SPACE
SCIENCE

UNIVERSITY OF CALIFORNIA
ENGINEERING AND PHYSICAL
SCIENCES EXTENSION SERIES

Howard Seifert, Editor · Space Technology
Robert L. Pecsok, Editor · Principles and Practice of Gas Chromatography
Howard Seifert and Kenneth Brown, Editors · Ballistic Missile and Space
    Vehicle Systems
George R. Pitman, Jr., Editor · Inertial Guidance
Kenneth Brown and Lawrence D. Ely, Editors · Space Logistics Engineering
Robert W. Vance and W. M. Duke, Editors · Applied Cryogenic Engineering
Donald P. LeGalley, Editor · Space Science

SPACE SCIENCE

Edited by

DONALD P. LE GALLEY
Space Technology Laboratories, Inc.

The Authors

LEVERETT DAVIS, JR.   California Institute of Technology

VON R. ESHLEMAN   Stanford University

BRIG. GEN. DON D. FLICKINGER   U. S. Air Force Medical Corps (RET.)

HERBERT FRIEDMAN   U. S. Naval Research Laboratory

LEO GOLDBERG   Harvard College Observatory

JESSE L. GREENSTEIN   California Institute of Technology

ALBERT R. HIBBS   Jet Propulsion Laboratory

GERARD P. KUIPER   University of Arizona

DONALD P. LE GALLEY   Space Technology Laboratories, Inc.

ALAN ROSEN   Space Technology Laboratories, Inc.

S. FRED SINGER   National Weather Satellite Center

EDWARD J. SMITH   Jet Propulsion Laboratory

CHARLES P. SONETT   National Aeronautics and Space Administration

HAROLD C. UREY   University of California, San Diego

JAMES A. VAN ALLEN   State University of Iowa

JOHN R. WINKLER   University of Minnesota

JOHN WILEY & SONS, INC., NEW YORK · LONDON

Library of Congress Catalog Card Number: 63–11438
Printed in the United States of America

FOREWORD _____

In the period since the earth's first artificial satellite, Sputnik I, was launched on October 7, 1957, our knowledge of space science has progressed with tremendous strides. From instrumentation carried aboard satellites and space probes like the Explorer and Pioneer series, new discoveries are being made in areas previously inaccessible to earth-bound man. Examples are the discovery of the Van Allen radiation belts and the large ring currents, which are now known to exist far above the earth's atmosphere but in its magnetic field. Also, much additional scientific information is being obtained about phenomena which a few years ago were little known. Examples are cosmic rays, micrometeorites, solar emissions, and interplanetary magnetic fields.

New discoveries and new scientific information about space have been accumulating so rapidly that it has been difficult for scientists and engineers to keep abreast of this expanding technology. Therefore, a book summarizing the present state of our knowledge of this field should prove both timely and useful. Since no one person is sufficiently knowledgeable in all of the scientific disciplines involved, it is particularly fortunate that it has been possible to obtain contributions from so many nationally recognized experts, each of whom has written a chapter covering his specialty.

In this way an authoritative treatise has been obtained covering not all but many of the scientific areas in space exploration, which will be of great value to the scientists designing space experiments and to the engineers designing spacecraft.

JAMES H. DOOLITTLE

PREFACE

The purpose of this book is to bring to the attention of scientists and engineers, especially those actively working on space programs, the most up-to-date information on the important aspects of "Space Science." During the five years since the first Sputnik was put into orbit, tremendous strides have been made in space science and space technology. To date, about 100 United States and 30 USSR satellites and space probes have been successfully launched into orbit, most of which have carried sophisticated equipment capable of making scientific measurements and sending back to earth information about inner and outer space. In addition to these data, a formidable amount of new and connected knowledge has been obtained in the fields of radio and optical astronomy. An attempt is made in this book to evaluate all of this information and to record the significant recent achievements in the field of science.

This book is an outgrowth of a series of 16 lectures given in a course entitled "Space Science," which was presented to about 1200 graduate students under the sponsorship of the University of California, Engineering and Physical Sciences Extension Departments during the Fall Semester of 1961. Although the chapters do not appear in the same order as the lectures were presented, they do cover the same material but in an expanded and improved form. Since no one person is knowledgeable in all of the fields of "Space Science," it was decided to select a nationally recognized authority to prepare a lecture on each topic. We were fortunate to obtain the support and cooperation of specialists from all over the country not only to give the lectures but also to prepare manuscripts for the chapters of the book. This book is a synthesis of the experience and knowledge of 16 experts and attempts to place at the disposal of scientists and engineers the latest and most up-to-date information from the frontiers of "Space Science."

Many individuals made contributions to this book while it was in the formative stage. As early as November 1959 Howard S. Seifert, editor of *Space Technology*, and Charles P. Sonett, author of Chapter 10 of this book, both then employees of Space Technology Laboratories, Inc., suggested that the course on "Space Technology" should be followed by a course on "Space Science." Both men made constructive suggestions in regard to topics that might appropriately be included in the course (and in the book) and to lecturers who might deliver them. In addition, Alan Rosen, author of Chapter 8, made some helpful suggestions about possible topics and authors. Others with whom the book and the course were discussed were Carl D. Anderson, Richard M. Sutton, and Jesse L. Greenstein (author of Chapter 2), all of the California Institute of Technology; Albert R. Hibbs (author of Chapter 6) of the Jet Propulsion Laboratory; and Donald H. Loughridge of the Aerospace Corporation.

In the early formative stages of the "Space Science" Lecture Series, the suggestions, guidance, and motivation of the UCLA Advisory Committee for this course were most beneficial. The Advisory Committee was composed of Clifford Bell, John C. Dillon, Harold M. Heming, Samuel Herrick, and John H. Lyman, all of the University of California; John W. McKee of the General Electric Company (TEMPO); Richard C. Potter and Donald P. LeGalley of Space Technology Laboratories, Inc.; and Jack Rosenberg, Consulting Engineer. The course was sponsored by the Engineering and Physical Sciences Extension Departments of the University of California and was under the direct supervision of Clifford Bell and John C. Dillon.

The editing of this book, with the myriad details involved, would not have been possible without the approval and support of the Professional Development Section of Space Technology Laboratories, Inc., of which Richard C. Potter is Manager.

DONALD P. LeGALLEY

Space Technology Laboratories, Inc.
December, 1962

CONTENTS _____

chapter 2   **STELLAR EVOLUTION AND HIGH ENERGY**
PHENOMENA IN ASTROPHYSICS   **58**
Jesse L. Greenstein, Mt. Wilson and Palomar
Observatories, Carnegie Institution of Washington,
California Institute of Technology

chapter 7   DYNAMICS, COMPOSITION, AND ORIGIN OF
             GEOMAGNETICALLY TRAPPED RADIATION   226
             James A. Van Allen, State University of Iowa

chapter 8   THE DYNAMICS OF THE OUTER RADIATION
             ZONE   275
             Alan Rosen, Space Technology Laboratories, Inc.

Contents   xv

chapter 13   **THE EARTH'S EXOSPHERE**   522
              S. Fred Singer, National Weather Satellite Center,
              United States Weather Bureau

Contents

chapter 15   THE SURFACE OF THE MOON   630
Gerard P. Kuiper, The University of Arizona

chapter 16   BIOASTRONAUTICS   650
Brigadier General Don D. Flickinger, U.S.A.F.M.C. (Ret.)

CHAPTER 1

INTRODUCTION—
SPACE EXPLORATION

DONALD P. LE GALLEY

Space Technology Laboratories, Inc.

On October 4, 1957, an event occurred that will greatly influence the future of all mankind. This event will affect us not only from a technical, scientific, and military point of view but also socially, politically, and economically. On that date the world's first artificial satellite, Sputnik I, was successfully launched into orbit, an occasion comparable in importance to Columbus' discovery of the Western Hemisphere, the flight of the first airplane, and the invention of the telephone, the radio, and the atomic bomb.

The launching of Sputnik I indicated that for the first time man had been able to overcome the earth's gravitational pull and that he had developed a new scientific and technical tool with which he could explore the space beyond the earth. This was the beginning of the space age. Up until that time man had been limited to pointing his telescope or his spectroscope toward the sky or to sending radio waves out into space if he wanted to explore the physical universe beyond the earth. This event proved that he now had sufficient scientific and technical knowledge of the laws of propulsion, structures, materials, aerodynamics, guidance, control, and trajectories to send out into space, vehicles containing instruments that could explore the physical universe around the earth, out as far as the moon and even the near planets. These instruments, which have been developed by man and which are designed to take his place as observer and experimenter (at least on the first flights), are intricate mechanical and electronic brains capable of making physical measurements, storing or remembering this information on digital computers, and, on command, sending it back to earth. Later, in addition to instruments, he would send animals out into space and, eventually, he would go himself. With this new tool and freed from the earth's environment, what would man like to know about the physical universe around him? In fact, what must he know about space environment if he is to travel there himself and return safely? Now that space exploration is possible, what experiments can be designed to obtain the necessary scientific information about the planetary system and the space it encompasses? What experiments would scientists like to conduct in space?

It should be pointed out that a great deal can be and has been learned about the universe in which we live from observations on the earth. For example, much has been learned from telescopic and spectroscopic observations made from the earth. In recent years telescopes and spectroscopes have been sent aloft in balloons and rockets in order to make observations above the earth's absorbing atmosphere. Then, too, there is that useful instrument known as the coronagraph, which, when applied in conjunction with the telescope, allows astronomers to examine the sun's corona as though the sun were in a total eclipse. Also, both passive and active radio waves are now being used to explore the moon, sun, and near planets. In the passive radio astronomy field new discoveries are being made almost daily about our own and distant galaxies, and, in addition, we can learn a great deal from cosmic-ray equipment placed at the earth's surface or by sending it to high altitudes in balloons. Furthermore, space conditions can be simulated for man and animals by the use of high-altitude chambers and centrifuges. Thus biological and medical experiments can be conducted under controlled conditions similar to those found in space.

To supplement the scientific information about space which has been obtained from earth observations, man now has the means for space exploration. Figure 1-1 indicates a few of the phenomena about which scientists would like to obtain more information. In order to obtain this information, scientists and engineers have and are de-

A. Solar emissions
B. Magnetic fields
C. Radiation belts
D. Ring currents

E. Cosmic rays
F. Lunar exploration
G. Biological and medical
   experiments

Figure 1-1 Space exploration experiments.

signing experiments to be carried aloft in satellites and space probes in what might be called a program of "Space Exploration." The purpose of this chapter and, in fact, the rest of the book is to describe what has been learned scientifically from space exploration and to describe some of the experiments and vehicles planned for the near future.

1-1 SPACE EXPLORATION EXPERIMENTS

Solar emissions

Since the sun is the center of our planetary system and the source of most of our energy, scientists would like to know more about its composition, its light- and particle-emitting abilities, its magnetic fields, the solar storms, the chromosphere, and the corona (5). They would like to know more about the radiation emitted by the sun in the visible region and in the infrared, ultraviolet, and X-ray regions. More information is needed on the solar emission of particles, such as the great clouds of hydrogen which the sun is continually throwing off. There is some evidence also that the sun discharges other light elements, including helium, lithium, beryllium, boron, and carbon, but in very small quantities.

In addition to the sun's ability to emit both radiation and particles in a steady state, it is now known that there are great solar storms (1) involving broad areas on the sun's surface, many of which are much larger than that of the earth. At the time of a solar storm there are large increases not only in the number of particles but also in the velocity with which they are emitted. There is experimental evidence that during a solar storm protons with energies in the multibillion electron volt (bev) range are discharged from the sun. It has been known for a number of years that sunspot cycles occur about every 11 years. It has now been determined that great magnetic disturbances accompany solar storms. Scientists would like to know more about these phenomena. In fact, we must have more information about them if man is to travel safely in interplanetary space. He must understand these radiations and be able to protect himself from them, for if he had been traveling in space unprotected by proper shielding during a storm like the one on September 28, 1961, he would not have survived.

Chapter 3, entitled "The Physics of the Sun—Its Nature, Structure, and Emission Properties," describes the present state of our knowledge about the sun and its emitting properties. Chapter 11, entitled "The

Production and Propagation of Energetic Particles from the Sun," describes some solar-emitting phenomena which have been discovered recently. Chapter 14, entitled "Rocket Spectroscopy," describes spectroscopic data obtained in recent years above the earth's atmosphere. The earth's atmosphere is highly absorptive of most radiation and transparent only for a very narrow part of the total spectrum. A narrow band of visible light gets through the atmosphere and reaches the earth's surface, but most of the ultraviolet and all of the X-ray wavelengths and some regions of the infrared are absorbed. Up until the time that it was possible to send spectrometers above the earth's atmosphere in balloons and in rockets, the information to be gained from observations on the earth's surface was extremely limited. With the advent of balloons and sounding rockets, and more recently, satellites and space probes, the facts obtained from spectroscopic measurements made from above the earth's atmosphere have greatly increased our knowledge of the universe.

Magnetic fields

More information is urgently needed about the direction and intensity of magnetic fields found in our solar system, and space exploration offers a promise of obtaining it. Direct measurements of the intensity and direction of magnetic fields have been made by both Russian and American spacecraft.

Although no rocket has been close enough to the sun to get direct measurements of its magnetic fields, measurements have been made from the earth with the use of a magnetograph invented by H. D. and H. W. Babcock of the Mt. Wilson and Palomar Observatories. Their observations show that at the surface of the sun the magnetic field changes greatly both in intensity and direction but that an average steady-state intensity value may be in the neighborhood of many gauss, varying from a few to a few hundred, and the direction may also change completely. For example, during the 1953 sunspot cycle the magnetic field was positive in the northern and negative in the southern hemispheres of the sun. However, between March and July 1957 the south polar field reversed its polarity, although the north field remained unchanged until 1958 when it was reversed from a positive to a negative field.

These changing magnetic fields give rise to magnetic storms on the surface of the sun and above it in the chromosphere, an effect that is propagated outward and certainly affects the earth (11). The great clouds of hydrogen which are shot out from the sun and are propagated throughout interplanetary space are now believed to be associated with magnetic storms on the sun. Measurements of the intensity and direction of interplanetary magnetic fields can be made by space probes carrying magnetometers, of which the flux-gate, spin-coil, and rubidium-vapor magnetometers are examples. These instruments are capable of measuring magnetic intensities within 0.01 gamma. (A gamma equals 10^{-5} gauss.) Pioneer I, Pioneer V, Explorer VI, Explorer X, Explorer XII, and other space probes have carried magnetometers and have provided useful data about the direction and intensity of interplanetary magnetic fields, but additional facts are urgently needed.

The importance of gaining more information about interplanetary magnetic fields is shown in the following examples. It is now well accepted that both the inner and the outer radiation belts are composed of ionized particles trapped in the earth's magnetic field and therefore definitely related to it. The recently discovered ring currents which encircle the earth at about 6 to 8 earth radii also are related to the magnetic field found at this altitude. Certainly, magnetic fields and magnetic storms affect the aurora borealis, radio communications, and even land-line communications. Therefore, it is essential to learn more about them by space exploration. Chapter 10, entitled "Rocket Experiments in Cosmic Magnetism and Their Significance," covers this topic in detail and describes the recent data obtained from rocket explorations. There are, in addition, Chapter 7 on "The Dynamic Composition and Origin of Geomagnetically Trapped Radiation," Chapter 8 on "The Dynamics of the Outer Radiation Zones," and Chapter 9 on the "Theoretical and Experimental Aspects of Ring Currents," which describe what is presently known about the relation of magnetic fields to these topics.

Radiation belts *

The trapped radiation belts were discovered by Dr. James A. Van Allen from experimental data obtained from the first American satellite, Explorer I, launched on January 31, 1958. These belts, composed of an inner and outer zone, exist at about $\frac{1}{2}$ and $2\frac{1}{2}$ earth radii above the earth's geomagnetic equator, respectively. In them the radiation intensity increases several thousandfold above that found in the surface of the earth. The inner zone is now thought to be composed mostly of high-velocity protons which have been caught in the earth's magnetic field and are caused to oscillate between mirror points located near the north geomagnetic pole and the south geomagnetic pole. The outer zone is now thought to be composed mostly of high-velocity

* The July 9, 1962, nuclear explosion over Johnston Island has greatly changed the radiation belts.

electrons oscillating between mirror points located near the north and south geomagnetic poles but in a belt farther from the earth, namely, about $2\frac{1}{2}$ earth radii. Figure 1-16 shows the location of these radiation belts.

The theory related to these trapped radiation belts was worked out earlier by Störmer (13) and others, but their exact nature and location were not completely predicted by the theory. The intensity of their radiation is such that a man could not remain in them for long periods of time without proper shielding. Although a number of satellites and space probes have carried counters, ionization chambers, and other equipment to measure the intensity of these radiation belts, more exploration must be done before man can safely venture into this area.

An experiment which was performed soon after the discovery of the Van Allen radiation belts and after their existence had been verified by several other satellites and space probes is known as the Argus Experiment. It was suggested and designed by N. C. Christofilos (2) of the Lawrence Radiation Laboratory and consisted of exploding three atomic bombs at high altitudes to see what effect the ionization they produced would have on the intensity of the radiation in the Van Allen belts on aurora borealis, etc. The explosions occurred over the South Atlantic on the nights of August 27 and 30 and September 6, 1958. Explorer IV, in orbit at the time, recorded increases in the radiation density in these zones. At the same time, increases in aurora displays were observed visually in many parts of the globe. This experiment shed additional light on the trapped radiation zones and indicated that, like solar emissions and magnetic fields, there is superimposed a fluctuating phenomenon which adds to and subtracts from the steady state. The subject of trapped radiation is discussed in detail in Chapter 7, "The Dynamic Composition and Origin of Geomagnetically Trapped Radiation," and in Chapter 8, "The Dynamics of the Outer Radiation Zones."

Ring currents

The experimental discovery from satellites and space probes of perturbations in the earth's magnetic field has led to the postulation of the existence of toroidal or ring currents of large magnitude which encircle the earth. To explain the perturbations detected would require the postulation of currents of several million amperes flowing in a westward direction around the earth at a geocentric altitude of 5 to 10 earth radii. A diagrammatic representation of the ring current is shown in Figure 1-2. The latest findings indicate that the toroid

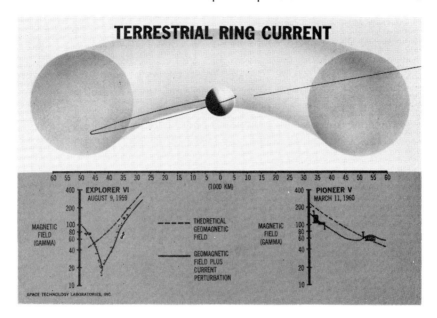

Figure 1-2 Terrestrial ring current.

may be more "tear" shaped, with the "tail" pointing away from the sun. The center of the toroid is approximately 8 earth radii from the center of the earth, and its radius is about 3 earth radii.

Although the total current flow may be several million amperes, the current density or the amperes per square meter is small because of the extremely large areas involved. The ring currents are postulated to lie outside the radiation belts but inside the magnetosphere, which is thought to be the region within which the earth's magnetic field is contained.

Magnetometers such as the spin coil, flux gate, and more recently the rubidium vapor have been flown on various satellites and space probes (e.g., Pioneer I, Lunik I, Explorer VI, Pioneer V, and Explorer X). The interpretation of these data, and their correlation or noncorrelation with theory, is given in Chapter 9, "Theoretical and Experimental Aspects of Ring Currents." The measurement of interplanetary magnetic fields and the determination of ring currents is an important scientific accomplishment. It is a physical quantity about which we should obtain more information, since it is related to magnetic storms, the ionosphere, solar winds, auroral phenomena, and probably the radiation belts.

Cosmic rays

Many of the satellites and space probes flown to date, including the Sputniks, Vanguards, Explorers, and Pioneers, have carried cosmic-ray measuring equipment. An effort has been made to obtain more information about cosmic rays to determine their origin, nature, and effects on matter.

Although cosmic-ray measurements can be made on the ground, both the earth's atmosphere and its magnetic field affect them, especially the softer components. Therefore, satellites and space probes offer a good platform from which to make these measurements.

At present it is thought that the primary cosmic rays are galactic in origin, are composed mostly of protons (i.e., ionized hydrogen), and have been accelerated to energies in the billion electron volt (bev) range. However, there is some evidence that other light elements such as helium, lithium, beryllium, and boron are included with the hydrogen but in much smaller amounts. The secondary cosmic rays are thought to be composed of electrons, photons, mesons, and strange particles which are produced when the primary cosmic rays strike our atmosphere. In addition, there are solar cosmic rays whose intensities increase when solar flares occur.

One phenomenon associated with cosmic rays, which was not fully understood until after measurements were made with satellites and space probes, is known as the Forbush decrease. On occasion it was observed that the cosmic-ray intensity on the earth decreased by as much as 25 percent. This phenomenon is now believed to be associated with huge clouds of hydrogen shot out from the sun and the magnetic field associated with them. This and other phenomena related to cosmic rays are explained in Chapter 12, "The Theoretical and Experimental Aspects of Cosmic Rays."

Lunar exploration

It has always been man's desire to "make a trip to the moon." Even Jules Verne wrote about such an imaginary voyage. But now we are leaving the realm of the imaginary and getting closer to reality with present-day and future spacecraft. The Russians, with Lunik II, were able to propel and guide a space vehicle well enough to impact the moon,* and with Lunik III they were able to take pictures of its back side and to transmit them back to earth (9). Since the moon always keeps one face toward the earth, no one had ever seen its other side. One of the purposes of the Ranger Program is to land instru-

---

* More recently Ranger 4 also impacted the moon.

ments on the moon's surface. The Surveyor Program includes landing a vehicle with instruments and equipment with which to make extensive physical and chemical measurements on the moon's surface and to transmit this information back to earth. This program would be followed by the Apollo vehicle, whose purpose is to land three men on the moon and return them safely to the earth. More details about these programs are given in Chapter 6, "Exploring the Solar System with Space Probes."

However, a great deal has been and can be learned about the moon's surface structure and history from telescopic observations and radio astronomy measurements from the earth. Chapter 15, "The Surface of the Moon," describes some of the things that we know about the moon from visual, photographic, and telescopic observations. Lunar atlases (8) have been published which summarize what is presently known about the moon and its surface. Chapter 5, "Radio Exploration of the Solar System," includes information about what has been learned by reflecting radar beams from the moon's surface. However, much remains to be learned from space explorations.

Biological and medical experiments

Before man can venture into space, where he will find a hostile environment which includes high g's, weightlessness, vacuum conditions, low temperatures, heat radiation, gamma rays, and strong varying magnetic fields, to name only a few, considerable biological and medical experimentation will have to be done. Chapter 16, entitled "Bioastronautics," describes what has been done and is being done to prepare man for space flight.

It is true that Astronauts Shepard, Grissom, and Glenn from this side of the Atlantic and Cosmonauts Gagarin and Titov from the other side have gone out into space and returned safely. However, none of these flights lasted for more than 24 hours, and a trip to the moon—which is our nearest neighbor—will require several days. Therefore, man must be prepared to withstand these environmental conditions for longer periods of time. If man is to undertake long space flights, biological and medical experiments must be done in space to understand the existing conditions. Extended visits to the regions of the Van Allen radiation belts without shielding might prove fatal. Also, it is known that some solar storms have occurred which, if man had been out in space unprotected, would have proved at least harmful if not fatal. Many experiments can be conducted on the ground, but many will have to be performed out in space if man is to be safe.

1-2 SATELLITES AND SPACE PROBES WHICH HAVE BEEN SUCCESSFULLY FLOWN—THE PURPOSE AND ACCOMPLISHMENT OF EACH (15)

In order to understand what has been accomplished scientifically in space, it is important to have some knowledge of the results of experiments carried on the satellites and space probes which have been flown to date (April 1962). Therefore, the rest of this chapter is devoted to a description of these accomplishments, with a few comments on future experiments. Figure 1-3 is a list of the major satellite and space-vehicle programs, the sponsoring agency, the number of vehicles successfully launched, and a few scientific details about each.*

Sputniks, Luniks, Vostoks

The Russians have a number of "firsts" to their credit when satellites and spacecraft are considered. Sputnik I was the first object to be launched into earth orbit. This occurred on October 4, 1957, and although the satellite weighed only 184 lb it heralded the beginning of the space age. Lunik II was the first earth-launched object to impact the moon. It was launched on September 12, 1959. Lunik III was the first space probe to carry automatic camera equipment to the other side of the moon, photograph it, and transmit the pictures to earth. Figure 1-4 is a composite picture of the far side of the moon, put together from Russian photographs taken from Lunik III. Figure 1-5 is a photograph of Lunik III. In addition, the Russians were the first to put a man in orbit around the earth and to safely recover him. This was Cosmonaut Major Yuri A. Gagarin, who made the orbital trip in Vostok I on April 12, 1961.

Figure 1-6 is a chart of all the Sputniks launched to date. The Luniks are shown in Figure 1-7 and the Vostoks in Figure 1-8. It will be noted from Figure 1-6 that beginning with Sputnik IV the Russians were capable of launching satellites weighing 5 tons and more. After Sputniks I and II were launched, and our Vanguard Program was not ready, it was decided to use a military booster, the

---

* The list is not complete, since some of the military programs such as Midas, Samos, Dyna-Soar, Advent and some of the communications satellites have not been shown. The number of Discoverer vehicles put in orbit is now 26, and the number successfully recovered is 12. Also, events are occurring so rapidly that it is difficult to keep this information up-to-date. For example, since Figure 1-3 was composed, Colonel Glenn has successfully completed his historic orbit of the earth, and Cosmos I, II, III, and IV have been launched into orbit.

Jupiter C, to launch our first satellite, Explorer I. Up until this time, the United States Space Program had not been permitted to use military boosters. The Russian use of military boosters was one of the reasons for their early success and head start in the space race. Later, we used the Thor as a booster, and still later the Atlas. Figure 1-9 * shows the launch-weight advantage that the Russians held in 1957, 1958, and 1959 and still hold over us.

Although the Russians have maintained a weight advantage over us, we surpassed them insofar as instrumentation is concerned. When large American military boosters were not available, our scientists and engineers were forced to design and build very sophisticated lightweight instruments to perform experiments in space which would require the superhuman efforts of several astronauts. For example, Pioneer V, which weighed only 95 lb, carried "Telebit," an intricate electronic brain capable of recording, remembering, and, on command, transmitting back to earth the data from six scientific experiments. Other American satellites and probes have carried intricate scientific experiments to measure cosmic rays, magnetic fields, solar radiation, and micrometeorites.

Other facts to be learned from Figure 1-6 are as follows: although the Russian experimenters did measure magnetic fields, electrostatic fields, cosmic rays, solar radiation, and did make many other scientific measurements, the main effort on their flights was in the biological and medical fields. Sputnik II carried into orbit the dog "Laika," about which much biological information was transmitted back to earth. Sputnik V carried two dogs in a capsule which was recovered after 18 passes. Sputnik VI carried a series of biological experiments, but was not recovered. Sputniks IX and X were devoted to animal studies preliminary to the manned flight of Vostok I. All of these spacecraft were successfully recovered over land. The United States has not yet achieved a land recovery. All of our recoveries, in both the Discoverer and Mercury Programs, have been over the water. Thus the Russians had acquired considerable recovery experience before attempting to orbit and recover a human being. Sputnik IV was their first attempt to recover a "dummy spaceman." Even though it failed, undoubtedly much was learned from it.

It might be pointed out that to recover an object out of orbit is a much more difficult technical problem than to place it into orbit. The position, attitude, and velocity of the orbiting vehicle must be accu-

---

* Figure 1-9 was devised by Dandridge Cole of the General Electric Missile and Space Vehicle Department and is used with his permission.

Name	Sponsoring Agency	Number Successfully Launched	Purpose/or Accomplishment
SPUTNIK	USSR	10	First satellite; back side of moon photographed
LUNIK	USSR	3	First dog in orbit; first recovery of dog from orbit
VOSTOK	USSR	2	First man in orbit; first recovery of man from orbit
VANGUARD	NRL, NASA	3	Designed for scientific exploration for IGY
EXPLORER	Army, AF, NASA	10	To explore space near earth
PIONEER	Army, AF, NASA	5	To explore lunar and planetary space
DISCOVERER	AF	18	Recovery of capsules from orbit (six to date)
MERCURY	NASA	2	Manned ballistic trajectories; man in orbit by 1961
SCORE (ATLAS 10B)	AF-ARPA Signal Corps	December 18, 1958	To test voice and teletype transmission between satellite and earth stations (President's Christmas message)
ECHO (THOR DELTA)	NASA	August 12, 1960	Inflated sphere 100 ft in diameter used to transmit messages between east and west coast
COURIER (THOR ABLE)	ARPA Army Signal Corps	October 4, 1960	Communication satellite received, stored, and transmitted 68,000 coded words per min; operated 18 days

Figure 1-3a Satellites and space probes, Part 1.

Name	Sponsoring Agency	Number Successfully Launched	Purpose/or Accomplishment
TIROS	NASA	4	Meteorological satellite
TRANSIT	Navy	4	Navigation satellite for ships and submarines
RANGER	NASA JPL	1961	Physical exploration of interplanetary space (will carry 8 experiments)
OGO	NASA Goddard	3 planned	Orbiting Geophysical Laboratory (OGO) equipped to conduct physical experiments between earth, moon, and sun
SURVEYOR	NASA JPL	7 planned	Designed for soft landing on moon; will sample and make chemical and physical analysis of moon's surface
PROSPECTOR	NASA JPL	1966–67	Mobile instrumented vehicle to travel over moon's surface by remote control
APOLLO	NASA JPL	3 planned	Design studies completed; proposed 3-man spacecraft to orbit moon, land, and return
MARINER A	NASA JPL	1962	Venus probe; to measure interplanetary magnetic fields and radiation intensities

Figure 1-3b Satellites and space probes, Part 2.

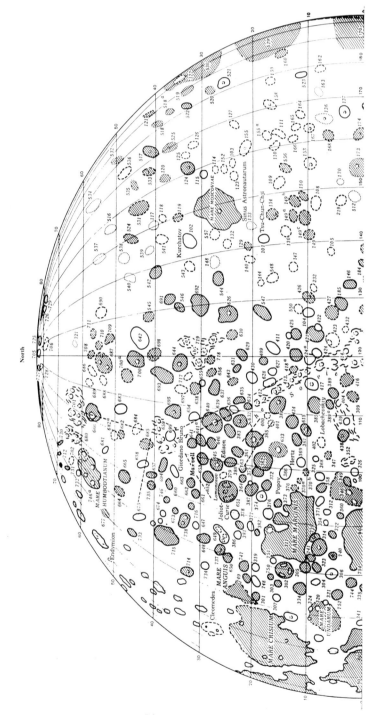

North

14

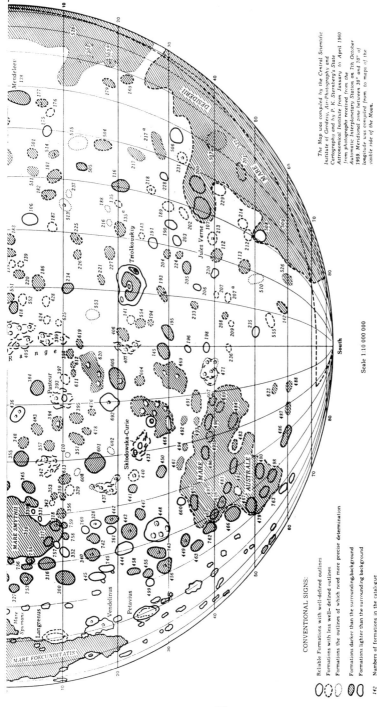

Scale 1:10 000 000

The Map was compiled by the Central Scientific Institute of Geodesy, Air-Photography and Cartography and by P. K. Sternberg's State Astronomical Institute from January to April 1960 from photograph received from the Automatic Interplanetary Station on 7th October 1959. Meridional zone between 30° and 70° of longitude was compiled from to maps of the visible side of the Moon.

Figure 1-4   Composite map of far side of moon.

15

Figure 1-5 Photograph of Lunik III.

rately known in space and the deorbiting signal given at exactly the
right time to provide landing in or near the designated area. The
signal to fire the retrorockets in Colonel Glenn's flight was given when
the capsule was over California. He landed southeast of Bermuda.
In spite of the great care used, several vehicles have gone astray;
Sputnik IV went into another orbit; Discoverer II landed near Spitzen-
berg instead of Hawaii. The Russians' ability to recover their capsules
over land is considered to be quite an accomplishment in guidance and
control.

Figure 1-10 is a diagram of Sputnik III, indicating the location of
scientific equipment. Sputnik III was the first large vehicle put in

Name	Launch Date	Lifetime or End	Weight in Pounds	Experiments/or Remarks
SPUTNIK I	Oct. 4, 1957	Jan. 4, 1958	184	First artificial satellite; telemetered internal temperatures and pressures
SPUTNIK II	Nov. 3, 1957	Apr. 14, 1958	1,120	Measurements on dog "Laika"; solar ultraviolet and X rays and cosmic rays
SPUTNIK III	May 15, 1958	Apr. 6, 1959	2,925	Earth's magnetic and electrostatic fields and atmospheric composition
SPUTNIK IV	May 15, 1960	May 19, 1960	Spacecraft 10,008 Cabin 5512	"Dummy spaceman" in 200-mile orbit; attempted recovery from orbit on May 19 failed
SPUTNIK V	Aug. 19, 1960	Aug. 20, 1960	10,120	Two dogs recovered alive after 18 passes; recovery made over land
SPUTNIK VI	Dec. 1, 1960	Dec. 2, 1960	10,060	Earth biomedical satellite; recovery unsuccessful
SPUTNIK VII	Feb. 4, 1961	Feb. 26, 1961	14,292	Test vehicle for SPUTNIK VIII (VENUS probe); precise orbit
SPUTNIK VIII	Feb. 12, 1961	Indefinite	14,292 Probe 1,419	VENUS probe launched from orbiting SPUTNIK VIII
SPUTNIK IX	Mar. 9, 1961	Mar. 10, 1961	10,340	Test vehicle for manned flight; orbit achieved; cabin containing dog, etc., recovered
SPUTNIK X	Mar. 25, 1961	Mar. 25, 1961	10,329	Biomedical satellite, test for manned flight; dog, etc., recovered

Figure 1-6 USSR satellites.

Name	Launch Date	Lifetime or End	Weight in Pounds	Experiments/or Remarks
LUNIK I (Mechta)	Jan. 2, 1959		3245	Orbit sun-15-month period; first artificial asteroid; interplanetary radiation, magnetic fields, etc.
LUNIK II	Sept. 12, 1959	Impacted Moon 9/13/59	858	Hit moon 1 min, 24 sec later than predicted; magnetic fields of earth and moon measured
LUNIK III	Oct. 4, 1959	Apr. 20, 1960	614	Automatic camera equipment; transmitted photographs of back side of moon

Figure 1-7 USSR space probes.

Name	Launch Date	Lifetime or End	Weight in Pounds	Experiments/or Remarks
VOSTOK I	Apr. 12, 1961	Apr. 12, 1961	10,418	First man in orbit; first man recovered from orbit; cosmonaut Major Yuri Gagarin
VOSTOK II	Aug. 6, 1961	Aug. 7, 1961	10,408	Second man to orbit earth and be recovered; Cosmonaut Major Gherman Titov

Figure 1-8 USSR spacecraft.

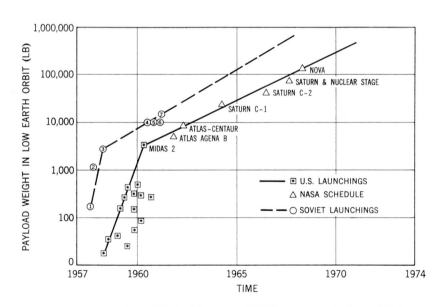

Figure 1-9 Comparison of United States and USSR space payload capabilities.

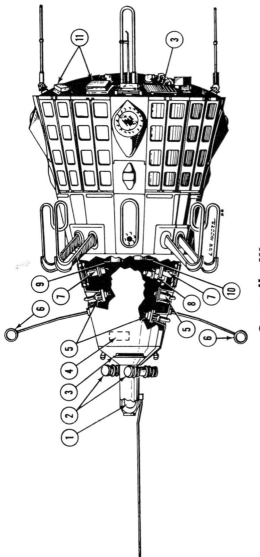

Sputnik III

1. MAGNETOMETER
2. PHOTO-MULTIPLIERS FOR THE REGISTRATION OF THE CORPUSCULAR RADIATION OF THE SUN
3. SOLAR BATTERIES
4. DEVICE FOR THE REGISTRATION OF PHOTONS IN COSMIC RAYS

5. MAGNETIC AND IONIZATION MANOMETERS
6. ION CATCHERS
7. ELECTROSTATIC FLUXMETER
8. MASS SPECTROMETRIC TUBE
9. DEVICE FOR THE REGISTRATION OF HEAVY NUCLEI IN COSMIC RAYS

10. DEVICE FOR MEASURING THE INTENSITY OF PRIMARY COSMI RADIATION
11. PICK-UPS FOR THE REGISTRATION OF MICROMETERS

Figure 1-10 Diagram of Sputnik III.

Figure 1-11   Photograph of Sputnik VIII.

orbit by the Russians. It weighed 1½ tons and was put in orbit about 15 months after Sputnik I. Figure 1-11 is a photograph of Sputnik VIII, showing the antennae arrays and the Russian attempt to use solar cells. The Venus probe was launched from Sputnik VIII.

The Vanguard Program

The Vanguard Program was initiated as a civilian space-exploration program to gather scientific information during the International Geophysical Year (July 1957–December 1958). The launching-vehicle schedule was not given a high priority; it was not permitted to interfere with military programs or to use military boosters. The design and construction of the booster was marginal, so that when the first two failed, and the Russians had put Sputnik I and Sputnik II into orbit, it was decided to use a military booster (Jupiter C) in an at-

Name	Launch Date	Lifetime or End	Dimensions in Inches	Weight in Pounds	Experiments/or Remarks
VANGUARD I	Mar. 17, 1958	2000 years	6.4	(50) 3.25	First use of solar cells; discovered earth pear shaped; this was test vehicle No. 3
VANGUARD II	Feb. 17, 1959	200 years	20	20.7	Cloud cover satellite used photocells to give cloud pictures (fourth attempt)
VANGUARD III	Sept. 18, 1959	30 to 40 years	20-in. sphere in 26-in. tapered tube	(100) 50	Earth's magnetic field. Solar X rays; frequency of micrometeorite impact (seventh attempt)

Figure 1-12   The Vanguard Program.

tempt to put a vehicle into orbit (Explorer I). Seven Vanguard vehicles were launched, of which three attained successful orbits. From these three flights considerable scientific data was obtained. In addition to measurements of the earth's magnetic field, solar X rays, and the frequency of micrometeor impacts, it was discovered that the earth is not strictly spherical nor precisely an ellipsoid, but slightly pear shaped with flattening in the south and a bulge of about 50 ft in the north. Vanguard II was the first satellite to take cloud-cover pictures and transmit them back to earth. Figure 1-12 gives some of the details of the Vanguard Program.

The Explorer and Pioneer Programs

The Explorers were designed to explore the space near the earth in concentric or slightly elliptical orbits, whereas the Pioneers were designed to explore farther out in space, including the moon and the near planets. Figure 1-13 lists the Explorers successfully launched and the accomplishments of each. Many scientific data, including measurements of the earth's magnetic field, momentum of micro-meteorites, solar X rays, density of the upper atmosphere, and cosmic rays, were obtained from the Explorers. However, the achievement for which this series is best known is the discovery of the Van Allen radiation belts. Figure 1-14 describes the experiments carried on Explorer VI, one of the most successful satellites from a scientific point of view. Figure 1-15 is a photograph of a model of Explorer VI.

The Pioneer series also made significant scientific discoveries. Figure 1-16 shows the trajectory followed by Pioneer III. It traversed the inner and outer radiation belts twice, verified their existence, and gave quantitative measurements throughout the region. Figure 1-17 lists the achievements of the Pioneers successfully launched. Of these, Pioneer V was the most outstanding. It was a veritable physics laboratory. It was launched into an orbit concentric with the sun but in between that of the earth and Venus. Figure 1-18 shows the trajectory followed by Pioneer V in relation to the sun, Venus, and earth; Figure 1-19 lists the experiments performed by Pioneer V. Valuable scientific data obtained from the six experiments are still being analyzed. In addition to the above, two scientific contributions were made by Pioneer V. Two-way communication was maintained over the longest distance ever achieved, namely 22.4 million miles, and, by tracking its trajectory, the astronomical unit was measured more accurately than it had ever been before.*

* The latest radar determination of the astronomical unit is 149,598,000 ± 3000 km (see Chapter 5).

Name	Launch Date	Lifetime or End	Dimensions in Inches	Weight in Pounds	Experiments/or Remarks
EXPLORER I (JUPITER C)	Jan. 31, 1958	3 to 5 years; stopped transmitting Feb. 28, 1958	80 x 6 cylinder	30.8	First U. S. satellite: discovery of Van Allen radiation belt; also measured micrometeorites
EXPLORER III (JUPITER C)	Mar. 26, 1958	Jun. 28, 1958	80 x 6 cylinder	31.0	Verified Van Allen radiation belt; data recorded on tape and read out on command
EXPLORER IV (JUPITER C)	Jul. 26, 1958	Oct. 23, 1958	80.4 x 6.3	38.4	Radiation belt; Geiger-Müller counters and scintillation counter to measure intensity and direction
EXPLORER VI (THOR-ABLE III)	Aug. 7, 1959	1 year	29 x 26	142	First paddlewheel solar cells; first TV cloud cover scan; micrometeorite; magnetometer and communication measurements
EXPLORER VII (JUNO II)	Oct. 13, 1959	20 to 30 years	30 x 68	91.5	Lyman alpha, X-ray, solar radiation, and temperature measurements
EXPLORER VIII (JUNO II)	Nov. 3, 1960	20 to 50 years	30 x 30	90.14	Measured positive ion and electron density; momentum frequency and energy of micrometeorites
EXPLORER IX	Feb. 16, 1961	Feb. 25, 1961		80	To inject inflatable sphere into earth orbit to determine density of upper atmosphere
EXPLORER X	Mar. 25, 1961				Map magnetic fields and solar winds

Figure 1-13a The Explorer Program, Part 1.

Name	Launch Date	Lifetime or End	Dimensions in Inches	Weight in Pounds	Experiments/or Remarks
EXPLORER XI	Apr. 27, 1961				To detect and map high-energy gamma rays from cosmic sources
EXPLORER XII	Aug. 15, 1961			83	To study the behavior of energetic particles—electrons and protons—that are present in space and affect geophysical phenomena on earth

Figure 1-13b The Explorer Program, Part 2.

1. Proportional counter (University of Chicago), ion chamber and Geiger-Müller counter (University of Minnesota), scintillation counter (STL) in order to measure the intensity and the energy levels of cosmic rays and the concentration of electrons.
2. A VLF transmitter (Stanford University) to perform "whistler-mode" experiment in order to examine the propagation of VLF radio noise along magnetic-field lines.
3. A search coil magnetometer, a flux-gate magnetometer, and an aspect indicator to measure magnetic fields and investigate auroral and ring currents.
4. Radio scintillation experiments to provide information about the size, shape, orientation, motion, and stability of ionospheric irregularities which cause amplitude and phase scintillations of radio waves.
5. A TV scanner and image transmission system to gather and transmit information on the composition of the earth's atmospheric cloud cover.
6. A micrometeorite momentum spectrometer to obtain data on the distribution of momentum among the micrometeorites.

Figure 1-14   Experiments carried on Explorer VI.

Figure 1-15   Photograph of model of Explorer VI.

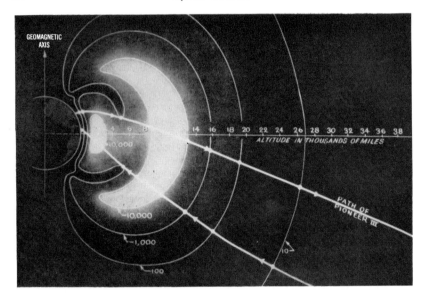

Figure 1-16 Trajectory of Pioneer III through Van Allen radiation belts.

Space tracking and communication network

Associated with any satellite or space-probe program must be a worldwide tracking and communications network. The network used for the Pioneer series might serve as an example. As shown in Figure 1-20, it consisted of a computing and control center in Los Angeles and five tracking and communication stations situated around the world so that at least one, but more often two, stations would be able to track the space vehicle simultaneously. The permanent tracking stations were located at Cape Canaveral, Jodrell Bank, Singapore, and Hawaii, and a portable station was set up near Salisbury, in Southern Rhodesia. Figure 1-21 shows the 250-ft dish at Jodrell Bank. In addition, the Millstone Hill Station of MIT Lincoln Laboratories and the Goldstone Tracking Station operated by JPL cooperated in tracking the spacecraft, especially in the early phases of launch. The Goldstone station was able to provide position data every 10 sec, accurate to 0.01 degree, which helped to determine early trajectories. All of these tracking stations were connected by an RF transmission link with the computing center at Los Angeles where a 709 IBM computer and later a 7090 IBM computer were available. After the vehicle was launched, tracking data were teletyped to the central station, where a recalculation yielded a more accurate estimate of the trajectory.

Name	Launch Date	Lifetime or End	Dimensions in Inches	Weight in Pounds	Experiments/or Remarks
PIONEER I (THOR-ABLE I)	Oct. 11, 1958	44 hr	30 x 29	84.4	First measurement of radiation in outer belt; first measurement of density of micro-meteorites
PIONEER (JUNO II)	Dec. 6, 1958	38 hr	23 x 20	13	Transversed both radiation belts and made additional measurements in each
PIONEER IV (JUNO II)	Mar. 3, 1959	1×10^6 years	20 cone	13.4	Space probe, in orbit around sun; 407-day period; good radiation data near earth
PIONEER V (THOR-ABLE IV)	Mar. 11, 1960		26 x 29	95	Space probe to Venus; period 315 days; used "Telebit"; successfully commanded communications to 22.5×10^6 miles

Figure 1-17 The Pioneer Program.

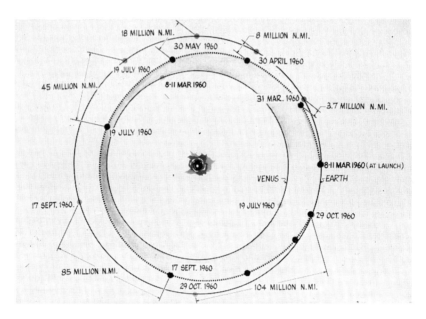

Figure 1-18   Trajectory of Pioneer V (Able 4).

1. First attempt to conduct controlled communications over long ranges (20 $\times 10^6$ miles). Used "Telebit" an intricate electronic brain, capable of storing the data from experiments carried in the spacecraft and transmitting it back to earth on command.   Equipped with 5-watt and 150-watt transmitters.

2. Used spin coil magnetometer and sun aspect indicator to measure two components of the magnetic fields in interplanetary space.

3. Carried a proportional counter "telescope" to explore the radiation emitted by the solar corona and the interplanetary primary cosmic-ray flux.

4. Carried an ionization chamber and Geiger-Müller counter to measure cosmic radiation found in interplanetary space.

5. Carried a micrometeorite momentum spectrometer to measure the number and the momentum of micrometeorites striking the spacecraft.

6. Used temperature measuring equipment to measure the temperature at strategic points within and without the spacecraft.

7. Spacecraft used to measure the astronomical unit by determining the vehicle's position from two widely separated times in the trajectory.

Figure 1-19   Experiments performed by Pioneer V.

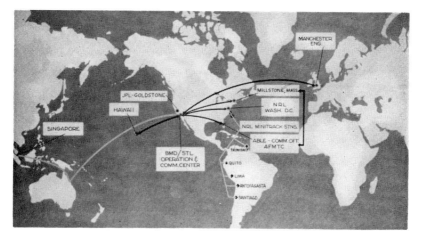

Figure 1-20   Space tracking and communication network.

These refined antenna-steering data were then provided to all ground stations. The recalculation of trajectories and steering data proceeded on a continuing basis for the useful life of the vehicle.

In addition to tracking the spacecraft, the tracking stations had the further responsibility of maintaining communication with the vehicle and relaying all data on its performance and the performance of the instruments it carried to the central control station. Since present spacecraft do not carry sufficient power for continuous transmission, a system is used whereby data are transmitted back to earth on a command basis. Future spacecraft will employ a system in which the information is recorded on a continuous basis, stored, and transmitted on command back to earth. For data on magnetic fields, cosmic rays, etc., the position of the vehicle in space is important at all times. The analysis of the scientific data obtained from a flight may continue for months or even years.

The Discoverer and Mercury Programs

The primary purpose of the Discoverer Program is to develop the ability, techniques, and knowledge to recover an object out of orbit. A secondary objective is to make scientific measurements under space-flight conditions. Experiments on cosmic rays, magnetic fields, and solar radiation, as well as biomedical questions have been carried on some of the flights.

The Discoverer vehicle is launched into a polar orbit from Vanden-

Figure 1-21   Jodrell Bank 250-foot tracking telescope.

berg Air Force Base, and, after a controlled number of orbits, is deorbited; it re-enters the atmosphere and is brought down by parachute into an area near Hawaii. Originally an Air Force modified C-119 aircraft, and more recently a C-130, equipped with a trapeze-type sling, then snatches the parachute-suspended capsule before it reaches the water. If the C-119 fails to catch the capsule, a navy team is available to make a water recovery. Figure 1-22 shows a modified C-119 snatching a Discoverer capsule.

Most of the Discoverers have been launched by using the Thor as a booster and the Agena A or the Agena B as the second stage. Some of these spacecraft did not achieve orbit, some did not eject out of orbit properly, some went into other orbits with a higher apogee, some burned during re-entry, some were not detected and therefore not recovered, and others hit the water and sank before recovery could be made.

However, in spite of these difficulties, the Discoverer Program has been successful. The first recovery occurred on August 11, 1960, when Discoverer XIII was recovered after 17 orbits. Nine days later, on August 20, 1960, Discoverer XIV was snatched in the air by a C-119 for the first airborne recovery. Since that time, a total of 12 recoveries has been made, eight of them air-snatched and four from the water. This is a remarkable achievement when the difficulties of recovering an object traveling 18,000 mph are considered. The Discoverer Program has contributed experience and knowledge of inestimable value to such programs as Mercury, Gemini, and Apollo.

The purpose of the Mercury Program is to develop the techniques and the skills necessary to put a man in orbit and to recover him safely. In order to do this, some human factors and considerations must be added to the engineering skills (e.g., propulsion, structures, aerodynamics, control, guidance, and re-entry) needed to put a satel-

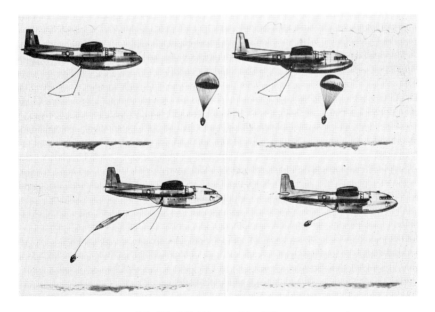

Figure 1-22 Modified C-119 snatching Discoverer capsule.

lite carrying instruments into orbit. The capsule must be designed so that the astronaut can withstand the 8-to-10-g load during launch and again on re-entry. The capsule is shown in Figure 16-1. The astronaut reclines on a foam-rubber couch form-fitted to his back. On launch the forces of the g's are across his body, pressing his back against the couch. During flight it is necessary for the astronaut to maneuver the capsule through 180 degrees so that he will come into the atmosphere back first. To do this, he can operate jet controls to orient the capsule.

As a safety precaution at launch, a framework containing three rockets is attached to the capsule. These rockets are oriented in such a way that they are capable of lifting the capsule away from the booster if a malfunction should occur at or near the launching pad. Once the launch is successfully underway, the frame is jettisoned.

The manned capsule must be equipped with a supply of oxygen and fresh air, a temperature control system, communications system, instrument panel, jet controls, periscope, drogue and main parachute, and an escape mechanism. Every precaution that is possible for the safety of the man is incorporated in the program. In addition to an extensive range instrumentation and communications system, fleets of aircraft and ships patrol the landing area preparatory to recovering the capsule.

Thus far there have been three successful suborbital and two successful orbital flights. The chimpanzee "Ham" was the first to make the suborbital flight. He reached an altitude of 155 miles and made his 420-mile trip downrange on January 31, 1961. This was followed by the flight of Commander Alan B. Shepard, Jr., on May 5, 1961, using the Redstone III as a booster. The capsule with Shepard aboard reached an altitude of 115 miles and a downrange distance of 302 miles. This flight was almost perfect in every detail, including the recovery of the capsule. On July 21, 1961, another suborbital flight carried Captain Virgil I. Grissom to an altitude of 118 miles and downrange 303 miles where he also was recovered, but the capsule was lost. Before attempting to put a man into full orbit, two practice flights were made, one instrumented and one carrying a chimpanzee called "Enos." In the case of Enos two complete orbits were made on November 29, 1961, before deorbiting and recovery occurred. Enos had been trained to operate certain levers and to close certain switches, which he did while in orbit.

At 9:47 A.M. on the morning of February 20, 1962, after a total of 10 "holds," Astronaut Colonel John H. Glenn, Jr., was launched into orbit by an Atlas D (see Figure 16-2). About 5 hours later, after three complete orbits, the retrorockets were fired while the capsule was over Southern California. The capsule re-entered the atmosphere and landed in the Atlantic Ocean, southeast of Bermuda near Grand Turk Island. The capsule was recovered by the destroyer *Noa*, and Colonel Glenn returned to the United States to receive a hero's welcome. Medical measurements on the astronaut were taken and telemetered throughout the flight, and a thorough medical examination was made before and after. Considerable medical and biological information and experience have been gained from the Mercury flights. Figure 16-3 is a photograph of the astronauts who have participated in the Mercury Program.

Communication satellites

1. Introduction. When future generations evaluate the present space effort, one of the most significant contributions they may find will be the communication satellites. Telephone and television transmission via synchronous or nonsynchronous satellites offers some interesting possibilities. Present transatlantic cables are crowded and will be saturated by 1965. Transcontinental lines are overloaded, and microwave link stations are expensive to install and maintain. Although passive-reflecting type satellites like Echo are satisfactory for certain communication purposes, they have serious limitations, especially when wideband telephone and television transmissions are attempted. For this purpose, the active-repeater type of communication satellite is far superior and much more reliable. The passive and active satellites now under consideration, with a few details about each, are described below. More information about communication theory and the development of new communication techniques is urgently needed.

2. Score. Score was launched into orbit on December 18, 1958, and is best known for its transmission of President Eisenhower's Christmas message. Its objective was to test the feasibility of a variety of combinations of voice and teletype transmissions and reception between a satellite and ground stations. The transmitter operated on 132.435 and 132.095 Mc, and the 8 watts of transmitted power was furnished by zinc and silver oxide batteries. In addition to transmitting recorded messages on command from the ground, the satellite accepted and relayed messages from ground stations located in Texas, Arizona, and Georgia.

3. Echo I. Echo I was put into orbit on August 12, 1960. It was an aluminum-coated, spherical balloon, 100 ft in diameter, which was inflated in orbit by gas-generating chemicals. It was the world's first passive communication satellite and attracted a great deal of attention because it could be tracked by the unaided eye and was visible in most parts of the world. President Eisenhower's message was transmitted across the country from the NASA facility at Goldstone, California, to the Bell Telephone Station at Holmdel, New Jersey, by reflecting it from Echo I. Two-way voice communication was transmitted between Cedar Rapids, Iowa, and Richardson, Texas, by way of Echo I on August 13, 1960. On August 19, 1960, picture transmission between these same stations occurred via Echo I. East-to-west transmission occurred at 960 Mc and west-to-east transmission at 2390 megacycles. The limitations and the possibilities of passive-communication satellites were explored by Echo I. The operational plan for Project Echo is shown in Figure 1-23. Additional Echos will be launched, but passive-communication techniques have serious limitations when compared to active-repeater types.

4. Courier. Courier IB was successfully launched into orbit on October 4, 1960. It consisted of an epoxy fiberglass sphere which measured 51 in. in diameter and contained 300 lb of electronic equipment. Its purpose was to test the delayed-repeater type of communication satellite. The 19,200 solar cells provide 62 watts of power to the nickel-cadmium batteries.

Much of the transmission equipment is transistorized, and in some cases redundant equipment which can be turned on by a command from the ground is carried. The transmitter includes four microwave FM transmitters and two telemetry transmitters. Frequencies in the

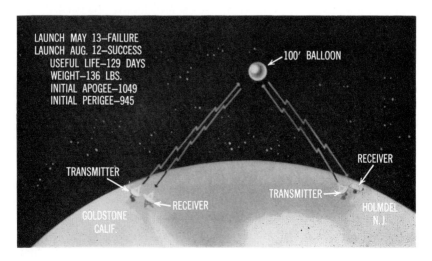

Figure 1-23   Project Echo.

Figure 1-24   Photograph of Courier 1B ready to launch.

200 to 7000-Mc range are used.   Courier IB is capable of simultaneously receiving, storing, and transmitting approximately 68,000 coded
words per minute.   Successful operation has occurred between Fort
Monmouth, New Jersey, and the Army Space Communication Center
near Ponce, Puerto Rico.   Figure 1-24 is a photograph of Courier IB.

5. Relay.   Relay is an active-repeater communication satellite being
built by the Radio Corporation of America under NASA's supervision.
It is planned to launch Relay in late 1962 into an orbit with a perigee
of about 900 miles and an apogee of about 3000 miles.   It is octagonal
in shape, will weigh 115 lb, and measures 29 in. in diameter and 32

in. high. It is the purpose of Project Relay to develop a satellite to receive and retransmit telephone, television, and other forms of wide-band transmission data on an international basis. The elliptical orbit will permit transmission on an intermittent basis between the American Telephone and Telegraph station at Rumford, Maine, and British, French, and possibly German stations in Europe. There will also be a link between an International Telephone and Telegraph station at Nutley, New Jersey, and a South American station at Rio de Janeiro, Brazil. Relay also will provide transcontinental communications between NASA stations at Goldstone, California, and Blossom Point, Maryland.

A UHF transmitter will be powered by storage batteries charged by 7500 solar cells. Two transponders, each receiving on 1725 Mc and retransmitting on 4170 Mc, will be employed. In addition, there will be two command-controlled receivers and decoders and a pulse-coded telemetry system. Efforts are being made to build an unusually high degree of reliability into the system.

6. Advent. Project Advent has as its objective an investigation of the feasibility of a worldwide microwave communication system for military purposes. Although the program is a tri-service effort, it is under the jurisdiction of the U. S. Army Advent Management Agency at Fort Monmouth, New Jersey.

Present plans call for three satellites to be injected into synchronous orbits (22,300 miles) about the equator, 120 degrees apart. Since the speed of each satellite would be synchronized with the earth's rotation, it would remain over a fixed point on the earth. Ground stations would be augmented by shipboard stations provided by the Navy. High-gain communication antennas will be used, which will be pointed toward the earth at all times by horizon sensors and a special attitude control system. The equipment will provide for multichannel wide-band microwave communication to permit simultaneous transmission of high-speed teletype and voice messages.

7. Syncom. Syncom, like Advent, will be a synchronous communication satellite (22,300 miles). However, instead of being launched into an orbit above the equator, it will be launched in an elongated figure-eight pattern which will extend 33 degrees north and south of the equator. Thus it will remain at the same longitude but will oscillate back and forth across the equator. Also, it will be considerably smaller than Advent, weighing only 50 lb.

Syncom will be an active-repeater satellite receiving at 8000 Mc and retransmitting at 2000 Mc. Initial models will have sufficient band-

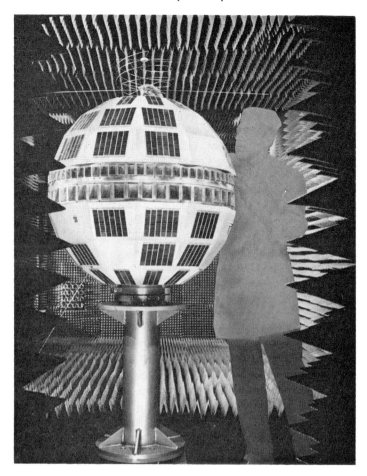

Figure 1-25   Photograph of Telstar.

widths to carry television transmissions. It is planned to launch the
first model in late 1962 by using a Thor-Delta booster.

8. Telstar.   Figure 1-25 is a photograph of the first model of Telstar
(4).   It will be this nation's first commercial satellite and is being
built by the American Telephone and Telegraph Company.   Telstar
will weigh about 150 lb, and it is planned to put it into an elliptical
orbit with a 600-mile perigee and 3000-mile apogee with a Thor-Delta
booster in late 1962.

Telstar will provide transcontinental and transoceanic wideband
telephone, telegraph, and television transmission.   It is an active-

repeater satellite whose power supply will be solar-cell-charged, nickel-cadmium batteries. Telstar will receive on 6390 Mc and retransmit on 4170 Mc, using a 3-watt traveling wave tube. Ground stations will be located at Rumford, Maine, and Holmdel, New Jersey.

Meteorological satellites

1. Introduction. When the peaceful uses of satellites are considered, meteorological satellites are probably second in importance only to communication satellites. Meteorological satellites offer the possibility of transmitting to ground stations cloud-cover photographs taken by television cameras and infrared sensing devices which indicate ground and sea temperatures, both on a worldwide basis. This meteorological information has proved useful in detecting and tracking storms, hurricanes, and typhoons and in making long-range weather predictions.

2. TIROS (12). The code word TIROS is taken from the initial letters of the phrase "Television Infra-Red Observation Satellite." The objective of the TIROS Program is to develop television and infrared techniques for a worldwide meteorological information system, which includes cloud-cover photographs for operational weather forecasting and infrared reflection measurements from clouds, land masses, and water surfaces for temperature determinations.

TIROS I was launched into a near-circular orbit on April 1, 1960, by a Thor-Able booster. The equipment included two television cameras, one with high resolution and the other wide angle, but both scanning 500 lines per frame and operating on a video bandwidth of 62.5 kc. The communication command and telemetering transmitters were frequency modulated and operated on 108.0 and 108.3 Mc. Power was supplied to nickel-cadmium batteries by 9200 solar cells. Ground stations were located at Fort Monmouth, New Jersey, and Kaena Point, Hawaii. Since the vehicle was spin-stabilized, the equipment was operated by command from the ground only when it pointed toward the earth and when that part of the earth's surface was in sunlight.

From the beginning TIROS I was successful in transmitting useful meteorological information back to earth. More than 22,000 pictures were transmitted by TIROS I, of which more than 60 percent were of sufficient quality to be used for meteorological research. New information was obtained on cloud systems, including spiral formations associated with large storms. It was discovered that both tropical and extratropical cyclones are characterized by a very distinct vortex or spiral-cloud pattern about their centers. Figure 1-26 is a photograph of TIROS I, showing one of the TV cameras.

TIROS I observed a storm off the coast of Madagascar and tracked it for 5 days. It also detected and tracked a typhoon in a region north of New Zealand. In the case of mid-latitude storms, it has been possible to detect the weather fronts associated with these storms from satellite observations.

TIROS II was successfully injected into a near-circular orbit on November 23, 1960. In addition to the transmission of cloud-cover pictures, the satellite provided useful infrared information on ground and water-surface temperatures. Infrared readings were taken in the 1-to-12-μ region.

TIROS III was successfully launched into a near-circular orbit on July 12, 1961. It carried a wide-angle television camera and improved

Figure 1-26   Photograph of TIROS I, showing one of the TV cameras.

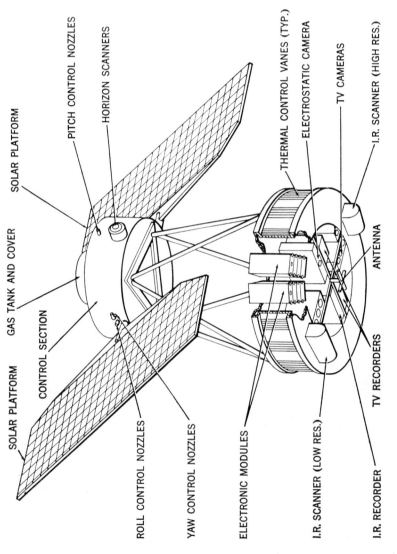

SOLAR PLATFORM

PITCH CONTROL NOZZLES

HORIZON SCANNERS

THERMAL CONTROL VANES (TYP.)

ELECTROSTATIC CAMERA

TV CAMERAS

I.R. SCANNER (HIGH RES.)

SOLAR PLATFORM

GAS TANK AND COVER

CONTROL SECTION

SOLAR PLATFORM

ROLL CONTROL NOZZLES

YAW CONTROL NOZZLES

ELECTRONIC MODULES

I.R. SCANNER (LOW RES.)

I.R. RECORDER

TV RECORDERS

ANTENNA

Figure 1-27 Diagram of Nimbus.

infrared equipment, both of which yielded useful information. TIROS III transmitted many photographs of tropical storms during the 1961 hurricane season and is credited with discovering hurricane Esther.

TIROS IV, with improved equipment aboard, was put into a near-circular orbit on February 8, 1962. Its perigee was about 475 miles and its apogee 525 miles. It has transmitted much useful photographic and infrared information.

3. Nimbus. Nimbus is a second-generation meteorological satellite. It will be more sophisticated than the TIROS satellites and will take advantage of recently developed attitude-control techniques so that its television cameras and infrared sensors will always face the earth. Also, its solar cells will always face the sun, thus providing constant power to the storage batteries.

Nimbus will be launched in polar orbit so that the entire earth will be scanned twice a day. It will carry six television cameras and improved infrared radiation sensors. Later models will carry a spectrometer for temperature measurements and an image orthicon camera for observing night cloud cover. Meteorological information obtained from Nimbus will be distributed to weather stations throughout the world by the United States Weather Bureau. Figure 1-27 is a diagram of Nimbus.

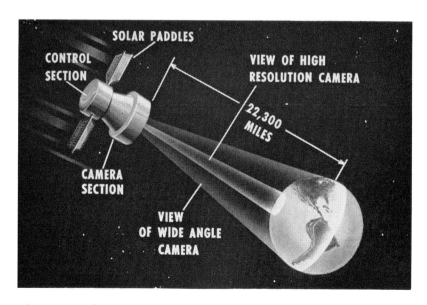

Figure 1-28   Diagram of Aeros.

4. Aeros. Aeros is the third-generation meteorological satellite. It will be a synchronous satellite (22,300 miles) and therefore will remain over a designated spot on the earth. Three such satellites will give complete world coverage. Its television cameras and infrared sensing equipment will be attitude-controlled so that they will always face the earth. Thus a storm, hurricane, or typhoon can be watched and tracked continuously.

A new feature that is being developed for Aeros is a remotely controlled zoomar-type lens for the satellite's television camera, which can be changed from high resolution to a wide angle sufficient to cover the diameter of the earth. Figure 1-28 is an operational diagram of Aeros.

Navigation satellites

1. Introduction. To date, the Transit Program (7) has furnished the only known operational navigation satellites. There have been seven launchings of Transit vehicles, of which five have been placed in orbit and have operated satisfactorily. The primary objective of the Transit Program is to establish an operational, worldwide, all-weather navigation system by the use of artificial earth satellites. Although the program was designed to provide an accurate navigation system for military ships, submarines, and aircraft, it also has commercial possibilities. Transit has as a secondary objective the scientific exploration of space near the earth. As a result, the last four Transit vehicles have carried pick-a-back satellites containing scientific experiments. These satellites were GREB to measure solar radiation, INJUN to measure the radiation in the inner and outer Van Allen radiation belts and to investigate auroral phenomena, LOFTI (Low Frequency Trans-Ionosphere) to measure the reception of radio waves in and above the ionosphere, and TRAAC (Transit Research and Attitude Control) to test the feasibility of a spacecraft-stabilization system utilizing the earth's gravitational field.

The Transit satellite carries a transmitter whose frequency is accurately known and is temperature-stabilized to 1 part in 10^9. Also, its orbit can be accurately determined from tracking data. From these two known facts, and by analyzing the Doppler signal between the satellite and a station anywhere on the earth's surface, it is possible to determine the latitude and longitude of the station. With present equipment it is possible to determine the position of a ship, submarine, or aircraft with an accuracy of about 500 ft. The accuracy of the navigation system is not limited by the precision of the equipment but by a lack of accurate information about physical quantities related to the earth. For example, additional information must be obtained about the size and shape of the earth and its gravitational field and about the refraction of radio waves by the ionosphere, especially in the auroral regions and during magnetic storms.

The feasibility of using an artificial satellite for an accurate, worldwide, all-weather navigation system has been demonstrated by the five Transit vehicles which have been put into orbit and all of which have operated satisfactorily. As a bonus, much useful scientific information has been obtained from the pick-a-back satellites GREB, LOFTI, INJUN, and TRAAC.

2. Transit I-B. Transit I-B was the first navigation satellite to be put successfully into orbit, although Transit I-A came close to succeeding. Transit I-A was launched from Cape Canaveral on September 17, 1959, but after it reached the desired altitude of 400 miles the third stage did not ignite and the capsule fell into the ocean west of Ireland. However, the equipment operated satisfactorily over a sufficient period (22 min) to demonstrate the feasibility of a satellite navigation system. Figure 1-29 is a cutaway diagram of Transit I-A.

Transit I-B was successfully launched into orbit on April 13, 1960, by a Thor-Able Star, and all equipment operated satisfactorily. In

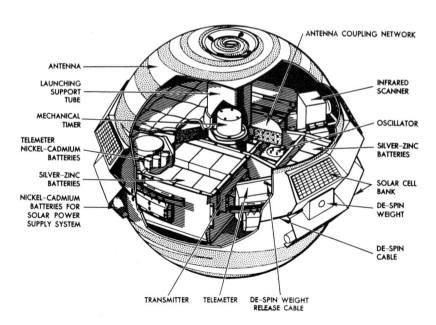

ANTENNA COUPLING NETWORK

ANTENNA

LAUNCHING SUPPORT TUBE

MECHANICAL TIMER

TELEMETER NICKEL-CADMIUM BATTERIES

SILVER-ZINC BATTERIES

NICKEL-CADMIUM BATTERIES FOR SOLAR POWER SUPPLY SYSTEM

INFRARED SCANNER

OSCILLATOR

SILVER-ZINC BATTERIES

SOLAR CELL BANK

DE-SPIN WEIGHT

DE-SPIN CABLE

TRANSMITTER   TELEMETER   DE-SPIN WEIGHT RELEASE CABLE

Figure 1-29 Cutaway diagram of Transit I-A.

addition to demonstrating the ability of a satellite to determine the position of a station on the earth's surface sufficiently accurate for navigation purposes, scientific information was obtained on the refractive effects of radio waves in the ionosphere and on the infrared albedo level of the earth. Also, the ability to retard the spinning rate of the vehicle while in orbit was demonstrated.

3. Transit II-A. Transit II-A carried pick-a-back satellite GREB-I with it into orbit. It was launched from Cape Canaveral on June 22, 1960, by a Thor-Able Star and operated satisfactorily as a navigational satellite.

GREB-I carried experimental equipment to measure solar activity above the atmosphere, particularly the Lyman-alpha line, and the X-ray spectrum below 8 Å. The experiments were designed by the Naval Research Laboratory. It also carried an experiment to measure cosmic radio noise above ionosphere which was designed by the Defense Research Telecommunications Establishment of Canada. All equipment operated as planned, and the data received is being analyzed.

4. Transit III-B. Transit III-B with a LOFTI (Low Frequency Trans-Ionosphere) attached as a pick-a-back satellite was launched into orbit on February 21, 1961, by a Thor-Able Star booster. The two satellites did not separate as planned and therefore went into an elliptical orbit rather than a circular one. However, the equipment on both satellites functioned and provided some results, though not so complete as had been hoped.

The LOFTI results indicate the possibility of using VLF for communication purposes between submarines and other stations either on the ground or on shipboard via a satellite traveling in and above the ionosphere. Transit III-B also functioned satisfactorily as a navigation satellite during its lifetime. Because of the ellipticity of the orbit, the perigee was low (102 statute miles), and the two satellites re-entered the earth's atmosphere after 37 days of operation. Figure 1-30 is a photograph of Transit III-B with LOFTI.

5. Transit IV-A. The first triple payload ever launched was put into a near-circular orbit on June 29, 1961, by a Thor-Able Star. It contained Transit IV-A, INJUN to make measurements of the inner and outer Van Allen radiation belts, and GREB-3 to make solar X-ray radiation measurements. The equipment on all three satellites functioned perfectly, and some very useful data has been obtained from the combined satellites.

A new feature, carried on Transit IV-A, was a small, lightweight, radioisotope-fueled thermoelectric generator to provide auxiliary

Figure 1-30 Photograph of Transit III-B with LOFTI.

power. It is known as SNAP (Space Nuclear Auxiliary Power) and is part of a series of power sources by this name, now numbering 12. The generator is about the size of a grapefruit and will provide the electrical power for two of the four transmitters for a period of many years.

6. Transit IV-B. Transit IV-B with TRAAC (Transit Research and Attitude Control) aboard was successfully put into a near-circular orbit on November 15, 1961. TRAAC was designed to test the feasibility of a spacecraft stabilization system using the earth's gravitational field. It is shaped like a doorknob, measures 43 in. in diameter and 16 in. high, and is connected to the top of the spacecraft by a tube. A coiled boom designed to provide the proper mass distribution for maintaining the desired attitude extends from the tube.

In addition to the experiment on attitude control, the satellite carried experiments (1) to delineate the number and density of protons in the inner Van Allen radiation belt, (2) to search for trapped particles heavier than protons, and (3) to check the cosmic-ray neutron albedo theory of the origin of the inner Van Allen radiation belt.

All equipment, including that used for navigation purposes, operated satisfactorily. Data received from Transit IV-B are now being analyzed, and it is considered to be a successful satellite.

1-3 FUTURE SPACE PROGRAMS

Lunar probes

1. The Ranger Program (3). The primary purpose of the Ranger Program is the scientific exploration of the moon. There are also a number of secondary purposes, such as the exploration of the space between the earth and the moon, interplanetary space, and the testing of control, guidance, tracking, and telemetry equipment for the spacecraft. Data obtained from Ranger flights will be utilized extensively in such later programs as Surveyor, Apollo, Prospector, and Mariner.

The purpose of Ranger 1 and Ranger 2 was not to reach the moon but to explore interplanetary space out to about 700,000 miles, which is about three times the distance between the earth and the moon, in order to make scientific measurements in this area and to test the operation of the spacecraft. Figure 1-31 is a diagram of Ranger 1. It weighs 675 lb, is 13 ft high, and, in orbital condition, 17 ft across the solar panels. Ranger 1 was launched into a parking orbit on August 24, 1961, by an Atlas D first stage and an Agena B second stage. This was the first attempt by the United States to launch a spacecraft from a parking orbit into another orbit. It failed when the Agena B apparently failed to restart, and as a result the spacecraft went into a much smaller orbit than planned and re-entered the earth's atmosphere on August 30, 1961. However, during the 7 days much valuable scientific information was obtained from the experiments carried on the spacecraft. The equipment included a solar corpuscular detector, a medium-range particle detector, a cosmic-ray ionization chamber, a triple-coincidence cosmic-ray telescope, a rubidium-vapor magnetometer, a solar X-ray scintillation detector, a Lyman-alpha telescope, a cosmic-dust detector, and a drag coefficient experiment. Ranger 2 was launched on November 18, 1961, and re-entered the earth's atmosphere 2 days later. Ranger 3 was the first Ranger built to go to the vicinity of the moon. It was launched on January 26, 1962, by an Atlas D and Agena B combination. It was designed to fly close enough to the moon to take television pictures,

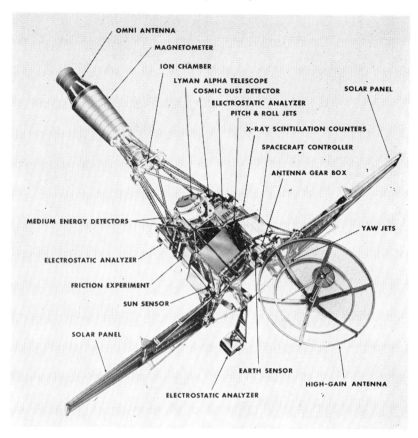

Figure 1-31 Diagram of Ranger 1.

and to perform scientific experiments. However, the Atlas guidance system imparted too great a velocity to the vehicle, and as a result it missed its target by approximately 22,800 miles. Nevertheless, the flight proved that the scientific equipment worked satisfactorily and that the spacecraft could be commanded to perform certain operational functions.

Ranger 4, which was a repetition of Ranger 3 insofar as objectives were concerned, was launched on April 23, 1962. A model of Ranger 4 is shown in Figure 1-32. It impacted the moon on April 26, 1962, but because of a faulty switch some of the experiments did not work satisfactorily. Additional Rangers are scheduled to be launched, some to the vicinity of the moon and others to make landings on the moon

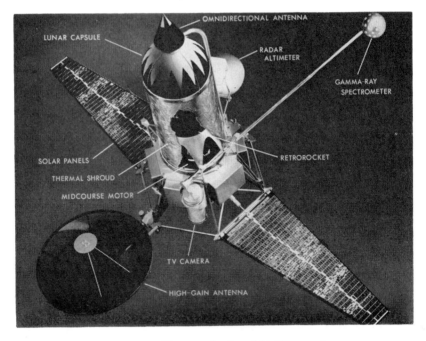

Figure 1-32 Photograph of model of Ranger 4.

and perform scientific explorations of the moon's surface. Some of the scientific experiments to be carried on Ranger spacecraft are the following:

a. Solar Corpuscular Radiation Analyzer. The purpose of this experiment is to determine the flow and movement of interplanetary plasma (clouds of charged particles) by observing their density and direction of motion and by measuring the energies of their particles. The experiment will try to determine whether the particles (primarily hydrogen) are streaming outward from the sun as a solar wind, or wandering at random in a comparatively stationary plasma.

b. Medium-Energy Range Particle Detectors. The purpose of this experiment is to observe charged particles in an energy range that overlaps the low energies of the particles in the interplanetary plasma and the high energies of the fast-moving cosmic rays. Six specially designed detectors have been prepared for this experiment, which was developed by Dr. Van Allen of the State University of Iowa and Dr. Simpson at the University of Chicago.

c. Cosmic-Ray Ionization Rate Measurements. In this experiment primary cosmic radiation and other ionizing radiation in the space beyond the earth's atmosphere will be measured by a quartz-fiber, integrating-type ionization chamber developed by Dr. Victor Nehr of the California Institute of Technology. It is known that storms on the surface of the sun produce many highly energetic particles that are hazardous to men in space. Therefore, it is important that this potentially dangerous radiation be measured.

d. Triple-Coincidence, Cosmic-Ray Analysis. The purpose of this experiment is to measure high-energy radiation in interplanetary space with the aid of two triple-coincidence telescopes consisting of an assembly of proportional-counter tubes. Similar experiments were carried on Explorer VI and Pioneer V. Since each telescope has a different amount of shielding, and by comparing the single-count data and the triple-coincidence data, it is possible to determine the radiation due to X rays and the amount due to protons or other high-energy charge particles.

e. Magnetic Field Analysis. The purpose of this experiment is to measure the magnitude and direction of the magnetic fields in interplanetary space beyond the influence of the earth's magnetic field. In order to do this, the experiment must include a rubidium-vapor magnetometer capable of taking measurements as low as 0.01 gamma. These measurements will be used to check various theories now existing, for example, regarding ring currents, solar winds, and the Forbush decrease. Although some very valuable information about these fields was obtained from the Explorers and from Pioneer V, additional data are needed.

f. Solar X-Ray Detection. The purpose of this experiment is to measure both the steady and the transient intensities of X rays given off by the sun. It is well known that the sun emits radiation in the X-ray region, but the intensity is not constant. Therefore, to measure the bursts of energy in this region, a pair of scintillation counters will be carried on the Ranger.

g. Neutral Hydrogen Geocorona. This experiment will employ a telescope and a detector sensitive to the Lyman-alpha region of the spectrum in an effort to determine whether the earth carries with it a cloud of hydrogen. A neutral hydrogen gas glow in the earth's upper atmosphere has been observed from sounding rockets, but there has not been an opportunity to observe it from outer space. If it exists, then its shape is important, since a "tear" shape, or a cometlike tail shape, would indicate that it is being affected by solar winds. If there is a glowing corona around the earth, it may be analogous to the corona of the sun. Pictures of the neutral hydrogen glow as Ranger proceeds from the earth will provide clarification of this phenomenon.

h. Cosmic Dust. As Ranger speeds through space, this experiment will measure the impact rate, energy, momentum, and direction of flight of dust particles in the interplanetary region. Analysis of the data will reveal both the mass and speed of the dust particles as well as their direction of flight. Their direction of flight is important since this will indicate whether the particles are rotating with the earth, the sun, or have any preferred direction. Since one theory states that our planetary system was formed by the condensation of great clouds of dust particles some 5 billion years ago, the measurement of the size and mass of these particles may throw some light on this theory.

2. The Surveyor Program. Although Rangers 6 to 9 may attempt a hard landing on the moon, the Surveyor Program is designed for a

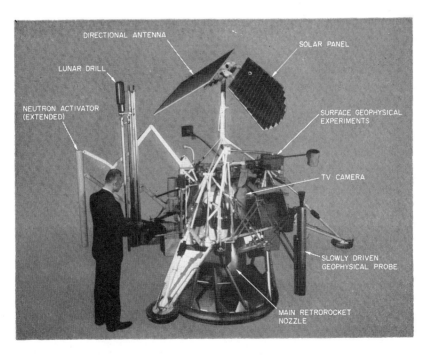

Figure 1-33 Photograph of model of Surveyor.

soft landing and exploration of its surface and subsurface. The space-craft will weigh about 750 lb. and will be landed on the moon's surface at 6 mph by solid-propellant retrorockets. Instruments to be carried on Surveyor include a seismometer, a magnetometer, and others to measure the lunar gravity, radiation, and atmosphere. Surveyor will carry a semiautomatic drill capable of penetrating the moon's surface to a maximum depth of 5 ft. The material obtained from the drilled hole will be analyzed by instruments carried on the spacecraft. In addition, Surveyor will carry four television cameras, one of which will monitor the drilling process. The spacecraft is designed to operate on the lunar surface for 1 month and should transmit back to earth valuable information about the moon's surface. Figure 1-33 is a photograph of the Surveyor spacecraft with some of its equipment.

3. The Apollo Program.* The purpose of the Apollo Program is to put three men on the moon by 1967 and return them safely. In order to accomplish this objective, a number of intermediate steps have been planned. The first Apollo vehicle will be known as Apollo A. It will weigh approximately 30,000 lb and will be boosted into an earth orbit by a Saturn C-1. It is planned in 1965 to put three men into a 14-day earth orbit and recover them as the initial step of the Apollo Program.

The second step will be taken by Apollo B in 1966, when it is planned to put a three-man crew into a circumlunar flight and return them safely to the earth. Apollo B will weigh about 50,000 lb and will be boosted by a Saturn C-5. The final step of placing three men on the moon for exploratory purposes will be taken by Apollo C. It will weigh approximately 200,000 lb and will require either a Saturn C-5 for a rendezvous flight or a Nova-type booster for a direct flight.

Planetary probes (10)

The purpose of the Planetary Probe Program is to develop an auto-matic unmanned spacecraft capable of orbiting and landing first on Mars and Venus and later on Mercury and Jupiter. The primary ob-jective of this program is the scientific exploration of these planets and interplanetary space. To accomplish it, three types of spacecraft are planned: Mariner R, Mariner B, and Voyager.

1. Mariner R. The primary objective of the Mariner R project is to develop and launch two spacecraft to the vicinity of Venus during 1962. The spacecraft will make radiometric temperature measure-

---

* After this section was written, NASA decided on the lunar-orbit-rendezvous method of landing men on the moon.

ments of the planet and telemeter this information back to earth. Venus is completely and continuously covered with clouds, so that very little is known about its surface or the atmosphere between the surface and the clouds (6). A secondary objective is to make scientific measurements in the interplanetary space between the earth and Venus and in the vicinity of Venus, including magnetic fields, radiation, and dust particles. Mariner R is a replacement for Mariner A. A diagram of Mariner A is shown in Figure 1-34.

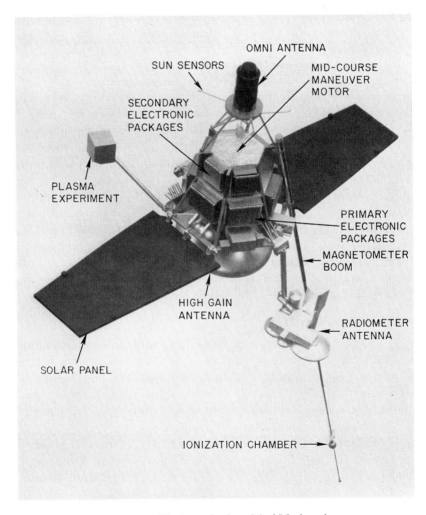

Figure 1-34 Photograph of model of Mariner A.

2. Mariner B. The primary objective of the Mariner B project is to make scientific investigations of the planet Mars and/or Venus during their periods of availability from 1964 to 1967. A secondary objective is to make scientific investigations in the interplanetary space between the earth and Mars and to gain experience and knowledge that will be helpful in the design of Voyager. The spacecraft mission will be designed as a flyby of Mars and Venus and may include dropping a capsule on these planets.

3. Voyager. Voyager will be a much more sophisticated planetary probe than either Mariner R or Mariner B. It will be launched with a Saturn vehicle and will be designed to orbit the planets. Before landing operations can be accomplished on the planets, careful observations must be made from orbiting vehicles. The landing of a capsule may be attempted, which then could relay detailed information back to the spacecraft. Data from the capsule, including television pictures, could be relayed back to earth via the spacecraft.

Scientific satellites

1. Orbiting Geophysical Observatory (OGO). OGO is the most sophisticated scientific satellite yet designed. It is sometimes called the "street car" satellite because it will carry as many as 50 experiments designed by scientists from many university, governmental, and industrial laboratories. Included are experiments to measure energetic particles, magnetic fields, cosmic rays, solar protons, solar winds, trapped radiation, ionospheric phenomena, and micrometeorites. It will carry both a search coil and a rubidium-vapor magnetometer, a mass spectrometer, and an ion trap. The micrometeorite detector is designed to measure the velocity, mass, and direction of flight of the micrometeorites. The satellite has a very sophisticated data-storage and telemetry system. Its attitude control system, which includes gas jets and reaction wheels, is unique in that it is designed to stabilize the solar cells so that they will always point toward the sun and one side of the satellite so that it will always point toward the earth. To protect the equipment, the spacecraft is thermally controlled so that its temperature will remain at approximately 70°F. Figure 1-35 is a photograph of a model of OGO. The vehicle will weigh approximately 1000 lb and will carry the magnetometers and the ion-capturing equipment on long booms that will unfold after launch.

The first version of OGO to be launched will be an Eccentric Orbiting Geophysical Observatory (EGO). It will be launched from Cape Canaveral in early 1963 by an Atlas-Agena B. Later, a Polar Orbiting

Geophysical Observatory (POGO) will be launched into polar orbit by a Thor-Agena B from the Pacific Missile Range.

2. Orbiting Solar Observatory (OSO). OSO-1, which weighed 458 lb, was launched from Cape Canaveral on March 7, 1962, with a three-stage Thor-Delta as the booster. It was put into a near-circular orbit of 350 miles apogee. The purpose of the OSO Program is to make scientific measurements of the sun from above the earth's atmosphere, in the ultraviolet, X-ray, and gamma-ray regions. OSO-1 carried 13 scientific experiments and is the first of a series of scientific satellites to study the sun during a solar cycle. The experiments included solar X-ray measurement of solar radiation in the 10-to-400-Å spectral region, gamma-ray monitoring, an ultraviolet test (1100 to 1250 Å), measurement of visible radiation in the blue region (3800 to 4800 Å), neutron monitoring, and a dust-particle experiment.

Preliminary results indicate that OSO-1 is a successful scientific satellite, that all 13 experiments are working satisfactorily, and that all are sending information back to earth with excellent clarity and quality.

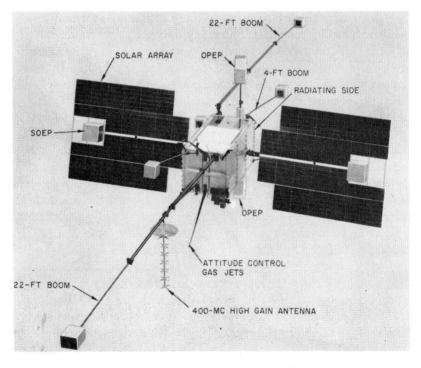

Figure 1-35 Photograph of model of OGO.

Figure 1-36 Photograph of a full-scale model of OAO.

3. Orbiting Astronomical Observatory (OAO) (14). The purpose of the OAO Program is to place an optical telescope above the earth's atmosphere in order to make observations of the stars, the planets, and possibly the sun. The first OAO will be launched in late 1963 with an Atlas-Agena B. It will weigh 3300 lb, and will carry a reflecting telescope with a 36-in. diameter and associated equipment. OAO will carry an attitude-control system capable of locking on a star and holding the telescope on it with an accuracy of less than 1 sec of arc. This is comparable to the accuracy of a terrestrial telescope. A wideband transmitting system will be employed to transmit television pictures back to earth. OAO will require 350 watts of power, which will be furnished by a large array of solar cells. Numerous universities, such as Wisconsin, Princeton, and Harvard, are cooperating in this scientific venture by supplying experiments. A photograph of a full-scale model of OAO is shown in Figure 1-36.

1-4 SUMMARY

In the five years that have elapsed since the first Sputnik was launched into orbit on October 4, 1957, a great deal has been accomplished both technically and scientifically insofar as space exploration is concerned. From an engineering or technical point of view, propulsion systems with large thrusts and long durations capable of overcoming the earth's gravitational pull and putting large objects into space have been developed. Structures able to sustain these objects in flight have been designed and built. The laws of supersonic aerodynamics have been well enough understood to produce vehicles that will withstand the aerodynamic forces of launching through the atmosphere and the thermal forces of re-entry heating. In addition, sophisticated methods of guidance, control, tracking, and telemetry have been perfected specifically for space vehicles. Complicated mathematical equations of motion and navigation, involving the use of the latest types of digital computers, have been worked out. All of these engineering advances have required scientific support in the way of research from nearly all of the scientific and mathematical disciplines.

The space-science accomplishments in this same period have been many and varied. The discovery of the Van Allen trapped radiation belts was not an accident. The discovery of ring currents circling the earth of several million amperes was made by scientific exploration of the magnetic fields surrounding the earth. The geodetic discovery that the earth is not a spheroid, but is slightly pear-shaped, came from one of the first satellites. The measurement of the astronomical unit more accurately than ever before achieved is certainly a space-science accomplishment. We know more about solar emissions, solar winds,

SPUTNIK I	Oct. 4, 1957	First artificial satellite put in orbit
SPUTNIK II	Nov. 3, 1957	First animal put in orbit (dog "Laika")
EXPLORER I	Jan. 31, 1958	Discovered Van Allen radiation belt
PIONEER III	Dec. 6, 1958	Discovery of second radiation belt
LUNIK II	Sept. 12, 1959	First object (from earth) to impact the moon
LUNIK III	Oct. 4, 1959	First photographs of back side of moon
PIONEER V	Mar. 11, 1960	Greatest radio communication distance $(22.5 \times 10^6$ miles)
TIROS I	Apr. 1, 1960	First extensive TV transmission of cloud formations
TRANSIT IB	Apr. 13, 1960	First navigation satellite
DISCOVERER XIII	Aug. 10, 1960	First recovery of capsule from orbit
SCORE	Dec. 18, 1958	First satellite used for communication purposes
SPUTNIK V	Aug. 19, 1960	First recovery of live animals from orbit
SPUTNIK XI	Apr. 11, 1961	First recovery of live man from orbit

Figure 1-37   List of "firsts" and accomplishments of space exploration.

and solar storms than we did before the first satellite was launched. Exploration of the earth's magnetic field out to distances of 10 earth radii and beyond have been made. We know more about cosmic rays, both galactic and solar, than we did before the space age began. Both rocket spectroscopy and radio astronomy have contributed useful scientific data to our space knowledge. In the biological and medical fields important discoveries have been made that will contribute to man's safety and comfort while traveling in space.

These are but a few of the technical and scientific developments of the last 5 years. The next 5 years should see even greater discoveries and accomplishments. Figure 1-37 shows a few of the "firsts" and outlines some of the results of space exploration to date.

REFERENCES

1. Chapman, S., Sun Storms and the Earth, *Am. Scientist,* 249 (September 1961).
2. Christofilos, N. C., The Argus Experiment, *Proc. Nat. Acad. Sci. U. S.* (August 1959).
3. Cummings, C., et al., Ranger in the Lunar Program, *Astronautics,* 22–37 (September 1961).
4. Findley, R., Communication Satellite—Telstar, *National Geographic,* **12,** 5, 638 (May 1962).
5. Goldberg, L., The Sun, Report of the Space Science Board of the National Academy of Sciences (February 1960).
6. Kellogg, W. W., and C. Sagan, The Atmospheres of Mars and Venus, Report of the Space Science Board of the National Academy of Sciences (Publication 944) (1961).
7. Kershher, R. B., The Transit Program, *Astronautics,* 36 (June 1960).
8. Kuiper, G. P., *Photographic Atlas of the Moon,* University of Chicago Press, Chicago, 1960.
9. Mikhailov, A. A., The Other Side of the Moon, *Astronautics,* 40 (March 1961).
10. Parks, R. J., The U. S. Planetary Exploration Program, *Astronautics,* 22 (May 1961).
11. Simpson, J. A., Physics of Fields and Energetic Particles in Space, Report of the Space Science Board of the National Academy of Sciences (February 1960).
12. Sternberg, S., et al., Tiros I, *Astronautics,* 32–44 (June 1960).
13. Störmer, C., *Polar Aurora,* Oxford University Press, London, 1955.
14. Viemer, R. R., Orbiting Astronomical Observatories, *Astronautics,* 36 (May 1961).
15. Much of the detailed information on satellites and space probes used in this chapter was taken from the "STL Space Log," published by Space Technology Laboratories, Inc., originally edited by John Herrick but now edited by Thomas L. Branigan.

CHAPTER 2

STELLAR EVOLUTION AND HIGH ENERGY PHENOMENA IN ASTROPHYSICS

JESSE L. GREENSTEIN

Mount Wilson and Palomar Observatories

Carnegie Institution of Washington

California Institute of Technology

Since the appearance of publications by Greenstein (1) and Fowler (2), not a great deal has been added to our fundamental knowledge of the energy-producing mechanisms in the stars. A belief that most or all of the chemical elements have been synthesized from hydrogen by thermonuclear processes inside the stars has gained wide acceptance. Elaborate machine computations of models of the density and temperature in stellar interiors have given us a more sophisticated, but certainly not final, picture of stellar evolution. A more detailed knowledge of the nuclear processes and many quantitative spectroscopic analyses of the stars have increased our confidence in the general picture of star birth, life, and death.

Matter is largely collected in stars like the sun; in addition, interstellar matter—gas and dust—also exists in each galaxy. A typical galaxy is about 100,000 light years in diameter, and has a mass of a hundred billion suns; about 1 to 10 percent of the mass is interstellar gas. On the basis of redshifts and current estimates of the distances of the galaxies, the expansion time, measured by the reciprocal of the Hubble constant, is about 13 billion years. The age of our Galaxy is now thought to be approximately 10 or 15 billion years, although a few years ago estimates as high as 25 billion were made.

Gravitational forces hold the stars together in clusters (10^2 to 10^5 solar masses) or in galaxies (10^9 to 10^{12} solar masses). Rotation is universal in spiral and probably in many elliptical galaxies, so that angular momentum is an important factor in many problems. In galaxies with a relatively large amount of interstellar gas and dust spiral arms are the loci of maximum abundance of the interstellar matter and of newly formed stars of high luminosity. Stellar rotation itself varies enormously, from equatorial speeds of 2 km/sec for stars like the sun to 500 km/sec for B stars at the margin of stability. In

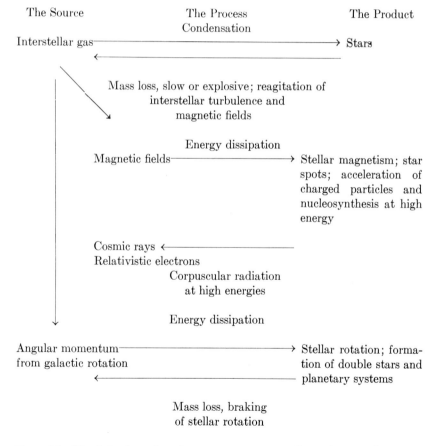

Figure 2-1   The interplay of various processes among the major constituents of a star system.

addition, many stars are double or multiple, reflecting the tendency toward multiplicity in the condensation process. The tiny system of planets around our sun is another manifestation of excessive angular momentum. In addition to gravitation, other important and unexpectedly large forces act on the interstellar gas. The spiral structure in galaxies is thought to be connected with interstellar magnetic fields. Cosmic-ray particles and the emission of radio-frequency noise are also directly connected with the existence of these fields. Magnetic A stars show very large, relatively simple, dipole fields at their surface ranging up to 34,000 gauss. Such a general field at the surface corresponds to an enormous field in the interior. The sun and probably many other types of stars have localized complex variable fields of a few thousand gauss (the sunspots).

Stars are born by condensation from interstellar gases, are heated by the release of gravitational energy, and then tap nuclear energy sources. By the conversion of mass into energy, H^1 into He^4, the energy balance is maintained. When the energy supply, dominantly hydrogen, becomes exhausted, the star "evolves" and begins to die. During the evolutionary dying phase, the star loses part of its mass to interstellar space, either by explosion or by slower methods "mass loss," evaporation, or corpuscular radiation; waste products of nuclear reactions inside the deep interior of stars are returned to space, mix with gases still containing the fuel, hydrogen, and recondense into a

The Source	The Process	The Product
Main energy source	$H^1 \longrightarrow He^4$ Proton-proton chain Carbon-nitrogen cycle	
Secondary energy losses or gains	Gains: helium burning. (C^{13}, O^{17}, Ne^{21}) $+ He^4 \rightarrow$ neutrons. Neutron capture on slow or rapid time scale. Very high temperature equilibrium processes among iron peak elements. Losses: endoergic reactions during star collapse; destruction of heavy elements; neutrino emission. Spallation formation of D, Li, Be, B.	Nucleosynthesis of heavy elements

Figure 2-2 Nuclear energy sources that drive processes in Figure 2-1 and that synthesize the chemical elements.

new generation of stars. A schematic set of cycles of star birth and death and important auxiliary processes is illustrated in Figure 2-1. Except for gravitational energy released during the contraction of a star and angular momentum available initially from galactic rotation or interstellar gas turbulence, nuclear energy is the driving force. The magnetic fields and the cosmic rays are indirect results of the nuclear energy release. Figure 2-2 is a diagram of the main lines and a few subsidiary lines in nuclear processes to illustrate the one type of interaction that seems to be irreversible and that energizes the cycles in Figure 2-1.

2-1 STELLAR EVOLUTION AND THE ORIGIN OF CHEMICAL ELEMENTS

Numerical integrations of a set of differential equations have been carried out step by step, as a star evolves through various stages, taking proper consideration of the energy sources, the pressure gradient, the opacity and temperature gradients that regulate the energy flow, and the change of composition with depth. In principle, once the mass and composition are given, the entire structure of the star is completely determined. Such a stellar model requires both a knowledge of physical processes and data, such as nuclear fusion, the opacity of highly ionized gases, and the hydrodynamics of convection, plus the full resources of large computing machines.

Major results of the study of stellar interiors and of the observations of the brightness, colors, masses and radii of stars are those that describe stars in stages:

1. Gravitational contraction from the low-density interstellar gas to an ultimately stable configuration. This is called the "contracting" or "T Tauri" stage.

2. The stable configuration for a given mass and initial composition. This is the normal main-sequence stage in which a star spends most of its life burning hydrogen. Central temperatures are 5 to 25 million degrees.

3. The evolving stage, that of the subgiants and red giants, which a star enters when it exhausts hydrogen in a certain fraction of its mass and burns other fuels. Here the greatest unsolved observational and theoretical problem is how a star loses mass. Central temperatures are several hundred million degrees.

4. The beginning of star death, when nearly all nuclear fuel is exhausted in the center of a star and the temperatures become extremely high, with an upper limit of about 4 billion degrees.

5. The death of stars—either through the long, slow decay of the white dwarfs radiating internal heat or through explosion as a supernova (if billion-degree temperatures have been reached).

Not all stars, depending on mass and composition, need go through all of these stages. The foregoing phases are characterized by different temperatures and densities and therefore by different nuclear processes. In giant stellar explosions (supernovae) in which the temperature reaches 2 to 4 billion degrees, essentially all possible reactions take place, heavy elements like iron are formed, or all matter is photodisintegrated into protons, neutrons, and alpha particles. Neutrinos may be emitted, carrying away a very large fraction of the stellar energy if the temperatures are sufficiently high.

Total energies; stellar lifetimes; star formation; evolution

The conversion of H into He^4 is accompanied by a mass decrease of 0.6 percent and therefore provides an energy yield of 6×10^{-3} cc^2 times the mass of hydrogen fuel available. Any further reaction, as shown, for example, in equation (2-1),

$$
\begin{aligned}
He^4 + He^4 &\rightleftharpoons Be^8 + \gamma, \\
Be^8 + He^4 &\rightarrow C^{12} + \gamma,
\end{aligned}
\tag{2-1}
$$

yields only an additional 0.06 percent mass decrease, and little is gained from reactions producing heavier elements. The yield from fission of uranium corresponds to a mass decrease of about 0.1 percent, but such heavy elements are very rare. Thus the lifetime of a star is greatest in the stage in which it is burning hydrogen fuel; all subsequent stages are short, except for the cooling-off stage of a dense white dwarf. The total energy output of a star of luminosity L, from all possible thermonuclear sources, is approximately

$$
\int L \, dt = 1.3 \times 10^{52} MF \text{ ergs.}
\tag{2-2}
$$

If we assume that all of its nuclear fuel can be burned (which is not true), $F = 1$; otherwise F is the fraction of the mass of hydrogen which can undergo nuclear processes. Gravitational contraction, from infinity to a minimum radius R (M and R in solar units) has available the approximate potential energy,

$$
|\Omega| = 2.4 \times 10^{48} \frac{M^2}{R} \text{ ergs.}
\tag{2-3}
$$

A considerable fraction of $|\Omega|$ could also be radiated. If a star of solar mass should contract to a small radius (possibly as small as 10^{-2}), the gravitational energy would be about 10^{51} ergs. But the contraction of the sun from the interstellar gas to its present radius yields only about 10^{48} ergs to balance radiation losses. The contracting stage A, already described, is relatively short-lived. Not more than 12 percent of the hydrogen can be burned on the main sequence, giving a nuclear supply of about 10^{51} ergs for the sun, from equation (2-2). These figures will be useful orders of magnitude for stellar energies. The total luminosity of a bright galaxy is 10^{45} ergs/sec, and the total possible nuclear energy output is between 10^{62} and 10^{63} ergs. The rotation of an entire galaxy of 10^{11} stars has a kinetic energy of only 4×10^{58} ergs, indicating that the mechanical energy storehouse is small compared to the nuclear.

If we limit ourselves to the burning of hydrogen into helium (a fairly good approximation), the maximum possible lifetime of the sun on the main sequence is almost 10 billion years. The luminosity L is a steep power of the mass M. A highly luminous blue B star with $L = 10^5$ has a lifetime of only 3 million years, whereas a faint red M dwarf with $L = 10^{-5}$ can live over 30 trillion years.

The interstellar gas from which the stars are born pervades the flattened, main plane of our Galaxy and is concentrated in spiral arms of gas and dust together with the bright short-lived stars. The gas now represents only a few percent of the total mass of the Galaxy. Star formation was much more rapid in the early history of the Galaxy, billions of years ago, than it is now. A counterbalance is the observed ejection of matter into interstellar space from stars at various late evolutionary stages, especially from the red giants; star death, and therefore ejection of mass into space, also was initially more rapid. There was an early period with a burst of rapid star formation in which much of the primeval gas was consumed. While some stars were still contracting, others were born, exhausted their nuclear fuel, and exploded or otherwise returned part of their mass to space where it was mixed with still unused gas. This mixture condensed into further generations of stars contaminated with the waste products of nuclear processes from stars that had already traversed many varieties of evolutionary histories.

We expect that there was also an early burst of formation of heavy elements. As a reasonable starting point, independent of cosmological models, we may assume that our Galaxy began as an uncondensed, rotating spheroid of gas, largely hydrogen, with small impurities of helium, and possibly small amounts of the heavy elements. In one cosmology, that of Hoyle, it is assumed that a galaxy begins with

pure hydrogen; in other models of a possibly very dense early stage of
the expansion of the universe it is possible that isotopes of hydrogen,
helium, and small amounts of a few other elements were synthesized.
In another speculative cosmology residues of matter in a different cycle
of expansion and contraction of the universe might be found. Some
small exchange of matter between galaxies is also possible.

Consideration of available energy is not all that is needed for an
understanding of stellar evolution. A wide variety of stars exists, as
is shown in Figure 2-3, a schematic Hertzsprung-Russell diagram.
Such a diagram relates the luminosity (as ordinate) to the surface
temperature, color, or spectral class (as abscissa). For homogeneous

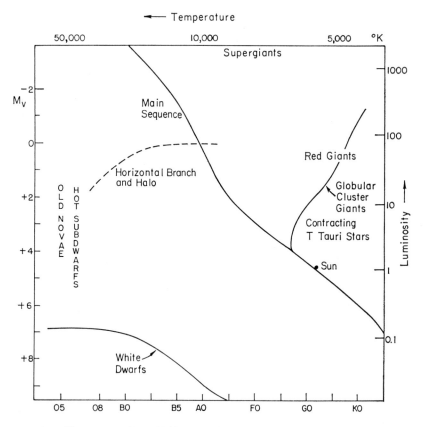

Figure 2-3 Hertzsprung-Russell diagram, showing stars of various masses and ages
at different stages of their evolution. This diagram is schematic and locates some
of the interesting types. Objects like the magnetic A stars lie close to the main
sequence.

stars of constant composition, location on the main sequence is uniquely determined by the mass. The faint dwarf M stars have masses about 0.1 $M_\odot$, the bright B stars about 20 $M_\odot$. The red giants are now thought to be inhomogeneous, with He^4, the nuclear ash, in their cores and with largely H envelopes. As a result, they are denser and hotter in their cores and have large relatively cool envelopes. The supergiants are evolved stars of large mass. Note that various types of hot sub-luminous objects exist at the left edge of the Hertzsprung-Russell diagram reflecting several alternate evolutionary tracks for stars that have exhausted substantially all nuclear fuel. These stars become fainter as they shrink (releasing gravitational energy in the process). Finally, in the lower left corner, we have the white dwarfs, electron-degenerate stars of constant radius without nuclear energy sources, which radiate only their internal energy. These stars will slowly cool into invisibility in hundreds of billions of years, traveling downward and to the right.

The prediction of the location of a star in the Hertzsprung-Russell diagram is theoretically simple but difficult in practice. Ideally, if all relevant physical laws are known, the mass and the composition of a star as a function of distance from the center at a certain time uniquely determine one point in the Hertzsprung-Russell diagram. If the effect of the nuclear reactions on the composition is known, the mass and the altered composition determine a neighboring point. A star therefore follows an evolutionary track. Idealized tracks based on the present theoretical computations are shown in Figure 2-4. Note the relatively great duration of the main-sequence stage during which the central temperature is constant and H is the fuel. When a star exhausts H in its core, stellar evolution toward the red-giant stage begins. The star becomes larger and brighter but cooler at the surface. Careful observations of a star of given mass can reveal whether it has reached the stage of turning off the main sequence, since it will be overluminous. A more approximate method of application of this concept has been enormously fruitful. In a cluster, a group of stars at the same distance from us, a study of the relation between brightness and color is sufficient to determine the upper limit of the main sequence; that is, we need only to measure the color and brightness at which stars depart from the main sequence. From equation (2-2), or from theoretically computed evolutionary tracks, a more sophisticated method, the observed data determine the age T of the group of stars. We can transform equation (2-2), if we assume that the star has an average luminosity $\bar{L}$ (in solar units) for T years, to read

$$T = 1.1 \times 10^{11} F \frac{M}{\bar{L}}. \tag{2-4}$$

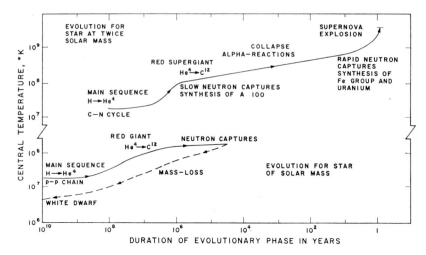

Figure 2-4 Schematic evolutionary tracks for stars of 1 $M_\odot$ and 2 $M_\odot$. The typical time spent in each stage is shown as abscissa, the temperature at the center of the star as ordinate. Also shown are the typical nuclear reactions that occur. The star of 1 $M_\odot$ presumably returns along the dashed line to the white dwarf stage. The star of 2 $M_\odot$ may reach such a high central temperature that implosion followed by explosion will be triggered by either endoergic reactions or by neutrino emission.

Since theory indicates that $F \approx 0.12$ and since initially the sun probably had only about 80 percent hydrogen, the life thus derived is about 10 billion years. Elementary theories give ages of young star groups (galactic clusters) as low as a million years and of old star groups (globular clusters) as high as 26 billion years. Elaborate machine computations have been made for the evolution of stars of low metal abundance such as exist in some of the oldest globular clusters. Ages from 20 to 26 billion years are derived, but it is quite probable that these calculations are incorrect by as much as a factor of two. Uncertainties arise from the composition and the effectiveness of the convective transport of energy in establishing a nearly adiabatic temperature gradient. It is possible to scale down the computed ages of the oldest systems arbitrarily to bring them near the "expansion" age of the extragalactic nebulae, about 13 billion, but it should be remembered that a somewhat rubberlike scale factor exists in the expansion age and in the absolute age dating of the star groups. Relative ages of the groups are more reliable, of course. The computational problems are reflected in equation (2-4) or more exactly in the proper evaluation of the integral of L over time, in equation (2-2), as well as in how much hydrogen can be burned, that is, the factor F.

Mass loss; composition

From our discussion of thermonuclear processes in stellar interiors, it is clear that a secular change in the He/H ratio in a star must occur. Heavy element formation (2) also occurs at late stages in stellar evolution, so that the ratio of metals/H also increases. If all of these reaction products are trapped within the star's core, no changes of composition will be observed by spectroscopic study of a star's surface layers, but there is little doubt that there is a large difference of composition between the oldest and youngest stars. As a consequence, we assume at present that a still unexplored stage of evolution exists. Machine computations have carried stars far into the red giant phase, in which even the helium has been exhausted (producing C^{12}, O^{16}, Ne^{20}, Mg^{24}) and in which the star's density and surface gravity are very low. The transition to the hot, subluminous subdwarf and white dwarf region has not been explored, nor have stars been clearly identified as in the process of moving to the left and downward in the Hertzsprung-Russell diagram (Figure 2-3). The speculative suggestion has been made that loss of the outer, low-density layers of the star begins during the giant stage and carries away as much as one solar mass in a few million years. Observational data on related problems are provided by spectroscopic study of close double stars and especially of the red supergiants (3) of extremely low density. This question is related to the problem of the "solar wind" (4), that is, the expansion of the hot outer layers of the solar corona into interplanetary space. Theoretical opinions differ greatly on the density and velocity of the material streaming outward from the sun. Observational data on the density and velocity of this substratum of normal solar plasma will be provided by interplanetary probes. In addition, the more violent outbursts connected with solar activity need to be monitored, since it is possible that a large fraction of solar mass loss occurs during violent activity. Biermann and Lüst (3) believe that in some stars the flux of acoustic energy heating the stellar outer corona may reach as high as 10 percent of the energy radiated by the star, which is a fraction about 1000 times larger than that in the sun.

On the basis of what is admittedly slender evidence the conviction has grown that even without explosion stars lose a substantial fraction of their mass to the interstellar gas from which they were born, even though considerable work must be done against gravity. For very old stars this fraction is substantial; evolving red giants have initial masses near 1.4 $M_\odot$, but the average mass of a white dwarf (5) is about 0.5 $M_\odot$, that is, two thirds of the red giant mass is lost. Thus in Figure 2-1 the return path cycling material once inside the stars to the interstellar gas is an important one. If this is true, changes in the heavy element composition of the interstellar gas occurs; He, C, N, and O, etc., are synthesized in ordinary stars and are returned to space. Exploding stars synthesize stable elements (2), such as Fe, and the very heavy elements, like U, in different nuclear processes. Neutron capture processes also occur in some red giants, and many elements of intermediate weight are synthesized. Thus on the average all heavy elements, which we call "metals" (M), are growing in abundance both inside stars and in the interstellar gas at the expense of H; that is, the M/H ratio is increasing with time. Recently formed stars have a larger M/H ratio. Detailed spectroscopic study has shown this to be true (6), and star colors can be used to show that the oldest stars are relatively metal-poor (7). A combination of the methods of age dating in clusters with spectroscopic and colorimetric analysis gives the results shown in Figure 2-5. Apparently, the M/H abundance in

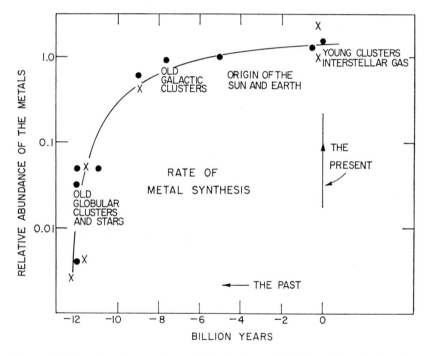

Figure 2-5 The abundance ratio, metal to hydrogen (M/H), relative to its value in the sun as a function of the age of star clusters (dots). For some individual stars (crosses), the M/H ratio is also given, although for these the ages are uncertain.

the oldest known star groups and in individual stars can be as low as 0.002 of that in the sun. Since $M/H \approx 10^{-4}$ for the sun, the value in old stars is amazingly low; the Galaxy consisted mainly of pure hydrogen, with a metal impurity of only 0.2 part per million! Note that the change in M/H in the last 5 billion years (i.e., from the formation of sun to the present) is small, at most a factor of two. An additional 5 billion years before the sun was formed shows little change; almost all the change occurred more than 10 billion years ago. It is suspected that not only the time of origin but the location in the Galaxy is reflected in the gas composition and therefore in the composition of the star. Table 2-1, reprinted from the *American Scientist* (8), gives an outline of individual anomalies in the abundances of particular elements or isotopes that are observed in various types of stars. It is not sufficient to consider only the M/H ratio. It is easier to establish a peculiarity in the abundance ratio of, say X/Y in a star, as compared to the same ratio in the sun. For many of the elements listed in Table 2-1 only the roughest quantitative results exist. Nevertheless, in many cases in which an element is enhanced or depleted by a factor of 10 to 100 there is little doubt of the reality of the effect. Consequently, in addition to the M/H ratio, about 30 elements plus most of the rare earths are found to vary in abundance from star to star.

A few recent studies of individual abundance anomalies provide significant examples. One effect of the first steps from H^1 beyond He^4 is the synthesis of C^{12} by

$$He^4 + He^4 \rightleftharpoons Be^8 + \gamma,$$
$$Be^8 + He^4 \rightarrow C^{12} + \gamma. \tag{2-5}$$

However, C^{13} is a by-product of the carbon cycle

$$C^{12} + H^1 \rightarrow N^{13} + \gamma,$$
$$N^{13} \rightarrow C^{13} + \beta^+ + \nu. \tag{2-6}$$

Some red giants have a high ratio C^{12}/H, and a few have high C^{13}/C^{12} abundance. We might conclude that in a completely hydrogen-deficient star C^{12} alone might be formed [equation (2-5)]. If the hot envelope of the star still had some H, C^{12} might be transformed into C^{13} [equation (2-6)]. Examples of both possibilities have been studied by quantitative spectroscopy. An interesting confirmation is that although its C^{12} abundance is high C^{13} is not found in a star that has little or no H left at the surface (8).

TABLE 2-1

Elements with Abundances Significantly Variable from Star to Star

Element	Remarks
H^1	Although normally the most abundant element, sometimes H is deficient by factors of 100.
D^2	Suspected present in excess during solar flares; almost certainly absent in stellar interiors.
He^3	Excessively abundant in two peculiar (magnetic?) B stars and observed in solar cosmic-ray bursts.
He^4	Normally $He^4/H^1 = 0.1$, but in many types of stars $He^4/H^1 \geq 1$. In certain white dwarfs and carbon-rich stars $He/H \approx 10^2$.
Li	Less abundant in most stars than in the earth and meteorites. In stars contracting from interstellar gas and dust clouds Li is enhanced more than 100-fold over the sun (surface or preplanetary reactions?).
Be^9	Variable from star to star, enhanced in some magnetic A stars (surface reaction?).
B	Rare; suspected in magnetic A stars.
C^{12}	Present in excess by factors up to 20 in red giants and in five white dwarfs. C/N ratio variable in some hot stars.
C^{13}	Normally $C^{13}/C^{12} = 0.01$ in the earth and stars. In some C^{12}-rich stars $C^{13}/C^{12} \approx 0.1$.
N^{14}	Greatly enhanced in late stages of evolution—N/C < 1 normally, but in hot subdwarfs and a few supergiants N/C > 1.
O	Usually constant, except for weakening in many peculiar magnetic A stars.
Ne	Strengthened in a few supergiants.
Si	Strengthened in some magnetic A stars.
P	Enhanced 100-fold in a peculiar B star, 3 Centauri A.
S	Depleted in 3 Centauri A which has excess P.
A	Enhanced in one supergiant.
Mn	Ratio to Fe abnormal in metal-poor stars. Also enhanced in magnetic stars.
Co, Ni	Possibly abnormal ratio to Fe in extremely metal-poor stars.
Ga, Kr	Greatly enhanced in 3 Centauri A.
Sr	Enhanced in magnetic A stars, and in "heavy-element" stars.
Y, Zr, Nb, Mo	Enhanced in "heavy-element" stars.
Tc	All isotopes are unstable. Present in cool red giants with abnormal heavy-element content (S stars). Probably Tc^{97}, with 2-million-year half-life.
Ba, La	Enhanced in "heavy-element" stars.
Ce-Dy	Same; most rare earths are also greatly enhanced in magnetic A and F stars, with Eu outstandingly strong in some magnetic A stars.
Hg	Suspected in magnetic A stars.

Another strange result provides an insight into a new complex of problems, that of nuclear reactions occurring at the surface of the stars. In Table 2-1 repeated mention is made of peculiar A stars. These objects represent a transitory stage in evolution of some A-type stars (15,000 to 8000°K surface temperature). They lie near the main sequence but are notable for large magnetic dipole fields, sometimes variable and ranging up to 34,000 gauss. Babcock (9) has studied the magnetic fields and proposes a magnetohydrodynamic pulsation as the origin of the variability of the fields. Such complex, nonradial, torsional oscillations of a large field provide a reasonable setting for electromagnetic acceleration processes. Even if the star has only large magnetic spots, neutral points in the magnetic field would exist, as in sunspots producing solar flares, and permit acceleration of the plasma. Without too much knowledge of the details, we should now merely note how many abundance peculiarities exist in the magnetic A stars.

One star related to the magnetic A stars is 3 Centauri A, a relatively young B star of extraordinary composition (10). We have found that

1. He is deficient compared to H;
2. $He^3/He^4 = 3$; D^2 is not seen, with upper limit $D/H < 0.01$;
3. He/H and O/H $= \frac{1}{6}$ normal; $N/H = 5 \times$ normal;
4. $P/H = 100 \times$, Ga $= 8000 \times$, Kr $= 1000 \times$ normal.

These extraordinary changes cannot be of thermonuclear origin. The temperatures at the center of a main-sequence, or even a red-giant, star are at most a few kev; reactions that would destroy He^4 or O^{16} require about 20 Mev. No thermal reactions could produce phosphorus without enormously altering the abundances of all elements of moderate nuclear charge; the production of Ga and Kr must also be nonthermal. We may search for reactions among heavy ions with energies of several Mev per nucleon. Reactions are also needed to release many fast neutrons that could be captured by abundant lighter elements, building P, Ga, Kr, and possibly many other spectroscopically unobservable heavy elements.

Other magnetic stars have shown deficiencies of O and excess of Mn, Si, Sr, and, most interestingly, of Be. About 20 percent of the magnetic stars have greatly enhanced Be, which has been a difficult element to observe, since its lines are near the ultraviolet limit of earthbound astronomical spectrographs. Significantly, the thermonuclear process in stellar interiors cannot successfully produce Be; if it does, Be will be quickly destroyed even at temperatures of less than 1 kev. Therefore, the Be observed must be a fragment of a heavier nucleus, produced by spallation. Collisions of protons with nuclei of $A > 20$ require 200 to 1000 Mev if the heavy nucleus is to be fragmented. If spallation occurs, nuclear fragments such as D^2, He^3, He^4, Li^6, Li^7, Be^9, B^{10}, B^{11} will be produced, so that we obtain the rare isotopes D^2 and He^3 and the elements Li, Be, and B, which cannot be made in stellar interiors.

2-2   MAGNETIC ACCELERATION PROCESSES

The probable location of the acceleration process is at or above the surface of stars, where magnetized plasma is in motion. The efficiency of conversion into high-energy protons or other forms of energy must be high. Even a star cannot afford the inefficiency of most earthbound accelerators! It is interesting to note that machines of relatively low energy, such as a cyclotron or small synchrotron, convert about 10^{-5} of their input power into high-energy particles in their output beam. However, the projected Stanford linear accelerator, or the projected 300-bev circular accelerator, has planned efficiencies of nearly 10 percent. Several mechanisms for acceleration in magnetohydrodynamic shock waves have been proposed for the astronomical environment, but this problem still remains one of the most interesting theoretical questions of contemporary astrophysics. There are fundamentally only two mechanisms (11). Fermi suggested that relativistic charged particles collide with moving magnetic fields and that collisions leading to acceleration of the proton are more frequent than decelerating ones. This statistical mechanism leads to the observed type of power-law for the differential energy spectrum of cosmic-ray protons (and probably also of any high-energy electrons). Another mechanism is the betatron type, in which the energy increment is proportional to the change of magnetic-field intensity. However, even in a hydromagnetic shock, the change of field is small. Schatzman has proposed repeated collisions with a clumpy transverse magnetic field, across which a shock wave is being propagated.

Physical conditions are different at or just above the star's surface and, of course, even more different in interstellar space. But observational evidence is overwhelming that the energy existing in ultrarelativistic protons and electrons is large and that an efficient acceleration mechanism is present in many types of astronomical environments (from the interstellar gas to the solar surface, magnetic stars, newly formed stars, supernova explosions, and radio sources in our own and other galaxies). The origin of cosmic rays in the sun and interstellar space has been treated elsewhere in this volume, but there are two other main lines of astronomical evidence that suggest the near universality of this phenomenon.

2-3 LITHIUM AND CONTRACTING STARS

A particularly interesting case history in the theory of the origin of the elements is that of our knowledge of the element lithium and the related problems of deuterium and beryllium.

Although lithium appears in the path of some elementary reactions, its lifetime against proton bombardment is extremely short. Where can Li be synthesized? The solar abundance of Li relative to the metals was found to be about one hundredth of that in the earth and meteorites (12). If the initial composition of the earth and sun were identical, mixing of solar surface and interior might since have reduced the Li content. Recently, 50 stars cool enough to show lines of Li (which is normally highly ionized) were observed. It was found that Li varied in abundance from star to star, but all stars contained even less Li than the sun. Again, convective mixing with the interior could be invoked. But why, then, is there any Li, D, Be, B at all? The search for objects with too much Li and Be has recently been successful, and several magnetic A stars have more Be than the earth.

There are faint variable stars, called T Tauri stars, which are connected with the denser gas and dust clouds of our Galaxy. These stars apparently are still in the process of contraction out of the gas and are somewhat unstable. They have rapid light variations, emission lines of hot surrounding gas clouds, and are connected with dense dark nebulae. Violent interaction still exists between gas and star. The star may brighten quickly and show a blue, essentially continuous spectrum, which fades away in less than an hour—very much like a solar flare, but on an enormously greater scale. Spectroscopic observations of these faint stars are difficult, but essentially all that could be studied (13) have shown abundances of Li 50 to 400 times the solar value, that is, even slightly higher than the earth. This surprising agreement with terrestrial values, and the fact that T Tauri stars have recently been through the process of gravitational contraction, suggests that the origins of Li, stars, and possibly planets have something in common. Perhaps even now the T Tauri stars have planets forming around them as each star goes through its final birth pangs, accompanied by the synthesis of lithium and probably of the other light elements.

A theory has been advanced by Fowler, Hoyle, and Greenstein (14) in a detailed discussion of both the astronomical and nuclear-physical aspects of this problem. The condensation of a star is not easy, since gravity must work against the magnetic tension of the interstellar fields as they become compressed and against the increasing centrifugal force of stellar rotation. The interstellar medium contains some angular momentum, and, as it is compressed, conservation of momentum results in an increase of rotational kinetic energy. The star becomes unstable and matter is expelled, carrying with it momentum and magnetic energy. The total energy to be dissipated has been estimated to be as high as 10^{48} ergs, an enormous supply, part of which, depending on unknown efficiency factors, may appear as high-energy phenomena. For example, twisted magnetic fields in a partially ionized plasma may produce high potentials and accelerate particles to relativistic energies, that is, cosmic rays. Such "flares" at or above the surface of the newly forming star could be responsible for the strange spectra and light variations of the T Tauri stars. Proton collisions, above a few hundred Mev, by spallation could produce, outside the star or in the small discoidal nebulae that eventually form the planets, the elements D, Li, Be, B, which are otherwise so difficult to explain. On such a hypothesis, they are formed only at the surface or in the preplanetary nebula. The high abundance of Li in the earth or in meteorites then becomes reasonable. The spallation process requires a large flux of high-energy particles and magnetic fields. We must turn to the interstellar medium and some of its properties to understand why it is now believed that angular momentum and magnetic fields carry a large store of the energy of the universe.

2-4   THE INTERSTELLAR MEDIUM

Some years ago it was estimated that approximately half the mass of our Galaxy existed in the form of interstellar gas whose composition resembled that of the young stars. The discovery of the hyperfine-structure emission line of neutral atomic hydrogen, at a frequency of 1420 Mc/sec, together with the rapid advance of radio astronomy, has resulted in determinations of the amount of neutral hydrogen in our own and other galaxies. The present result is that only about 3 percent of the mass of the Galaxy is neutral hydrogen. Whether any appreciable amount of hydrogen is molecular or ionized H_2 is not yet known. Satellite experiments on the ultraviolet spectrum of the stars may show lines of H_2, and infrared experiments have also been proposed. Such experiments might possibly reveal an important and hitherto unobservable fraction of the mass of the universe. But even if the mass of hydrogen should prove to be only 3 percent of the mass of the stars, the interstellar medium still plays an important role as the birthplace of new stars. As noted earlier, mass loss by red giants to the interstellar gas is an important postulate of current theories of stellar evolution.

The material in stars has been cycled a few times through space, so that both the angular momentum and the seed magnetic fields of the interstellar gas are important factors in stellar formation, rotation, and magnetism. The rotation of our Galaxy is at the rate of 10^{-15} rad/sec; the observed random motion of gas clouds is about 8 km/sec, which at a typical spacing of about 100 parsecs gives the relative angular speed of two clouds as about 3×10^{-15} rad/sec. Thus a characteristic turbulent angular shear exists, reflected in rapid rotation when a star is condensed out of interstellar gas. If the space density is about 10^{-21} gm/cm^3 in a dense interstellar cloud, the radius must be 10^{18} cm to provide a solar mass. The shrinkage to a stellar radius of 10^{11} cm, with conservation of angular momentum, produces rotation of 10^{-1} rad/sec, or a linear velocity near that of light! Therefore, the star cannot contract without losing some matter, which must carry away preferentially a very large amount of angular momentum. Small interstellar magnetic fields can be increased by twisting lines of force into loops, which with the plasma are expelled into space. Particle acceleration may occur and even planets may be formed. Stellar radiation, through heating and ionization, continues to feed mechanical energy into the interstellar gas, so that the turbulent, gas-cloud motions are not damped out. Thus a continued recycling between the gas and the stars makes magnetic phenomena of universal importance.

Proof of the existence of the interstellar magnetic field, however, is still elusive. Chandrasekhar and Fermi (15) argued that the spiral arms of our Galaxy would collapse gravitationally if not balanced by the pressure of the magnetic lines of force; fields of strength above 7×10^{-6} gauss were needed. It should be remembered that cosmic rays seem to be essentially isotropic. Unless a galactic magnetic field exists, this isotropy would require that they come from other galaxies, so that the total energy in the universe in the form of cosmic rays would have to be multiplied by an enormous factor. The containment in the Galaxy of cosmic rays with energies above 10^{18} ev also requires a similar field.

Astronomical evidence for the interstellar magnetic field is largely based on the theoretical interpretation of the observed polarization of starlight. In addition to the gas, there is a small amount of solid matter, detectable by the absorption and reddening of the light of distant stars. Its mass is estimated as about 1 percent of that of the gas. Small solid particles of diameter near the wavelength of light can be shown to be very efficient absorbers of light, with absorption cross sections reaching 10^5 cm^2/gm. The particles might be quasi-metallic (like tiny meteorites), they might be optically active giant molecules, or they might be dielectric frozen gases. If the material is anisotropic, or if the grains are elongated, the scattered light will be a function of angle in a plane perpendicular to that of propagation. Therefore, the transmitted light that we observe can be polarized linearly. The question of a mechanism that could align elongated particles over the enormous distances of interstellar space has been explored extensively. The generally accepted theory, that of Davis and Greenstein (16), is that a magnetic field exists more or less parallel to the galactic plane along the spiral arms of our Galaxy. The grains are spinning rapidly because of collisions with the gas atoms. If the grains are paramagnetic and have internal losses, or are ferromagnetic, the rapidly varying internal magnetic field induces torques that gradually orient the grain until its long axis is perpendicular to the lines of force. For paramagnetic substances with reasonable losses we derive an expression for the tendency towards orientation from the ratio of the magnetic to the collisional torques:

$$F_l = \frac{6.3 \times 10^6 B^2}{a T^{\frac{1}{2}} n T_g}, \tag{2-7}$$

where B is the absolute value of the field, a, the radius of the grain, about 10^{-5} cm, n, the interstellar gas density, T, its temperature, and T_g, the temperature of the grain. If F_l is near unity, the grains will be highly oriented. The grain temperature is probably between 4 and 20°K; the gas kinetic temperature, about 100°K, so that for $n = 1$ hydrogen atom/cm^3 B must be near 10^{-5} gauss. Since the polarization is observed to be high for stars of only moderate absorption and reddening, the orientation mechanism must be efficient and the magnetic field large and fairly regular.

The only direct proof of the existence of a magnetic field would be the use of the Zeeman effect, which broadens and shifts the 21-cm line of hydrogen. Circular polarization can be observed when the line of sight is parallel to a longitudinal field. In certain regions a cool hydrogen cloud lies between us and an intense source of radio emission which has a continuous spectrum. Such a cloud produces an absorption line, and if the gas has small turbulent velocity the line will be sufficiently sharp for a Zeeman experiment. So far only two radio sources have been observed for circular polarization of the absorption line, and still yields negative results, at the Manchester, Cambridge, and Cal Tech radio observatories. The upper limit to the component of the field along the line of sight is now set at about 3×10^{-6} gauss in one cloud, although the experiment is an extremely difficult one. A magnetic field shifts the circularly polarized components of the line from their zero-field position by approximately 2.8 Mc/sec/gauss. Thus frequency shifts of only 8 cps must be detected in a line broadened by 5000 cps for each km/sec of thermal or turbulent velocity. Further work on the possible Zeeman-effect polarization and widening of the 21-cm line will be carried out, since a positive effect, even in one region, would be the first actual proof of the existence of an interstellar magnetic field.

2-5 SYNCHROTRON RADIO-FREQUENCY EMISSION AND RADIO GALAXIES

The sun, certain peculiar gaseous nebulae, interstellar space, other galaxies, and possibly three other stars are known sources of a continuous spectrum of radio-frequency emission. Such a continuum could arise from black-body emission or from thermal emission from an ionized gas. In that case the maximum emission would have an intensity given by the black-body law, which is linearly dependent on the temperature at these low frequencies:

$$P_\nu \, d\nu = \frac{8\pi k T \nu^2 \, d\nu}{c^2}. \qquad (2\text{-}8)$$

The power received should increase with ν^2; but, in fact the observed radio-frequency spectra can be represented by the law $1/\nu^n$, with $0.2 < n < 0.7$ in general, so that thermal emission is excluded. A thin gas would have $n = 0$ and would emit less than equation (2-8) predicts. Plasma oscillations are usually nearly monochromatic or have discrete spectra consisting of the plasma frequency and several overtone frequencies; these have been observed only in the sun. The only process successful in representing the observed radio continuous spectra is the so-called synchrotron emission. Electrons of high energy, that is, ultrarelativistic electrons, are spiraling about magnetic lines of force. Since there is an acceleration in circular motion, there must be radiation; the synchrotron emission is a continuous set of high harmonics of the electron's fundamental spiraling frequency. Some of this radiation is observed in laboratory electron synchrotrons as a blue glow accompanied by infrared and radio emission. The physical theory has been developed classically and later by Schwinger and others, and applications to the astronomical situation have been discussed by many authors (17), particularly by the Soviet astronomers (18). If only electrons of one energy, E, are present, the highest frequency at which there is substantial emission is a critical frequency, ν_c, given by

$$\nu_c = 6.27 \times 10^{18} BE^2. \tag{2-9}$$

We see that to obtain a continuum reaching up to high radio frequencies, say $\nu = 3000$ Mc/sec, with $B = 10^{-6}$ gauss, E must be about 10^{-2} erg or 10^{10} ev! The shape of the spectrum emitted by a single ultrarelativistic electron is one with an exponential cutoff for $\nu > \nu_c$ and a slowly decreasing (power-law) spectrum for $\nu < \nu_c$. Since this does not resemble the radio power emitted by any natural radio source, the electrons are not monoenergetic. Since the cosmic-ray protons have a number density given by a power law, let us assume the same law to hold for high-energy electrons:

$$N(E)\, dE = VN_0 E^{-\beta}\, dE. \tag{2-10}$$

Here V is the volume and β an index to be fitted to the observations. The expression for the radiation by one electron, as a function of $\alpha(=\nu/\nu_c)$, is then to be mathematically folded into equation (2-10) to give the total power radiated at frequency ν by electrons of all energies. A complicated function, $F(\alpha)$ (integrals over fractional Bessel functions), appears, as well as the limiting values of α_1 and α_2, which might occur if there are cutoffs on the energy spectrum. The total power radiated at frequency ν is

$$P_\nu = 1.17 \times 10^{-22} N_0 V k^{(\beta-1)/2} B^{(\beta+1)/2} \nu^{(1-\beta)/2} \int_{\alpha_1}^{\alpha_2} F(\alpha) \alpha^{(\beta-3)/2}\, d\alpha. \tag{2-11}$$

The constant $k = 6.27 \times 10^{18}$, $F(\alpha)$ is a tabulated function, and the integral, in practice, proves to be nearly a constant lying between 1.5 and 2.0. The radiation increases as $B^{(\beta+1)/2}$, which will prove to be about $B^{1.6}$. Note that p_ν varies as $\nu^{(1-\beta)/2}$; the observations suggest that $(1-\beta)/2 = -0.6$, that is, $\beta = 2.2$, not very far from the cosmic-ray-proton, power-law index of 2.8. The total power radiated over all frequencies is obtained by integrating equation (2-11) and evaluating the $F(\alpha)$ integral for reasonable cutoffs α_1 and α_2. An approximate value of the integrated power between two cutoff frequencies is

$$p = \int_{\nu_1}^{\nu_2} p_\nu \, d\nu = 2 \times 10^{-22} N_0 V k^{(\beta-1)/2} B^{(\beta+1)/2} \int_{\nu_1}^{\nu_2} \nu^{(1-\beta)/2} \, d\nu. \quad (2\text{-}12)$$

Table 2-2 gives the results of computations of the total energy that must be present in relativistic electrons, U_{CR}, and magnetic field, U_B, to account for the radiation from a synchrotron radio source of observed total radiated power, P. Specific cutoffs in the electron spectrum and in the radio emission have been adopted to simplify the table. The total electron energy is U_{CR}, obtained by integrating equation (2-10). By setting the predicted emission p equal to the observed P, equation (2-12) gives the magnetic field required and permits us to evaluate its total energy from $U_B = VB^2/8\pi$. Finally, the minimum value U_0 of U_{CR} and U_B, if the source is to emit power P, is found when the U_{CR} and U_B are set equal to each other:

$$U_0 = U_{CR} = U_B = N_0 V \int_{E_1}^{E_2} E^{1-\beta} \, dE = V \frac{B^2}{8\pi}. \quad (2\text{-}13)$$

Thus observation of the radio power P and volume V determine N_0, the magnetic field, B, and the total number of ultrarelativistic electrons.

When the synchrotron emission theory is applied to various types of astronomical objects, some surprises are encountered. Some solar radiation is synchroton (the so-called Type IV bursts). In the remnants of a supernova, the Crab nebula, which is a strong radio source, the discovery was made that polarized light of optical frequencies

TABLE 2-2

Electron (U_{CR}) and Magnetic Field (U_B) Energy in a
Radio Source of Power, P, and Volume, V

β	n Spectral Index	$F(\alpha)$ Integral	U_{CR} Electron Energy	U_B Magnetic Energy	U_0 Equipartition Energy
2.0	0.50	2.00	$[+0.88]N_0V$	$[+6.28]B^{1/2}P/N_0$	$[+3.55]B^{1/4}(PV)^{1/2}$
2.5	0.75	1.77	$[+2.50]N_0V$	$[+3.26]B^{1/4}P/N_0$	$[+2.88]B^{1/8}(PV)^{1/2}$
3.0	1.00	1.61	$[+4.40]N_0V$	$[+0.90]P/N_0$	$[+2.65](PV)^{1/2}$

Note. A bracket denotes a logarithm with base 10.

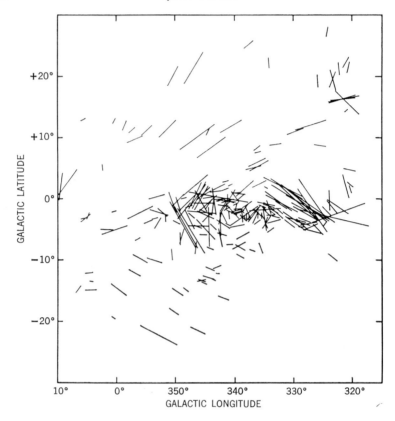

Figure 2-6 On galactic coordinates, polarization of starlight by interstellar dust grains as seen in the direction of the center of our Galaxy. Each line represents the direction of the maximum electric vector and the amount of polarization. If the grains are elongated and aligned by a magnetic field, the lines of force lie along the directions of the maximum electric vector. The field so indicated is chaotic but tends in places to parallel the galactic plane.

was also emitted (see Figure 2-6). A reasonable model of the Crab nebula requires that a field of 10^{-3} gauss fill about a cubic parsec and that electrons of energies up to 200 bev be present. The total energy in the field and the electrons is about 10^{48} ergs. Since a supernova outburst originally involves about 10^{51} ergs, the fact that 10^{48} ergs still remain in fields and particles more than 1000 years after the supernova explosion may or may not seem surprising, depending on the reader's taste! It is, however, in the distant radio galaxies that we encounter the most serious energy problem.

2-6 RADIO GALAXIES

In addition to a rather featureless background of radio noise from our own Galaxy, about 1000 small sources of radio emission have been discovered. These are uniformly distributed over the sky, unlike stars in the Milky Way; the radio sources could be either faint stars very close to the sun or very distant galaxies. Their number $N(I)$ increases with decreasing apparent brightness, I, nearly as $I^{-3/2}$, which would be the expected behavior for distant objects homogeneously and isotropically distributed through space. Some observed deviation from this law, incidentally, has played an important part recently in the theory of cosmology and may help to decide between steady-state and explosive relativistic cosmologies. It is now generally assumed that most of the radio sources are distant galaxies; about 50 have been so identified. The first object identified was called Cygnus A; it is one of the brightest radio sources, yet it is about 500 million light years distant. In addition, it was found not to be a small point, or even a spherical source, but to consist instead of two emitting regions, each 100,000 light years in diameter and separated by about 250,000 light years. Figures 2-7 and 2-8 show two other radio galaxies. One, NGC 5128, is a peculiar spiral nebula possibly in collision, quite close to us, with a complex structure. An inner small double source is superposed on a large halo extending over a million light years. Another, 3C33, is like Cygnus A, but the two radio centers are separated by about 600,000 light years. (I am indebted to Dr. T. A. Matthews for these data and photographs.) Both Cygnus A and 3C33 have strong emission-line spectra, revealing the presence of gas at an unusually high level of ionization; for example, forbidden lines of [NeV] are strong. Collision of gas clouds at high velocities may be involved in the excitation of the emission lines, but the radio emission is located clearly outside the region in which most of the gas and stars are found. Our Galaxy and the optically detectable galaxies in radio sources are only 100,000 light years in diameter, and most of the gas is in a disk 500 light years thick. If the synchrotron process is the source of the radio emission, we need magnetic fields and ultrarelativistic electrons in an enormous volume outside the visible galaxy. If some event, an explosion or collision, has expelled jets of plasma and field, as seems to have occurred in the double radio sources, the expansion should enormously decrease both the magnetic field per unit volume and the particle density. In fact, if the field decreases, the electrons would eventually break loose from the field and travel outward with the velocity of light. Thus the large radio sources must be short-lived, perhaps 10^6 to 10^7 years.

Let us consider one example to determine how the total radiated power, volume, field, and high-energy particle density are evaluated. The double radio source, Hercules A, has an observed flux at the earth of 7.4×10^{-25} watt/meter^2/cps at 960 Mc/sec. The total power over all radio frequencies is difficult to estimate, but if we arbitrarily set a high-frequency cutoff of 10^4 Mc/sec the total received radio power at the earth can be set at about 4.6×10^{-15} watt/m^2 or the intrinsic radio luminosity at $5.5 \times 10^{31}R^2$ watts, where R is the distance in megaparsecs ($= 3 \times 10^{24}$ cm). No direct measure of the distance is possible for the faint galaxy that we believe to be at the center of the double radio source. Nevertheless, we succeeded in obtaining a spectrum at Palomar and found a velocity of recession of 46,000

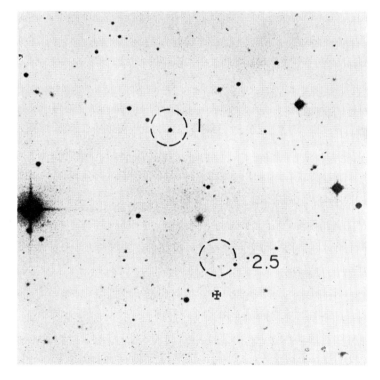

Figure 2-7 A typical complex radio source, 3C33. The circles represent the double, radio-emitting region; the galaxy is a faint, diffuse object just above the lower circle. The cross represents the probable error of the coordinates. The galaxy is at a distance of 600 million light years and has a peculiar, emission-line spectrum.

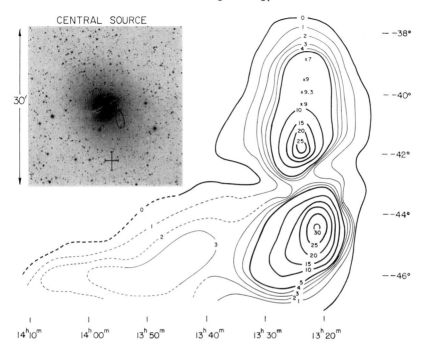

Figure 2-8 The complex, nearby radio source, Centaurus A, and the galaxy NGC 5128. The inner double source is shown at the right with its coordinate error. The isophotes of the much larger halo, diameter about a million light years, are shown at the left.

km/sec. If we use the current estimate of the rate of expansion of the universe, 75 km/sec redshift per megaparsec, the distance R derived from the redshift is 620 megaparsecs, and the intrinsic luminosity becomes 2×10^{37} watts, or $P = 2 \times 10^{44}$ ergs/sec. In addition, we need the emitting volume; the separation of the two emitting regions is 360,000 psc, their volume, about 9×10^{70} cm³. (Even if they exploded out of the center of their galaxy at the velocity of light, they could not be less than half a million years old.) We can insert P and V into our equations and derive the energies; in fact, we shall take more typical data (19) for strong radio sources, $P = 4 \times 10^{44}$ ergs/sec and $V = 2 \times 10^{70}$ cm³. The results for U_{CR} are shown in Figure 2-9. This figure shows not only U_0, the minimal value of the energy in equipartition, but also the dependence of the particle energy on B. The total energies have minimal values in the range 2×10^{60} to 2×10^{61} ergs. We must also allow for the presence of cosmic-ray protons; suggested acceleration mechanisms have a ratio, p/e, of pro-

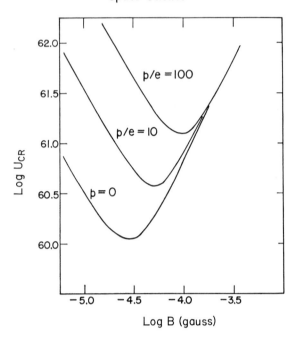

Figure 2-9 The total energy in a strong, large radio source in the form of magnetic fields and ultrarelativistic electrons depends on the assumed magnetic field B. The curve, $p = 0$, holds when electrons alone are present. The others show the total energy when ultrarelativistic protons exist in ratio of energies $p/e = 10$ and 100. The minimal energies of the system are between 10^{60} and 10^{61} ergs.

ton to electron total energy of 10 to 200; the other curves in the figure show that the total energy must be multiplied by about $(p/e)^{1/2}$. The electrons are probably secondary in origin, presumably decay products of proton collision. In our Galaxy p/e is about 100, and the ultrarelativistic electron energy is about 3×10^{52} ergs, vanishingly small compared to that in intense radio galaxies.

In our Galaxy structures such as spiral arms may owe their stability to a balance between gravitational attraction and the disruptive forces of the magnetic fields and cosmic rays. But how can an intense radio source be stable and how can it contain its magnetic fields against their tendency to explode? It should be remembered that the particles react on the field so that they also tend to pull the field apart. Actually, it is the gravitational attraction of the stars on the neutral gas that anchors the field; the thermal ions collide with the overwhelmingly neutral atoms, and the field cannot move through the ionized gas.

Stabilization, however, is essentially impossible if the high-energy particles are too numerous. An effort has been made to find plausible models of massive, gas-rich galaxies, which have sufficient gravitational attraction on the gas, but without success. Unless a whole galaxy can have a completely force-free field, it is unlikely that 10^{60} ergs or more can be contained. The entire gravitational potential of our Galaxy is only 10^{60} ergs, but it is largely stars, not gas, and we cannot imagine any direct interaction that would permit the stars to anchor very large interstellar magnetic fields. In addition, we see that the typical scale of lengths is about 10 times that of a normal galaxy, which further reduces the potential energy of radio sources. The probable gravitational potential of the gas is, in fact, about 2×10^{56} ergs, far too small for stabilization in a nonforce-free field.

The problem is a serious one; either the theory of synchrotron emission must be replaced, and no good alternative has been suggested, or the radio galaxies are very extraordinary objects. From optical observations, a few peculiarities can be noted. These galaxies tend to be more luminous than average; they are sometimes double and some may be in collision. They are not necessarily gas-rich, although the probable collision cases sometimes show strong, high-excitation emission lines. Some are quite old systems, elliptical galaxies with only small angular momentum and probably poor in gas. The radio power, about 4×10^{44} ergs/sec, is equivalent to the total optical luminosity of 10^{11} suns, that is, about the same as the total luminosity of our Galaxy. Can there be a mechanism that, with high efficiency, converts ordinary stellar radiation of a few electron volts per photon into cosmic ray particles at billions of volts? Perhaps some fundamental process still remains to be found. Otherwise, we must imagine a very efficient sequence in which the stellar thermal radiation heats the gas and maintains interstellar turbulence. The magnetic fields are then increased by the twisting of lines of force, and the electrons and protons, injected from stars or supernovae, are accelerated so that their energy density, in equipartition with the magnetic field, finally reaches a very high value. In addition, this must occur almost catastrophically, for once the energy density exceeds the small gravitational potential both fields and particles will escape.

Even before the magnitude of the difficulty was realized the suggestion was made that some type of stellar catastrophe was involved. Supernova remnants in our Galaxy are strong radio sources. They have shock waves with exploding gas velocities of 2000 to 10,000 km/sec, initially, and the Crab nebula is probably still regenerating fields and ultrarelativistic particles 1000 years after it exploded as a supernova. Other supernova remnants are in the 10^4-to-10^5-year age group and are still radio sources. We have found what appears to be a genuine radio star, 3C48, which has negligible gas around it, a very strange optical spectrum, and which may be the collapsed remnant of an old supernova. Nevertheless, the total energy released in a supernova outburst is only 10^{51} ergs (about the same as the total radiation of the sun in 10^{10} years). This is far too small, and only if a very large number of supernovae appeared in a short time could there be the 10^{60} ergs of ultrarelativistic particles needed. G. R. Burbidge (20) has made the interesting suggestion that a chain reaction of exploding supernovae could occur in a region of high star density. For example, there might be stars near the end of their evolutionary life, perhaps red giants, in the center of a rich galaxy. The shock wave of one supernova penetrates and compresses the inner layers of a nearby star. Sudden increase of thermonuclear energy rates then make the second star unstable and lead to its explosion. The stars must be closely spaced, to keep the shock strength high, and the shock wave must be able to penetrate into a spherical object with density increasing inward (which seems implausible). With the newly found large energies of 10^{60} ergs, the explosion of 10^9 to 10^{10} supernovae within a million years is required. The normal rate of supernova occurrence is about one in 300 years per galaxy. The containment is no longer a problem; the burst of increased magnetic field and high-energy particles would travel outward at high velocity. Although this hypothesis is extremely speculative, it remains as one of the few attractive in this field.

It is clear that the radio galaxies provide numerous unsolved problems. The apparently high density of ultrarelativistic particles should have other observational consequences. When cosmic-ray protons collide with stationary nuclei, not only spallation but numerous electrons and mesons are produced. Gamma rays are a decay product of some mesons; they travel in straight lines unaffected by fields; satellite-borne experiments may reveal small sources of gamma rays. Experiments from the earth also may detect localized sources of emission of cosmic rays from our own and other galaxies. The higher energy protons would not be completely isotropic, on this hypothesis, in spite of the magnetic fields. The problems of high-energy phenomena on the borderline between physics and astronomy are fascinating and largely unsolved.

REFERENCES

1. Greenstein, J. L., *Modern Physics for the Engineer,* ed. Ridenour, Chapter 10, McGraw-Hill, New York, 1954; *Les Processus Nucléaires dans les Astres,* Liége, 1953.
2. Fowler, W. A., *Modern Physics for the Engineer,* Second Series, ed. Ridenour and Nierenberg, Chapter 9, McGraw-Hill, New York, 1961; E. M. Burbidge, G. R. Burbidge, W. A. Fowler, and F. Hoyle, *Rev. Mod. Phys.,* **29,** 547, 1957.
3. See *Stellar Atmospheres,* ed. Greenstein, Chapters 6, 8, 12, 15, 17, University of Chicago Press, Chicago, 1960.
4. Parker, E. N., *Ap. J.,* **134,** 20, 1961; and other papers by Parker; see also J. W. Chamberlain [e.g., *Ap. J.,* **133,** 675 (1961)].
5. Greenstein, J. L., *Encyclopedia of Physics,* **50,** 161, ed. S. Flügge, Springer Verlag, Berlin, 1958.
6. Wallerstein, G., *Ap. J., Suppl.,* **61,** 407 (1962); L. H. Aller and J. L. Greenstein, *Ap. J. Suppl.,* **5,** 139 (1960).
7. Arp, H. C., *Science,* **134,** 810 (1961).
8. Greenstein, J. L., *Am. Scientist,* **49,** 449 (1961).
9. Babcock, H. W., in *Stellar Atmospheres,* ed. Greenstein, Chapter 7, University of Chicago Press, Chicago, 1960.
10. Jugaku, J., W. L. W. Sargent, and J. L. Greenstein, *Ap. J.,* **134,** 783 (1961); Sargent and Jugaku, *ibid.,* p. 777.
11. Parker, E. N., *Phys. Rev.,* **109,** 1328 (1958).
12. Greenstein, J. L., and R. S. Richardson, *Ap. J.,* **113,** 536 (1951).
13. Bonsack, W. K., and J. L. Greenstein, *Ap. J.,* **131,** 83 (1960); W. K. Bonsack, *ibid.,* **133,** 340 (1961).
14. Fowler, W. A., J. L. Greenstein, and F. Hoyle, *Geophys. J.,* **6,** 148, 1962; *Am. J. Phys.,* **29,** 393 (1961).
15. Chandrasekhar, S., and E. Fermi, *Ap. J.,* **118,** 113 and 118 (1953).
16. Davis, L., and J. L. Greenstein, *Ap. J.,* **114,** 206 (1951).
17. Smith, F. G., *Radio Astronomy,* Penguin Books, Baltimore, 1960; G. R. Burbidge, *Ap. J.,* **124,** 416 (1956); J. H. Oort and Th. Walraven, *Bull. Astron. Inst. Neth.,* **12,** 285 (1956).
18. Shklovskii, I. S., *Cosmic Radio Waves,* translation, Harvard University Press, Cambridge, 1960.
19. Maltby, P., T. A. Matthews, and A. Moffet, *Ap. J.* (in press, 1962); J. L. Greenstein, *ibid.*
20. Burbidge, G. R., *Nature,* **190,** 1053 (1961).

CHAPTER 3

THE PHYSICS OF THE SUN— ITS NATURE, STRUCTURE, AND EMISSION PROPERTIES

LEO GOLDBERG

Higgins Professor of Astronomy

Harvard College Observatory

The sun is a dwarf star of a type that is found rather commonly in the universe. It is unique because it happens to be about 250,000 times closer to the earth than its nearest stellar neighbor. All other stars are in fact so far away that it is much beyond the capability of even our greatest telescopes to resolve them as disks. On the other hand, the sun is so close that areas as small as 400 km² may be isolated for study under the best observing conditions. Thus the sun affords a unique opportunity for the study of the anatomy of a typical star.

The sun also controls and regulates its environment, including the planets, satellites, and the interplanetary medium. Transient events on the sun cause frequent and unpredictable changes in the environment, which at present disturb man's activity on the earth and in the near future may hinder seriously his activity in space.

A description of the many ways in which the sun's radiation can be observed is outside the scope of this chapter, however, two basic limitations on its observation, which are imposed by the earth's atmosphere but which can be removed by the use of space vehicles, should be mentioned. First, the turbulence of the atmosphere smears fine details in the solar image and prevents the resolution of details smaller than about ½ sec of arc, or 400 km in linear measure. Second, atmospheric absorption selectively "blacks out" most regions of the sun's radiation spectrum. All radiation of wavelength shorter than about 3000 Å, and longer than about 30 meters, is completely extinguished (although very long radio waves may sometimes be received through transient "holes" in the ionosphere). Radiation of intermediate wavelengths is transmitted through a number of more or less transparent "windows" in the atmosphere, notably between 3000 Å and 11,000 Å and between 1 cm and 20 meters at radio wavelengths.

The mass of the sun is 2×10^{33} gm, and the radius of its visible surface is about 700,000 km. The average density of the solar gases is therefore about 1.4 times that of water. The total flux of solar radiation at the distance of the earth is the so-called *solar constant*, equal to 2.00 cal/cm²/min, from which it can be deduced that the sun radiates 3.6×10^{33} ergs/sec. Because of uncertainties in correcting for absorption by the earth's atmosphere, the probable error of the solar constant is about 2 percent; and, to this degree of accuracy, no certain variation in the sun's total radiative output has been detected. We shall see later, however, that localized areas on the sun exhibit large variations in brightness, more or less in unison with the sunspot cycle. Future, more refined measurements of the solar constant may well reveal some intrinsic variability.

The solar gases are so highly opaque that only radiation from the extreme outer periphery, consisting of about one part in 10 billion of the total mass, escapes into space. However, even though the solar interior cannot be directly observed, its gross structure at least can be rather safely deduced from such known facts as its mass, luminosity, radius, and chemical composition. The continued existence of the sun in a stable configuration requires that its central temperature and density be extremely high—about 15,000,000°K and about 70 gm/cm³, respectively. Under these conditions, thermonuclear reactions transform hydrogen into helium at a rate sufficient to account for the observed rate of energy release at the surface. The total mass converted into energy in this way is 4×10^{12} gm/sec, by the transformation of 5×10^{14} gm/sec of hydrogen into helium. As large as this number is, it represents only one part in 5×10^{18} of the sun's present mass, and since 64 percent of this is hydrogen—the remainder being 35 percent helium and about 1 percent heavier elements—the life expectancy of the sun, measured in billions of years, is high indeed.

The energy liberated in the interior leaks slowly outward to the exterior, each original high-frequency quantum being degraded into thousands of lower frequency quanta by successive absorptions and re-emissions. The extreme outer envelope of the sun, from which the radiation finally escapes, is called the "atmosphere," as distinguished from the interior.

It has been found that the atmosphere consists of three zones with entirely different physical and radiative properties. First, the *visible* radiation of the sun, as recorded in white light, is emitted from the lowest of the three zones in a layer a few hundred kilometers thick called the *photosphere*. Second, a zone about 15,000 km thick, called the *chromosphere*, lies immediately above the photosphere. It was first observed during total solar eclipses, when it appeared as a fiery red ring, at the instant when the bright disk of the sun was occulated by the moon. Third, an enormously distended outer envelope, greenish-white in color, as seen during solar eclipses, and called the *corona*, is observed to extend for many millions of kilometers into the solar system, possibly as far as the earth and beyond. The properties of each of these zones is discussed in turn.

3-1 THE PHOTOSPHERE

When the sun is photographed in white light (see Figure 3-1), it appears to have a very sharp boundary, which is caused, not by the absence of material beyond the boundary, but by the high opacity of the solar gases coupled with an extremely steep density gradient. So rapid is the fall in density that just inside the edge of the sun a tangential column of gas along the line of sight is completely opaque; and just outside, less than a second of arc farther out, it is virtually transparent. The outer edge of the sun as observed in visible light defines the upper boundary of the photosphere. Also, by definition, the photosphere includes all lower layers down to the level at which the gases become completely opaque. The thickness of the photosphere defined in this way is about 350 km.

All but a minute fraction of the sun's radiation is emitted by the photosphere. The spectrum of the photosphere is basically continuous, but it is crossed by the well-known Fraunhofer absorption lines, which are formed in the upper layers of the photosphere essentially because the temperature decreases outward (Figure 3-2). Early determinations of the temperature were based on comparisons of the sun's continuous radiation from the center of the disk with that of a black body; that is, by measuring (1) the total energy radiated at all wavelengths, (2) by noting the wavelength of maximum intensity, and (3) by fitting the spectral energy curve to an appropriate Planckian curve. All three methods agreed in assigning a temperature of about 6000°K

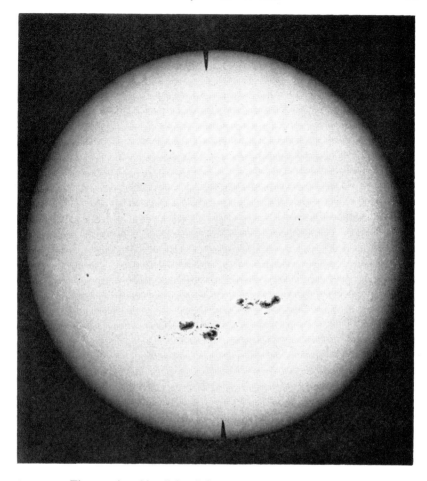

Figure 3-1   The sun in white light, July 31, 1949 (Mount Wilson and Palomar Observatories).

to the photosphere. The agreement was rather surprising because simple inspection of a white-light photograph shows that the disk is not uniformly bright but darker at the limb than at the center (Figure 3-1). Since the solar gases are opaque, the radiation from the darkened limb must emerge from higher and therefore cooler layers than that from the center of the disk. Thus the photosphere cannot have a single temperature; its radiation is composed of contributions from layers of different temperatures, the contribution from each depth being weakened by absorption in traversing the layers above. At the

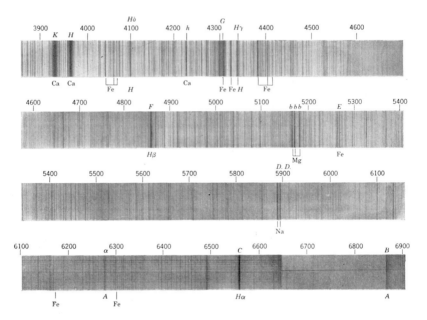

Figure 3-2 The Fraunhofer Spectrum λ3900–λ6900 (Mount Wilson and Palomar Observatories).

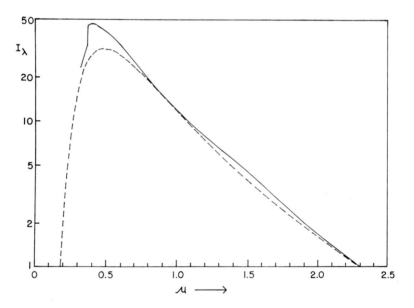

Figure 3-3 Observed spectral intensity distribution of solar radiation (solid line) compared with that of black body at $T = 6000°$K (dashed line). Ordinates in arbitrary units, abscissas in microns (McMath-Hulbert Observatory, University of Michigan).

top of the photosphere the temperature is about 4500°K; at the bottom it is about 8000°K. The resulting curve of emergent intensity versus wavelength of radiation from the center of the disk happens to coincide rather closely with that of a black body at $T = 6000°K$, as shown in Figure 3-3.

The temperature and opacity of the photosphere

Information on the temperature gradient of the photosphere can be obtained by a number of different methods, some theoretical and some empirical. The most straightforward route is by analysis of accurate measurements of the limb darkening. When such measurements are performed in different parts of the spectrum, they also yield the wavelength dependence of the cross section for continuous absorption, which helps to identify the mechanism that causes the opacity. Figure 3-4 shows the intensity profile of the solar disk as it appears in two different wavelengths. In Figure 3-5 the limb darkening is plotted as a function of wavelength for a number of fixed points on the solar disk, according to the value of cos θ, where θ is the angle between the line

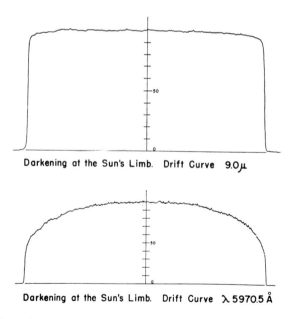

Darkening at the Sun's Limb. Drift Curve 9.0μ

Darkening at the Sun's Limb. Drift Curve λ 5970.5 Å

Figure 3-4 Intensity profile of the solar disk: upper: wavelength 9.0μ (90,000 Å), lower: wavelength 5970.5 Å (McMath-Hulbert Observatory, University of Michigan).

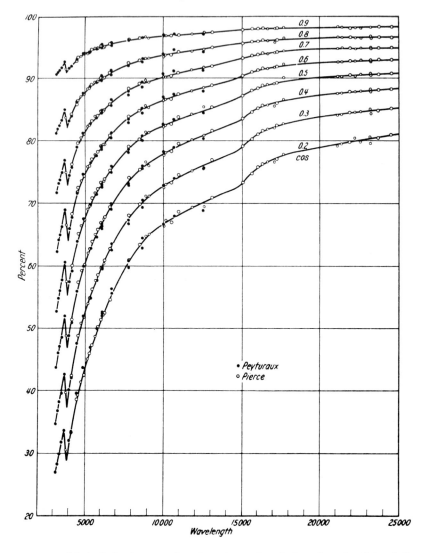

Figure 3-5 Limb darkening as a function of wavelength for selected points of the solar disk defined by cos θ (*Handbuch der Physik*, Vol. 52, p. 7, 1959).

of sight and the normal to the sun's surface. At the center of the disk cos $\theta = 1$, and at the limb cos $\theta = 0$. Note that the contrast between the center of the disk and the edge increases rapidly toward shorter wavelengths, which reflects the fact that the ratio of Planckian intensities for two values of the temperature is greater at shorter than at longer wavelengths.

The theoretical expression for the limb darkening may be obtained as follows. First, it can be shown that the intensity emergent from the photosphere at angle θ in units of ergs/cm²/sec and in unit solid angle and wavelength interval may be expressed as

$$I_\lambda(\mu) = \int_0^\infty B_\lambda(\tau_\lambda) e^{-\tau_\lambda/\mu} d\frac{\tau_\lambda}{\mu}, \qquad (3\text{-}1)$$

where $\mu = \cos\theta$. The quantity τ_λ is called the optical depth and is defined as

$$\tau_\lambda = \int_x^0 k_\lambda \, dx, \qquad (3\text{-}2)$$

where x is the geometrical depth, measured radially inward, and k_λ is the absorption coefficient per centimeter of the solar gases at wavelength λ. In equation (3-1) $B_\lambda(\tau)$ is the value of the Planck function at optical depth τ and wavelength λ. Thus the observed brightness in direction θ is the sum of contributions from all depths in the atmosphere, each reduced by the factor $e^{-\tau_\lambda/\mu}$ by the absorption of the layers above. Unit optical depth is seen to correspond to the geometrical distance over which the intensity is diminished by the factor $1/e$.

The expression for the limb darkening is therefore

$$\frac{I_\lambda(\mu)}{I_\lambda(1)} = I_\lambda^*(\mu) = \int_0^\infty B_\lambda^*(\tau_\lambda) e^{-\tau_\lambda/\mu} \frac{d\tau_\lambda}{\mu}, \qquad (3\text{-}3)$$

where

$$B_\lambda^*(\tau_\lambda) = \frac{B_\lambda(\tau_\lambda)}{I_\lambda(1)}. \qquad (3\text{-}4)$$

The left-hand side of equation (3-3) is an observed quantity from which $B_\lambda^*(T_\lambda)$ is to be derived. The usual procedure is to seek an analytic expression for B^* with unknown constants, which, when substituted into equation (3-3), yields the correct shapes of the observed limb-darkening curves. The following analytic form has been found useful:

$$B_\lambda^*(\tau_\lambda) = a_\lambda + b_\lambda\tau_\lambda + c_\lambda E_2(\tau_\lambda), \qquad (3\text{-}5)$$

where E_2 is the integral exponential function. Integration of equation (3-3) gives

$$\frac{I_\lambda(\mu)}{I_\lambda(1)} = a_\lambda + b_\lambda\mu + c_\lambda \left[1 - \mu\ln\left(1 + \frac{1}{\mu}\right)\right], \qquad (3\text{-}6)$$

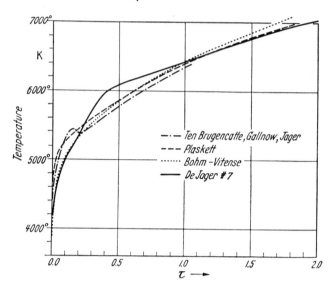

Figure 3-6 Temperature distribution versus optical depth in the photosphere by different observers (*Handbuch der Physik*, Vol. 52, p. 23, 1959).

after which the constants a_λ, b_λ, and c_λ are evaluated by least squares from the limb-darkening observations.

The analysis gives relative values of $B_\lambda(\tau_\lambda)$ in terms of the absolute intensity of the radiation from the center of the disk, which is also a measured quantity. Since $B_\lambda(\tau_\lambda)$ is a Planck function, its derivation leads to the determination of the temperature T as a function of the optical depth τ_λ. Some typical determinations are shown in Figure 3-6. If now the function $T(\tau_\lambda)$ has been determined for a broad range of wavelengths, the variation of τ_λ with λ also may be derived for fixed values of T, which correspond to fixed values of the geometrical depth. By equation (3-2) the derivative $d\tau_\lambda/dT$ is proportional to $k(x)$, the absorption coefficient per centimeter. The results of this analysis are shown in the left-hand side of Figure 3-7, in which the absorption coefficient is plotted against wavelength for a number of values of the parameter $\theta = 5040/T$. The shapes of the curves are generally similar at all values of T and closely resemble that of the negative hydrogen ion H^-. Below $\lambda = 16,000$ Å the absorption is caused chiefly by the photoionization of H^- and above $\lambda = 16,000$ Å by free-free transitions in the field of neutral hydrogen atoms. The photoionization of neutral hydrogen also plays a part in the deeper layers (smaller values of θ), as evidenced by the discontinuities at the Balmer, Paschen, and Brackett series limits.   The set of curves on the right has been calculated from theory and shows that on the whole the observed opacity of the photosphere is fairly well understood.

Once the temperature and absorption coefficient have been derived for each level in the photosphere, the pressure and its gradient may be calculated on the assumption of hydrostatic equilibrium.   Thus the analysis of observations of the sun's continuous radiation leads to the derivation of a model of the photosphere, in which the temperature and pressure are tabulated as a function of the optical depth at some standard wavelength, usually 5000 Å, and also as a function of the geometrical depth x.   One such model, by H. H. Plaskett, is given in Table 3-1.   Similar models have been obtained by many investigators; they differ only in minor respects, except at the very top and bottom of the photosphere, where the results are most uncertain. Successive columns in the table give the optical depth at 5000 Å, the geometrical depth in kilometers measured upward from $\tau = 3.00$, the temperature, the density, and the total pressure.

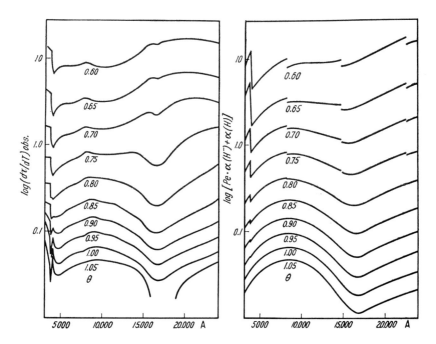

Figure 3-7   Wavelength dependence of absorption coefficient at different depths in the solar photosphere according to the parameter $\theta = 5040/T$: (left), observed; (right), computed absorption by neutral hydrogen and negative hydrogen ions (Handbuch der Physik, Vol. 52, p. 25, 1959).

TABLE 3-1

Model of the Solar Photosphere

(After H. H. Plaskett: *Vistas in Astronomy*, Vol. I,
ed. by Beer. London: Pergamon Press, 1955.)

τ	h (km)	T (°K)	ρ $(10^{-8}$ gm/ cm^3)	P $(10^4$ dyne/ cm^2)
0.0		4649	0	0
0.03	318	5033	4.2	1.7
0.06	261	5162	5.8	2.5
0.09	227	5246	7.1	3.1
0.12	203	5312	8.2	3.6
0.24	145	5505	11.2	5.1
0.36	113	5680	13.2	6.2
0.48	93	5838	14.4	6.9
0.72	67	6118	15.9	8.0
0.96	49	6356	16.8	8.8
1.20	37	6555	17.4	9.4
1.80	19	6959	17.9	10.3
3.00	0	7535	18.0	11.2

Convection in the photosphere

The temperature gradient derived from limb-darkening observations throws light on the important question how energy is transported through the photosphere. It can be shown that if the temperature gradient is not too steep most of the energy will be carried upward by radiation, but if the gradient exceeds that corresponding to adiabatic equilibrium an unstable situation may result. Radiation transfer is then inadequate to maintain the required energy flux and convection sets in. The observed temperature gradient indicates that radiative transfer prevails in the outer photosphere but that in the deeper layers convection must play an important role.

That convection does indeed occur in the photosphere is evident from examination of the visible surface with high magnification. It is found that the surface is not uniformly bright but has a mottled, granular structure consisting of small bright regions separated by darker and cooler areas. The pattern of granulation is not stable but has a mean life of 3 to 4 min.

It has long been generally accepted that the granulation is visible

evidence of convection in the sun—the bright granules are the tops
of turbulent columns of hot gas moving upward, whereas the darker
regions signify downward moving material that has cooled. However, the precise character of the convection has eluded description
until recently. For example, is the pattern of granulation in the
form of Bénard cells, as would be expected if the flow were laminar,
or are the fluctuations in brightness purely random and irregular, as
in random aerodynamic turbulence? The reason for the ambiguity is
that the scale of the granulation pattern is close to or smaller than
the smallest features that can be resolved by another kind of turbulence, that of the air through which telescopes look at the sun. The
turbulence is both inherent in the atmosphere and aggravated by the
solar heating and reradiation of metallic telescope structures. The
problem has now been solved in two ways. First, a number of observers, notably Rösch in France, have obtained superb photographs
of the sun by choosing moments when the atmosphere was exceptionally steady and by cooling the focal plane of the telescope. Second,
Schwarzschild of Princeton University sent a telescope aloft in an
unmanned balloon to a height of 80,000 ft, above the turbulent layers
of the atmosphere, and recovered what are probably the finest photographs ever made of the sun.

The following are some of the conclusions reached by Schwarzschild
from inspection and measurement of his best photographs, one of which
is shown in Figure 3-8:

1. The bright granules are irregular but often polygonal in shape.
2. There is a striking asymmetry between the bright and dark
regions, the bright ones occupying a much larger area.
3. On the average, the bright granules are about 100°K hotter than
the darker areas.
4. The range of sizes of the granules is rather great—between
<300 km and about 1800 km.

In general, the granules can be described as having an irregular
but cellular structure. They are therefore not a random phenomenon
like that of aerodynamic turbulence. They also cannot be Bénard
cells, which are in any case stable structures, whereas the granules
last but a few minutes. The observed pattern is actually strikingly
similar to that of nonstationary convection, which is midway between
the other two extremes. The new observations are not yet fully
explained because theoretical considerations based on the value of
the Rayleigh number to be expected in the sun seem to require fully
developed aerodynamic turbulence.

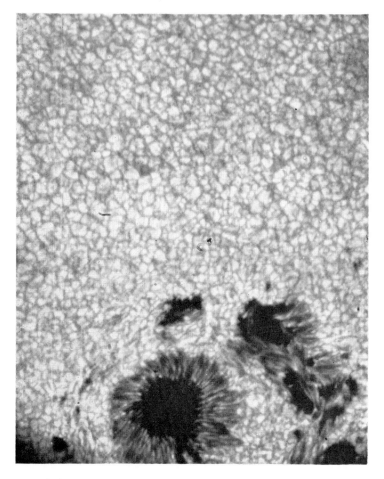

Figure 3-8 Solar granulation and a large sunspot photographed from a balloon at 80,000 ft altitude (Princeton University, Office of Naval Research and National Science Foundation).

The Fraunhofer spectrum

We have seen that a great deal of important information about the photosphere can be obtained from the observation of its continuous radiation alone. Much more can be learned from consideration of the wavelengths, intensities, and shapes of the Fraunhofer absorption lines, which tend to be formed mostly in the higher layers of the photosphere. Time does not permit more than mention and a few brief illustrations of the wealth of interesting problems that can be solved by studies of the line spectrum. The Fraunhofer spectrum is essentially an atomic-line spectrum, although bands of 14 diatomic molecules have also been identified. On the whole their lines are quite weak, with the exception of CN, C_2, and CO. Many different parameters determine the intensity of an absorption line, among them the structure and physical state of the photosphere, the abundance of the element, and the transition probability of the line. When the other relevant factors are taken into account, the observed line intensities can be used to derive the chemical abundances of all elements giving rise to lines in the observable region of the spectrum. Table 3-2 contains a recent compilation of abundances for 43 of the 60-plus chemical elements that have fairly certainly been identified in the solar spectrum. The absence of the other elements can be reasonably explained on the grounds of low abundance, location of their strongest lines in the inaccessible ultraviolet, and the short lifetimes of radioactive atoms.

Apart from determinations of chemical abundance and the testing

TABLE 3-2

Composition of the Solar Atmosphere *

(According to L. Goldberg, E. A. Mueller, and L. H. Aller, Astrophysical Journal Supplement No. 45, 1960.)

Element	log N	Element	log N	Element	log N
H	12.00	Se	2.82	Y	2.25
Li	0.96	Ti	4.68	Zr	2.23
Be	2.36	V	3.70	Nb	1.95
C	8.72	Cr	5.36	Mo	1.90
N	7.98	Mn	4.90	Ru	1.43
O	8.96	Fe	6.57	Rh	0.78
Na	6.30	Co	4.64	Pd	1.21
Mg	7.40	Ni	5.91	Ag	0.14
Al	6.20	Cu	5.04	Cd	1.46
Si	7.50	Zn	4.40	In	1.16
P	5.34	Ga	2.36	Sn	1.54
S	7.30	Ge	3.29	Sb	1.94
K	4.70	Rb	2.48	Ba	2.10
Ca	6.15	Sr	2.60	Yb	1.53
				Pb	1.33

* The table gives values of log N, the logarithm of the number of atoms per gram of solar material, relative to that of hydrogen, which is arbitrarily set at 12.00.

of theories of line formation, the most important uses to which the Fraunhofer lines have been put in recent years have been in the measurement of weak magnetic fields and in the study of the hydrodynamical properties of the solar atmosphere. We shall see later that the most violent kind of activity can take place in localized regions of the solar atmosphere, in which jets of gas are flung about at speeds of several hundred kilometers per second in the presence of magnetic fields as strong as several thousand gauss. The origin and buildup of such transient activity is very likely connected with the fact that the entire photosphere is in a constant state of turbulent motion and that the moving gases are magnetized in a highly random and irregular pattern. Both the velocities and the fields are extremely weak, on the order of 1 km/sec and a few gauss, respectively, and it has been only recently that spectroscopic techniques have become sufficiently refined to permit their measurement.

Local velocity fields

It was suggested earlier that the granulation implies the presence of up-and-down moving columns of gas. Therefore, if the slit of a high-resolution spectrograph is placed across the solar disk, the Doppler effect should cause the Fraunhofer lines to display a zigzag appearance. This expectation has been fully verified, as shown in Figure 3-9, on a photograph made at the McMath-Hulbert Observatory. The line shifts correspond to velocities of about 1 km/sec or less, the root-

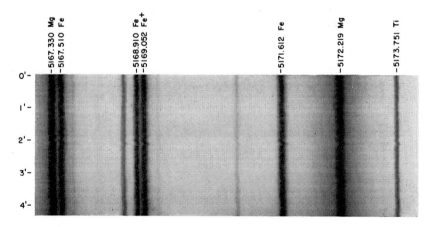

Figure 3-9 Local Doppler shifts in Fraunhofer lines near 5170 Å. The vertical scale is in minutes of arc on the solar disk (McMath-Hulbert Observatory, University of Michigan).

mean-square value being about 0.4 km/sec at the center of the disk. Some very new work by Evans and Michard at the Sacramento Peak Observatory and by Leighton at the Mount Wilson Observatory has established the remarkable fact that the motion is oscillatory in a period of about 4 min. This does not mean that the entire photosphere pulsates as a unit, since the phases of the individual gas bubbles are distributed at random, but the period is everywhere the same.

Leighton has devised an ingenious technique for the study of velocity fields in the solar atmosphere by an interesting modification of the spectroheliograph. This instrument is commonly used at many solar observatories to make monochromatic photographs of the sun in the light of individual spectral lines. In Leighton's modification, photographs are also made in individual lines, but light and dark areas now represent not fluctuations in the line intensity but regions in which

Figure 3-10 Velocity map of the sun by R. B. Leighton (Mount Wilson and Palomar Observatories).

material is moving along the line of sight in directions toward and away from the observer, respectively. A typical photograph of this kind, made in the light of the neutral calcium line $\lambda = 6103$ Å, is shown in Figure 3-10.

In this representation large fluctuations in brightness would denote large velocities, whereas low contrast would signify small velocities. It is apparent from the photograph that the contrast is lower in the center of the disk than near the limbs. This suggests that the motion is not only radial but has an even larger horizontal component. Away from the center of the disk one also sees large numbers of roughly circular structures, bright in the direction toward the center of the disk and dark on the opposite side. These are large gas bubbles, about 15,000 km in diameter, which are apparently expanding as they rise. It must be emphasized that the features observed in the spectral lines come from much higher levels in the atmosphere than the granules observed in the continuous radiation. Both are related but different manifestations of the convective currents that originate at relatively greater depths below the photosphere.

Magnetic fields

Intense magnetic fields up to several thousand gauss in strength are associated with sunspots. Such strong fields are easily revealed by the Zeeman splitting of spectral lines. After discovering them in 1908, George Ellery Hale set upon the much more difficult task of searching for the weaker general magnetic field that the sun was expected to possess. Hale's efforts were not entirely successful, but continued work at the Mount Wilson Observatory by H. D. and H. W. Babcock led to their invention of the magnetograph, a device for measuring fields as small as two or three tenths of a gauss. The sensitivity of this device is extraordinary when one considers that the Zeeman splitting of a spectral line at 5000 Å is only about 2×10^{-5} Å/gauss.

Some typical magnetic maps of the sun's photosphere are shown in Figure 3-11. The distance between the parallel lines equals a deflection of about 1 gauss; the direction of the deflection indicates the magnetic polarity. The small deflections of opposite polarity near the north (up) and south (down) poles are caused by the general magnetic field, which has an average intensity of about 1 gauss. Superposed on the general field are many large areas, generally lying within 60 degrees of the equator, which have bipolar magnetic fields ranging from two to several tens of gausses. The Babcocks have also discovered extensive areas containing unipolar fields not exceed-

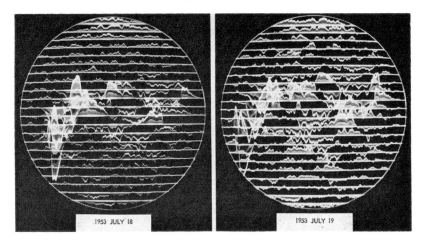

Figure 3-11 Solar magnetograms showing intensity and polarity of weak magnetic fields (Mount Wilson and Palomar Observatories).

ing about 2 gauss, which may be regions from which solar cosmic rays escape to the earth.

The magnetograph began operation in about 1953, during the minimum of the sunspot cycle. At that time, the polarity of the general, or poloidal, field was positive in the north and negative in the south. Between March and July 1957 the south polar field reversed its polarity, but the north field remained unchanged until late in 1958, when it reversed from positive to negative.

3-2 THE CHROMOSPHERE

As recently as 25 to 30 years ago it was thought that the faint, outer envelope of the solar atmosphere, which flashes into view during the brief seconds of a solar eclipse, was merely a highly rarefied extension of the photosphere; its temperature being rather less than 6000°K (see Figure 3-12). Indeed, the emission spectrum of the chromosphere at visible wavelengths, which may be photographed at solar eclipses, resembles that of the photosphere in its general level of excitation and ionization. The spectroscopic evidence did include a number of warning flags, however, which eventually signaled the true state of affairs. The first was that although the spectrum of the chromosphere consists mainly of emission lines that would be expected to appear at a temperature of 6000°K or less there are also numerous lines of neutral helium, which require temperatures in excess of

Figure 3-12 The solar corona, June 8, 1918 (Mount Wilson and Palomar Observatories).

10,000°K for their excitation, and even one or more lines of ionized helium, which are not expected at temperatures much less than 20,000°K. Second, the spectrum of the corona, which extends above the chromosphere to a distance of many solar diameters, was observed to consist entirely of about two dozen diffuse emission lines, none of which could be identified with any spectral lines observed in the laboratory.

The subsequent identification of the coronal lines by the Swedish physicist Edlén in 1941, as arising from such highly ionized atoms as Fe X to Fe XIV, Ni XII to Ni XVI, and Ca XII to Ca XIII, proved that in reality the corona is a hot plasma at a temperature of about one million degrees. This meant that somewhere in the chromosphere, the temperature, which decreases outward through the photosphere, must turn sharply upward from 4500 to 1,000,000°K in the relatively short space of a few thousand kilometers. The maintenance of such a negative temperature gradient and high coronal temperature requires a steady input of energy, which is probably supplied from below by the mechanical energy carried upward by the photospheric granules. It has been estimated by Schwarzschild that the rate of upward energy transport by the granules is about 3×10^{29} ergs/sec, which is about 100 times greater than the total rate of energy radiated by the chromosphere and corona. The granules therefore provide an ample supply of energy and the problem, which is still not finally solved, is to find the exact process or processes by which the mechanical energy is transformed into heat.

Several mechanisms for heating the chromosphere and corona have been proposed, all of them equally plausible in the absence of sufficient information to test them rigorously. For example, Schwarzschild and Biermann have proposed independently that turbulence in the granules generates acoustic waves, which are transformed into shock waves by the lower density in the chromosphere, the shock waves being then dissipated into heat. Since the photospheric gases are magnetized, the upward moving disturbances may be magnetohydrodynamic waves, as suggested by Alfvén.

If a theory of chromospheric heating is to be completely acceptable, it must be fully in accord with what is actually observed. Unfortunately, although there is a large body of observational data about the chromosphere, conditions there are so fantastically complex that it has not even been possible to construct a single physical model of the chromosphere that accounts for all of the observations. To begin with, the chromosphere, unlike most of the photosphere, is not in thermodynamic equilibrium and therefore measurements of intensity in the spectrum cannot be easily converted into meaningful values of the temperature and density. In general, one can derive three different types of temperatures from spectral measurements. The first is the electron or kinetic temperature T_e, which is defined by the Maxwellian distribution of electron velocities and can be deduced, for example, from the distribution of intensity in the continuous spectrum beyond the limit of the Balmer series of hydrogen. Second, the distribution of atoms of a given species among its various excited levels, as derived from relative line intensities, defines an excitation temperature, T_{exc}, according to the Boltzmann formula. Finally, the relative abundance of neutral and ionized atoms of the same element specifies an ionization temperature, T_{ion}, according to the Saha equation.

In thermodynamic equilibrium the three kinds of temperatures are identical, but in the chromosphere the differences are often great. The excitation and ionization temperatures differ not only from one another and from the electron temperature but also from one line to another. The only really significant temperature is the electron temperature, but this can be deduced only from a relatively small fraction of the observational data.

A second complication is the extreme heterogeneity of the chromosphere for which there is both direct and indirect evidence. The spectrum of the low chromosphere, below about 400 km, reveals the presence of both low-excitation lines of the metals, indicative of temperatures of about 5000°K and high-excitation lines of helium, which signify temperatures three or four times as great. To explain this anomaly, Giovanelli suggested that the chromosphere might have a heterogeneous structure consisting of alternate columns of high and low temperature. Observations made during good observing conditions show that the chromosphere is indeed made up of a multitude of tiny jets, or spicules, which are often seen to be exploding outward at speeds up to 30 km/sec (see Figure 3-13). In the view of Thomas and Athay, the spicules represent the cool component of the chromosphere, the interspicular regions being much hotter. Furthermore, the

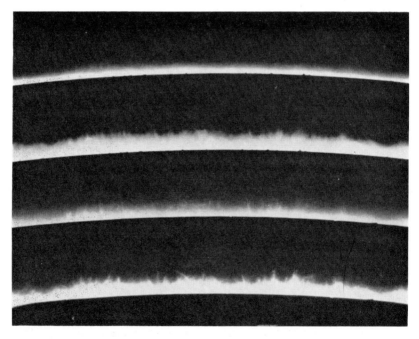

Figure 3-13 Jet structure of the chromosphere (Sacramento Peak Observatory, Geophysics Research Directorate, AFCRL).

TABLE 3-3

A Suggested Working Chromosphere Model

(L. H. Aller)

Height (km)	Spicule log N	T	Interspicule log N	T
500	11.60	5,300		
1,000	11.43	5,800	11.43	6,300
1,500	11.18	5,850	11.05	9,000
2,000	10.95	5,900	10.70	10,000
2,500	10.72	6,050	10.35	12,000
3,000	10.50	6,200	10.15	15,000
4,000	10.15	6,500	9.88	22,500
5,000	9.88	7,000	9.63	35,000
6,000	9.64	8,000	9.43	56,000
7,000	9.45	11,000	9.27	90,000
8,000	9.30	20,000	9.12	140,000
10,000	9.10	53,000	8.88	500,000

speeds of the spicules are supersonic, which leads to the formation of shock waves that can provide a source of mechanical energy for heating the upper chromosphere and corona.

The construction of a physical model of the chromosphere is one of the major goals of solar research. Many such models have been derived, but they differ so drastically that none can be regarded as more than working hypotheses. A recent model by Aller is presented in Table 3-3 merely as an illustration of the present concept of the chromosphere as a filamentary structure in which the temperature increases steeply upward. It must also be emphasized that any two-component model grossly oversimplifies the heterogeneity of the chromosphere and further that no model can even faintly resemble reality without including the dynamical aspects of the chromospheric structure.

The ultraviolet spectrum of the chromosphere

The far-ultraviolet spectrum of the sun has been photographed frequently during the last 15 years with spectrographs mounted in high-altitude rockets. We have seen that at visible wavelengths the radiation from the disk of the sun comes almost entirely from the photosphere. Only the central parts of the strongest Fraunhofer lines are formed in the low chromosphere. The situation is completely reversed at far-ultraviolet wavelengths. The continuous radiation from the center of the sun's disk closely simulates that of a black body at a temperature of about 6000°K over the entire wavelength range from 4000 to 25,000 Å. At longer and shorter wavelengths the opacity is greater, and the radiation tends to emanate from the higher and cooler layers. Thus below 4000 Å the radiation is characterized by a temperature of 5000°K or less and at 11 μ (110,000 Å) a recent measurement by Saiedy and Goody yields a temperature of 5000°K. The intensity of ultraviolet radiation from a 5000°K black body falls off rapidly with decreasing wavelength. At the same time, the emission from the high-temperature layers of the chromosphere increases, until, at about 1700 Å, the radiation of the photosphere fades out completely and the solar spectrum consists entirely of emission from the chromosphere.

The foregoing ideas are fully documented by actual photographs of the far-ultraviolet solar spectrum obtained by Purcell and Tousey of the Naval Research Laboratory. The strongest line in the spectrum is, as would be expected, the resonance Lyman-alpha line of hydrogen. Other members of the Lyman series are also present, together with lines of carbon, nitrogen, oxygen, silicon, and sulfur in many stages of ionization, including O VI, N V, and S VI. The wealth of high-temperature lines is a remarkable feature of the spectrum, as contrasted with the predominantly low-temperature spectrum found in the visible, but it is readily explained as a consequence of the extreme range in temperature that prevails in the chromosphere.

3-3 THE CORONA

Observations of the solar corona, made during total eclipses of the sun, show that it reaches to a distance of more than 40 solar radii; it may ultimately be found to extend well beyond the orbit of the earth. The density of its lowest regions is about 10^{-15} gm/cm^3, as compared with about 10^{-8} gm/cm^3 in the photosphere and 10^{-3} gm/cm^3 for the bottom of the earth's atmosphere. Hence, despite its temperature of about 2 million degrees, the corona radiates only a millionth as much energy as the photosphere in visible wavelengths, and about 97 percent of the visible radiation is simply continuous photospheric light scattered by free electrons in the highly ionized coronal gas.

Apart from scattered sunlight, the coronal spectrum exhibits 31 emission lines between 3000 and 11,000 Å, most of which have been identified as the so-called forbidden lines of metallic atoms in high stages of ionization (see Table 3-4). Although none of the coronal lines can be observed under laboratory conditions, the locations of the atomic energy levels concerned with their formation have been sufficiently well established by measurement of theory that there is no doubt of the correctness of the identifications.

The energies required to produce these ions are in the range of several hundred electron volts and therefore demand temperatures on the order of a million degrees. Many other lines of evidence also lead to the same conclusion. For example, if the extreme broadness of the lines (about 1 Å) is attributed to the random Doppler effect, the temperature required is about 2 million degrees. The gradient of the electron density, which can be derived from the radial decrease in intensity of the scattered photospheric light and its polarization, also leads to the same temperature, from considerations of hydrostatic equilibrium. Finally, and most important, the corona is observed to emit strongly at radio wavelengths in the meter band, the intensity being such that the temperature cannot be less than a million degrees.

A million-degree plasma like the corona would be expected to emit both short-wave ultraviolet radiation and soft X rays above about 20 Å. Indirect evidence for such radiations is the existence of the E and F layers of the ionosphere. Thus the E layer requires radiation in the wavelength range 40 to 100 Å for its maintenance and the F_2 layer is probably formed by the absorption of radiation in the band 100 to 1000 Å. Observations of far-ultraviolet and X rays from the

TABLE 3-4

Coronal Emission Lines

Wave-length	Identi-fication	I.P. (volts)	Wave-length	Identi-fication	I.P. (volts)	Wave-length	Identi-fication	I.P. (volts)
3329	Ca XII	589	4086.4	Ca XIII	655	5444.5	Ca XV	814
3388.0	Fe XIII	325	4232.0	Ni XII	318	5535	A X	421
3454.1	—	—	4256.4	K XI	—	5694.4	Ca XV	814
3534.0	VX	—	4351.0	Co XV	—	6374.5	Fe X	233
3601.0	Ni XVI	455	4359	—	—	6535.5	Mn XIII	—
3642.9	Ni XIII	350	4412.4	A XIV	682	6701.83	Ni XV	422
3800.4	—	—	4566.8	—	—	7069.6	Fe XV	390
3885	Mn XII	—	4586	—	—	7891.7	Fe XI	261
3987.2	Fe XI	261	5116.03	Ni XIII	350	9024.21	Ni XV	422
3998	Cr XI	—	5302.86	Fe XIV	355	10746.80	Fe XIII	325
						10797.95	Fe XIII	325

corona have now been made from rockets. Most of the emission lines above 100 Å are formed in the chromosphere, but a certain number, notably those of Mg X at 625 Å, Si XII at 500 Å, and Fe XVI near 350 Å, are clearly of coronal origin.

Observations of solar X rays have been made by Friedman and his co-workers at the Naval Research Laboratory in a number of wavelength bands between 1 and 100 Å (see Chapter 14). The observed flux is highly variable and connected with solar activity, but even when the sun is quiet it is consistent with a temperature of 1,500,-000°K. The observational techniques are still too limited to permit the resolution of the X-ray spectrum into individual lines, but this development may be realized in the near future.

To summarize, the radiation of the undisturbed or quiet sun is spread throughout the electromagnetic spectrum and is therefore not typical of any one temperature. In fact, the emitting layers vary in temperature from 4500°K at the top of the photosphere to about 2,000,000°K in the corona. In general, radiation typical of various temperature ranges is concentrated in different parts of the spectrum. Thus, between 4000 and 25,000 Å, the sun radiates like a black body at 600°K, whereas at longer infrared wavelengths the effective temperature is about 5000°K or less. At short radio wavelengths between a few millimeters and a few centimeters the radiation comes from the low chromosphere and is typical of temperatures in the range 8000 to 10,000°K. The effective radio temperature then increases rapidly with wavelength to the million-degree range at meter wavelengths because long radio waves can escape only from the upper layers of an ionized gas when the density decreases outward.

Below 4000 Å, the solar radiation is roughly consistent with a temperature of 4500°K down to about 1500 Å, where the emission line spectrum of the chromosphere begins to dominate. As the wavelength decreases, the line spectrum is characteristic of higher and higher temperatures until at 100 Å it arises entirely from the corona.

3-4 SOLAR ACTIVITY

Up until now we have been concerned with the structure and radiation of what has been called the "quiet" sun. However, its close proximity to the earth makes possible the observation of a whole series of complex stormlike disturbances, which are connected with the presence of sunspots but are not necessarily caused by them. These disturbances, which are often referred to as *solar phenomena* or *solar activity*, are usually shortlived in duration and take place in relatively local and confined regions of the solar atmosphere, but their sheer violence and the dramatic effects they often produce on the earth make them a fascinating subject for study.

The best known and most easily observed of the solar disturbances are the sunspots, which can be seen in ordinary white light photographs or visually when the sun's image is projected through a telescope on a white card. The number of spots that can be observed on the disk of the sun at any one time varies in a somewhat irregular period, averaging 11 years, this variation being known as the sunspot cycle. In general, the level of solar activity goes up and down in phase with the same cycle, but individual events of great magnitude are sometimes observed when the face of the sun is relatively spotless. The appearance of the sun during a typical sunspot maximum is shown in Figure 3-14. Sunspots do not appear everywhere on the

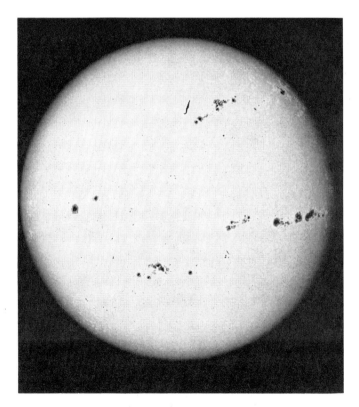

Figure 3-14   The sun at sunspot maximum, December 21, 1957 (Mount Wilson and Palomar Observatories).

face of the sun; they are confined to latitudes between 5 and 40 degrees on either side of the equator. As the sunspot cycle progresses from minimum through maximum, new spots tend to break out first at the highest latitude, after which their place of occurrence moves ever closer to the equator as the cycle progresses to maximum. Sunspots generally appear in groups, centered about two main spots which grow to a maximum size in a period of a few days to about a week. A large group of spots may persist on the sun for as long as a few weeks or months. Observations of sunspots first established the fact that the sun is rotating, but not as a solid body, since the period of rotation increases from 24.6 days at the equator to 32 days at a latitude of 75 degrees. However, the duration of spot groups is such that the same group has been observed during as many as four transits across the disk.

Whitelight photographs also show the presence in sunspot zones of large areas that are brighter than the surrounding photosphere and are called faculae. Such areas are usually associated with sunspots and seem to be present both before a spot has developed and after the spots have dissipated.

A typical large sunspot is shown in Figure 3-15. It appears dark because it is about 2000°K cooler than its surroundings. All sunspots are characterized by strong magnetic fields, and spots such as these may have fields as large as 3000 to 4000 gauss. Sunspots consist of a dark central region, called the umbra, surrounded by a lighter periphery, the penumbra, which has a granular filamentary structure. The largest spots may have diameters approaching 150,000 km, and a large group may extend over a distance of nearly 300,000 km.

Not only the magnitude but also the direction of the magnetic field can be measured from the Zeeman splitting of spectral lines. Usually the direction of the field is perpendicular to the surface, and the spots frequently occur in pairs of opposite magnetic polarity. Some complex groups contain a mixture of spots of opposite polarity. When the spots occur in pairs, the leading member, in the direction of the sun's rotation, always has the same polarity, which is opposite that of the following member. However, spots in opposite hemispheres tend to have opposite magnetic polarity, and the direction of the polarity reverses in alternate 11-year cycles.

It now seems quite certain that a sunspot is formed as a consequence of the buildup of an intense magnetic field. Because the magnetic field inhibits the convection of hot material from below, the sunspot becomes cooler than its surroundings. The sunspot cycle itself can probably be explained as a consequence of the large-scale hydrodynamical motions of magnetized material.

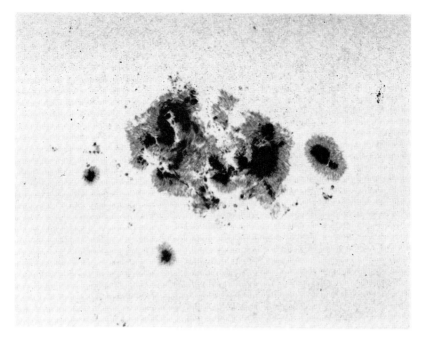

Figure 3-15 Large sunspot group, May 17, 1951 (Mount Wilson and Palomar Observatories).

Plages and filaments

Sunspots and faculae are located in the photosphere. Activity in the chromosphere can be revealed by visual or photographic observations of the sun as it appears in monochromatic radiation at the center of a strong spectral line, such as Hα of hydrogen or the H and K lines of ionized calcium. Although the continuous spectrum is formed entirely in the photosphere, the radiation at the centers of strong lines comes entirely from the chromosphere. By using lines with a progression of intensities, one can obtain cross-sectional views of the solar chromosphere at different heights. Figure 3-16 shows the appearance of the sun, first in white light, second in Hα of hydrogen, third in the K line of ionized calcium, and fourth in the Lyman-alpha line of hydrogen. It will be seen that activity in the chromosphere is much more pronounced than in the photosphere. The large bright areas called *plages* are usually found to surround sunspot groups. Actually, they appear to be upward extensions of the faculae. The large sinuous dark threads seen on the Hα photograph, which are called *filaments*, are actually large clouds of relatively cool, low-

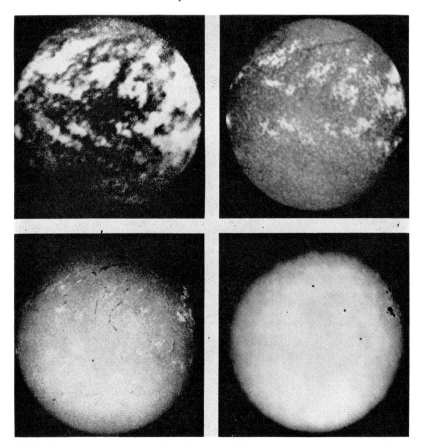

Figure 3-16 Images of the sun on March 13, 1959, photographed in white light (*lower right*), in Hα of hydrogen (*lower left*), in K of ionized calcium (*upper right*), and in Lyman-alpha of hydrogen (*upper left*) (U. S. Naval Research Laboratory).

density material, sometimes extending to heights of tens of thousands of kilometers, and are visible in projection against the solar disk. The filaments sometimes undergo remarkably abrupt disappearance after persisting for many weeks, but sometimes the disappearance is followed by an equally abrupt reappearance at the same place and in nearly the same form.

Prominences

At times of solar eclipses fiery-red protuberances of gas can often be seen to jut out from the chromosphere and to extend for tens of thousands of kilometers into the corona. *Prominences*, as they are called, were first discovered in this way but are now observed daily at all solar observatories, usually in the monochromatic light of Hα, but also in the K line of ionized calcium. They appear as filaments when seen in projection against the disk. Prominences are found in many sizes and in many forms. Their motions are so complicated that they can be studied only by motion-picture techniques and even so defy mathematical description. Attempts to classify prominences according to form and behavior have generally been unsuccessful, owing to the large number of subdivisions that are required and also because prominences may progress from one type to another during their lifetimes.

Prominences occur much more frequently and numerously near the maximum of the sunspot cycle than at other times, especially those that appear over sunspot zones. Their forms seem to be shaped by the lines of force issuing from magnetized regions on the solar surface below. Loop formations are exceedingly common, and the fine structure of the material is decidedly filamentary. It is not uncommon to observe material in rapid motion along the loops, and stable or quiescent prominences in particular appear to lie across the lines

Figure 3-17 A large solar prominence (Sac Peak Observatory, Geophysics Research Directorate, AFCRL).

of force connecting two magnetic regions of opposite polarity on the disk. Prominences sometimes undergo violent and spectacular eruptions during which the entire object may be hurled upward over a distance of several hundred thousand kilometers before turning and falling back into the sun (see Figure 3-17). Other gas clouds may appear to leave the sun entirely and to be cast out into the interplanetary medium. Velocities of more than 1000 km/sec have been observed and the escape paths of some prominences traced to distances between 1 and 2 million km.

Temperatures of prominences so far determined indicate that the range is between about 8000 and 30,000°K and the particle density is about $2 \times 10^{10}/cm^3$. In the surrounding corona the temperature is about 2 million degrees and the density about 10^8; therefore, prominences are relatively cool, dense formations embedded in a much hotter and rarer medium. Evidently magnetic lines of force play an important role in causing the coronal medium to condense and cool.

Flares

The greatest of all transient solar disturbances are the solar flares. Although they show a variety of observable effects, they are most commonly seen in Hα light (see Figure 3-18) as a rather sudden brightening of portions of a plage region followed by a much slower decline in brightness that may last for several hours. The area, brightness, and duration of flares vary over a large range. The greatest flares may cover areas as large as a few tenths of 1 percent of the area of the solar disk. The early visual observers of flares assigned them to Classes I, II, or III, in order of increasing importance of the event, and this rough quantitative description is still found useful, although it has become necessary to subdivide further by the addition of pluses or minuses to the numbers. Thus the weakest flares are classed as 1−, and the strongest as 3+. Other lines in the visible spectrum also brighten during the flare, in addition to Hα, and a few of the brightest flares, including the first one discovered in 1859, have been observed in white light. Flares are also accompanied by greatly enhanced emission at the two opposite ends of the spectrum, at radio frequencies, and in the ultraviolet and X-ray regions. Flares also usually generate and eject high-speed charged particles, which, for most flares, have energies in the vicinity of 100 Mev but which are sometimes as high as 20 bev.

As far as its general level of excitation is concerned, the spectrum of a flare at visible wavelengths is not unlike that of the chromosphere, although many individual lines display grossly anomalous behavior,

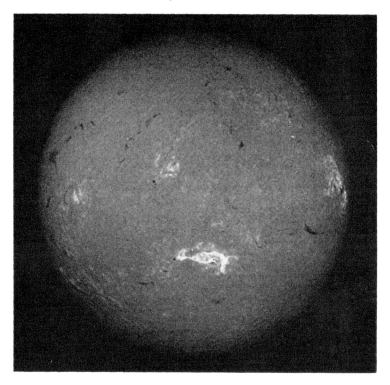

Figure 3-18   Great Class III flare of November 12, 1960, photographed in Hα light (Sacramento Peak Observatory, Geophysics Research Directorate, AFCRL).

and in general the visible spectra are characteristic of temperatures in the range 10,000 to 20,000°K. However, the X-ray and radio-frequency spectra tell quite a different story. Friedman, Chubb, and their associates at the Naval Research Laboratory have flown a number of X-ray detectors responsive to the three wavelength bands 2-8 Å, 8-20 Å, 44-60 Å and to hard X rays with energies to 100 kev both during and in the absence of solar flares. During three flights in 1959 the average total flux in X rays at the top of the earth's atmosphere was 0.4 erg/sec/cm², of which 0.14 was contained in the narrow band 44-60 Å. On August 31, 1959, a flight was made to coincide with a Class 2+ solar flare. At this time the total X-ray flux was 9.8 erg/sec/cm², an enhancement of more than a factor of 10 over the quiet sun. Furthermore, there was an enormous increase of emission of high energies greater than 20 kev, and photon energies as high as 70 kev were observed. The corresponding wavelength would be less than 0.20 Å. Although the normal X-ray emission from the quiet sun is consistent with a temperature of about 1,000,-000°K, the X-ray flux during bright solar flares simulates temperatures as high as 100,000,000°K.

Great flares are always accompanied by spectacular bursts of radio waves at meter wavelengths, which can be observed with radio telescopes and sweep-frequency receivers that display the radio-frequency spectrum as a function of time (see Figure 3-19). Five different classes of radio bursts have been distinguished, according to the way in which the intensity and frequencies change with time. Type I bursts seem to occur high up in the corona and show no change in frequency during their duration of about 0.10 sec in the course of prolonged noise storms that may last for hours or days. The noise storms, but not the individual bursts, seem to be associated with solar flares. Both Type II and Type III bursts are closely connected with flares and seem to originate in the corona above them. Their frequencies decrease with wavelength on the average, relatively slowly in the case of Type II and rapidly in Type III. Type II bursts seem to originate in disturbances traveling outward from the sun with speeds up to 1500 km/sec. They are rare occurrences, lasting for many minutes, unlike the Type III bursts, which are frequent and last for about 10 sec. The speeds associated with Type III events are enormous—as high as a few tenths of the velocity of light. The radio emission connected with Types II and III appears to result from plasma oscillations excited by fast-moving streams of ionized gas.

The spectrum of a Type IV burst extends over a broad band of frequencies, and the emission usually lasts for several hours. Type V events also show continuous emission over a broad band of frequencies but last for only a minute or two. There is considerable evidence that the Type IV and V bursts can be ascribed to synchrotron radiation resulting from the motions of relativistic electrons in magnetic fields.

The enhancement of X-ray, ultraviolet, and particle radiation accompanying solar flares produces some rather striking effects upon the earth. For example, the enhancement of solar X rays greatly increases the ionization of the D layer, the lowest layer of the ionosphere, which thereby absorbs meter waves used for radio communications on the earth instead of reflecting them. Such sudden ionospheric disturbances, or SID's, as they are called, frequently accompany solar flares and lead to fadeouts in short-wave radio communications that may last for several hours. The sudden increase of electrical cur-

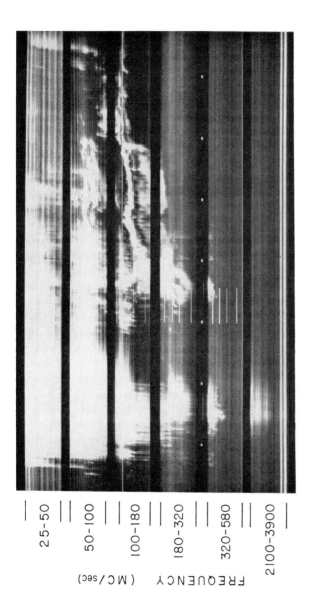

Figure 3-19   Three-dimensional record of a great solar radio event at both meter and centimeter wavelengths observed at the Fort Davis, Texas, Radio Astronomy Station of Harvard College Observatory. The frequency decreases upward, time increases from left to right, and the brightness of the images is a measure of the intensity of the radio emission. Several types of bursts are shown on the record (Courtesy Alan Maxwell).

rents in the ionosphere also induces erratic fluctuation in magnetic compasses.

The impact of high-speed electrified particles from the sun results in showers of cosmic rays, blackouts of radio communication in the polar regions, geomagnetic storms, and brilliant displays of aurorae. These and other consequences of solar radiation are discussed in more detail in later chapters.

GENERAL REFERENCES

Kuiper, G. P., ed., The Sun, Vol. I, *The Solar System;* University of Chicago Press, Chicago, 1953.

Flügge, S., ed., The Solar System, Vol. 52, *Handbuch der Physik,* Springer Verlag, Berlin, 1959; articles by L. Goldberg, A. K. Pierce, and C. de Jager.

Berkner, L. V., and H. Odishaw, eds., *Science in Space,* Chapter 17, The Sun, L. Goldberg and E. R. Dyer, Jr.

Papers by many authors on ultraviolet radiating from the sun and stars in Proceedings of Tenth Astrophysical Colloquium at Liége, July 1960, *Mem. Soc. Roy. Sci. Liége,* Fifth Series, **IV** (1961).

CHAPTER 4

THE ORIGIN AND EVOLUTION OF THE SOLAR SYSTEM *

HAROLD C. UREY

University of California, San Diego

La Jolla, California

The problem of the origin of the solar system has been discussed by scientists for centuries. In some ways the solar system has a simple structure and this perhaps leads us to expect that the process of the formation of the system would be a simple one. As time has passed, we have realized more and more how complex the problem is and how little information we have on which to build the theory required. The general structure of the solar system has been known for a long time. The planets have orbits that lie nearly in one plane. The orbits are almost circular, and all the planets move in one direction about the sun. Most of the angular momentum of the system is in the planets. The regular satellites of the planets may be classified as regular and irregular. The satellites have orbits lying in the plane of the equator of the planet, and their orbital rotation has the same direction as the planetary rotation. One wonders very much how these

* This chapter reviews the lecture given for the University of California Extension Course in September 1961. The same subject was covered in four lectures given before the Institute of Space Studies in New York during October 1961 and before the Tata Institute for Fundamental Research in Bombay during January 1962.

objects got into these regular orbits. The irregular satellites are moving in orbits distributed at various angles to the plane of the equator of the primary and in some cases have a retrograde direction. Among the larger satellites, the moon of the earth and Titan have orbits whose planes do not lie near the equatorial planes.

Many years ago Titus and Bode called attention to an approximate regularity in the distances of the planets from the sun, this regularity being known as the Titus-Bode law. It is very likely that this is not a natural law except insofar as it agrees with the fact that the spacing of the planets increases with distance from the sun in a not very regular way. The variation of mass with distance has been commented on repeatedly: there is a maximum of mass at the distance of the earth from the sun, a minimum in the asteroidal belt, a maximum again at Jupiter, followed by a falling off at greater distances.

These facts in regard to the solar system have been known for many years; the data have been slightly improved in recent years, but the improvement does little to help us understand the possible origin of the system. Most astronomical discussions of the past have been concerned with these problems and their explanation. In recent years much more information has been obtained in regard to certain features of the system of a more chemical and physical character, and it is the purpose of this chapter, while not neglecting the older astronomical facts, to point out the contributions to an understanding of the subject which arises from a more careful study of the moon, the meteorites, and the chemical composition of the system and to apply astrophysical theory to the problem.

4-1 THE MOON *

Physical characteristics

The density of the moon is well established from a fairly exact knowledge of its mass and radius as 3.34 gm/cm³. This density, of course, applies to the moon with a considerable pressure on the interior and undoubtedly a higher temperature on the interior than

---

* The author has given a rather detailed description of the structure of the moon as it bears on the origin of the moon in *Physics and Astronomy of the Moon,* edited by Z. Kopal, Academic Press, New York, 1962. The reader should refer to the author's chapter in this book for many details and will find all chapters interesting. It would be difficult to review the material without essentially covering precisely the same ground again. Only a brief summary, without mathematical details, is given here.

that at the surface. The pressure distribution in the moon can be calculated with considerable certainty, assuming a uniform density throughout, from the well-known hydrostatic formula,

$$p = \tfrac{2}{3}\pi G\rho^2(a^2 - r^2).$$

The temperature is much more difficult to estimate, and various estimates have been made. Urey (48) estimated the density at low pressures and terrestrial surface temperature from approximate values for the temperature distribution and from the calculated pressure as 3.38 to 3.41 gm/cm³. A round value of 3.40 is reasonable and can hardly be changed by future calculations by any significant amount. It is then possible to estimate the composition of the moon, making assumptions by comparing materials of approximately the composition of the meteorites. It is immediately evident that the moon is less dense than the chondritic meteorites, which consist of two rather distinct groups with mean densities of 3.57 and 3.76 gm/cm³. These densities are calculated, assuming the mineral composition as observed, and are probably more accurate than the means reported for not very accurate observational data. The assumption is made that except for the element iron the composition of the moon is the same as that of these chondritic meteorites. The results of the calculation depend somewhat on the possibility of high-density modifications of certain minerals in the interior of the moon, but the percentage of iron calculated is approximately 10 to 14 by weight, whereas the two groups of chrondritic meteorites average 22.33 and 28.58. Thus it appears that the composition of the moon is different in its iron content from the meteorites, and various estimates that have been made indicate that the earth, Mars, and Venus could possibly have about the same composition as that of the chondritic meteorites, as judged from calculations of their densities at low pressures. The moon definitely seems to have a different composition from the earth and other planets; it is more nearly that of the sun. Mercury has a higher density and probably contains more iron than the other terrestrial planets.

It has been evident from the studies of Stratton, Jeffreys, and others that the moon has an irregular shape that is not an equilibrium one under the centrifugal and gravitational forces operating on the moon at any distance from the earth. From the dynamical motions of the moon, it is possible to calculate a value for the ratios of differences in the moments of inertia of the moon, and from this value the height of a bulge toward and away from the earth. Jeffreys (20) has calculated the equilibrium values from theory under the combined effects of the gravitational fields and the centrifugal forces. The two are in definite disagreement and indicate that the shape of the moon is not an equilibrium one if the density is uniform with angular position on the moon. Also, Stratton (40) studied carefully the ratio of the moments of inertia of the moon and deduced as the best value at that time for its ratio $\dfrac{C - B}{A} \Big/ \dfrac{C - A}{B}$ a value of 0.5. More recently, studies indicate that the ratio may be, in fact, 0.60 to 0.85, whereas the theory requires that this ratio be 0.25. Recent calculations for the three radii of the moon are $a = 1738.57$, $b = 1738.21$, and $c = 1737.58$ km. This indicates a bulge toward and away from the earth of 0.99 km as compared with the radius toward the poles. This value has now been in the literature for a number of years, and only recently slight improvements in the estimate have been accomplished. The result of this calculation shows that the moon has an irregular shape, not consistent with the forces acting on it.

Surface elevations of the moon have been studied for many years. Watts (56) has made a careful study of this problem and reports great differences near the limb of the moon. One, for example, between Mare Orientale and the D'Alembert Mountains amounted to 9.8 km. Similar observations have been made as a result of the work of Saunders and Franz, which has been reviewed by DuFresne (10) and Baldwin (4). These studies indicate that the observational data are neither very good nor very reliable, but the results seem to indicate definitely that considerable differences in elevation exist on the moon's surface, even within the smooth areas of the maria.

Rather simple calculations show that such differences in elevation could not exist on the surface of the earth for long periods of time unless there were marked differences in the densities of materials at different parts of the surface. This follows from the fact that the elevations of Canada and Scandinavia have been rising since the Ice Age, when these areas were covered with thick layers of ice. If the moon had a "viscosity" comparable to that of the outer parts of the earth, the differences in elevation indicated by these studies could not be maintained for more than some hundreds of thousands of years. This evidence indicates that the moon is now a rigid object, a conclusion that is valid regardless of the origin of the moon or how the irregularities were established.

Some years ago the writer attempted to estimate the thermal history of the moon. The first calculations were made with data which have been very substantially revised since that time, both with respect to the concentration of the radioactive elements and with respect to the age of the moon. These calculations have been revised in the years since, and MacDonald (32) has made similar calculations. The thermal history cannot be given with great confidence because of the uncertainty of the constants employed. The concentration of the radioactive elements used are the same as those of the chondritic meteorites, but there is considerable doubt that these concentrations are really representative of an object such as the earth or the moon. The thermal conductivity of the matter is not well known and is usually reported to only one significant figure. Urey (45, 49, 50) used 0.005 and 0.01 and thought that the true value probably lay between the two. MacDonald (32) has used 0.006 and has also included radiative transfer. The results of such calculations show that an initially cold moon formed, say, at approximately ordinary temperatures would be melted now in the deep interior. It is difficult to show that its irregular shape would be maintained under these conditions. However, it is also evident from these calculations that an initially melted moon would still be at a high temperature on the interior, probably near the melting point, even if all radioactive substances had been concentrated at the surface, which seems highly improbable. There is also the uncertain question, in regard to a moon with a melted interior, whether extensive lava flows would occur on the surface of such an object. Lava of the earth comes from some hundreds of kilometers below the surface, and there is no indication that substantial pockets of liquid material remain below the surface of the earth for more than limited periods of time. With the smaller gravitational field of the moon and its colder exterior, no certainty in regard to this question can be reached. If the moon were originally melted, it would solidify from the interior outward, since the highest melting silicates, namely olivines, have a higher density than the liquids, as is usual and would undoubtedly sink to the deep interior. A distribution of melting point with depth would thus depend not only on pressure but also on composition. It seems likely that the radioactive elements would not be quantitatively removed to the surface in the initial melting process, but the presence of even a small fraction of the radioactive elements in the deep interior would keep it nearer the melting point for all of geologic time. Thus the irregular shape of the moon would be difficult to account for on this basis.

Another suggestion that has been made to account for the irregular density distribution is that the moon is not uniform in composition with respect to angular position (52). Thus the limb and the pole of the moon may lie in regions in which the mean density is greater than that along the axis pointing toward and away from the earth. In this case an initially cold moon would take an irregular shape, and this irregular shape would not disappear with time unless convection currents could be set up that would transfer the higher density material to the deep interior and allow the lower density material to flow above it. This would involve a very considerable reorganization of the moon and a considerable convection in solid materials; hence such irregular density distribution would account for the observed facts. This, in turn, requires a cold origin for the moon and its accumulation from a substantial number of bodies having variable densities.

It is not possible to come to a definite conclusion in regard to this problem at the present time, though it seems most likely that the solution lies in an incorrect estimate of the amount of radioactive elements in a body such as the moon. Gast's (13) observations in regard to the ratio of rubidium to strontium in the earth being less than that in the chrondritic meteorites indicates that rubidium for some reason is much too abundant in the meteorites relative to its abundance in the earth. Because of the chemical similarity of potassium and rubidium, it is very probable that the same situation occurs with respect to potassium, and even a rather modest decrease in the amount of potassium in the materials of the moon would mean that thermal calculations would result in a cold and rigid interior for this object. Thus no difficulties in respect to its irregular shape would be experienced, provided the moon was formed as a rather cold object.

The observation of the great differences in elevation at the surface of the moon indicates that lava flows could not have come from its interior after these irregularities were established. Melting of the materials of the moon would require temperatures comparable to those beneath the surface of the earth. If temperatures comparable to those in the outer parts of the earth had existed in the moon, then we can expect that isostatic adjustment of the lunar surface would have obliterated the differences observed by Watts on its eastern limb. Since this has not occurred, we conclude that the moon has been cold at comparable distances throughout its history and that there have been no great lava flows. This means that the smooth areas of the moon, if they are lava, must have been the result of other processes than those observed for lava flows on the earth's surface. Gilbert (14) suggested that these areas were produced by the energy of the great collisions with the surface of the moon. It is also possible that these smooth areas are not composed entirely of lava but are in part great masses of finely divided dust, sand, and rubble produced by the collisions. There is some slight indication from the surface features of the moon that this may indeed be the case.

Others have maintained that the maria are filled with lava produced from the moon's interior. If this is the case, it must have come from so deep in the lunar interior that the strength of the thick outer layers is sufficient to support the surface irregularities.

Keith Runcorn has suggested that the bulge of the moon toward and away from the earth as well as the differences in moments of inertia may result from two convection cells in the moon's interior. The rising currents are postulated to occur toward and away from the earth and the sinking currents beneath the limb regions. It has been the opinion of the present author that very little evidence or possibly none at all exists in the surface features for such convection, but it is difficult to be at all confident that the outer parts could not be so rigid that no folding of the surface region would occur. Runcorn's suggestion might be included in the general description of the lunar structure and history starting from a cold origin of the moon as presented in this chapter.

On the other hand, the postulate of a cold origin for the moon was advanced in order to account for the nonequilibrium shape of the moon, and if this characteristic can be explained by convection cells it would be well to explore the possibility of a high temperature origin of the moon due, for example, to short-lived radioactivity. If such a heat source was present, complete melting followed by slow solidification should have occurred, with certainly some and possibly much segregation of potassium, uranium, and thorium at the lunar surface. Runcorn's convection cells must be driven by radioactive heating, hence an adequate amount of these elements must have remained in the deep interior if his hypothesis is to be energetically reasonable. To the present writer, there are many questions in regard to this suggestion that have not been answered even approximately. Would the outer parts of the moon have remained sufficiently rigid to have prevented the formation of folded mountains or other effects such as the San Andreas type fault for all geologic time during which the radioactive heating has been varied by about a factor of 10? Would sufficient radioactive elements have remained in the deep interior to provide the energy required for convection cells? If the "bulge" is now 1 km in height, would it not have been higher when the heating was greater and would no evident marks of these effects have remained? There are also problems of the mechanisms of such cells. Convection in the mantle of the earth has only recently been seriously considered and only on the basis of much more evidence than exists for the lunar situation. Nevertheless, the possibility of convection in the moon must be kept in mind and, if possible, observational methods should be devised for deciding which explanation for the deserved facts is the true one.

Surface features

Most of the craters of the moon are surely due to the collision of objects with its surface. At the same time, there are small craters that must be of plutonic origin, although their general appearance is not that of terrestrial volcanoes. The craters range in size from the smallest objects that can be seen on the lunar surface to the great maria hundreds of kilometers in diameter.

The great Imbrian collision first described by Gilbert in 1893 is most informative with respect to the origin of the lunar surface. This area is the great smooth plain lying in the northeast quadrant of the moon. Figure 4-1 is a photograph of this area with the foreshortening eliminated. It was taken by projecting pictures of the moon on a sphere and then photographing the area from a position directly above the projected image. It will be seen that the mare is nearly

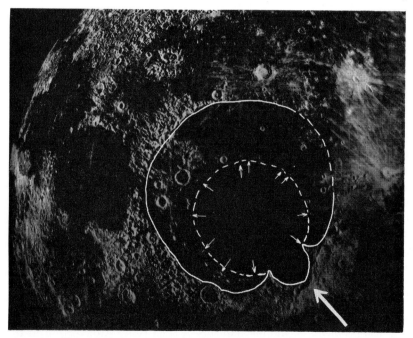

Figure 4-1 Mare Imbrium, with foreshortening eliminated. Mare Imbrium is outlined by the solid curve. Sinus Iridum is the bay at the lower right. The arrows indicate mountainous masses just outside the collision area. Three of these arrows point to masses not visible in this photograph but easily seen on others. (University of Chicago photograph)

circular in shape, with an inner ring eccentric to the center of the mare lying just in front of Sinus Iridum. It appears that an object came in from the northeast, plowed out the area of Sinus Iridum,* produced a great hole in the moon outlined by the inner circle, probably created a great bulge in its surface in all directions, and sprayed material over a wide region. Evidence of this spray of material can be found clear to the center of the moon's disk in the form of great ridges and grooves. The edge of the mare was probably produced by a breaking off of material from the great wave that settled back toward the interior of the moon to a greater extent than did the mountainous edge of the mare. Some of the craters in the region, such as Ptolemäus, were evidently premare in origin because of the great erosion effects shown in its crater walls, whereas other craters such as Copernicus are certainly postmare. The radiating ridges south of Mare Serenitatis indicate that the colliding object consisted partly of lower density material, that is, silicates, and the grooves in the surface near the center of the moon's disk indicate that high-density objects, that is, iron-nickel, have plowed through these regions. The Alpine Valley radiates from the region of the collision, as do many of the mountainous masses in the region of Oceanus Procellarum. Other circular maria exist on the moon's surface—Mare Serenitatis, Mare Crisium, Mare Nectaris, and Mare Humorum. Presumably, these also were made by collisions of rather large objects with the moon. The other maria of the moon, such as Oceanus Procellarum, Tranquillitatis, Nubium, and Foecunditatis, appear to be flooded, that is, produced by flows of liquid material. It is generally assumed that these smooth areas of the moon consist of solidified lava flows. In particular, Mare Tranquillitatis looks very much like a lava flow that extended over this area and filled in little bays and valleys between the mountainous masses. It appears that the lava distorted craters that had been present on the moon before it arrived. Distortion of craters in the region of Oceanus Procellarum is certainly not evident. There is a controversy in regard to the origin of this lava. Some maintain that it came from the interior of the moon, and others, following Gilbert, have supposed that it

---

* Some students of the moon believe that Sinus Iridum is the remnant of a great crater that was partially destroyed by the Imbrian collision. The writer was not present when the collision occurred, hence has no conclusive information on the subject. However, Sinus Iridum lies precisely before the collision area and could hardly be moved 50 km without destroying the symmetrical pattern. Simple calculation shows that the probability that it occupied such a position is about 1 in 10,000. The entire pattern is probably due to a single event.

was produced by the energy of the collisions. Objections to the first hypothesis rest in the generally cold structure of the moon indicated by the calculations referred to above. In general, one cannot expect that a small object like the moon, with a larger surface-to-volume ratio than that of the earth, for example, would have a temperature as high as that of the earth and be capable of producing lavas as the earth has done. It is difficult to understand how the moon wou'd have supported the mountain ridges in the neighborhood of these maria if the subsurface regions were warm enough to produce lavas, as is done on the earth. Arguments in regard to the second hypothesis have been advanced; namely, that collisions do not produce melting, as observed on the earth, but rather finely divided powder. It seems to the writer that the second hypothesis is likely to be correct and that the arguments against this source of melted material are possibly false because of our difficulty in estimating what large inhomogeneous objects in collision would do to dissipate their energy. Also, it is probably true that great masses of dust, sand, and rubble would be produced in such collisions. Granting a temporary atmosphere, these materials might very well have become distributed over wide areas of the moon and thus over the so-called flooded maria, such as Oceanus Procellarum. In fact, the crater Prinz is partly covered with smooth material, and one wonders how lava could have covered one wall of the crater and not the other, whereas the falling of great clouds of dust could quite possibly have produced such an effect. It is also difficult to understand how the great craters in the south of the moon become filled with lava unless one postulates a general and substantial heating of the moon, and in this case there is no explanation for its great rigidity. But, if this smooth material should turn out, at least in part, to be masses of dusty, sandy, rubbly material which fell in clouds after the great collisions, the smooth character of the interior of the craters would be understandable. The controversy in regard to the interpretation of the maria and the craters will probably continue for some time in the future until we are able to make landings on the moon and study the surface carefully.

The relationship of Mare Serenitatis to Mare Imbrium is an interesting one. One may well ask which circular maria was produced first. If it were Imbrium, then one would expect a great deal of destruction of the radiating ridges to the south of Mare Serenitatis, which quite definitely are centered on the collision area of Mare Imbrium. Thus it seems that Serenitatis was not produced after Mare Imbrium. But, if Serenitatis were produced first, one wonders why there are not mountain ranges on Mare Serenitatis also radiating from the collision areas of Mare Imbrium. The suggestion that immediately comes to mind is that Mare Serenitatis was still fluid at the time that the collision of Mare Imbrium occurred. This means that the two events that produced these maria occurred near to each other in time—perhaps some thousands of years. This, in turn, has a bearing on the origin of the moon and its capture by the earth, as will be discussed later. The whole distribution of craters and maria on the moon suggests that there were many collisions occurring at some time. At first craters were formed, then a mare, then other craters, then another mare, etc. Then within a relatively short period of time the whole bombardment stopped, and little has happened since except the stray meteorite-type collision that should have occurred during geologic time. It has been the writer's opinion that the collisions that fashioned the surface of the moon occurred during the terminal stage of the formation of the earth-moon system and that for the most part they are ancient, with only a few craters having been formed since; for example, the ray craters of the moon.

At various places on the moon, but prominently west of Copernicus, there are small craters that are not of the collision type. One cannot expect a row of craters to be placed in a crack in the moon by means of a collision mechanism. After one becomes accustomed to looking at these craters, he realizes that there are many in the immediate neighborhood that may also have a similar origin. Then his eye wanders over other parts of the moon, and he realizes that there may be small craters distributed in many places on its surface. In trying to estimate the origin of these features, it is well to keep in mind the law of conservation of energy. Great expenditures of energy are required to produce the maria of the moon, and it must have been concentrated at sharply localized points. There appears to be no way to produce such large areas on an object such as the moon, considering all the evidence in regard to its probable thermal history, by any other mechanism than a collisional one. The rather small activity indicated by the limited number of craters of a plutonic origin is not inconsistent with the moon's thermal history.

Kozyrev (22) recently observed gases coming from the interior of the moon within the Alphonsus crater. He identified fluorescent bands of the C_2 molecule in the gases emanating from a point near its central peak. Various suggestions have been made to account for this molecule. Some have suggested that graphite is volatilized in some way. Volatilization of graphite would require exceedingly high energy, and, if it were volatilized in this way, then many other things would be volatilized as well. There seems to be no method of producing C_2 by such a process. It appears likely that C_2 may have originated from acetylene, which, in turn, could be produced by the action of water on calcium carbide (46). Silicon metal has been detected in the meteorites, and the methods for the production of silicon and calcium carbide are very nearly the same. Thus this gas might easily be explained in this way.

The composition of the moon as a whole was referred to above, but the surface of the moon may not have the average composition at all. The great collisions have undoubtedly brought in some metallic iron-nickel as indicated by the grooves mentioned before, and certainly our knowledge of the meteorites would indicate that some material would arrive in this way. How much is very difficult to say. We do not know how thick a bombardment layer may exist on the moon. It may well be that the whole surface of the moon is composed of material of about the same composition as that of the meteorites. This material would have a higher density than that of the moon as a whole. As indicated above, the smooth areas may be solidified melts of silicates. In the solidification of these melts a differentiation occurs, as observed on earth, with the more basic material sinking to the bottom of the pools and the more acidic materials solidifying last on the surface. We may find differentiation of the surface of the moon into basalts and granitelike materials to some extent. If this material of the maria is indeed lava that has flowed from the interior of the moon, then our terrestrial experience would indicate that it should be primarily basalt. The amount of granite on the earth is fairly large and its origin is not well understood. Perhaps we will find some granitic material at the surface as well. On the other hand, if the outer parts of the moon are due principally to the collision of objects having the general composition of the meteorites, then we can expect the surface of the moon to have a composition similar to that of the meteorites, which, for the most part, is quite different from basalt and granite. Only a minor group of stone meteorites of the achondritic variety has compositions somewhat near that of basalt. One of the curious things about this basaltic type of achondrite is that the concentrations of the alkaline metals are much lower than they are in the basalts of the earth. Thus potassium has a concentration less than one tenth of 1 percent in the meteorites, whereas in the igneous rocks of the earth it averages about 2.6 percent. One of the first things that should be learned as a result of the Space Program is whether the surface of the moon has a composition similar to that of the meteorites or to that of the earth's surface.

The albedo of the moon is on the average about 7 percent, but there are certain areas of the moon's surface that are blacker. Mare Tranquillitatis is a particularly black spot on the moon. There are patches west of Copernicus in which the mountainous regions are a very dark color. From his study of the reflection of light from the moon, Van Diggellen (54) concluded that he could duplicate his observations on a metal surface in which many holes were drilled and which was covered with a mixture of magnesium oxide and graphite. These observations would indicate that the ultimate surface of the moon may consist of many pockets and that the material of the surface may have some black materials, such as graphite, mixed with it. There are some craters, several of which occur within Alphonsus crater, that are occasionally distributed over the moon and are surrounded by a black patch. It seems possible that this patch was produced by the escape of acetylene from the moon's interior, which was then decomposed by sunlight to give the C_2 molecules observed by Kozyrev, and these collected on the surface of the moon to form a graphite surface that would be very black indeed. At least this seems to be one explanation of these curious black patches. It may well be that substantial areas of the moon's surface contain materials similar to the carbonaceous chondrites, which incorporate considerable quantities of carbon, water, and sulfide.

It is not possible to recognize the composition of the surface of an object when it must be viewed from a distance of 384,000 km. The surface materials of the moon have undoubtedly been affected by the collisions of meteoritelike objects on its surface and by very fine grains that rain into the atmosphere of the earth and must collide with the moon's surface at high velocity. Such objects may spray material off the moon, hence may produce a net loss as Whipple has suggested. It may be also that the whole surface of the moon is a mixture of its original surface and the materials that have come from space for more than 4.5 billion years. This layer has been affected by the high-speed particles from the sun and its ultraviolet light until it probably has a physical structure quite different from any materials we have on earth. Beneath such a layer we may find a surface that was produced 4.5 billion years ago by the collisions which formed the numerous big craters and the maria of the moon's surface. It is quite evident that if we are going to understand the structure of the moon's surface much more detailed exploration of its surface must be made by methods other than photographs and spectroscopy of the lunar surface by instruments placed on earth.

The question of the origin of the moon is an interesting one from the standpoint of the origin of the solar system, and this problem is discussed later.

4-2 METEORITES

The meteorites have been studied for the last century and a half with considerable detail. Much valuable work was done during all of this time, and the general composition of these objects and their physical structure were mapped most effectively. During the last 10 years, or more, very intensive studies have been made on these objects, using the latest chemical and physical methods available, and it is to be expected that outstanding work will be done in the future.

The meteorites proved to be exceedingly complicated objects, and they have an age estimated from radioactive dating methods of 4.5 to 4.7 AE. It therefore seems likely that they acquired most of their chemical composition and physical structure during the process of the origin of the solar system. Hence the study of these objects has a very direct bearing on the subject of this chapter. A complete review of meteorite structure would require a very lengthy treatise in itself. The object here is to review certain points believed to have a direct bearing on the problem of the origin of the solar system.

The iron meteorites

The iron meteorites are composed principally of iron-nickel. The amount of nickel varies from a minimum of around 6 percent to more than 50 percent by weight, most of the objects lying in the range just above 6 percent. There are many minor constituents in these objects, the more abundant being iron-nickel sulfide, phosphide, and carbide. Small amounts of the so-called siderophile elements also are present. There is considerable variation in the abundances of these rare constituents. It is particularly difficult to understand how certain of the noble metals of the palladium and platinum group can exist in such variable concentrations in relation to one another. It seems likely that various processes and conditions must have been present during the formation of these objects in order to produce these variations in composition. The Widmannstatten figures, due to the crystallization of kamacite along the octahedral planes of the taenite crystals, must have required a long period of time for their formation, and the evidence surely indicates that they were produced by a slow cooling process.

The irons vary in size from a few kilograms to masses of many tons.

Holes in their surfaces are often larger on the interior than their exterior openings. In rare cases, such as the Horse Creek meteorite, these holes have been observed to be as much as eight times the diameter of the opening. Henderson and Perry (17), who pointed this out, have argued that these holes indicate that the iron meteorites were not part of larger objects because they could not have been broken along their surfaces with such holes in their interiors. It is also true that the pallasites consist of a mixture of metal and silicate, mostly olivine, in about equal proportions by volume, and this mixture appears to constitute the surface between metallic pools and silicate walls. In the case of Brenham Township, we have a piece of material, one part of which is a typical octahedrite metallic meteorite and the other part attached to it is a typical pallasite. Thus in one case we actually have the surface region presented to us. Since 8 percent as many pallasites have been found as iron meteorites, the surface regions of the parent bodies must have been large compared with their volumes. It appears, therefore, that the parent bodies of the meteorites had a raisin-bread structure with iron masses of limited size embedded in silicate bodies. If this is true, general internal heating of the parent bodies of the meteorites is not possible as a means of accounting for the production of the melted metal masses, for they would surely have drained to the deep interior of objects of this kind and would have produced a core that is contrary to the observations here discussed.* Also, internal heating due to radioactivity must have been adjusted carefully so that the iron-nickel was melted but the olivine was not, for otherwise a smooth boundary would have resulted. This internal heating requires that the interior of the object be higher than the outer parts of an object. Also, an intermediate sulfide layer would be expected to be present.†

The stone meteorites

The stone meteorites are divided into two main groups: the so-called chondrites and the achondrites. The chondrites contain small rounded objects known as chondrules. The achondrites do not con-

---

* The grooves in the lunar surface produced by the spray of objects during the Imbrian collision indicate that metallic masses were embedded in the planetesimal that collided with the moon (50).

† Fish, Goles, and Anders have called attention to the fact that the proportion of pallasite material at the surface of a core to the metallic material in the core should be a constant. This follows from a consideration of the strength of the field that produces the separation of phases, which is imperfect. However, the Brenham Township octahedrite-pallasite is still a specific example of the surface between the two phases.

tain these objects, or at least only a very few of them do. A chondrite consists of a mixture of these chondrules, broken up bits of chondrules, and the irregular silicate masses, and mixed very uniformly throughout the whole mass are substantial amounts of iron sulfide and bits of iron-nickel particles. These particles consist of both the kamacite and taenite varieties of iron-nickel, namely, the body-centered cubic and the face-centered cubic crystals. One can say immediately that these objects did not solidify from a melt into their present forms. They must, in fact, be conglomerates of materials which acquired their structures elsewhere. In some cases the chondrules show a crystalline structure radiating from a point, indicating that they were once liquid and that crystallization had been started by a scratch or a break on the surface of the glass droplet. Possibly, all chondrules originated by solidification of liquid drops.

The metal particles have been studied by Urey and Mayeda (53), by Kvasha (25), and by Massalski (34), and these authors are in essential agreement regarding their structure. They consist of kamacite and taenite, sometimes as separated phases, sometimes as phases in contact with each other, and sometimes rather crudely mixed. The kamacite phases appear to be more irregular in shape, as though they had been deformed by pressure of the silicate particles in their neighborhood. The taenite particles are sometimes broken cleanly across. They generally have a diffusion border when etched with appropriate agents, indicating that equilibrium with the other phase was attained very slowly. This is also true for the metallic crystals of the iron meteorites. Sometimes a taenite particle has been broken and the broken border has no diffusion border. This fact indicates that they did not come to equilibrium in the positions in which they are now found by any mechanism that would transport iron and nickel from one phase to the other. The indications are that very intense brecciating processes existed. The chondritic meteorites sometimes have veins in which sulfide particles are finely distributed, often in what appear to be small melted spheres. There is some indication of secondary heating and even melting in the veins and in the taenite particles. These features have been interpreted by the authors working on this problem as indicating an intense crushing action, which is thought perhaps to have occurred because of collisions between small and large ones so that a surface effect occurred on the larger object. Fredriksson (12) has been able to produce some of the features of veins by submitting meteorites to the shock of an explosion. In particular, he has been able to produce the small spherical iron sulfide particles. Fish, Goles, and Anders have argued that these veins are the result of the injection of sulfur vapor. This explanation is exceedingly doubtful because of the great difficulty of forcing hot sulfur vapor through even small amounts of material and at the same time maintaining both the high temperature in the vein and low temperatures in its immediate neighborhood, that is over distances of 0.1 mm or less as indicated by the fact that taenite particles have not lost their diffusion borders. It appears that the Fredriksson explanation is preferable.

A suggestion has been made by Ringwood (38) that ferric chloride or carbonyls were able to transport the iron and nickel from one particle to another, hence to build up *in situ* the particles observed. If this has occurred at some time, then subsequent to the process the taenite particles in some cases have been broken again by a crushing action, as indicated by the taenite particles without diffusion borders over part of their surfaces.

Chondritic meteorites are fragile and difficult to polish. In fact, they must be embedded in plastics before polishing can be done. This indicates that the chondritic meteorites are compacted breccia and were probably not part of a large planet, as Ringwood has suggested.

The chondrules consist of olivine and hypersthene or their mixtures. In addition, they are found to contain small amounts of metal and sulfides of iron, magnesium, and calcium. They are often glassy in appearance, though they may indeed be microcrystalline in all cases. The minerals of the chondritic meteorites appear to be those that result from the solidification of silicate melts, though in some cases the solidification must have occurred rapidly to form a glassy feldspar or other glassy-appearing silicate minerals. The objects, once they secured their present structure, were never annealed even at moderate temperatures for any appreciable length of time, for they surely would have acquired a much more crystalline structure than is characteristic of many of them.

The composition of the chondrites is remarkably constant, though variations within limits of many of the constituents have been certainly established. Many years ago Prior pointed to a general relationship between the amount of metallic iron and oxidized iron. Chondrites with increased amounts of metal had lesser amounts of the oxidized elements. Urey and Craig (51) pointed out that Prior's findings could not be explained as the result of a simple oxidation and reduction process but required that the relative proportion of iron to the silicates be changed at the same time. In fact, there are two prominent groups of chondrites, each one of which obeys Prior's law without the necessity of simultaneously changing the oxidation state and content of iron. These are referred to as the low- and high-iron group chondrites. The average amount of iron is 22.33 and 28.58 percent, respectively. Wiik subsequently investigated a number of meteorites and confirmed these conclusions by most careful modern analyses. There are other groups of chondrites not so prominent. Yet on the whole the composition of the chondrites is remarkably constant, compared with our experience with terrestrial rocks. Suess and Urey (41) used the low-iron group chondrites for the preparation of abundance tables of the elements.

There have been two interpretations of these results. Urey, Craig, and Suess have taken the point of view that if there are two prominent groups with rather definite differences in iron content and grouped around a mean value in each case then certainly these materials would seem to indicate that they are coming from two different positions, and it is not possible to say which of these two gives the fundamental abundances of the elements; in fact, one does not know whether to use the average or whether the true primitive abundance value would lie outside both means. Others have been content to use the average of all meteorites as giving an estimate of the abundances of the elements. The carbonaceous chondrites contain substantial amounts of carbon and water and somewhat more iron sulfide in general than the other chondrites. Approximately 4 percent of all observed falls belong in this group, and because they are fragile objects one suspects that the percentage of material of this kind in the primordial reservoir for meteorites, wherever it may be, is larger than would be indicated by the 4 percent datum. In some way the curious situation exists that most of our meteorites are dry (0.10 percent of water or less), whereas a group of them has large amounts of water (up to 20 percent). The percentage of water in the earth as a whole is surely very low, probably $\frac{1}{10}$ of 1 percent, and thus more nearly in accord with the water content of the dry meteorites. In some way it appears that neither the carbonaceous nor ordinary chondrites are an average of the materials that formed the earth. The carbonaceous chondrites belong to the high-iron group of Urey and Craig. Recently, Nagy, Claus, Meinschein, and Hennessy (36) reported the presence of objects in these meteorites which resemble fossil microscopic forms.

The achondritic meteorites vary in composition considerably more than the chondrites and are classified into a considerable number of types of objects. Some of the achondrites have high calcium content and indeed have a type of composition somewhat characteristic of the basalts, whereas others have low calcium content and high magnesium content and are similar in composition to the chondrites, though the similarities are not exact at all. One of the curious things about the meteorites generally is that they have low concentrations of potassium and sodium; this is true even of the basaltic-type achondrites. Whereas the basalts on earth have potassium contents in the neighborhood of 1.4 percent, the basaltic achondrites contain more nearly 0.05 percent of potassium. It would appear that in the melting that produced the minerals of the achondrites some volatilization process carried the alkalis away from these objects.

There is considerable evidence to indicate that in important ways the chondritic meteorites do not give us a correct average of the abundances of the elements in the solar system. There is the prominent iron difficulty and also the very curious situation in regard to indium, thallium, and bismuth, whose abundances are low compared to the elements in their immediate neighborhood in the periodic system. Gast (13) has noted that rubidium is much lower in relation to strontium in the earth than it is in the meteorites. It seems likely that this is the case with respect to potassium and the other alkalis as well. It has been thought that the chondritic meteorites give us a correct average for the material in the body of the earth and other planets. Evidence accumulated in recent years indicates that this is not the case.

Composition of the sun, planets, and meteorites

During the last 30 years, astronomers have attempted to deduce the composition of the sun and stars from the intensity of their absorption lines in the spectra. Considerable variation in these determinations has occurred, but as time has gone on the values reported have varied less and less, and today substantial agreement is being secured by the various workers in this field. A recent review by Goldberg, Mueller, and Aller (15) reviewed the subject extensively. In general, these abundances agree fairly well with those deduced from a study of the composition of the meteorites. There are, however, several prominent differences, the most important of which probably is the abundance of iron in relation to neighboring elements in the periodic system. Table 4-1 compares the abundance data as secured from the meteorites by Suess and Urey and those of the sun as given by Goldberg, Mueller, and Aller. It will be noted that fair agreement is secured except that iron must be either too low in the sun by a factor of about 4 or too high in the meteorites by this factor. The comparison with cobalt is particularly interesting, for both the de-

TABLE 4-1

Comparison of Abundance Data as Secured from the Meteorites and the Sun

The data of Suess and Urey (41) are used for the meteoritic values and those of Goldberg, Mueller, and Aller (15), for the astronomical values. Only what appears to be the more reliable data is included. Abundances are given relative to Si = 10^6.

Element	Solar	Meteoritic	Ratio Met./Solar
Na	6.31×10^4	4.38×10^4	0.69
Mg	7.94×10^5	9.12×10^5	1.15
Al	5.01×10^4	9.48×10^4	1.89
Si	10^6	10^6	1
K	1.58×10^3	3.16×10^3	1.99
Ca	4.46×10^4	4.90×10^4	1.10
Sc	2.09×10	2.8×10	1.27
Ti	1.51×10^3	2.44×10^3	1.61
V	1.58×10^2	2.2×10^2	1.38
Cr	7.41×10^3	7.80×10^3	1.05
Mn	2.51×10^3	6.85×10^3	2.76
Fe	1.17×10^5	6.00×10^5	5.12
Co	1.38×10^3	1.8×10^3	1.30
Ni	2.57×10^4	2.74×10^4	1.07
Zn	7.94×10^2	4.86×10^2	0.62
		Geometric mean excluding Fe	1.25
		Ratio of Fe ratio to geometric mean	4.10

terminations of iron and cobalt appear to be reliable. The chemical similarities of iron and cobalt are fairly great, cobalt being more noble than iron. Yet the ratio of cobalt to iron in the sun is higher than this ratio for the meteorites by a factor of about 4. The comparison between iron and nickel is very similar to the comparison of the iron and cobalt, but the abundance of nickel in the sun is uncertain. It should be noted that the two groups of chrondrites—high- and low-iron group—have a different ratio of iron to nickel, though the difference is small compared to the difference in this ratio as observed between the meteorites and the sun. Suess and Urey used the low-iron group chondrites for the tables. The use of the average of all chrondrites would make the discrepancies greater. One must conclude that the meteorites and the sun do not have the same composition with respect to these so-called nonvolatile elements.

The composition of the planets varies. This was pointed out some years ago by Urey (50), and revision of the data in recent years has changed the conclusions but slightly. Recent determinations of the radius of Mercury during its last transit was observed by a number of astronomers who agreed in regard to the radius secured as approximately 0.38 of the radius of the earth. Table 4-2 shows a comparison of the densities of the planets as observed and an estimate of their

TABLE 4-2

Comparison of Density of Planets and Estimate of
Their Densities at Low Pressures *

Planet	Mass $M_\oplus = 1$	Radius $R_\oplus = 1$	Density
Moon	0.012304	0.2728	3.34
Mercury	0.0543	0.377	5.59
Venus	0.8137	0.957	5.12
Earth	1	1	5.515
Mars	0.1077	0.520	4.22
		0.530	3.99
Jupiter	317.42	10.97	1.33
Saturn	95.05	9.03	0.71
Uranus	14.49	3.72	1.55
Neptune	17.60	3.38	2.51

* The masses for the planets are taken from Brouwer and Clemence (1961), who reviewed the latest data. The radius of Mercury was reported at a meeting of the Astronomical Union (1961) as an average of the work of several astronomers during the last transit of Mercury and has a probable error of about 1 percent. Values for Mars set by Trumpler (1927) and Camichel (1954) are used. Camichel's results vary from 9'.24 to 9".48 at unit distance. The hazy atmosphere possibly makes measurements too high rather than too low. Those of Jupiter and Saturn are from Russell, Dugan, and Stewart. The radius of Venus is that reported at the International Astronomical Union meeting and has a probable error of 0.5 percent. The values for Uranus and Neptune are from Kuiper (1952). These are considerably lower than the older values. No details of the measurements on which these data are based have been published. The mass and radius of the earth are 5.975×10^{27} g and 6.37123×10^8 cm, respectively.

densities at low pressures. There is uncertainty in regard to the calculated values for all of these objects, but it would be very difficult indeed to make Mercury agree in density at low temperatures and pressures with the densities of the other planets, and the density of the moon can hardly be made to agree with the densities of any of the planets. It appears that there was a real fractionation of the elements during the formation of the planets and the moon and that the composition of none of these agrees with that of the sun. Gradually, results are becoming more certain with time, and the conclusion can be safely accepted that in the formation of the solar system substantial variations in composition have actually occurred.

Other possible explanations have been put forward. Ringwood has suggested that Mercury consists of iron carbide. An estimate of the density of Mercury on this basis has been attempted, and a maximum of about 4.7 gm/cm^3 at ordinary temperatures and pressures has been secured. Several models for the moon have been tried, assuming that it consists of chrondritic meteorite material, except that the iron content is low. This leads to a conclusion that the amount of iron in the moon may be 10 percent or perhaps slightly more, whereas the amount of iron in solid material of the nonvolatile kind such as in the earth and meteorites calculated for solar material would be only 6 percent. The moon appears to have more iron in its content than the sun and less iron than the earth or other terrestrial planets or the meteorites [Urey (47)].

Urey (50) gave an explanation for the differences in the terrestrial and solar compositions that may still be acceptable. Silicate materials were driven from the solar system rather than the denser metallic material during the period of accumulation of the earth and moon. At first, more nearly average material accumulated in both, but the earth by chance grew more rapidly and acquired an effective field. Toward the end of the process the earth captured material more rapidly than the moon, and at this time it contained more metal. However, the moon acquired less of this higher density material, hence has a composition intermediate between the compositions of the earth and sun.

It seems likely that these differences are real and that they must have been produced by some process taking place during the origin of the solar system. Alternatives are that the moon contains some graphite or water. It would require about 10 percent of graphite or 2 or 3 percent of water to account for the density difference of the moon and meteorites [Urey (48)]. In the latter case, melting points of silicates should be markedly lower, extensive lava flows should have occurred, and surface regions of the moon should contain large amounts of water. Exploration of the moon's surface will answer these questions. If the moon were produced from the earth, which is an old but presently not generally accepted hypothesis, we still must explain the difference in composition of meteorites and the sun. Possibly the planets originated from a different dust cloud than the sun, but in this case the physicists should maintain that both types of composition—that of the sun and the meteorites—would have been produced during the synthesis of the elements, which is not the case. Another possibility is that the astronomers are wrong about the composition of the sun, but at present there appears to be general agreement in regard to the solar composition with respect to iron and other more abundant elements.

The ages of meteorites and the solar system *

Much work has been done on dating the meteorites by the lead-lead, rubidium-strontium, and potassium-argon methods, and it is not intended to review this work. It is assumed that the Canyon Diablo meteorite lead is the primitive lead of the solar system and that the lead of the chondritic meteorites differs from it because of the decay of uranium and thorium. In this way ages in the neighborhood of 4.5 to 4.7×10^9 years have been secured. (A difficulty exists, however, for it appears that at least in some cases there is not sufficient uranium and thorium in the stone meteorites to account for the observed radiogenic lead. In fact, it is possible that the composition of the lead of the stone meteorites cannot be accounted for in this way. There is some indication that some lead was injected into these objects some 500 million years ago.) The rubidium-strontium ages are not precise but are consistent with the lead ages. The potassium-argon ages vary from rather low values up to 4.5×10^9 years. Since argon may have escaped from the meteorites, the errors are likely to be on the low side, and students of the subject have assumed that these low ages are indeed due to such loss. Cosmic-ray ages determined from the concentration of inert gases present in the meteorites indicate ages for the stone meteorites in the neighborhood of some tens of millions of years, and in the case of iron meteorites, in the neighborhood of 500 or 600 million years, with one lone age of about 1.5×10^9 years. Inert gases of primordial composition are included in the meteorites, so that at some time during their formation the primordial inert gases were deposited in meteorite minerals. In the

* Anders (2) has given an excellent summary of the data on the age of meteorites.

case of the Pantar meteorite, for example, chunks of a light-colored chondrite are embedded in the general dark chondritic mass. The primordial inert gases are found only in the dark gray mass, which probably means that they were injected at some date by some process.

Certain of the stone meteorites contain an increased amount of Xe^{129} that must have been produced from I^{129}, which has a half-life of approximately 16 million years. This indicates that the meteorites acquired a structure and temperature such that xenon was not lost within some 100 million years after the last synthesis of the elements. Following this work of Reynolds (37), Murthy (35) showed that the troilite of some iron meteorites contains increased amounts of silver-107, indicating that it was produced by the decay of palladium-107, which has a half-life of some 7 million years. It appears that some melting process, in which silver was removed from the region where palladium was preserved, occurred within some 10 million years after the last synthesis of the elements. All of this indicates that the process which produced the solar system occurred in a very short period of time after a synthesis of the elements.

Some general anomalies in the abundances of the isotopes of xenon, barium, and molybdenum have now been observed. In the case of xenon, the ratio of the lightest to the heaviest isotope differs by approximately 30 or 40 percent from this ratio in terrestrial xenon. The effect in the case of barium is only some 2 percent (43). In the case of molybdenum, the ratio of the lightest to the heaviest isotopes in one of the iron meteorites is less than that of the earth by some 7 percent and in a second meteorite by some 4 percent (35). It thus appears that there is a general variation in the isotopic composition of various samples of matter within the solar system. The origin of these variations is quite unknown at the present time.

A review of ideas concerning the origin of meteorites

Fish, Goles, and Anders (11) have adopted the traditional point of view that the meteorites come from asteroidal bodies and that the amount of matter in the asteroidal belt has always been approximately the same as that existing there now, except possibly for the solar proportion of gaseous substances which have obviously escaped from the region of the terrestrial planets. They also assume that the heating that has produced the silicate minerals and the large metal masses of the meteorites was produced by radioactive nuclides. It seems likely that Al^{26} is the only nuclide that could have remained after the synthesis of the elements in sufficient amounts to have produced this melting. But, since the half-life of Al^{26} is about 740,000 years, the amount that was preserved may have been very small indeed and quite inadequate. Some years ago the writer suggested the possibility of Al^{26} as the heating agent for the melting of the minerals of the silicates and discarded it because of the short time span indicated and because the physical shapes of the iron meteorites indicated, as explained above, that the parent bodies of these objects were not much larger than those now observed. If the iron meteorites come from small objects of the same order of magnitude as the observed meteorites, then, of course, heating on the interior of asteroidal-type bodies by radioactive substances is inconsistent with this observation, since internal heating should have produced asteroidal cores. Anders and his colleagues have explored the possibility of this type of heating on the assumption that the effects cited can be explained in some other unknown way.

The general process envisioned by these authors is that objects of approximately the dimensions of the present asteroids accumulated quickly after the last synthesis of the elements and that radioactive nuclides heated them to temperatures on the interior of 3000°K or more. It was assumed that the asteroidal body acquired a zone structure with a metallic core, a sintered or melted mantle, and a surface region that remained cold. It was assumed also that volcano-like ejections of matter occurred from the deep interior and sprayed melted silicates above the surface, which then fell in the form of chondrules onto the surface. The rubble is assumed to have piled up on the surface, and with time the heating slowly disappeared. The materials of the iron meteorites cooled slowly to give the Widmannstatten figures, and as a result we have chondrites on the surface, achondrites somewhat below, and an iron-nickel core in the center. Extensive calculations on the heat balance of such systems have been presented. These authors also postulated that the decomposition of iron sulfide occurred at high temperatures and that sulfur penetrated the overlying layers and caused a sinking of the chalcophile elements such as indium, thallium, bismuth, and lead.* They have made a point of explaining the low concentration of these elements as the result of a sort of Soxhlet extraction process by which these elements were removed to the interior, while other more volatile chalcophile elements were returned to the surface to be mixed with the chondritic meteorites in approximately the primordial abundances.

---

* In terrestrial regions lead is not present in increased amounts in magmatic sulfides but is found in the silicates instead. The lead deposits of the earth are hydrothermal deposits, and it is not clear that lead would be carried with the other chalcophile elements in the melting process.

They have also explained the veins in meteorites as due to the injection of sulfur into cracks in the overlying chondritic layers.

The present writer's objections to this model are summarized briefly: Extraction of chalcophile elements in the way described above should have removed metallic iron from the chondritic meteorites as iron sulfide while the nonvolatile chalcophile elements were being removed. This would leave the chondritic meteorites with too little iron, and at present they have too much iron as compared with the sun. Instead of a factor of 4 calculated above for the excess of iron in the meteorites relative to the sun, the factor might become 10, or something of this sort—completely out of line with the abundance problem. Other suggestions of a similar kind might be made to account for the low abundance of indium, bismuth, thallium, etc., but always one runs across the difficulty of returning the observed iron sulfide to the chondritic meteorites without carrying with it the correct proportion of the chalcophile elements. If additional iron sulfide necessary to supply the missing elements is added to the chondritic meteorites, an enormously increased concentration of iron must be expected. Thus we eliminate one difficulty by replacing it with another.

In order to produce chondrules, volcanic processes are involved. Present terrestrial volcanoes produce mostly coarsely melted materials. Pressures within the earth do not greatly exceed overburden pressures. Breakthrough to the surface occurs, lava flows result, and some rather large bombs are thrown above the earth. Pressures within smaller objects should be less. Packing and consolidation of the outer layers should be less because of the smaller gravitational field; a silicate sintered shell should be weak and fractured, and the condition for producing finely divided material should not exist.

The model for producing the veins by the injection of sulfur seems most unrealistic. These veins are narrow, and pictures published of them show the broken taenite fragments with an undisturbed diffusion border in two parts separated by a vein. It seems completely unrealistic to believe that iron sulfide in a melted condition could be produced between fragments of this kind without heating them to some $700°K$, at which temperature the diffusion border would disappear completely. As stated above, the present writer believes that the veins must be due to shock as Fredriksson maintains. Also, Anders et al. assume high pressures on the interior of the asteroid which causes the explosive ejection of materials, and they postulate tensile strength in the silicate materials of the mantle of these objects. Silicates have no great tensile strength, and it seems most likely that imperfections would always be present. Long before the temperature reached a value at which explosive ejections could take place a flow of melted material from the interior to the surface would occur. Thus no thick mantle of chondritic material would be observed.

No provision is made in this theory for the variation in composition of the sun and planets, and no mechanism for the accumulation of asteroidal bodies is provided. It seems certain that no accumulation of asteroidal fragments is now occurring.

The writer has never been able to accept the Fish, Goles, and Anders model. First, it requires that the molten metal must accumulate in a core, and the evidence from the holes in some iron meteorites and from the proportions of pallasites and irons indicates that the metal meteorites do not come from a planetary or asteroidal core. Second, the writer has not been able to construct a model for the moon that appears to be consistent with its structure and thermal history if radioactive heating was available during its accumulation. No accumulation process, after all the heating processes in asteroidal bodies postulated in this model were over, seems to this writer to be consistent with the chemical composition of the moon.

Although there are objections to this theory on many points, it must be noted that no model is available to explain many of the difficult features associated with the meteorites. For some years Professor Suess has maintained that the chalcophile elements are indeed partly missing from the meteorites because of a separation from the mass of iron sulfide containing these elements. It appears that in some way some material has been lost from the meteorites and never returned to them, and thus the meteorites are a special material that is not at all the average of the solar system. Although the writer recognizes that chemical processes of a type discussed by Fish, Goles, and Anders are required, it does not seem to be necessary to accept their model for the processes.

Ringwood (38) and Lovering (30) have proposed that the meteorites come from the interior and surface regions of a fairly large planet. This suggestion seems to the writer to be quite impossible, for there is no obvious method to break up a large planet, and at the present time there are no residues in the solar system to indicate that it ever existed. Moreover, most of the material of a large planet would not have the fragile structure such as we find in the meteorites. A large planet should have been fairly warm on the interior with considerable probability at least; hence annealing of the meteorites should have been usual in this case. It is very difficult to see how the metal particles or the chondrules could possibly have been present even a moderate distance below the surface of a planet such as the earth or possibly the moon. Also, Ringwood has used quite impossible physical-chemical processes to produce the chondritic meteorites. He postulates the solution of water and carbon dioxide in order to form small masses of finely divided material presumed to be similar to the chondritic meteorites. The great difficulty here is that there is so little water in these objects now. How does one achieve the melting of silicates by dissolving water in the melt and at the same time show only exceedingly dry minerals as a result of the crystallization of that mass? This seems to be a most improbable suggestion. Lovering has found that the stone meteorites have a remanent magnetism and concludes, therefore, that they were formed in the body of a planet, using the earth and its magnetic field as a model. It seems to the writer that there must have been methods of producing other magnetic fields during the time of the formation of the solar system aside from such fields as found on the earth. Current ideas in regard to the origin of the solar system postulate that great magnetic fields were present in the past and, in fact, that they were the mechanism by which the sun transferred its angular momentum to a gas cloud. The writer is exceedingly skeptical in regard to these suggestions of Ringwood and Lovering.

The suggestion has been made that the meteorites are coming to us from the surface of a planetary body such as the moon or Ceres. This suggestion goes back to a paper by Urey and Craig (51), in which it was assumed that the asteroidal bodies had been bombarded by objects during the early history of the solar system which splashed partly melted materials to a great distance over their surface. Modifications of this suggestion have been made from time to time. In this model the chondrules are assumed to have been melted by heat produced by collisional processes. There is some doubt that collisions will produce melting, though all arguments are doubtful because of our difficulty in understanding these large-scale phenomena. It is assumed that the chondrules are produced by such processes and that bits of iron-nickel fragments are simultaneously produced; they are deposited together in the surface of a planetary object, and the material so deposited is compacted by settling or by compression in some way. The energy required for melting the silicate and metal is assumed to come from the adiabatic compression of gases, as will be discussed later.

It was suggested that possibly the objects required structures as large as the moon because of the presence of diamonds in meteorites.

But Lipschutz and Anders (27) have shown that these diamonds are almost certainly produced during collisions of objects with the surface of the earth; hence this suggestion is unnecessary to account for the diamonds but it is not excluded by their arguments.

It was also suggested that the objects may come from the moon not only to account for the structures, as mentioned above, but also for the low age of the stone meteorites measured by cosmic-ray bombardment, namely, some tens of millions of years. Difficulties have been encountered in this connection, for the Pzribram meteorite was moving in an orbit out to the asteroidal belt and can reasonably be estimated to have had a mean lifetime of about 200 million years, whereas the observed concentration of inert gases would indicate that it had been only 12 million years in space, thus disagreeing with this possible explanation of the cosmic-ray ages (39). Apparently the stone meteorites are destroyed by collisions in the asteroidal belt. The idea that the meteorites may arrive from the moon also meets with objections because the meteorite orbits are apparently predominantly of asteroidal shape, that is, going from the asteroidal belt and crossing the earth's orbit, as shown by Wood (58). The carbonaceous chondrites contain carbon compounds that might well be primitive carbon compounds produced by the action of light, gamma rays, and high-speed particles on materials in space. However, the objects have the composition of the high-iron group chondrites, approximately, and they look as though they had been produced by the action of water on the high-iron group chondrites, the water being assumed to have contained carbonaceous material, sulfide, and perhaps some of the other elements as well. It is difficult to see how one can impregnate an ordinary chondritic meteorite with materials from interplanetary space, and in this case it must be assumed that the carbonaceous chondrites have accumulated from such material. The writer proposed this some years ago and discarded it. It has been brought up again by Ringwood (38) and Mason (33). The difficulty of this suggestion is that there is no constant chemical composition in the carbonaceous chondrites, and one wonders which one of them could have accumulated in this way. Though some variation in isotopic abundances has now been observed, the extent of this type of fractionation is much less than would be required to account for the variations in the carbonaceous chondrites. The writer is exceedingly skeptical of this proposal.

The meteorites appear to have had at least two stages in their development, which may have been associated with two or more sets of bodies, namely, a place where melting occurred, followed by a breakup process, and then by an accumulation on another body. It was proposed that the first set of bodies was of lunar size and that the second was the asteroids. This suggestion is unsatisfactory. The particles of the chondrites in many cases show that they have been crushed and fragmented without having been widely separated from each other. Hence the secondary objects were identified with the moon or the surface of other fairly large objects. This suggestion is similar to that put forward by Urey and Craig (51).

The meteorites appear to be exceedingly complicated structures—they are not an average of solar material of the nonvolatile kind. They appear to have a preferred probability of arriving at the earth, and they have passed through exceedingly complicated chemical processes which have still not been satisfactorily explained. It seems most likely that extensive investigations by the methods of space research will be necessary before an agreement can be reached in regard to the origin of these objects and their exact bearing on the origin of the solar system. Details of Urey's model will develop as an outline of the origin of the solar system is presented.

4-3   THE GENERAL PROBLEM OF THE ORIGIN OF STARS

During the years of this century it has become apparent that stars are originating in the Galaxy, that they are going through an orderly development, and that they are disappearing in the graveyard of stars. They begin by the accumulation of a mass of gas and dust in space, which then goes through gravitational contraction that results in an increased luminosity and density. The temperature of the interior of the star rises until nuclear reactions become possible. The first to occur is probably the burning of deuterium and helium-3 to helium, followed by reactions in which hydrogen combines to give helium, which supplies an enormous amount of energy to the star. The time that the star spends in the different parts of this history depends on the amount of energy available. The gravitational loss of energy and the reactions of D and He^3 to form He^4 require only short times, but the burning of H^1 to He requires a long time. A small star such as the sun will probably require some 10 billion years for the effective burning of hydrogen to helium. The star then moves out of what is called the main sequence of stars into the red giant stage; this probably explodes as a supernova and the residue remains as a white dwarf. The history being discussed lies in the region when the star is large and at low temperatures before it reaches the main sequence.

In certain regions of space we observe stars that appear to have been formed recently. These are the T Tauri stars that are located in areas having considerable amounts of dust. They expel considerable amounts of matter into space, and possibly during this stage of their development they lose as much as a solar mass. The time required for the development of these stars from the first accumulation of dust to the T Tauri stage, or somewhat beyond, has been generally supposed to be of the order of 50 million years. This figure is a rough one, however, because essentially it assumes a constant luminosity of the radiating mass, and the time on this assumption is only that calculated for the radiation of the gravitational energy into space. Recently, Hayashi (16) has given reason for supposing that in these early stages the star behaves as a red giant and has an enormous luminosity, much larger than that of the present sun; hence it evolves from the dust stage to the main sequence in the course of some 5 to 10 million years, thus within the limits that might be expected from the calculation on the production of the fossil nuclides Xe^{129} and Ag^{107} from their radioactive progenitors. This history at present is not inconsistent with the times indicated from the concentrations of these fossil nuclides in meteorites.

A mass of gas in space should have a very considerable angular momentum, much larger than that at present possessed by the solar system. Interstellar gas has a density of about 10^{-24} gm/cm³ or about 1 hydrogen atom/cm³, and if a quantity of gas with a mass equal to that of the sun and a density of 10^{-24} should be rotating with the angular velocity of the rotation of the galaxy, namely, 10^{-15} rad/sec, then its angular momentum should be approximately 10^{56} gm cm²/sec. Stars apparently do not originate in such dilute masses of gas. If the density of gas were 10^{-20} gm cm⁻³ and was rotating with this angular velocity, its angular momentum would be 2×10^{53} gm cm² sec⁻¹; and if 10^{-18} gm/cm³, then the angular momentum would be 10^{52} in the same units. Densities within this region do not appear to be unreasonable, neither does it seem to be unreasonable to expect that the original angular velocity could be assumed to be that of the rotation of the Galaxy.

Various suggestions in regard to the development of a rotating mass of gas have been made. Alfvén (1), in particular, has pointed out that the transfer of angular momentum within the developing solar system may account for the changed velocity of rotation of the sun in relation to the planets, so that most of its angular momentum in the course of the development has been transferred to a solar nebula. Alfvén, however, does not consider in his discussions any of the data that have been developed in the course of this chapter except those of the older astronomical facts relating to the shape and distribution of mass in the solar system. His model seems completely unable to account for the enormous amount of data that have been accumulated in the last decade concerning the composition of the planets and the solar system generally, as presented in this chapter.

Hoyle (18) has suggested a rather complicated development in which magnetic fields are used in a qualitative way to account for the observed facts of distribution of mass and angular momentum in the solar system. His paper gives the impression that the particular values for the angular momentum selected by him follow in a natural way from fundamental theory. It is the belief of the present writer that the values used are arbitrary and in no way limit the discussion to the particular model proposed. The residual angular momentum for the evolution of the system is just that of the present planets plus the cosmic proportion of gases which have obviously been lost from it. This gives us no method of accounting for the increased density of the terrestrial planets relating to the material of the sun, as discussed in this chapter. It also seems artificial to the present writer to propose that a contraction of the sun within the orbit of Mercury was followed by an expulsion of the materials of the planets out to Neptune by means of magnetic fields. This whole theory appears to the present writer to be quite artificial.

Schmidt discussed the origin of the solar system in papers that often presented quite unacceptable mechanical ideas, such as the capture of solid objects from space. However, other astrophysicists of the USSR have suggested ideas qualitatively similar to those of the present writer. Levin (28, 29) has given reviews of these ideas. Solid objects are assumed to have accumulated to form the planets from a dust cloud of low temperature. Condensation of solid hydrogen and other gases at various parts of a solar nebula are mentioned, as is gravitational instability, without showing quantitatively how these effects could come about. The later versions of these theories assume that a nebula was captured by the sun.

Various writers discussing this subject have assumed quite different massive nebulae. Von Weizäcker (55) proposed a rather massive nebula approximately one tenth the mass of the sun. This nebula was adopted essentially by Kuiper (24) in discussing his protoplanets. Also, massive nebulae have been suggested by the present writer and by Cameron (7). These two authors assume nebulae more nearly that of a solar mass. On the other hand, the Schmidt school, Alfvén, and Hoyle have assumed nebulae of a much lower mass of the order of 1 percent of the mass of the sun—that is, barely sufficient to account for the present planets plus the gases that have been lost, assuming that the amounts of nonvolatile materials indicated by densities of the planets have been retained. It is the purpose of the next section to review the assumptions of the present writer in regard to this problem.

4-4 THE ORIGIN OF THE SOLAR NEBULA

All writers of the subject have assumed that in the early history of the solar system a nebula lying in the plane of the ecliptic consisting of gas and dust existed at some time and that the rotation of the planets and their nearly circular orbits and the fact that they lie very nearly in one plane can be accounted for by the development of such a nebula.

Jeans (19) discussed the instability of rotating masses of gas and found that one type of instability results in the loss of matter at the equator of the rotating mass. He developed this for the conditions of an incompressible spheroid and for a model with all the mass at the center and an atmosphere of negligible mass moving in the field of the central mass; he then discussed in an approximate way an adiabatic model of gases and indicated that the conditions for the loss of material in the equator should be intermediate between the two models. He assumed that the mass rotated as a solid body with no differential rotations throughout the mass. He gave no justification for this assumption, although today it seems likely that it might not be too far wrong because of the presence of magnetic fields within the rotating gas that would increase its viscosity most markedly if it were highly conductive, as it would be at higher temperatures. He showed that material will be left behind at the equatorial plane when $\omega^2/2\pi G\bar{\rho}$ lies between 0.18712 and 0.36075, and he estimated that for the adiabatic model this constant would be 0.31. There appears to be a numerical error on p. 263 of his book for equation 239.1, as derived from equation 238.1. The correction suggests that perhaps his constant of 0.31 should be 0.28. For the purposes of the present discussion, either the minimum or maximum value could be used without serious error. In this equation ω is the angular velocity, $\bar{\rho}$ the mean density of the rotating mass, and G the gravitational constant.

It is assumed in the present model that an unstable star of this kind occurred, that it began to lose mass in this way when the equatorial radius was somewhat greater than the equatorial radius of Neptune, and that a solar nebula was left behind as the sun contracted. Jeans also concludes that the density of material that is left behind at the equator must conform to the following inequality:

$$\bar{\rho} \text{ (nebula)} > 0.36075\bar{\rho} \text{ (sun)}.$$

At present it is not possible to say whether the loss of mass from such a rotating body would indeed produce the nebula used in the following discussion. Possibly in the years ahead modern computers will be able to prove or disprove the assumption made.

A mass of dust and gas rotating about the sun must assume a plane configuration, and the gas will be distributed above and below the median plane because of the component of force due to the sun in the direction perpendicular to the plane and because of the self-gravitation of the gas itself. The centrifugal force of the rotating gas will be balanced by the gravitational force of the sun. If both the gravitational field of the sun and of the nebula are included in the mathematical development, a troublesome mathematical problem will result. If we are working with a massive nebula of the order of one tenth of the mass of the sun or more, then the gravitational field of the sun can be neglected and the solution of the problem is much simpler. Ledoux secured for the distribution of mass above and below the plane the following equation:

$$\rho = \rho_o \operatorname{sech}^2 \frac{x}{H}, \qquad H = \left(\frac{RT}{2\pi G \mu \rho_o} \right)^{\frac{1}{2}},$$

where ρ_o is the density at the median plane, μ is the molecular weight, and x is the distance from the median plane.*

In this it is assumed that the nebula is isothermal. The surface density is easily shown to be $2H\rho_o$. In deriving this formula, Ledoux assumed an infinite plane of gas that was not rotating; in this case

---

* The derivation of this formula follows from Poisson's equation and the hydrostatic equation

$$\nabla^2 \psi = \frac{d^2 \psi}{dx^2} = -4\pi G \rho$$

and

$$dp = -g\rho \, dx, \qquad \text{where } g = d\psi/dx \quad \text{and} \quad p = RT/\mu\rho.$$

Substitution with appropriate differentiations gives

$$\frac{d^2 \ln \rho}{dx^2} = \frac{4\pi G \mu}{RT} \rho.$$

The solution of this equation is that given n the text.

the gravitational energy for each finite element of gas becomes infinite, and the virial theorem requires that the kinetic energy also be infinite. However, as applied to our problem, the plane of the gas is not infinite, and the distribution of gas above and below the plane will be determined mostly by the matter in the immediate neighborhood and not by that at great distances. Also, both the potential energy and the kinetic energy are approximately those of a particle in the field of the sun; hence the virial theorem is not violated, and an exact calculation should, of course, be possible in accordance with the virial theorem.

Jeans made a calculation of the masses that would separate from a three-dimensional nonrotating mass of gas and secured the following formula for the wavelength above which the mass of gas would break up into finite masses,

$$\lambda^2 = \frac{RT\gamma\pi}{G\mu\rho}, \qquad \text{where } \gamma = \frac{C_p}{C_v}.$$

The density multiplied by the cube of this wavelength gives an approximate formula for the masses produced in this way. Chandrasekhar (9) investigated this formula for the case of a rotating three-dimensional mass of gas and found a slight correction factor to Jeans's formula which is negligible for the velocities of rotation to be expected in the solar nebula. Bel and Schatzman (5) have studied the problem of instabilities in a rotating plane of gas and have secured formulas that are approximately the same as those of the Jeans. Ledoux' formula is $m(\text{critical}) = 2H\rho_0\lambda^2 = 4\pi RT/G\mu\rho_0$. For the purpose of this discussion, any of these formulas are satisfactory.

It will be noticed that in order to apply these formulas it is necessary to choose a value for the temperature of the gas and to estimate the density and the molecular weight. The density is assumed to be the minimum required to make it possible for a gaseous mass to be held together by its gravitational field under the influence of the gravitational field of the sun, as assumed by Kuiper (24). The temperature was also assumed by the writer (52) to be that which would give approximately lunar-sized masses, in this way attempting to account for diamonds in the meteorites. As explained above, this limitation is not needed at the present time. Still we have the moon with a composition somewhat similar to that of the nonvolatile material of the sun; also, there are six other satellites in the solar system with masses within a factor of 2 of that of the moon. All other satellites have masses less than 3 percent of the lunar mass. Thus lunar-sized objects are prominent in the solar system, and we retain the assumption that objects of approximately the lunar mass are required. The molecular weight can be estimated as that of a mixture of molecular hydrogen gas to helium gas of approximately 16 to 4.1 in ratio, other gaseous substances contributing little to this quantity; the solids are of negligible mass compared with the mass of the gas. Table 4-3 gives the results of calculations of this kind made some years ago by the writer, using Ledoux' formula and assuming that the temperatures within the nebula were such that some hydrogen gas was condensed at the median plane of the nebula and assuming a density equal to $10^{-6}/cm^3$. Using the Jeans formula for the unstable mass and taking the value for the density in this formula equal to one half the Roche density, that is, $2.1 \times 10^{-6}/cm^3$ as calculated above, leads to the temperatures of Table 4-4, in which it is assumed that the unstable masses throughout the solar system would produce objects of lunar mass plus its component of cosmic gases. It will be seen that the temperatures in the first set of calculations are fairly low, but perhaps not unreasonable if the sun at the time we are discussing was screened by a cloud of gas and dust lying in the nebular plane and near the sun. In the second calculations the temperatures again do not appear to be unreasonable so far as the terrestrial planets

TABLE 4-3

Data on Planets

$$\rho_o = \frac{10^{-6}}{c^3}, \quad m = 2H\rho_o\lambda^2 = \frac{(32\pi)^{\frac{1}{2}}}{\rho_o^{\frac{1}{2}}}\left(\frac{RT}{G\mu}\right)^{\frac{3}{2}}$$

Planet	Density (gm/cm³)	Temperature (°K)	H (cm)	$2\rho_o H$ (gm/cm²)	Unstable mass (gm)	Time years
Mercury	1.72×10^{-5}	10.26	7.4×10^9	2.6×10^5	1.1×10^{27}	1.3×10^7
Earth	10^{-6}	8.09	2.7×10^{10}	5.5×10^4	3.2×10^{27}	5.9×10^6
Asteroids	4.6×10^{-8}	6.53	1.1×10^{11}	1.0×10^4	1.1×10^{28}	2.9×10^6
Jupiter	7.1×10^{-9}	5.85	2.7×10^{11}	3.9×10^3	2.4×10^{28}	1.8×10^6
Neptune	3.7×10^{-11}	4.55	3.4×10^{12}	2.5×10^2	2.2×10^{29}	7×10^5
Pluto	1.6×10^{-11}	4.44	5.0×10^{12}	1.6×10^2	3.3×10^{29}	5×10^5

$$2\rho_o H = 5.5 \times 10^4/cm^{1.59}$$

Total mass of nebula $= \dfrac{2.24 \times 10^{26}}{1.99 \times 10^{33}} \displaystyle\int_{0.3}^{35} 2\rho_o H 2\pi c.dc \approx 0.35\ M_\odot$. (It is assumed that the nebula did not extend beyond 35 Å.)

Lunar mass 7.35×10^{25} gm. Lunar mass plus cosmic gases $= 2.2 \times 10^{28}$ gm.

The calculated masses using the formula of Table 4-4 would be 1.66 times as large as those listed in this table.

TABLE 4-4

Temperatures Required for Lunar Masses

$$\rho_o = \frac{2.1 \times 10^{-6}}{c^3}, \quad m = \left(\frac{RT\gamma\pi}{G\mu}\right)^{\frac{3}{2}} \frac{1}{\rho^{\frac{1}{2}}}$$

where ρ is taken to be $\frac{1}{2}$ of ρ_o, $\gamma = 1.44$, $\mu = 1.61$, that is, the ratio of hydrogen molecules to helium atoms is 16 to 4.1. Calculations are made for the temperature required for lunar masses, namely, $m = 300 \times 7.35 \times 10^{25} = 2.2 \times 10^{28}$ gm, that is,

$$T = m^{\frac{2}{3}}\rho^{\frac{1}{3}} \frac{G\mu}{R\gamma\pi}$$

Distance	Temperature
Mercury	59
Earth	23
Asteroids	8.3
Jupiter	4.4
Neptune	0.8

Mass of the nebula $= 0.30 \ M_\odot$.

are concerned, although the temperature for the outer major planets is low. The mass and angular momentum of the nebula calculated for the first case is 0.35 of a solar mass and 1.2×10^{53} gm cm²/sec, respectively, and these quantities in the second example are not greatly different.* This angular momentum is that expected for the original gas mass rotating with the angular velocity of the galaxy and having a density of 2×10^{-20} gm cm³. If the density of the nebula is increased, then the same size of objects will be produced if the temperatures are somewhat higher. Of course, the over-all mass of the nebula increases substantially in this case. What is indicated is that the application of Jeans's stability formula to the nebula together with approximate estimates for the density of this nebula lead to the conclusion that objects of something like lunar mass or smaller should form spontaneously due to gravitational instability, and attempts to use other values of T and ρ are not satisfactory. If ρ is higher, the objects are smaller, but the mass of the nebula becomes

* The angular momentum is calculated on the assumption that the nebula is acted on by the field of the sun only. Since the gravitational field of the nebula is not negligible, the angular momentum may be some 10 percent larger than that given.

larger. If it is smaller, then large objects should be formed, and the gravitational fields of these objects could be so large that the gases could not escape from them and only Jupiter's would have remained. The reader should attempt to devise other conditions. Rather narrow limits to a reasonable nebula will be found in this way.

The following approximate outline of events is proposed. First, a nebula was produced from a rotating sun as it contracted. The sun's radiation was screened from the nebula by gas and dust in the immediate neighborhood of the sun and lying toward the plane of the equator of the sun. The nebula cooled by radiation into space until fairly low temperatures existed. (The times required are given in Table 4-3.) Objects of approximately the mass of the moon, together with its cosmic gases, formed by gravitational instability in this mass. Then, the solids present in the gas accumulated on the interior of these gaseous masses. The temperatures within such objects can be estimated from Emden's tables for gas spheres as long as pressures are not too high. Modifications of these formulas have been calculated recently by Mrs. Janet Bainbridge (3), using nonideal gas laws. These calculations are complicated and lead to the conclusion that temperatures on the deep interior could well have been as high as 2000°K. It is difficult to get much higher temperatures because those of nonideal gases do not increase rapidly at high pressures due to adiabatic compression. Following this process the gas escaped from the solar nebula due to radiation processes from the sun. This may have begun first in the neighborhood of the sun and gradually extended outward, or indeed the processes may have developed as contraction of the sun and the formation of the nebula took place. When the gas had escaped almost completely, a breakup of the solid objects formed in this way was produced by collisions, and silicate dust was carried into space along with the residue of the gas, thus leaving behind material containing increased amounts of high-density elements. The accumulation of the planets occurred at this time, and the planets thus have a greater amount of iron compared to the sun. The moon is one such object that by chance escaped breakup and accumulation into the bodies of the terrestrial planets and was captured in a special orbit after some capture of high-density material similar to that which makes up the earth. Its composition is thus intermediate between that of the sun and that of the earth and other terrestrial planets and the meteorites.

The settling of dust within a gaseous spherical mass will depend on several parameters, such as the size of the particles, convection in the gas mass, temperatures that may produce evaporation of particles, and the growth of such particles to larger size. Convection might aid settling by transferring dust to the interior or it might prevent accumulation. The size and composition of the solid particles may have been different in the various parts of the nebula because of differences in temperature of the equatorial regions of the contracting sun as the nebula separated. In the outer parts, for example, in the regions of the major planets, condensation of water and carbonaceous material may have occurred and gravitational separation of hydrogen and helium and other gaseous materials should have been possible. Also, at the temperatures assumed in the preparation of Table 4-3 solid hydrogen would be present at the median plane. Such separations may have been partly preserved as the unstable masses were formed, and in this case convection in the gaseous approximately spherical masses would be modified. The writer has attempted to study these processes and has found it impossible to set up any plausible models for such a complex and uncertain physical situation.

One may ask how the disintegration of objects of approximately lunar size could occur. We know of no way by which internal explosions could accomplish it. Pressures due to radioactive heating might build up within such objects, but it is observed that pressures much higher than the overburden pressure are never contained within the earth. It is to be expected that planetary objects will always discharge gases into their surroundings when this overburden pressure is exceeded. The outer part of the object simply lifts and cracks and the gases escape. Silicate materials have no great tensile strength.

As long as the lunar-sized objects retain the gaseous envelope, it might be expected that they would collide gently with each other and perhaps remain in nearly circular orbits about the sun, but as soon as the gaseous envelope is lost we can expect that collisions will occur and, moreover, that perturbations between the objects will immediately begin to distribute objects into noncircular orbits. The direction of the perturbation effect can be stated immediately. The principle of equipotential of energy requires that the mean kinetic energy in the three degrees of freedom shall be equal. It is also possible to estimate how rapidly such perturbations might scatter the objects. For objects in the region of the terrestrial planets we can expect that a few tens of millions of years would be adequate.*

Although explosions of objects cannot occur, it can be expected that internal pressures in collisions would be effective in disintegrating

---

* This is discussed in an article presented by the writer at the December 1960 Symposium on the moon in Leningrad (44). The details are not repeated here.

the interior of such objects. Perhaps comparison to the explosion of mountains of the earth such as Krakatoa would be informative. Pressures of water vapor build up on the interior of a mountain such as Krakatoa, and when the pressure exceeds some critical value the top of the mountain is lifted, the pressures are reduced on the interior, and exceedingly fine dust is produced, which in the case of Krakatoa traveled completely around the world and persisted for some time. A precisely similar effect should be expected in the collisions of the lunar objects postulated above. Perhaps only the outer parts of these objects would remain as sizable objects. The fine dust from the interior would be easily blown into space by particle and light pressure from the sun, whereas the outer parts heated by the adiabatic compression of the gases would contain substantial bodies of metal and well-compacted silicates, and these would remain to be accumulated into the planets.

Such collisions are possible in the region of the terrestrial planets, but it is not at all clear that they would be in the region of the major planets because of the much greater volumes over which these objects would be distributed. It should be noted that although we have postulated the accumulation of solid bodies of the mass of the moon on the deep interior of these gaseous masses it is not necessary that this should always occur and it may be that in parts of the solar system large bodies such as the moon did not form. This may be the reason for the absence of such bodies in the asteroidal belt, and it may be that in the region of the major planets gaseous materials were dissipated into space without the formation of solid bodies which are postulated for the region of the terrestrial planets.

A suggestive but not at all unique explanation for the differences between the major and terrestrial planets may be proposed. At the equatorial edge of the contracting sun, where the nebula is being left behind, it can be expected that the temperatures may vary from very low at the Neptune distance to higher, but still low, within the orbit of Jupiter. The solid fraction of the nebula may have been finely divided so that it did not settle completely in the gaseous masses formed by gravitational instability in this region; hence all material, both in the gaseous and solid states, was largely driven into space from this region. In the region of the asteroids and terrestrial planets silicate materials may have condensed from the gaseous state in the region of the nebula being formed, and the solid particles could have grown to larger size and settled rapidly in the gaseous bodies to form smaller solid bodies at the asteroids and larger ones in the region of the terrestrial planets.

It is possible that there are other processes that could account for differences of this kind. It would be most interesting to know whether these gross features of the solar system, the asteroidal belt, the terrestrial and major planets, the maxima in mass at the earth and Jupiter are also characteristic of other solar systems.

4-5 SUMMARY

The model advanced in this chapter follows from certain well-studied processes: (1) Jeans's instability of a rotating mass as a means of securing a solar nebula and (2) gravitational instability formulas of Jeans, Chandrasekhar, and Bel and Schatzman. The model accounts for certain observed data: (1) the differing compositions of the planets and (2) the composition of the moon are explained; (3) the improbability of capture of the moon by the earth is alleviated, since it is only one of many moons that were captured by a terrestrial planet.

Certain properties of the meteorites may be explained: (1) the iron meteorites could have been produced as small pools of molten metal in the outer parts of the lunar objects by adiabatically heated gases; (2) the achondrites may come from pools of silicates so melted; (3) the chondrites may be conglomerates of silicates produced during the collision processes, or, as Suess would prefer, the chondrules may be droplets of silicates that condensed on the interior of the heated gas masses; (4) the meteorites give some evidence that they are bodies with a high probability of reaching the earth, and they may come predominantly from surface regions of lunar- or asteroidal-sized objects produced by processes made available by the model. The many detailed observations on meteorites may be explainable in terms of this model, but it has not been possible to propose unique chemical and physical processes for the origin of all the observed characteristics.

The model is not inconsistent with certain other requirements of the problem: (1) magnetic fields probably transferred the angular momentum of the sun to the solar nebula, as Alfvén and Hoyle maintain, and the model is not obviously inconsistent with this requirement even though it is in disagreement with the details of their models; (2) such magnetic fields may have accelerated protons to high velocity and provided the transmutation agents required by Fowler's process for the production of deuterium and other nuclides during the origin of the solar system. This would have occurred when most of the gas had been lost and before the many solid objects had been accumulated to form the planets. Whether this model could be modified to agree with Cameron's massive solar nebula is difficult to decide.

APPENDIX

It is probable that many people believe that the model for the origin of the moon is too complicated to be considered seriously. But it can be said that there is no model for the origin of the moon that is not complicated and does not appear to be very highly improbable. Sir George Darwin suggested that the moon escaped from the earth because of a resonance between the period of the tides and the natural frequency of vibration of the earth. This model has had very considerable acceptance in the past, but at present it is not looked on favorably. It should be noted that in its rotation the bulge on the earth produced by the tides would be required to travel with the speed of rotation of the earth, and as the condition of separation approached, and indeed long before it, enormous frictional forces would be set up. It seems highly improbable that separation of the moon in this fashion could occur. Perhaps a modification of this idea presented by Dr. Donald U. Wise is more plausible. He suggests that the earth accumulated as a body of uniform density with an angular velocity near the critical velocity for disruption. Following this, radioactive heating melted the metallic iron which sank to form the core and thus decreased the moment of inertia. The conservation of angular momentum therefore required that the angular velocity increase, and if the earth as it first accumulated was just barely stable with respect to rotational disintegration the increased angular velocity of rotation might have been sufficient to cause the moon to separate. The idea has never been worked out in detail, and indeed Lyttleton (31) maintains that the separation into two objects as Jeans argued cannot occur. Since the moment of inertia of a sphere of uniform density is $0.4 Ma^2$ and an earth of uniform composition would still have an increased density on the interior due to compression, the moment of inertia would be less than this; hence only a small change in angular velocity could be expected. Again we must postulate exceedingly special conditions to account for the escape of the moon. This suggestion has the virtue that it does account for the difference in composition of the earth and moon.

It has been suggested that the earth and the moon grew in the neighborhood of each other by the accumulation of objects. There are two objections that may be raised to this postulate. A small earth and a small moon would attract each other with a small gravitational force. Hence the angular velocity of rotation would have to be small at the beginning in order for the centrifugal and gravitational forces to be equal. As they grew in size, the gravitational forces would become greater and the angular velocity would have to increase in a very exact way, for otherwise the two objects would either collide with each other or move an infinite distance apart. Again, a very special condition would be required. In the second place, it is necessary to assume some process in the accumulation which would account for the difference in chemical composition of the earth and the moon. The writer previously suggested that this occurred during the process of fractionation of the high-density metal particles and the low-density silicate particles in the solar system. At first both accumulated low-density material, and as time went on they accumulated high-density material, but the earth by chance became larger than the moon; hence its accumulation toward the terminal stage of the accumulation was more rapid than that of the moon. It therefore added many metal objects to its body during this terminal phase while the moon added little. Again, it should be noted that a very special process for the formation of the earth-moon system would be required.

The third possibility is capture of the moon by the earth. If only one moon had been formed in the solar system at the time of this capture, the formation of the earth-moon system by a capture process would have been an exceedingly special event since the two objects had to approach each other in a very exact way with the dissipation of energy either to the sun, as required for the three-body problem, or by tidal dissipation in the earth and moon. This argument is an exceedingly improbable process. Again, it is necessary to account for differences in composition of the earth and moon by special assumptions such as those discussed above.

It should be noted that the proposal in this chapter avoids some of these improbabilities. The moon is assumed to have accumulated primarily out of solid material of solar composition by the settling of dust particles in a gravitational field. It was one of many objects of this kind; hence it is not so improbable that one of these objects should have been captured by a terrestrial planet. In fact, if the moon was captured by the earth, it seems very probable indeed that there were at one time many moons in the solar system that were destroyed by capture into the planets and by the destructive processes we have discussed. This model requires that some material of terrestrial composition has been added to a moon of solar composition. The calculated iron content of the moon is in accord with this.

REFERENCES

1. Alfvén, H., *On the Origin of the Solar System*, Oxford University Press, London, 1954.
2. Anders, E., Meteorite Ages, *Rev. Mod. Phys.* (in press, 1962).
3. Bainbridge, J., *Astrophys. J.*, **136**, 202 (1962).
4. Baldwin, R., *The Face of the Moon*, University of Chicago Press, Chicago, 1949.
5. Bel, N., and E. Schatzman, *Rev. Mod. Phys.*, **30**, 1015–1016 (1958).
6. Brouwer, D., and G. M. Clemence, *Planets & Satellites*, ed. G. P. Kuiper, University of Chicago Press, Chicago, 1961.
7. Cameron, A. G. W., preprint, 1961.
8. Camichel, H., *Bull. Astron.*, **18**, 185 (1954).
9. Chandrasekhar, S., *Vistas in Astronomy*, Pergamon Press, New York, 1955, p. 344.
10. DuFresne, E. R., *Astrophys. J.*, **124**, 638 (1956).
11. Fish, R. A., G. G. Goles, and E. Anders, *Astrophys. J.*, **132**, 243 (1960).
12. Fredriksson, K., private communication, 1962.
13. Gast, P. W., *J. Geophys. Res.*, **65**, 1287 (1960).
14. Gilbert, G. K., *Bull. Phil. Soc. Wash.*, **12**, 241 (1893).
15. Goldberg, L., E. A. Mueller, and L. H. Aller, *Astrophys. J.*, Supp. **5**, 135 (1960).
16. Hayashi, C., Paper presented before the International Astronomical Union, Berkeley, California, 1960.
17. Henderson, E. P., and S. H. Perry, *Proc. U. S. Natl. Museum*, **107**, 339–406 (1958).
18. Hoyle, F., *Quart. J. Roy. Astron. Soc.*, **1**, 28 (1960).
19. Jeans, J., *Astronomy and Cosmogony*, Cambridge University Press, Cambridge, 1929.
20. Jeffreys, H., *The Earth*, Cambridge University Press, Cambridge, 1929.
21. Kopal, Z., *Physics and Astronomy of the Moon*, Academic Press, New York, 1962.
22. Kozyrev, N., *Sky & Telescope*, **18**, 184 (1959).
23. Kuiper, G. P., *Atmospheres of the Earth and Planets*, University of Chicago Press, Chicago, 1952.
24. Kuiper, G. P., *Proc. Natl. Acad. Sci. U. S.*, **37**, 1; Chapter 8, *Astrophysics*, ed. J. A. Hynek, McGraw-Hill, New York, 1951.
25. Kvasha, L. V., *Meteoritika*, **20**, 124, Akad. Nauk, USSR (1961).
26. Ledoux, P., *Ann. Astrophys.*, **14**, 438 (1951).
27. Lipschutz, M. E., and E. Anders, *Geochim. Cosmochim. Acta*, **24**, 83 (1961).
28. Levin, B., *Origin of the Earth and Planets*, Foreign Languages Publishing House, Moscow, 1956.
29. Levin, B., *New Scientist*, **13**, 323 (1962).

30. Lovering, J. F., *Geochim. Cosmochim. Acta*, **12**, 238–252, 253–261 (1957). (Urey has made some criticisms of these papers: *Geochim. Cosmochim. Acta*, **13**, 335–338.)
31. Lyttleton, R. A., *The Stability of Rotating Liquid Masses*, Cambridge University Press, Cambridge, 1953.
32. MacDonald, G. J. F., *J. Geophys. Res.*, **64**, 1967 (1959).
33. Mason, B., *J. Geophys. Res.*, **65**, 2965 (1960). [See also H. C Urey, *ibid.*, **66**, 1988 (1961).]
34. Massalski, T. B., private communication, 1962.
35. Murthy, V. R., *Phys. Rev. Letters*, **5**, 539 (1960); *Geochim. Cosmochim. Acta*, **26**, 481–488 (1962); *J. Geophys. Res.*, **67**, 905 (1962).
36. Nagy, B., W. G. Meinschein, and D. J. Hennessy, *Ann. N. Y. Acad. Sci.*, **93**, 25; G. Claus and B. Nagy, *Nature (London)*, March 24, 1962.
37. Reynolds, J. H., *Phys. Rev. Letters*, **4**, 4, 351 (1960); *J. Geophys. Res.*, **65**, 3843 (1960).
38. Ringwood, A. E., *Geochim. Cosmochim. Acta*, **24**, 159 (1959).
39. Stauffer, H., and H. C. Urey, *Bull. Astron. Inst. Czechoslovakia*, **13**, 106 (1962).
40. Stratton, F. J. M., *Mem. Roy. Astron. Soc. (London)*, **59**, 257 (1909).
41. Suess, H. E., and H. C. Urey, *Rev. Mod. Phys.*, **28**, 53 (1956); see also *Handbuch der Physik*, **51**, 296 (1958).
42. Trumpler, R. J., *Lick Obs. Bull.*, **13**, 19 (1927).
43. Umemoto, S., *J. Geophys. Res.*, **67**, 375 (1962).
44. Urey, H. C., *Proc. Leningrad Symposium*, December 1960, ed. Z. Kopal and Z. Kadia, Academic Press, London, 1962.
45. Urey, H. C., *Physics and Astronomy of the Moon*, ed. Z. Kopal, Academic Press, New York, 1962.
46. Urey, H. C., *Astrophys. J.*, **134**, 268 (1961).
47. Urey, H. C., Space Research, *Proc. First International Space Sci. Symposium*, 1114, North Holland, Amsterdam, 1960.
48. Urey, H. C., *J. Geophys. Res.*, **64**, 1721 (1959).
49. Urey, H. C., *Phys. Chem. Earth*, **2**, 46–77 (1957).
50. Urey, H. C., *The Planets*, Yale University Press, New Haven, 1952.
51. Urey, H. C., and H. Craig, *Geochim. Cosmochim. Acta*, **4**, 36 (1953).
52. Urey, H. C., W. Elsasser, and M. G. Rochester, *Astrophys. J.*, **129**, 842 (1958).
53. Urey, H. C., and T. Mayeda, *Geochim. Cosmochim. Acta*, **17**, 113 (1959).
54. Van Diggellen, J., *Rech. Astron. Obs. Utrecht*, **14**, No. 2 (1959).
55. Von Weizäcker, C. F., *Z. Astrophys.*, **22**, 319 (1944).
56. Watts, C. B., private communication, 1960.
57. Wood, J. A., preprint, 1962.
58. Wood, J. A., *Mon. Not. Roy. Astron. Soc.*, **122**, 79 (1961).

GENERAL REFERENCES

The Planets, H. C. Urey, Yale University Press, New Haven, 1952. The author's ideas have changed on the origin of the solar system and abundances of the elements, but the discussion of the moon remains essentially as presented. New ideas on the problems of the origin of the solar system are summarized in the present chapter.

The Moon, ed. Z. Kopal, Academic Press, New York, 1962. Several authors present different aspects of the subject.

The Face of the Moon, Ralph Baldwin, University of Chicago Press, Chicago, 1949 and 1962. The first edition started much of the recent study of the moon. The second edition will be out soon. It is a comprehensive review of the entire literature. The author discusses the views of others in detail, whether he agrees with them or not; thus this book is most unusual.

Leningrad Symposium on the Moon, December 1960. This report should appear very shortly.

The Solar System and Its Origin, H. N. Russell, Macmillan, New York, 1935. This is an older book, but it summarizes the classical studies very well.

CHAPTER 5

RADIO EXPLORATION OF THE SOLAR SYSTEM

VON R. ESHLEMAN

Stanford University

The subject of this chapter is the study of the solar system by the techniques of radio and radar astronomy. Both approaches are based upon the emission, propagation, and reception of radio waves. In radio astronomy the natural emissions from celestial objects are received and studied for whatever information they may yield about their source and flight through space. Radar astronomy involves the use of man-made transmissions to obtain echoes for the study of the echoing object or the intervening regions of space. Only those aspects of radio astronomy that relate to the solar system are included here. Radar astronomy studies are naturally limited to the solar system because of the reduction of echo strength as the inverse fourth power of distance.

The sun, moon, and Venus have been detected by both radio emission and radar reflection, and Jupiter appears to emit radio waves by at least three distinct processes. Although much has been learned from these studies, it seems that more new mysteries have been generated than old problems solved. The past results and present status of the radio * study of these objects is reviewed. Excluded from further consideration here are the very extensive studies of meteor trails and the earth's ionosphere and magnetosphere by radio techniques and the recent radio astronomy discoveries of weak thermal

* The general term "radio" may apply to both radio astronomy and radar astronomy.

emissions from Mars, Saturn, and Mercury having about the predicted strengths.

A description of the types of equipment used in the radio exploration of the solar system is not included in this chapter. However, it is important to point out that advances in these studies are based on the combined use of the latest developments in large antennas and antenna arrays, low-noise receivers, data-processing equipment, and, for radar astronomy, powerful transmitters. For example, the 1961 radar studies of Venus were made at four laboratories in the United States, England, and Russia, with each group using advanced radar equipment and techniques of data analysis (1, 2, 3, 4). It is interesting to note, however, that an echo of up to 1000 times stronger could have been obtained if the best components of each of the four systems had been used to build a single radar system at one location. On the other hand, some of the radar astronomy facilities now being built are even more sensitive than such a combined system.

The radio exploration of the solar system is complementary to the direct probing into space with rocket-launched instruments. The radio studies can provide advanced information and a continuity of study that will make the space-probe measurements more meaningful. Also, the ground-based facilities can be used in conjunction with future space-borne terminals to make measurements that would not be feasible with only one technique.

In the following an attempt is made to introduce the reader to the results and potentialities of the radio studies. Because of the introductory nature of the text material, extensive bibliographical references within the text have not been made, although a list of references is included.

5-1 RADIO ASTRONOMY

The sun, moon, Jupiter, Venus, Mars, Saturn, and Mercury have all been detected by the radio waves they emit (5, 6). These waves carry important clues about the characteristics of the solid surfaces, dense atmospheres, or tenuous plasmas from which they emanate. The deciphering of these clues, and the advancement of the measuring techniques, constitute the challenge of the radio astronomy study of the solar system.

Thermal and nonthermal sources

All matter emits electromagnetic energy. At the radio wavelengths of interest here (from centimetric to metric waves, $10^{-2} < \lambda < 10$

meters), it is common to speak of the radiated energy as being either of thermal or nonthermal origin. The source in each case is accelerated electrons, with thermal emission resulting from random motions of independent electrons. The nonthermal emission of interest here results from the coordinated motions of a large number of electrons, such as electric currents in a plasma or a radio antenna. We are not concerned with nonthermal emission resulting from atomic processes, such as those responsible for the $\lambda = 21$ cm emission from atomic hydrogen in the galaxy and the line spectra of solar emission at optical wavelengths.

Both thermal and nonthermal radiation received from the sun, moon, and planets are described in terms of an apparent black-body disk temperature. The actual radiation received is compared with the thermal radiation that would be received from a hypothetical body of perfect emissivity (a black body) which subtends the same solid angle as the visible disk of the actual source. The apparent black-body disk temperature is the temperature required for the black body in order for its radiation to equal that of the observed radiation at the given wavelength.

The emissivity and absorptivity of a black body is unity, and thus its reflectivity is zero. Actual material bodies have some reflectivity so that their emissivity and absorptivity are always less than unity. Thus the physical temperature of the emitting material of an actual thermal source is somewhat greater than its apparent black-body temperature.

The physical temperature of a nonthermal source may bear no relationship with its apparent black-body temperature. For example nonthermal radiation from the sun has momentarily been so intense at a given wavelength that a black body the size of the sun would have to be at 10^{13} °K to equal this radiation by thermal emission. Although it is obvious that no region of the sun actually reaches such a temperature, it is convenient to use this fictitious temperature as a way of describing the intensity of the nonthermal radiation.

For almost all radio applications thermal emission can be described in terms of the Rayleigh-Jeans approximation to the classical Planck's law for radiation from a black body. Thus,

$$b = \frac{2kT_b}{\lambda^2}, \tag{5-1}$$

where b = the "brightness" of radiation from a black body at absolute temperature T_b in free space,

λ = the wavelength,

k = Boltzmann's constant (1.38×10^{-23} joules °K^{-1}).

The mks units of b are joules meter^{-2}. In practice, it is more informative to give the equivalent units as watts meters^{-2} (cps)$^{-1}$ steradians^{-1}. A receiving system with an effective antenna area A and receiver bandwidth B would pick up $\frac{1}{2}ABb\Omega$ watts of thermal noise from a source that subtends at the receiver a solid angle Ω, assuming that the antenna beam angle exceeds Ω. The factor $\frac{1}{2}$ results from the fact that only one of two orthogonal components of polarization of the randomly polarized emission is accepted by the antenna. The effective antenna beam angle Ω_a is related to its effective area by $\Omega_a = \lambda^2 A^{-1}$, so that the received noise power is kT_bB watts for a source that fills the antenna beam. For $\Omega_a > \Omega$ the received noise power is kT_aB, where T_a is defined as the effective antenna temperature given by

$$T_a = \frac{\Omega}{\Omega_a} T_b. \tag{5-2}$$

In the foregoing discussion it is assumed that T_b is constant over the source or that it is the average brightness temperature over Ω or Ω_a, whichever is smaller.

From equation (5-1) it can be seen that if the brightness does not vary as λ^{-2} then the source cannot be thermal (assuming that the emissivity is not a function of λ). Conversely, if it is found that $b \sim \lambda^{-2}$ so that T_b is constant over a wide range of wavelengths, it is likely that the source is emitting thermally.

The radio moon

The principal aims of the radio astronomy studies of the moon are the determinations of the density, temperature, thermal and electrical conductivity, dielectric constant, heat flux, emissivity, and "roughness" of the lunar surface and subsurface materials. These determinations are not simple, and usually it is necessary to combine measurements, assumptions, and theoretical calculations to come up with a proposed numerical value for one or a combination of several of these fundamental lunar characteristics. As a result, there is still much uncertainty about most of them, although certain guide lines are emerging.

Radio astronomy observations of the moon have been made over the wavelength range from 4.3 mm to 75 cm. The principal results of these measurements are listed below (6).

1. Within the accuracy of measurement, the time average blackbody disk temperature appears to be constant with wavelength at a value of about 200°K. This value checks well with expectation

based on the input of heat from the sun and an emissivity at radio wavelengths between 0.9 and unity.

2. There is a sinusoidal component of temperature that is dependent on the cyclic change in solar illumination. The amplitude of this component decreases with increasing wavelength, and the time of occurrence of its maximum value occurs several days after full moon. The sinusoidal component is too weak to be measured at wavelengths much longer than 3 cm. For short wavelengths (infrared) the fundamental component of the observed radiation is in phase with the solar heat source, since the radiation comes from the surface. Radio waves penetrate into the surface to a depth depending on the characteristics of the surface material and the radio wavelength, with the temperatures observed at increasing wavelengths corresponding to the temperatures existing at increasing distances below the surface. Considerations of the flow of heat flux and radio wave absorption indicate that the amplitude of the variable component should decrease with increasing wavelength and its phase should lag behind the solar illumination.

3. At the shortest wavelength (4.3 mm) the moon has been resolved in angle, and it appears that the radio brightness decreases rather rapidly with increasing latitude. It also appears that the lunar maria heat up and cool more rapidly than the mountainous regions, although Mare Imbrium is an exception to this general rule. The temperature variations with position are not nearly so pronounced at 8 mm wavelength.

4. Recent measurements with high angular resolution show a limb-darkening effect that may lead to better estimates of the surface characteristics and heat flow from the interior (7, 8). Here the relative temperature at various depths can be measured with precision because the change in effective depth is due to the changing angle of incidence as one scans over the lunar disk. Average disk temperatures measured at various wavelengths also correspond to different depths, but here the calibration from one receiving system to another is not accurate enough to permit deductions about changes in average temperature with depth.

Although some of the gross features of lunar radio emission correspond to expectations, a simple model of a single surface material does not appear to explain the measurements within the precision of these measurements. Many different models have been hypothesized to explain various measured characteristics. Although the measurements are apparently sufficiently accurate to rule out a simple model based on one surface constituent, they are not precise enough to allow a reliable fit to a more complicated model. A possible model appears to be one in which parts of the lunar surface consist of deep, homogeneous dust deposits, and other parts have a very thin layer of dust over a material whose thermal conductivity is like that of porous rock, such as pumice. Some measurements seem to indicate that the average dielectric constant of the surface is about 3.5, whereas several more recent measurements based on high angular resolution have led to estimated values not much greater than unity. Similar uncertainty has arisen in the radar studies of the moon. It is clear that considerably more experimentation and theory must be done before it will be possible to specify reasonably precise characteristics of the lunar material.

Another aspect of radio astronomy has been used to determine a preliminary density of the lunar atmosphere. When the moon passed in front of the strong radio noise source in the Crab nebula on January 24, 1956, it was found that the time of occultation was changed by about 25 sec because of refraction near the moon (9). This leads to a lunar atmosphere only two parts in 10^{13} as dense as that of the earth.

Radio noise from Venus

If Venus were a perfect absorber of solar energy, a perfect heat conductor, and a perfect radiator, its average temperature would be about 325°K. The corresponding figure for the earth, which is farther from the sun, is 280°K. However, largely because of atmospheric clouds, the earth and Venus do not absorb all of the solar radiation (whose energy is concentrated at optical wavelengths). Also, their emissivity at the infrared wavelengths where their emission energy is concentrated is not perfect. The first factor would tend to lower the equilibrium surface temperature, whereas the second factor would raise it. For the earth these two effects almost compensate, the trapping of infrared radiation by the atmosphere, or "greenhouse effect," being as effective in raising the surface temperature as the optical reflectivity of clouds and surface is in lowering it. The net flow of heat from the earth's interior has very little effect on surface temperature, and the total input of solar energy is very nearly the same as the total energy emitted by the earth.

The observational results for the apparent black-body disk temperature of Venus from 0.8- to 10.2-cm wavelength (6) are presented in Figure 5-1. Note that in the range of about 3 to 10 cm the temperature is approximately constant at 600°K. At the shorter wave-

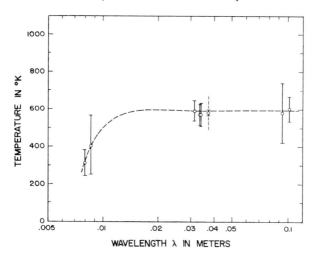

Figure 5-1 Apparent black-body disk temperature of Venus determined from its radio emission (6).

lengths the temperature decreases to the order of 300 to 400°K, with the observed infrared temperature at about 250°K.

From the constancy of radio temperature over the wide wavelength range from 3 to 10 cm, it would appear that this radiation is of thermal origin. The lower temperatures at the shorter radio wavelengths and at the infrared may result from the fact that the origin of this radiation is above the surface of the planet, whereas the radio emission is coming from the surface. If this interpretation is correct, Venus must be an efficient absorber of the solar energy that penetrates the cloud cover and a very inefficient emitter of infrared energy in order for its surface to reach such a high equilibrium temperature. This temperature corresponds to more than 600°F, which is hotter than most ovens used in baking.

Several models have been suggested in an effort to explain the apparent high temperature of Venus (10). In the greenhouse model it is assumed that Venus has a cloud layer and atmosphere that is relatively transparent to sunlight in the visible and near infrared. On the other hand, the atmosphere may contain enough water vapor and carbon dioxide to be nearly opaque to the outgoing thermal emission in the far infrared. With this model, the observed infrared temperature would be due to a cloud cover of ice crystals, which would be expected to form at about 30 to 40 km above the surface. The observed temperature at the shortest radio wavelengths would be due to the region between the clouds and ground. The 3- to 10-cm microwave radiation would not be affected by the atmosphere, so that the surface would actually be at a temperature on the order of 600°K.

In an entirely different model the atmosphere below the visible clouds is an extremely dry and dusty region kept in constant motion by winds, thermally driven from above (11). In such an atmosphere the temperature would increase with increasing depth below the top of the clouds. In this model the winds would heat the surface by friction to a temperature of 600°K. The loss by the surface would be small because the dust in suspension makes the atmosphere virtually opaque at infrared while remaining transparent to radio wavelengths longer than 3 cm.

Each of the foregoing models has its strong and weak points. A third alternative which has been suggested is that Venus has a very thick and dense ionosphere that is highly absorbing at centimeter wavelengths. This would require a number density of electrons more than 1000 times greater than the maximum of the terrestrial ionosphere over a thickness of several hundred kilometers. Since the ionosphere would be totally absorbing at wavelengths longer than 3 cm, the 600°K temperature observed with microwaves would correspond to the temperature of the ionosphere. With this model the surface temperature of Venus would be more inviting to future visits by astronauts. It should be pointed out, however, that this explanation would appear to preclude the radar reflections that have been obtained from wavelengths between about 13 and 70 cm; that is, we cannot have an absorbing ionosphere to produce a high black-body disk temperature and at the same time have a transparent or reflecting ionosphere to explain radar echoes.

It is obvious from the foregoing that many mysteries remain concerning the characteristics of the surface and atmosphere of our sister planet. Continuing ground-based studies should go a long way toward solving some of these mysteries, although final answers may not be available until instrumented probes reach the surface of Venus. For the time being, the observed microwave radiation from Venus leading to an apparent black-body disk temperature of 600°K must remain one of the principal mysteries of the solar system.

Noise bursts from Jupiter

Another first-order mystery of the solar system is the source of the intense emission from Jupiter at wavelengths longer than about 10 meters. The spectral characteristics and the time variability indicate that this emission is definitely not of thermal origin. At these wavelengths Jupiter is often the most intense radio noise source in the sky. Because of many natural and man-made terrestrial sources of impulsive radio noise at these wavelengths, the identification of Jupiter as the origin of emission of this type was overlooked for many years (12).

The principal features of the burst noise from Jupiter include (12, 13):

1. The duration of isolated, well-defined bursts varies from about 0.2 to 1 sec, with a most likely value of 0.6 sec. There is a marked tendency for grouping of pulses with the group lasting for some minutes.

2. Strong bursts are so intense that the equivalent black-body disk temperature of Jupiter at this wavelength can reach $10^{12}\,^{\circ}\mathrm{K}$.

3. The time of occurrence of bursts indicates a very stable planetary rotation at a period of 9 hr 55 min 29.36 ± 0.01 sec.

4. The bandwidth of an individual burst is usually on the order of 1 mc, although some bursts are much wider in bandwidth. For a group of bursts, there is a tendency for the frequency to progress from low to high frequency.

5. It appears that a wavelength of about 17 meters is optimum for receiving noise bursts from Jupiter. Very few bursts are received at wavelengths shorter than 10 meters. In Figure 5-2 the relative probability of emission is plotted as a function of wavelength (14).

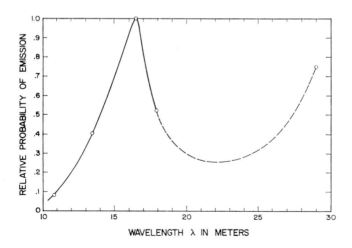

Figure 5-2 Relative probability of emission as a function of wavelength for burst noise from Jupiter (14).

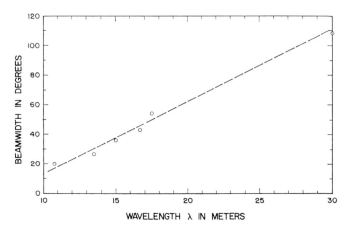

Figure 5-3 Cone angle of the beamed emission of burst noise from Jupiter at various wavelengths (14).

6. There are marked differences in the characteristics of the burst noise at wavelengths that differ by less than a meter.

7. It appears that the emissions are limited in cone angle, with the angle of the cone increasing with increasing wavelength. The extent of this effect is illustrated in Figure 5-3 (14).

Although the burst emission from Jupiter has characteristics in common with terrestrial lightning emissions, the intensities are such that the Jovian lightning bolt would have to be a billion times more intense than its terrestrial counterpart. The stability of the rotation period of the sources, as opposed to the variable rotation of the visible atmospheric markings, has led to the conclusion that these radio sources may be tied to a solid core. From considerations of this type, it has been suggested that the source of the emission may be associated with violent effects in the solid planetary mantle which have their closest terrestrial counterpart in earthquakes and vulcanism (13). Such an explanation would require some mechanism for transforming the energy into electromagnetic radiation. One possibility might be that a sound wave travels to an ionospheric region where it excites plasma oscillations. The durations of the individual bursts on this model might be related to the relaxation time of the ionosphere. However, a simple explanation of propagation of radio waves through an ionosphere would cause limiting cone angles to change with wavelength in the opposite sense to that observed (see Figure 5-3).

It is indeed surprising that Jupiter is comparatively far more active than the sun. Regardless of the mechanism of the generation and emission of the energy, it is obvious that the radio measurements have uncovered a mystery whose existence could not have been guessed from optical measurements alone.

Trapped particle radiation from Jupiter

The first microwave measurements of emission from Jupiter were made at wavelengths near 3 cm. They indicated an apparent black-body disk temperature of about 150°K, in reasonably good agreement with theory and infrared measurements of the thermal emission. Later measurements at longer wavelengths, however, were extremely puzzling. It appeared that the longer the wavelength used in the observation, the "hotter" the source (50,000°K at a wavelength of 68 cm). The results for apparent black-body disk temperature measured at various wavelengths are given in Figure 5-4 (16). Clearly, Jupiter is not behaving like a simple thermal source at these wavelengths.

There appear to be long-term changes in the intensity of the radiation from Jupiter, which provide additional evidence that the radiation is not of simple thermal origin. However, by far the best clues to the source characteristics can be found in the results of a series of careful interferometric and polarization measurements at

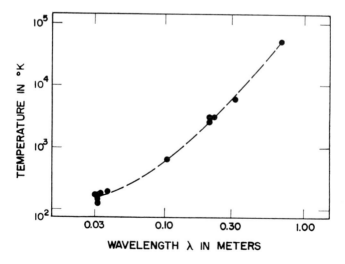

Figure 5-4 Apparent black-body disk temperature of Jupiter determined from its radio emission (6).

31 cm (15). It appears that the diameter of the source is some three times the diameter of Jupiter, and that the radiation is preferentially linearly polarized (30 percent) with the electric vector approximately parallel to the equator of Jupiter. These characteristics strongly suggest that the radiation is due to trapped electrons spiraling in a Jovian magnetic field. Both synchrotron (relativistic electrons) and cyclotron (nonrelativistic electrons) mechanisms of emission have been suggested [see reviews in (6) and (12)].

In order to explain the intensity of the observed radiation in terms of synchrotron emission, it would be necessary to have a magnetic field of about 5 gauss and a density of energetic electrons 10^4 to 10^6 that of the Van Allen belts of the earth. In order to account for the radiation in terms of cyclotron emission, Jupiter would require a magnetic field of greater than 1200 gauss at the poles.

It appears that an explanation based on either relativistic or non-relativistic particles near Jupiter leads to some difficulty with regard to the required number density of particles or the strength of the magnetic field. Nevertheless, the evidence based on the angular size and polarization of the radiation is such that a theory of this type appears to be called for. It is interesting to note that only recently has it been discovered that the particles in our own magnetic field may also radiate radio noise of sufficient intensity to be observed on the earth (16).

At wavelengths shorter than about 3 cm it appears that most of the observed radiation is of thermal origin, since derived temperatures check well with infrared measurements. Thus three distinct types of radio emission apparently have been observed from Jupiter, so that radio astronomy constitutes a powerful technique for the determination of the conditions on and near this giant planet.

Thermal radio noise from the sun

The apparent black-body disk temperature of the sun at millimeter wavelengths is about 6000°K. However, the temperature, increasing with wavelength, reaches the order of a million degrees in the meter range. Although the apparent temperature corresponding to the radio emission varies with wavelength, it does not follow in this case that the source is nonthermal. The temperature of the plasma in the chromosphere and corona increases with height above the photosphere. Thus thermal emission would be expected to produce a rising apparent temperature as the wavelength is increased and the effective source of radiation mounts higher and higher in the plasma

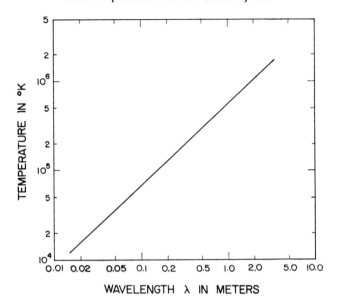

Figure 5-5 Disk temperature as a function of wavelength for the basic thermal component of radio emission from the sun (17).

surrounding the sun. In addition, there are many nonthermal sources of solar emission, which are described in the next section.

A basic thermal component of solar emission occurs at all times and is the only source when the sun is quiet (no sunspot areas). The temperature of the basic component is plotted as a function of wavelength in Figure 5-5 (17). Since the description of this radiation involves complicated considerations of the equation of transfer, propagation paths, and emission from a deep plasma, it is necessary to go into considerable detail to predict the variation of temperature with position on the solar disk. Figure 5-6 shows some results of computations of this type (18). Graphically illustrated here is the complex change in brightness temperature with radial position on the solar disk for various wavelengths and coronal electron temperatures.

It would be expected that the apparent black-body temperature, starting at wavelengths greater than about 1 meter, would decrease with increasing wavelength. This would not be due to a lower temperature at the level of origin, but rather it would result from a decrease in the emissivity or absorptivity. This characteristic is important in considerations of radar reflections from the solar corona, since decreasing emissivity implies increasing reflectivity.

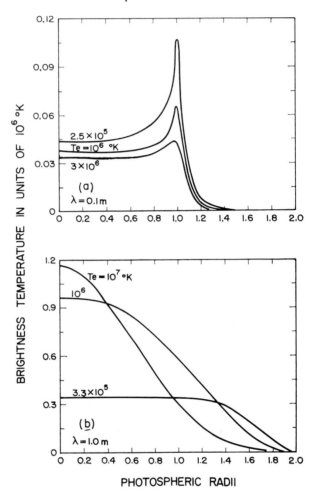

Figure 5-6 Theoretical brightness temperature of the basic component of solar radio emission plotted as a function of disk radius at wavelengths of 0.1 meter (a) and 1.0 meter (b) for various values of electron temperature T_e (18).

In addition to the basic component, there is a slowly varying thermal component with a period equal to that of solar rotation. The variable component rises and falls in phase and magnitude in a way that closely corresponds to the area of calcium plages, those centers of activity marked by the unusual emission of spectral lines from calcium. These are a common and long-lived feature of the sun. Two-dimensional maps made at Stanford University of the thermal emission at a wavelength of 9 cm are given in Figure 5-7a, b. These show active regions and their rotation with the general rotation of the sun. It appears that the slowly varying component, which may reach intensities equal to the basic component, is associated with the magnetic field of sunspots, which raises the level of origin of radiation from the relatively cool chromosphere into the million-degree corona.

Nonthermal solar emission

In addition to the basic and slowly varying components of solar emission, there are also intense and highly variable emissions of obvious nonthermal origin. This component is only rarely observed

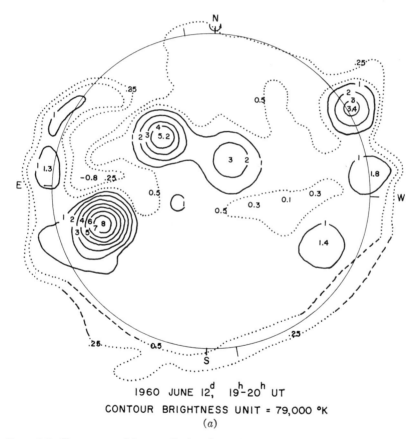

1960 JUNE 12,^{d} 19^{h}-20^{h} UT
CONTOUR BRIGHTNESS UNIT = 79,000 °K
(a)

Figure 5-7 Two maps of 9-cm radiation from the sun, showing active regions and their changing position on the disk due to solar rotation (G. Swarup, *Scientific Report No. 11*, Contract AF 18(603)-53, Stanford University). (Figure 5-7 continued on p. 184.)

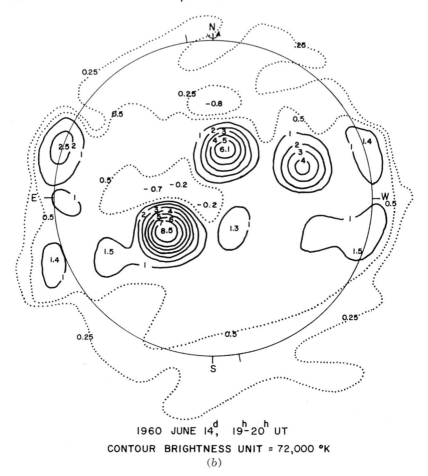

1960 JUNE 14^d, 19^h-20^h UT
CONTOUR BRIGHTNESS UNIT = 72,000 °K
(b)

Figure 5-7 (Continued)

at centimeter wavelengths, but it becomes intense and often predominant at decimeter and meter wavelengths.

Many observations of these nonthermal noise emissions have been gathered over the last few years. Examination of their spectral characteristics suggests that the majority can be classified in five groups (19):

Type I. "Storm" bursts occur in numbers from hundreds to thousands and are characterized by a bandwidth of only a few megacycles and durations of less than a few seconds. The emissions are strongly circularly polarized, and they often appear above a background-noise continuum which is polarized in the same way.

Type II. "Slow-drift" bursts are strong events lasting up to 10 min and occur after certain large flares. They are characterized by a slow drift in frequency from high to low frequencies at about 200 kc/sec.

Type III. "Fast-drift" bursts are common events which last on the order of 10 sec. They occur in groups at the start of solar flares and drift in frequency from high to low at a rate 100 times faster than Type II bursts.

Type IV. "Long continuum" bursts are extremely rare, but they last for hours and start late in the life of certain large solar flares which follow a Type II burst. The spectrum is broad and has no distinct markings. The polarization is circular.

Type V. "Short-continuum" bursts are events lasting about one minute. They follow immediately after certain Type III bursts and have a broad and featureless spectrum.

All of these emissions appear to be associated in one way or another with solar flares. In some major flare disturbances all of the radio events are present. Types III and V are simultaneous with the sudden expansion of the flare. A few minutes later Type II events may start. This is followed by or merges into the start of the Type IV bursts, which continue for hours.

It now appears that the following sequence of events may be responsible for most of the emissions described above (19). There is an explosion near the photosphere that is observed optically as a solar flare. A stream of relativistic electrons is emitted which escapes immediately at velocities near that of light into the outer layers of the corona. In addition, a shock wave is started which carries more relativistic trapped particles with it as it travels up through the corona at speeds on the order of 500 to 1500 km/sec. The initial relativistic particles high in the corona are responsible for the Type V bursts. The rapid transport of these particles up through the corona produces the Type III bursts by exciting plasma oscillations in the corona at the local plasma frequency. The slower moving shock wave excites the Type II bursts by a similar mechanism. This would explain the characteristic increase in wavelength of the emission with time and the difference in the time scale of these two emissions. Synchrotron emission from relativistic electrons carried up by the shock wave to three or four solar radii may be responsible for Type IV emissions.

Important geophysical effects may result from this same disturbance (19). On the order of 20 min after the start of a flare there may be a large cosmic ray increase on the earth. Because this time delay is greater than would be expected for particles going near the speed of light, it may be that the cosmic rays are the delayed relativistic particles that also cause the Type IV bursts. From 1 to 3 days after a large flare there may be a sudden commencement of a terrestrial magnetic storm. This would appear to be associated with a corpuscular stream from the sun traveling at about 1000 km/sec and suggesting a relationship with the shock front that causes the Type II emissions. Correlation between Type II bursts and geomagnetic storms has been well established, although there is no one-to-one correlation.

5-2 RADAR ASTRONOMY

In radio astronomy the nature of the source is determined by the characteristics of its natural radiation. In radar astronomy the experimenter controls the characteristics of the radiated energy, and information about the object of study must be gleaned by its effects on this radiation. Different characteristics are susceptible to study by these two techniques. The most obvious use of radar is in the measurement of distance. However, this is just one of several areas in which radar astronomy may make a contribution to the continuing studies of the solar system.

The radar moon

Because of the proximity of the moon to the earth, its radar echo is about 10^7 times the strength of an echo from Venus at its closest approach to the earth. The first radar echoes from the moon were obtained in 1946. However, serious study of the moon by radar has only begun.

Echoes from the moon provide new information about the surface material, although much more work appears to be required to determine an accurate model to explain both the radio and radar astronomy results. A technique of resolving separate regions on a spherical rotating body has been demonstrated by deriving a two-dimensional radar map of the lunar disk, as described in the next section. Reflections from the moon are being used to study the structure and dynamics of the ionospheric and interplanetary medium between the earth and the moon by the slight effects of the plasma on wave propagation. Accurate distance measurements are improving our knowledge of the size and shape of the earth-moon system and of the earth itself. It also appears that radio reflections from the moon may be a new mode for long-range communications.

Simple energy considerations show that the total power reflected directly backward from the moon will be about the same for a slightly irregular surface as for a perfectly smooth surface with the same reflection coefficient. This is the basis for determining the reflectivity of the moon by equating the returned power to the reflectivity times the expected returned power from a perfectly smooth and perfectly reflecting target. It appears that the reflectivity of the surface at wavelengths near 1 meter is between 5 and 10 percent. From measurements of this type, the computed dielectric constant of the material on the surface of the moon is on the order of 3, which is about half that of terrestrial rocks (20). However, it has also been proposed, partly on the basis of the small apparent change of echo power with wavelength, that the dielectric constant may be only about 10 percent greater than that of free space, indicating material of very low density (21). This uncertainty is similar to that which has resulted from the different kinds of radio astronomy measurements. However, all of these results are still being studied and it may be possible to reconcile these apparent differences in terms of a better model of the moon.

Powerful radar systems have been used recently to study the variation of signal strength for all the positions between the center of the disk and the limb (20, 22). It appears that there are two types of scattering—a "specular" component near the center of the disk, which accounts for about 80 percent of the total returned power, and a "diffuse" component from the whole of the disk containing the remaining 20 percent. Studies of the change in strength within the specular component have led to estimates that the average slope of the lunar landscape is about 1 in 15. This result applies for wavelengths between 10 cm and 3 meters, so that it would appear that the surface irregularities which cause the moon to be almost uniformly bright at visual and infrared wavelengths must be many times smaller than 10 cm. The diffuse component is attributed to the small-scale features on the surface which have dimensions on the order of 1 meter. It appears from the measurements that only about 5 percent of the surface is covered by such a structure (20).

If the moon were perfectly smooth, its use in communications would be ideal, since its reflection would not distort the information being transmitted. Actually, there is a certain amount of distortion. It would not be feasible to send a wideband television signal via the moon, although reasonably good voice communications could be maintained. However, the most important factor limiting the use of the moon in communications is the fact that it is available only half of the time.

Another use of lunar reflections is for the study of the terrestrial ionosphere and the interplanetary gas between the earth and the moon. For these experiments the reflections from the moon serve only to return the energy to the earth for analysis. The study of the medium is based on its effects on the polarization and velocity of the waves. Near the earth the earth's magnetic field combines with the free electrons to cause a "Faraday" rotation of the plane of linearly polarized waves. Knowing the strength of the magnetic field allows one to compute from polarization measurements the total content of the ionosphere. Farther from the earth, where the magnetic field becomes extremely weak, measurements of the plasma density are based on slight changes in group and phase velocity. Since the frequency and timing of the transmitted and received wave can be measured with great precision, slight effects of the propagation medium can be determined.

The range from a radar site to the reflection point on the moon has been measured with a precision of about 300 meters (23). The departure of these measurements from the computed distance is variable with an average discrepancy of about 10 km. Both the variability and the average difference remains unexplained, although it would appear that uncertainties in the size and shape of the earth, the lunar topography, the scattering characteristics, and the lunar orbit may combine to cause these effects. Conversely, the radar measurements may be used to correct some of these parameters.

Radar mapping

The clarity of optical photographs and radio-astronomy brightness maps (illustrated in Figure 5-7) is limited by the resolving power of the measuring instrument, or the stability of the propagation path, in allowing discrimination in angle. Angular scintillation of light rays in the atmosphere limits astronomical photographs taken from the earth's surface to a resolution of about 1 sec of arc. Practical antenna size has limited angular resolution in radio astronomy to about 1 min of arc. This same limitation also applies to radar astronomy. However, resolution in angle is not the only way to obtain a map of a radar target.

A preliminary radar map of the moon is presented in Figure 5-8. This map was made at the Lincoln Laboratory's Millstone Hill radar site, using an antenna beam broader than the moon, so that essentially no angular resolution was possible (20). However, because the

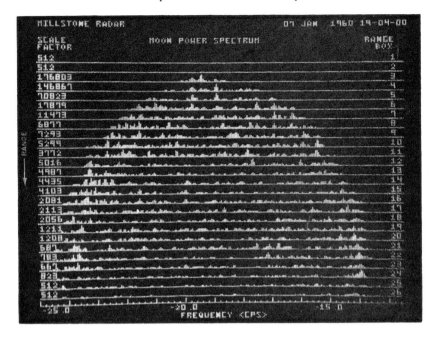

Figure 5-8 Preliminary radar "map" of the moon made at the Lincoln Laboratory field site near Boston, using a wavelength of 0.68 meter (20).

flight time and radio frequency of the received pulses could be measured with great precision, a detailed map could be made based on range-Doppler coordinates.

In the figure each horizontal section corresponds to a particular range from the radar to a portion of the moon. The nearest point at the center of the lunar disk gives the signals in the first (top) range increment. The last range increment corresponds to echoes at the greatest delay, which are returning from the regions of the moon near the limb. For each range increment there is a spread in the radio frequencies caused by the apparent rotation of the moon. The response at a particular range and Doppler frequency on the map is caused by two small areas on the disk of the moon; that is, there is a correspondence between a particular range-Doppler response and a limited region of the moon, making possible a radar map. Since two separate areas contribute to each response, the circular disk is mapped into a half circle, but there are techniques for removing this ambiguity.

The resolution in this kind of mapping is determined by how narrow a range interval can be used and how narrow a frequency increment can be measured. In practice, these quantities are limited primarily by the strength of the echo. With increasing sensitivity of radar systems, it is conceivable that future radar maps of Venus and Mars could delineate surface features to a greater precision than can be seen in an optical telescope. In the case of Venus, the radar waves can be used to map surface features that are totally hidden from optical study by the dense cloud cover. Although only very weak echoes have been obtained from Venus, radars are being built with 10,000 times the sensitivity of the present systems so that crude radar maps may soon show whether Venus has mountain ranges and oceans.

The astronomical unit

The special forte of radar is the accurate measurement of distance and velocity. It was obvious that one of the first tasks in radar astronomy, once radar echoes from a planet could be obtained, would be the accurate determination of the astronomical unit, which is defined as the time-average distance between the center of the sun and the center of the earth. It is also the semimajor axis of the elliptical orbit of the earth.

From years of optical observations of the planets, accurate measurements in angle and time made it possible to determine the shape of the solar system to a high precision. Although the distance between two planets could be given in terms of the astronomical unit to a high degree of accuracy, it was not possible to describe the distance in terrestrial units, such as kilometers, with similar precision; that is, the shape of the solar system was known better than the size. Thus the situation before the advent of radar studies appeared to be that once one accurate range or velocity measurement was made all distances in the solar system could be described with similar accuracy. Tracking of space probes, such as Pioneer V, also provides techniques for improving the precision of the astronomical unit.

In 1958 the Lincoln Laboratory of the Massachusetts Institute of Technology announced that they had apparently received the first weak radar reflections from Venus (24). Extensive data processing and analysis were needed to obtain the echo indications. Two separate measurements of echo delay corresponded to a value for the astronomical unit of 149,467,000 ± 2000 km. From the echo intensity, it appeared that the reflectivity of Venus was near unity. The measured values of the Doppler frequency shift appeared to be in good agreement with predictions.

In 1959 the experiment was repeated with improved sensitivity, but no echoes were found. That same year measurements in England, using the 250-ft antenna at the Jodrell Bank Experimental Station of the University of Manchester, yielded what appeared to be echoes at the same range found by the American group (25). Then, at the 1961 conjunction the Russians announced a value of the astronomical unit based on radar of approximately the same value as the previous determinations (26). In spite of this agreement, based on measurements taken by different organizations in different years, it is now evident that the astronomical unit is markedly different than appeared to be indicated by these preliminary measurements.

During the 1961 conjunction radar echoes were obtained at the Lincoln Laboratory, Jodrell Bank, and the Jet Propulsion Laboratory of the California Institute of Technology, as well as in Russia (1, 2, 3, 4). The published American and English results for the astronomical unit measured in 1961 check very well. The earliest Russian announcement, which gave a value near the incorrect 1958 figure, can be explained by the fact that their measurements had a periodic uncertainty based on the regular sequence of transmitted pulses. One of these values corresponds to the other 1961 results, and indeed further processing of the Doppler shift shows that this value is unique. In addition, a new processing of the 1959 Lincoln Laboratory recordings also checks with the other 1961 results (27).

The present status of the radar determinations of the astronomica. unit is illustrated in Figure 5-9 (28). It appears that an accuracy of at least one part in 50,000, with an apparent average value of 149,598,700 km, has been obtained. This represents an improvement in precision of about 30 times over the spread of values derived from previous optical determinations.

One measurement of range would serve to pin down the size of the solar system if its shape were perfectly known. However, it appears that the radar measurements, taken over several months, are so accurate that they exceed the precision of the shape information; that is, by the use of the present shape description, no single assumed value for the astronomical unit can fit the radar measurements, there being a systematic trend in the comparison of measurements and predictions (27). In fact, the uncertainty quoted above for the radar value of the astronomical unit results from this limitation rather than from inaccuracies in individual range measurements. Continuing radar studies of planets over appreciable parts of their orbits should make it possible to prescribe both the size and the shape of the solar system to an accuracy approaching that of our knowledge

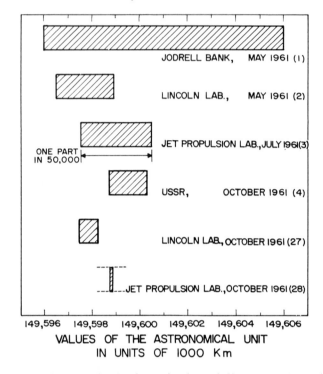

Figure 5-9   Results of radar determinations of the astronomical unit.

of the velocity of light, which has a precision of about one part in a million.

Radar studies of Venus

The initial radar studies of Venus have provided preliminary information about the reflectivity and roughness of the surface and about the planet's period of rotation. Radar provides a particularly important approach for the study of Venus, since the surface is hidden to optical study by a nearly featureless cloud cover.

Both the Lincoln Laboratory and Jet Propulsion Laboratory measurements indicate a surface reflectivity of 10 to 15 percent, the measurements being made at wavelengths of about 70 and 12.5 cm, respectively (28). There was no obvious change of reflectivity on the various days that measurements were made. The measured reflectivity indicates a dielectric constant on the order of 4, which is higher than that of the moon but still less than what would be expected for material such as terrestrial surface rocks. This value seems to preclude a body of water (which has a dielectric constant of about 80) at the reflection point. It is interesting to note that if a body of water as small as 4 km in diameter were precisely at the center of the disk, the planet would appear to be a nearly perfectly reflecting sphere, having about the same reflection characteristics as it would if it were completely covered with water.

From polarization measurements made at the Jet Propulsion Laboratory, it appears that the orthogonal polarization is reduced about a factor of 10 from that corresponding to the transmitted polarization. This indicates that Venus has about the same roughness or depolarizing effect as does the moon. The Lincoln Laboratory measurements show a slight echo-pulse lengthening due to surface roughness which again checks with the specular component of moon echoes, after scaling for the difference in diameter. At radio wavelengths the moon is relatively smooth, having average slopes on the order of 1 in 15. It appears, therefore, that Venus also is relatively smooth at scales on the order of 0.1 to 1 meter.

It was evident to all the radar experimenters that a measure of the Doppler spread of the echo could yield information about the unknown rotation speed of Venus. Both the Lincoln Laboratory and the Jet Propulsion Laboratory groups found the Doppler spectrum extremely narrow, and, based on the fact that Venus appears to have about the same scale of roughness as the moon, they deduced that the rotation period of Venus very likely corresponds to its year; that is, Venus may turn once on its axis in 225 terrestrial days so that, like Mercury, it maintains the same face toward the sun. However, the Russian measurements seem to indicate a wider Doppler spread, from which they have deduced a rotation period of about 10 days. It must be recalled that in all of these instances weak echoes are involved so that it is difficult to determine their characteristics.

The question of the period of rotation of Venus on its axis has important implications with regard to the weather and wind circulation and also to the possible existence of a magnetic field on Venus. More radar studies are required to differentiate between the two values suggested by the 1961 measurements. It should also be noted that the sense of rotation and the orientation of the axis are not immediately evident from Doppler measurements, although these are amenable to more sophisticated radar measurement.

During future conjunctions of Venus, more powerful radars will be used to study the surface and rotation features with greater precision. Radar may also be used to study the atmosphere and ionosphere of Venus. In addition, we can look forward to the time when it will be possible to use the radar mapping technique to tell us more about the change of surface features with position on our sister planet.

Solar radar astronomy

The sun in all probability will be the most important object for future radar astronomical investigations. It is a different kind of target than the planets in that the waves are reflected from highly ionized coronal gases instead of a solid surface. From visible studies of the sun during eclipses, it is known that the corona is a highly variable region, changing markedly with the changing activity in the lower chromosphere and photosphere. Knowledge of the changing size, shape, temperature, and density of the corona should prove valuable in basic solar studies and in predicting the various effects of the sun on the earth, such as auroras, solar cosmic rays, radiation belts, ionospheric and magnetic storms, and radio blackouts.

Radar waves will not penetrate to the photosphere or visible disk of the sun. The depth of penetration depends on wavelength, with the longer wavelengths being reflected as much as several solar radii from the sun's center. The shorter wavelengths penetrate further into the hot coronal gas, where particle collisions cause the waves to lose considerable energy before they reach the reflecting level. Therefore, the choice of wavelength in solar radar astronomy is crucial. It appears that wavelengths on the order of 10 meters are ideal, for considerably shorter wavelengths are probably almost totally absorbed.

In April and September of 1959 weak radar echoes from the sun were obtained at the Stanford University Radioscience Laboratory with a radar system at a wavelength of 12 meters (29). The radar components included an antenna that covers about 14 acres, a 40-kw transmitter, and a digital computer for data processing. From these preliminary measurements, it appeared that reflection was taking place at about 1.7 solar radii (i.e., 0.7 radii above the photosphere) and that the spectral width of the echo was greater than could be produced by solar rotation.

During the first half of 1961 a longer series of measurements was made near El Campo, Texas, by a group from the Lincoln Laboratory of the Massachusetts Institute of Technology (30). Their radar system operates at a wavelength of 8 meters with a power output of 500 kw. The antenna consists of 1024 dipoles in an array 100 ft wide by 750 ft long. The computed sensitivity of this radar is on the order of a hundred times that of the Stanford system. Although

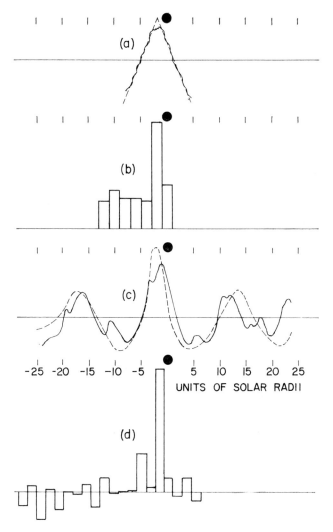

-25 -20 -15 -10 -5   5   10   15   20   25

UNITS OF SOLAR RADII

Figure 5-10 Indications of radar echoes from the sun obtained at Stanford University: (a), (b), (c), see (29) and also R. C. Barthle, *Scientific Report No. 9*, Contract AF 19(604)-2193, Stanford University and the Lincoln Laboratory field site in Texas (30). (d) The solid line in (a) shows the cross correlation of echo recordings, made in April 1959, with the transmitted code; the dotted line is the idealized shape for reflection at 1.7 solar radii. In (b) the same data are presented in a different way to illustrate echo and noise characteristics, with the echo indication appearing at the expected range. In (c) the two lines show ideal and measured correlations for data taken in September 1959, where the range ambiguity has been improved over the previous measurements. In (d) echo energy as a function of range (in units of solar radii) is plotted from measurements made on a number of days during the period April to July 1961. In each graph the circle represents the size of the solar photospheric disk relative to the range scale.

195

computations of the expected signal strength indicated that the echoes should be about equal to the solar and galactic noise intensity, the measurements revealed that the average echo was 30 to 100 times weaker.

The echo indications for the Stanford and Lincoln Laboratory experiments are compared in Figure 5-10. The techniques of data reduction and presentation are markedly different, yet the indicated echo range seems to be about the same in each presentation.

From the longer series of experiments taken by the Lincoln Laboratory, it appears that the strength of the echo is highly variable from day to day, and there is some preliminary indication that the echo strength may increase considerably at times of solar noise storms (28). This effect may explain an apparent difference in average signal strength obtained in the two series of experiments, since the Stanford measurements were taken when the average sunspot activity was about twice the early 1961 activity. In addition, the small difference in wavelength may cause a marked difference in signal strength. Figure 5-11 illustrates a computation of expected radar cross section of the sun as a function of wavelength for different values of coronal electron temperature and density. Note in particular that if the temperature were only $0.5 \times 10^{6}°K$ the echo strength would be expected to drop rapidly as the wavelength is decreased.

Many other methods of measuring coronal electron temperatures indicate values of more than $10^{6}°K$. However, some of these methods are based on electron motions, which are assumed to be of thermal origin only. If there are coordinated mass motions of electrons due to turbulence, these deduced temperatures would be too high. The radar spectrum measurements at an 8-meter wavelength indicate that the energy is spread more than 8 kc (28). Since rotation could account for no more than about 10 percent of this Doppler spread, it appears that turbulence is a prevalent characteristic of the corona. The radar measurements also show a slight shift of the center of the spectrum, indicating a general outflow of gas toward the earth.

New radar systems are being constructed for continuing studies of the sun. Based on the system capabilities that are coming into being, the future of solar radar astronomy looks bright indeed. From multiwavelength resolution in echo range, Doppler, amplitude, and angle, it should ultimately be possible to monitor the changing size, shape, density, temperature, and motion of the coronal gas. Related radar studies include the search for direct echoes from solar streams of gas far from the sun, and the study of propagation effects in radar

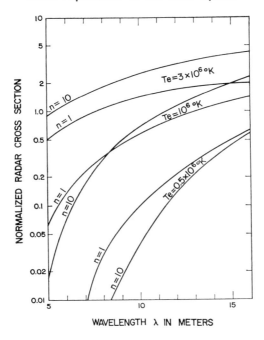

Figure 5-11   Computed radar cross sections (apparent radar "sizes") of the sun as a function of radio wavelength for various electron temperatures, T_e, and coronal densities (n-values). The cross sections are normalized by the photospheric disk size (see P. Yoh, *Scientific Report No. 2*, Contract AF 19(604)-7436, Stanford University).

echoes from the planets near superior conjunction where the waves must pass twice through the solar corona.

5-3   THE FUTURE

The subject of the radio exploration of the solar system includes the use of space-probe-borne terminals (1) to provide a remote terminal for one-way propagation of man-made signals for studying the intervening medium, (2) to get above the ionosphere and atmosphere to use and study radio wavelengths longer and shorter than those that can pass through these regions, and (3) to get closer to the object of study. Although significant steps have been made in these directions, the space-probe aspect has not been discussed, since there are few results for regions in the solar system beyond the ionosphere of the earth. Future developments along these lines are expected to be fruitful, although earth-based radio and radar measurements will continue to be important. It would be expected that earth-space, earth-only, and space-only radio measurements would be complementary, each making the other two more meaningful. In the first two the same ground facilities can be used to advantage, so that improvements in these systems should continue to be stressed.

REFERENCES

1. Thomson, J. H., G. N. Taylor, J. E. B. Ponsonby, and R. S. Roger, A New Determination of the Solar Parallax by Means of Radar Echoes from Venus, *Nature* (*London*), **190**, 519–520 (1961).

2. Staff, Millstone Radar Observatory, Lincoln Laboratory, Massachusetts Institute of Technology, The Scale of the Solar System, *Nature* (*London*), **190**, 592 (1961).

3. Victor, W. K., and R. Stevens, Exploration of Venus by Radar, *Science*, **134**, 46–48 (1961).

4. Kotelnikov, V. A., Radar Contact with Venus, Paper presented at XII International Astronautical Congress, Washington, D. C., October 4, 1961.

5. Denisse, J. F., "Les Sources d'émissions radioelectriques du soleil, Paper 14, *Paris Symposium on Radio Astronomy,* ed. R. N. Bracewell, Stanford University Press, Stanford (1959).

6. Mayer, C. H., Radio Emission of the Moon and Planets, Chapter 12, *The Solar System, Vol. III: Planets and Satellites,* ed. G. P. Kuiper and B. M. Middlehurst, University of Chicago Press, Chicago, 1961.

7. Salomonovich, A. E., Paper presented at the International Astronomical Union Symposium No. 14, Leningrad, USSR, December 1960, to be published by Cambridge University Press, England.

8. Cudaback, D. D., Thermal Emission of the Moon at 10 cm Wavelength, to be submitted to the *Astrophys. J.*

9. Elsmore, B. E., Radio Observations of the Lunar Atmosphere, Paper 6, *Paris Symposium on Radio Astronomy,* ed. R. N. Bracewell, Stanford University Press, Stanford, 1959.

10. Kellogg, W. W., and C. Sagan, The Atmospheres of Mars and Venus, a report of the Space Science Board, *Publication 944*, National Academy of Sciences—National Research Council, Washington, D. C. (1961).

11. Öpik, E. J., The Aeolosphere and Atmosphere of Venus, *J. Geophys. Res.*, **66**, 2807–2819 (1961).

12. Burke, B. F., Radio Observations of Jupiter. I, Chapter 13, *The Solar System, Vol. III: Planets and Satellites,* ed. G. P. Kuiper and B. M. Middlehurst, University of Chicago Press, Chicago, 1961.

13. Gallet, R. M., Radio Observations of Jupiter. II, Chapter 14, *The Solar System, Vol. III: Planets and Satellites,* ed. G. P. Kuiper and B. M. Middlehurst, University of Chicago Press, Chicago, 1961.

14. Smith, A. G., Radio Spectrum of Jupiter, *Science*, **134**, 587–595 (1961).

15. Radhakrishnan, V., and J. A. Roberts, Polarization and Angular Extent of

the 960-Mc/sec Radiation from Jupiter, *Phys. Rev. Letters*, **4**, 493–494 (1960).

16. Egan, R. D., and A. M. Peterson, Auroral Noise at HF, *J. Geophys. Res.*, **65**, 3830–3832 (1960).

17. Pawsey, J. L., and R. N. Bracewell, *Radio Astronomy*, Oxford University Press, London, 1955.

18. Smerd, S. F., Radio-Frequency Radiation from the Quiet Sun, *Australian J. Sci. Res.*, **A3**, 34–59 (1950).

19. Wild, J. P., Solar Radio Spectroscopy, *Rend. Scuola Intern. Fis.*, *XII Corso*, 296–312 (1960).

20. Pettingill, G. H., Lunar Studies, Chapter 10, *Radar Astronomy*, ed. J. V. Harrington and J. V. Evans, McGraw-Hill, New York (in press).

21. Senior, T. B. A., and K. M. Siegel, Radar Reflection Characteristics of the Moon, Paper 5, *Paris Symposium on Radio Astronomy*, ed. R. N. Bracewell, Stanford University Press, Stanford, 1959.

22. Leadabrand, R. L., R. B. Dyce, A. Fredriksen, R. I. Presnell, and J. C. Schlobohm, Radio Frequency Scattering from the Surface of the Moon, *Proc. IRE*, **48**, 932–933 (1960).

23. Yaplee, B. S., N. G. Roman, K. J. Craig, and T. F. Scanlan, A Lunar Radar Study at 10-cm Wavelength, Paper 4, *Paris Symposium on Radio Astronomy*, ed. R. N. Bracewell, Stanford University Press, Stanford, 1959.

24. Price, R., P. E. Green, Jr., T. J. Goblick, R. H. Kingston, L. G. Kraft, Jr., G. H. Pettingill, R. Silver, and W. B. Smith, Radar Echoes from Venus, *Science*, **129**, 751–753 (1959).

25. Evans, J. V., and G. N. Taylor, Radio Echo Observations of Venus, *Nature (London)*, **184**, 1358–1359 (1959).

26. Kotelnikov, V., and I. Shklovsky, *Izvestia*, Moscow, USSR, May 11, 1961.

27. Pettingill, G. H., Paper presented at XII International Astronautical Congress, Washington, D. C., October 4, 1961.

28. Papers presented at the session, Exploration of the Solar System by Radar and Radio Astronomy, XII International Astronautical Congress, Washington, D. C., October 4, 1961.

29. Eshleman, V. R., R. C. Barthle, and P. B. Gallagher, Radar Echoes from the Sun, *Science*, **131**, 329–332 (1960).

30. Abel, W. G., J. H. Chisholm, P. L. Fleck, and J. C. James, Radar Reflections from the Sun at Very High Frequencies, *J. Geophys. Res.*, **66**, 4303–4307 (1961).

CHAPTER 6

EXPLORING THE SOLAR SYSTEM WITH SPACE PROBES

ALBERT R. HIBBS

Jet Propulsion Laboratory

California Institute of Technology

Under the direction of the National Aeronautics and Space Administration, work has begun on a series of spacecraft intended to explore the moon and planets. These spacecraft are designed to carry a variety of instrumentation to the moon or the target planet, to conduct the required series of measurements automatically, and to return the resulting information to earth by radio link.

Eventually, human explorers will land on these other bodies to participate directly in this exploration program. However, for the first several years data will be obtained by the use of remote automatic instrument systems. It is the purpose of this chapter to describe the scientific objectives of this exploration program, some of the specialized instrumentation that is being developed to meet these objectives, and the spacecraft designed to carry these instrument systems.

6-1 THE LUNAR PROGRAM

Introduction

The surface of the moon looks quite different from the surface of the earth. The level maria are more extensive than any equally level area on the earth's surface, and the lunar craters, the most typical of the moon's markings, are far more extensive and developed than any similar markings on the earth. On the other hand, the moon has no extensive mountain chains such as those found on earth; it is, of course, completely without liquid water on its surface, and shows no sign of any past erosion by moving water.

Origin of the lunar features has been a subject of controversy ever since they were first observed in detail by Galileo about 350 years ago. In his dialogues on the two chief world systems Galileo described the surface of the moon (1):

> The prominences there are mainly very similar to our most rugged and steepest mountains, and some of them are seen to be drawn out in long tracts of hundreds of miles. Others are in more compact groups and there are also many detached and solitary rocks, precipitous and craggy. But what occur most frequently there are certain ridges (I shall use this word because no more descriptive one occurs to me), somewhat raised, which surround and enclose plains of different sizes and various shapes but for the most part circular. In the middle of many of these there is a mountain in sharp relief and some few are filled with a rather dark substance similar to that of the large spots that are seen with the naked eye; these are the largest ones, and there are a very great number of smaller ones, almost all of them circular.

In the three centuries since the days of Galileo we have improved our astronomical techniques to the extent that we now have an order-of-magnitude better in resolution for details on the surface of the moon than was available in those first observations. Nevertheless, we are still seriously limited and cannot resolve photographically surface features smaller than approximately 1 km. (Trained observers have reported visual observations with a resolution of about half this distance.)

Most of our knowledge of the nature of the moon has resulted indirectly from an increased understanding of geophysical phenomena which affect the development of any large body. But here again our knowledge has really not progressed far in comparison with the extent of what we do not know.

The history of our understanding of the moon is well exemplified by the history of the controversy surrounding the nature of the lunar craters. For many years these craters were thought to be the remnants of massive lunar volcanoes. Although no volcanic craters on the earth ever reached such a size, there were a few formations on the surface of the earth called "crypto volcanoes" that seemed to show a similarity in shape and size to the craters on the moon, at least if one took into account the erosion effects on the earth.

Although meteorite impact was occasionally suggested as an alternate to volcanoes for the production of lunar craters (the splashed appearance of the rayed craters has always been suggestive), the first serious discussion of the impact phenomena in crater formation on the moon was given by G. K. Gilbert (2), then director of the U. S. Geologic Survey, in 1898.

Since that time, the impact theory has steadily been gaining ground at the expense of the volcano theory. It is rather interesting to note that astronomers had always used vulcanism, a geologic process, to account for lunar craters; but when this geologist came into the field he used an astronomical process, the fall of meteorites, for his explanation.

In recent years the impact theory has gained even more ground by the study of meteorite impact sites on the surface of the earth. The most famous is Canyon Diablo or Meteorite Crater near Winslow, Arizona. Not only have numerous pieces of meteoritic iron been found in the vicinity of this formation but also the high-pressure silicate mineral coesite has been discovered in many of the shattered rocks near the crater.

Several other less obvious impact craters have been found around the world, several of which were shown up by analysis of airplane photographs. In fact, many of the "crypto volcanoes," once used to help justify a volcanic explanation for the lunar craters, are now being identified on earth as the result of meteorite impact. It is interesting to note that many of these crypto (or "hidden") volcanic structures occur in sedimentary rock—a situation that has always been difficult to explain.

In the vicinity of these meteorite craters on the earth coesite and shatter cones (or "astroblemes" as Dietz has identified them) have been reported (3, 4).

Of course, there are still some formations on the moon that appear to require a volcanic origin. For example, there are linear arrays of small craters that might be difficult to explain as the result of random meteorite impacts and might more sensibly be described as volcanoes along a surface crack. There are small rounded domes (small compared to other resolvable lunar formations, i.e., 5 km across or less), some with a visible indentation in the top, which appear to be volcanoes. But even in these cases explanations have been offered to show how these formations could be the result of impact phenomena (5, 6).

Even though our attitude toward lunar craters has changed, beginning with Gilbert, this change has not resulted from more detailed observations of the moon but rather from a more thorough investigation of geophysical processes and geologic materials here on the earth. Our observations of the moon are constrained not only by the 240,000 miles of distance separating us but also by the turbulent blanket of atmosphere which limits the resolution of even our most strategically placed telescopes. Thus the spacecraft that will be flown to the moon in the NASA Lunar Program will have an essentially unexplored region to work in.

The Ranger spacecraft

The program of lunar exploration will be initiated with the Ranger series of spacecraft. The first two (Ranger 1 is shown in Figure 6-1)

Figure 6-1   The Ranger 1 spacecraft in its open preflight condition.

were built for development flights of the many engineering innovations involved in the Ranger design. The Ranger is an attitude-controlled vehicle which derives its electrical power from solar batteries and communicates with the earth by means of a 4-ft parabolic directional antenna on the spacecraft and the 85-ft diameter receivers of the deep space instrumentation facilities at Goldstone, California, Woomera, Australia, and Johannesburg, South Africa.

The first two Rangers were launched during the third quarter of 1961. Malfunctions in the second stage of the launching rocket prevented these spacecraft from achieving the intended orbit with an apogee at a distance from the earth of approximately 1 million km. Nevertheless, both spacecraft behaved properly under the more limiting conditions of the obtained near-earth orbit at an altitude of between 100 and 200 miles above the surface.

In its structural concept, the Ranger is divided into two major portions. First is the hexagonal-base structure (Figure 6-2), to which are attached the solar cell panels and the directional antenna. Around

Figure 6-2 The hexagonal base structure of the Ranger spacecraft showing the electronic equipment boxes with surfaces plated and painted to maintain radiative temperature control. Two sets of proportional counters mounted in cylindrical "telescope" arrays can be seen on the upper surface of the right-hand box.

this hexagonal base are six boxes containing electronic components of the several subsystems of the Ranger. The exterior surfaces of these boxes are treated with the appropriate paint or plating to maintain proper temperature control. Attached on the forward or upper section of this hexagonal base is a superstructure (Figure 6-3) which contains most of the scientific experiments and carries on its forward end an omnidirectional antenna designed to give telemetered data on the behavior of the system in case the attitude-control subsystem should fail to point the directional antenna at an earth-based receiver.

Several scientific experiments (7) were carried on the first two Rangers designed to take advantage of its intended distance from earth and comparatively long flight time (2 or 3 months). Of course, the near-earth orbit actually achieved by the launching rocketry prevented the gathering of useful information from these experiments.

The second group of Rangers, numbers 3 through 5, is designed to make close-up observations of lunar characteristics and land a working instrument on the surface of the moon designed for a two-month operation. The design of this group of Rangers evolves in a natural manner from the first two. The basic structure, including the six equipment boxes, the solar panels, and the directional antenna, remains essentially unchanged, but the superstructure is replaced. For the Ranger 3, 4, and 5 design, as shown in Figure 6-4, the superstructure is replaced by a combination of retrorocket and survival sphere to be detached from the basic bus at an appropriate altitude above the moon. At this point the retrorocket is ignited to slow down the surviving sphere to a speed at which the equipment can survive the resulting impact.

The scientific subsystem of this group of Ranger spacecraft (8) involves four types of measurements of lunar characteristics. A gamma-ray spectrometer will measure the intensity of gamma rays in the spectro region characteristic of potassium-40 emissions. This spectrometer involves a blank crystal, a photomultiplier, and a pulse-height analyzer to record the intensity of gamma rays with energies around this line.

This gamma-ray information will give us our first direct measurement of the chemical nature of the surface of the moon. Crustal rocks of the earth contain considerably more radioactive material, such as potassium 40, than the rock of meteorites. It is assumed that this indicates a differentiation of crustal material on the earth which has resulted from the thermomigration of the heat-producing radioactive rocks upward, whereas the average composition of the earth is presumed to be the same as the average composition of meteorites.

Figure 6-3 Superstructure of the Ranger 1 with the proof-test model of the Ranger 1 spacecraft in the background. Near the bottom of the superstructure is an array of particle counters. The small sphere near the upper end of the truss structure is an ionization chamber. A rubidium vapor magnetometer is housed within the aluminum-covered truncated cone at the top of the superstructure; an omnidirectional transmitting and receiving antenna is at the upper end.

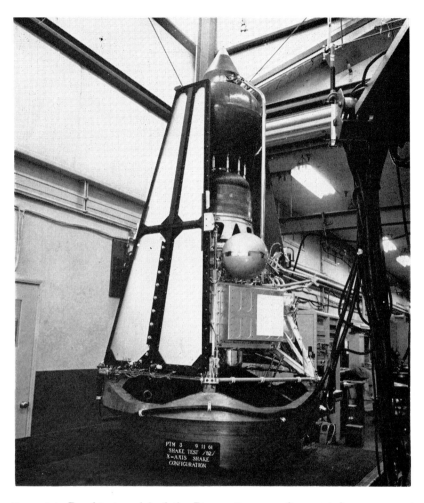

Figure 6-4 Proof-test model of the Ranger 3 spacecraft mounted on a support fixture for a vibration test. A conical omnidirectional antenna is at the upper end. The large ball below it is a balsa impact-absorbing shell containing in the center a single-axis seismometer, together with its power supply, amplifier, transmitter, temperature control, righting mechanism, and antenna assembly. Below that is a solid-propellant retrorocket motor in a fiberglass case. The sphere to the right and below that contains the detector of the gamma-ray spectrometer.

In order, then, to estimate whether the moon has had a thermodynamic history similar to that of the earth, it is of great importance
to know whether the surface of the moon also contains a higher
abundance of potassium 40 than the meteorites.

The gamma-ray spectrometer is located on a boom that will be
extended out away from the spacecraft after the completion of the
midcourse rocket maneuver—a course-corrective action designed to
direct the Ranger toward the moon on a preselected impact trajectory.

As the spacecraft approaches the moon, its orientation will be
changed. Instead of having its head end pointed toward the sun
(as is required for adequate illumination of the solar panels), the
spacecraft will be reoriented so that its base will be aimed directly
at the moon. In this position, using a special Cassegrain telescope
(Figure 6-5), it will take a series of vidicon photographs of the surface and relay them back over the communication link once every

Figure 6-5 The Cassegrain telescope of Ranger 3 used in conjunction with the
vidicon television tube to photograph the surface of the moon. The main structural component of the telescope is a fused quartz tube 8 in. in diameter which
maintains the proper spacing between the primary and secondary mirrors.

13 sec. This will result in a series of pictures of increasing resolution and decreasing surface area coverage.

The target material of the vidicon is designed to hold the image for well over the 10 sec necessary for the readout—a readout time required by the limited bandwidth of the communication system. During the remaining 3 sec of the vidicon cycle, the image will be erased to prepare for the next photograph.

The first of the series of more than 100 photographs will show lunar-surface features at a resolution similar to that now available in earth-based photographs. However, the last photograph, taken at an altitude of 50 to 100 km above the surface and read out during the remaining stable portion of the spacecraft flight should show a picture approximately two orders of magnitude better in resolution than any now available. The spacecraft impact trajectory is designed so that each succeeding picture will overlap that preceding.

During this approach trajectory a radar altimeter will be in operation. The fundamental purpose of this altimeter is to trigger the retrorocket for the survival sphere at the appropriate altitude. However, the strength of the return signal to the radar will be telemetered to give some indication of the reflectivity characteristics of the area of the moon directly under the spacecraft. This information will help us to interpret radar measurements on the moon made from the surface of the earth.

The flight time to the moon will be approximately 66 hr. At the conclusion of this period, at an altitude of approximately 20 km, the radar altimeter will signal the initiation of the retrorocket sequence. The retrorocket and survival capsule will detach from the bus section of the spacecraft, spin up around its longitudinal axis in order to maintain its aiming direction, and fire. At the conclusion of burning of the solid propellant retromotor, the survival capsule should be at an altitude of approximately 1100 ft above the surface, traveling with zero velocity in relation to the surface of the moon. At this point it will be detached from the retrorocket and fall freely the rest of the way. The instrumentation in the sphere is surrounded by a thick shell of balsa wood (Figure 6-6) designed to withstand the estimated impact which will occur at a speed of approximately 125 mph. If the retrorocket does not perform exactly according to specifications, the burn-out altitude could be either above or below the designed 1100 ft, and the burn-out speed could differ from zero. In this case the impact speed could vary significantly from the design value of 125 mph. The survival sphere is designed to withstand im-

Figure 6-6 A portion of the shock-absorbing structure designed to protect the seismometer and its associated equipment at impact with the lunar surface.

pacts of several thousand g's which might result from an impact speed some 300 mph on reinforced concrete. The instrument system designed to withstand this impact contains a single-axis seismometer. It contains also power supply, amplifier, transmitter, temperature-control system, and righting mechanism. The complete package is designed to detect and transmit lunar seismic data for a period of 1 to 2 months.

The natural seismicity of the moon, if any, will tell us a great deal about the moon's structure and current thermoactivity. Even without internal seismic disturbances, the seismometer may still obtain detectable signals from the impact of meteorites in its vicinity. Considering the average flux of meteorites in the vicinity of the earth-moon system, it is estimated that during the 1-to-2-month operating time of the seismometer, the chances are 9 out of 10 that a meteorite of sufficient size will land close enough to give a detectable signal. The detailed nature of the resulting vibrations from any seismic source, meteoritic or internal, will give information on the thickness of any surface layer in the vicinity of the seismometer.

The Ranger series will continue with four more flights, numbers 6 through 9, devoted to the acquisition of detailed photographic information on the lunar surface. For these spacecraft, the superstructure will be replaced by a structure containing a battery of television cameras and a pair of transmitters. These cameras will operate sequentially during the last portion of a lunar impact trajectory and are designed to give information on small segments of the lunar surface to a resolution of at least a fraction of a meter. No attempt at survival will be made for any instrumentation in this series of flights, and the experiment will terminate when the spacecraft impacts the moon.

The Surveyor spacecraft

The Surveyor spacecraft (Figure 6-7) is designed to land softly a package of instruments for a detailed inspection of the lunar surface. This spacecraft, complete with its loaded retrorocket, will weigh more

Figure 6-7 A model of the Surveyor spacecraft with landing legs extended and a main retrorocket motor (the large gold sphere in the center with the gold nozzle) still attached. In this photograph two omnidirectional antenna booms are shown extended and the solar panel and antenna array at the top of the spacecraft are shown partially unfolded, although in actual operation the deployment of these components would await landing on the surface of the moon.

than a ton—approximately three times the size of the Ranger space-craft. Its instrument system contains a range of geophysical and geochemical devices intended to make a very detailed analysis of the portion of the lunar surface under and immediately around the Surveyor landing site.

It will also contain a number of television cameras designed for panoramic, stereoscopic observation of the surrounding lunar terrain and for close-up mineralogical investigation of the material immediately below the Surveyor.

The physical nature of the lunar surface will be investigated by an array of separate devices. These devices will measure the shear strength and bearing strength of the lunar surface material as well as its density, thermoconductivity, magnetic susceptibility, and acoustical propagation speed.

The Surveyor spacecraft will be able to extend its analysis to material below the surface of the moon. It carries a drill designed to penetrate 18 to 60 in. below the surface, depending on the hardness of the surface material. As the drill penetrates into the crust, the fragments of crustal material from the drill hole are carried upward and distributed to several instruments for chemical and mineralogical analysis.

The investigation of lunar seismicity, which is begun with the Ranger spacecraft, will be continued with the Surveyor. A larger, and therefore inherently more sensitive, seismometer can be carried by the Surveyor. The additional weight-carrying capacity of the Surveyor makes possible the inclusion of a three-axis seismometer in contrast to the single-axis instrument carried in the Ranger capsule.

Both the steady-state and variable components of the moon's magnetic field will be measured by a magnetometer carried by this spacecraft. In addition, the radiation level near the moon's surface and the density of the rare lunar atmosphere will be measured by Surveyor equipment.

The availability of a soft-landing spacecraft such as the Surveyor permits the inclusion of a wide variety of instrumentation too delicate for the rough-landing techniques of the Ranger. To take advantage of this soft-landing feasibility, a number of different instruments are being designed and developed. For example, a gas chromatograph is now under development which might be able to detect the existence of complex molecules in lunar surface material. This would, of course, be of great importance if organic molecules were to be found on the moon. Although actual living organisms are not likely there, it is possible that organic molecules could have developed on the surface or have been deposited there by the fall of carbonaceous chondrites or could result from spores drifting through space after having escaped from some planet with an active life form (perhaps the earth?). This last possibility is, of course, the panspermia hypothesis suggested more than half a century ago by Arrhenius to account for the origin of life on earth.

The discovery of organic substances on the surface of the moon will not in itself resolve the conflict between various theories on the origin of life on earth. Instead, it will point the way toward more detailed chemical analyses of whatever molecules are so discovered. This subsequent detailed analysis of any such material might indeed be a major step in man's search for the secret of life's beginning.

To analyze the chemical and mineral nature of lunar material, X-ray fluorescence spectrographs and X-ray diffractometers are being developed. These instruments must operate remotely and automatically on a power supply considerably more limited than that which is customarily employed with earth-based X-ray equipment. Furthermore, they must be able to accept samples that can be prepared by reliable, remote, automatic equipment from the material removed by the lunar drill. In spite of these considerable problems, the developers of these instruments are confident that they will operate satisfactorily and give us an accurate picture of the elemental nature of the lunar material over a wide range of important constituents.

An effort is under way to develop a remote-operating petrographic microscope with a television readout. The availability of such an instrument would considerably enhance our ability to identify lunar material and to relate it to similar material—if any—found here on earth.

The physical nature of the lunar surface is also of primary importance, not only for an understanding of the nature of the moon, its origin, and its history, but also for the adequate design of subsequent vehicles designed to roam over the lunar surface—vehicles that will eventually carry a man. In order to conduct such experiments, the techniques of soil measurement are being applied to the development of remote equipment to measure the shear strength, bearing strength, and hardness of the lunar surface.

The lunar orbiter

The first Surveyor soft-landed vehicles will be stationary and will make a careful analysis of the lunar material in their immediate vicinity. Their range of exploration will be limited by the mechanical reach of the various arms and booms that deploy the instruments. Of course, the television cameras on the Ranger will be able to survey the lunar surface as far as visual range from the stationary Surveyor permits.

A series of several Surveyors will be flown, so that a number of separate sites will receive thorough investigation. Then, in order to relate the results of these stationary measurements to conditions over the rest of the moon, it is expected that the Surveyor soft-lander will be complemented by the operation of a lunar orbiter. A series of such orbiters are now in the planning stage.

It is intended that these lunar orbiters be placed in a fairly well-controlled circular orbit a few hundred kilometers above the surface. In order to complete a survey of the moon, the orbiter would have to operate for one lunar period—about a month. During this time, if it were launched into a polar orbit, it would have made one pass over all portions of the lunar surface twice—once in sunlight and once in shadow. During the sunlight passage it could photograph the lunar surface and take the spectral measurements that depend on reflected sunlight. The gamma-ray analysis of the surface material could be carried out over the complete orbit, regardless of sunlight conditions.

The lunar orbiter is an extremely powerful tool for completing a thorough survey of the lunar surface. It is to be compared to the airplane (rather than a satellite) in the survey of the surface of the earth. Since no clouds or other atmospheric disturbances will impede the observation of the surface from the orbiter, the surface resolution that could be obtained from photographs taken with an orbiter depends primarily on the design of the photographic system.

Preliminary design studies have been carried out in an effort to determine the most efficient way to obtain and transmit to earth accurate photographs of the lunar surface.

In the case of airplane surveys of the surface of the earth, one of the major efforts concerns the processing of the resulting photographs for the creation of maps, etc. For the lunar orbiter, the same problem arises. A major portion of the lunar-orbiter photographic system will be the ground-data-processing facility. This may well involve the creation of a brand new skill—the lunar photo interpreter. It is very likely that lunar features, resolved on the scale of a few meters, will be so unlike any features occurring on earth, either natural or man made, that completely new approaches to photo interpretation will be required.

The Prospector

The title "Prospector" is used to apply to a class of spacecraft differing in two ways from the Surveyor and lunar orbiter. The Prospector is thought of as being larger than the Surveyor and thus would be launched with a larger booster; second, the Prospector is considered to involve primarily a surface-roving vehicle.

Within the presently defined plans, the Prospector class of lunar spacecraft should be operating at about the same time as the preliminary flights in the manned lunar program. For this reason it is natural to suspect that there will be close correlation between the Prospector spacecraft utilization and the lunar exploration required for landing-site survey and selection. It is also reasonable to suppose that the Prospector spacecraft design will be carried out in conjunction with the design of the manned lunar landing craft, since these two craft will share many design objectives and design problems.

No detailed plans have been made for the scientific experiments to be carried out with the Prospector vehicle. It is reasonable to assume that the experiments conducted with the Surveyor will be extended during the Prospector series; that is, with the roving Prospector vehicle, experiments similar to those in the stationary Surveyor can be conducted over a wide variety of lunar terrain. Of course, it is quite likely that the results of the Surveyor experiments will reveal unimagined problems that will dictate a different course for the scientific program of the Prospector mission.

6-2 THE PLANETARY PROGRAM

Introduction

If the several objectives of the lunar exploration program were to be grouped together into one subject of natural philosophy, then its title would be, "The Question of the Origin of the Solar System," for we expect to find written on the surface of the moon the early history of the formation of the planets. Such a history was undoubtedly written on the surface of the earth, but in the subsequent 5 billion years the earth's crust has been so overturned, so worn away, and so modified that this record is now forever lost. On the moon, where we expect geological forces to have been much less active, this record very likely still remains, awaiting our detailed examination.

In this same sense, the objectives of our first step in exploring the planets can also be grouped into a single fundamental subject of natural philosophy, and that is, "The Search for the Origin of Life."

It is not likely that we will find the origin itself, or even the history of the origin, on any other planet in the same sense that the history of the solar system's formation can now be seen on the surface of the moon. Rather, we hope to find in the life form of another planet one more example of the way in which life can grow.

In spite of the many forms that life appears to take on the surface of the earth, the difference between a sea slug and a sequoia tree is really no more than a variation in the structure of the fundamental genetic molecule desoxyribonucleic acid (DNA). This molecule carries from generation to generation the genetic information that enables the species to reproduce itself continually, and its variations account for the variations between the species and between the cells in an individual.

How this is accomplished, of course, we do not yet understand, but we have at least identified this basic chemical constituent of all life on earth. So, in the most basic terms, there is only one form of life on earth, and thus we know of only one way in which nature can create living matter. On Mars we might be able to find another form of life, and it is possible that we will find a second way in which nature can make life. If this is true, we will immediately double the number of examples we have of life forms.

Mars is chosen as an example because observations of this planet over many years are certainly indicative of some form, at least, of vegetable life on its surface. There is the well-known seasonal change in the dark markings; that is, a color change progressing from the poles toward the equator during the seasonal warming up of the particular hemisphere and the associated evaporation of the polar frost cap. There are the observations of large, new areas, thousands of square miles in extent, of sections of Mars that were light in color for many years and then within a few Martian years changed to dark—a modification possible for growing plants but extremely difficult for a geologic process. There is the ability of the dark areas to survive and "show through" after a planet-wide dust storm (at least "dust storm" seems the most likely explanation of the yellowish clouds that grow up and cover the planet from time to time). Finally there is the work of Sinton (9, 10), who observed the infrared spectrum of Mars in the region between 3 and 4 μ and found there clear evidence of absorption at wavelengths corresponding to the absorption of the hydrogen-carbon bond in a large organic molecule.

Of course, there are alternate explanations for these individual observations. But still there are no adequate explanations (at least in the writer's opinion) other than a life form, which can account for all of the observations. Certainly, the existence of life on Mars has not been proven, but its likelihood has been so well established that it is accepted as a reasonable basis for the fundamental mission objectives of our early Martian exploration program. Simply the unambiguous proof of the existence of life will be enough for the first step. After that, the chemical analysis of this life will follow.

Planning for the activities in the planetary program has one unique aspect that separates it from all other missile flight programs so far undertaken: the flight schedule is determined not simply by the booster development program or the availability of launching pads but primarily by the intractable orbits of the planets themselves. This implies that a slipped schedule would have truly shattering consequences.

Although, in principle, one could undertake a flight to a planet at any time, since trajectories can be computed with the known equations of motion for any geometry at all, the flight itself under almost all circumstances is hopelessly impractical. Except for a very short interval, the order of 1 or 2 months in as many years, the energy that a rocket would require in getting from here to there is just not available. However, during the practical launch interval (commonly called the "launch window") presently available booster rocket systems have the capability to launch a few hundred pounds toward either Mars or Venus.

The Mariner R

The first attempt to take advantage of this launch-vehicle capability will make use of a spacecraft called the Mariner R. It is planned to launch this spacecraft on an orbit that will take it past the planet Venus after a flight time of approximately 100 days. During its flight, the Mariner R will take measurements of the particle radiation in the space between the orbit of earth and the orbit of Venus and will also measure the magnetic field in this region. As it passes the target planet, microwave and infrared radiometers will scan back and forth over the surface.

The Mariner R is similar in many ways to the Ranger spacecraft. It has a hexagonal base structure, two panels of solar batteries, and a 4-ft-diameter parabolic antenna for communication with the earth. Its general appearance (Figure 6-8) is similar to the Ranger 1; however, the Mariner R weighs approximately half as much as the first Rangers and carries considerably fewer instruments.

The microwave radiometer uses a single parabolic reflector and two receivers: one at 13 mm and one at 19 mm. Microwave radiometric

Figure 6-8 A model of the Mariner R spacecraft with the parabolic reflector for the microwave radiometer located in the center of the structure.

measurements carried out from the surface of the earth have shown that Venus has an apparent temperature of several hundred degrees centigrade. At least in the longer wavelength region of several centimeters the radiating strength of Venus is so high that it requires such a temperature if this strength is due to radiations from the planetary surface. At shorter wavelengths, from a few millimeters down to the infrared, the radiative power of Venus corresponds to a considerably cooler temperature. The signal-to-noise ratio of these measurements is very poor because of the low strength of the energy radiated by Venus in this region and the great distance to the planet. Thus the probable error on these temperature measurements is considerable; that is, the order of 100°K in a total reading of 400 to 600°K. Nevertheless, the general trend of cooler temperatures at short wavelengths and hot temperatures at long wavelengths seems by now substantiated.

It is reasonable to believe that the difference between these two measurements is caused by the presence of the atmosphere of the planet; that is, at longer wavelengths the atmosphere is transparent and the surface itself is being detected. At the shorter wavelengths radiations from the surface are absorbed in the atmosphere, and it is the upper atmosphere, considerably colder than the surface, that is responsible for the detected radiation. The two wavelengths chosen for the Mariner R experiment correspond to the transition region between the short and long wavelength regimes of this experiment. Since the Mariner R will pass within approximately 10,000 to 20,000 km of the surface, the signal-to-noise ratio will be greatly enhanced for these radiometric measurements. Therefore, accurate readings can be obtained of the radiation in this critical wavelength region. Furthermore, the passage near Venus is close enough and the beam width of the antenna narrow enough (2 degrees between half-power points) that the distribution of temperature over the surface of the planet can be resolved. This resolution is beyond the capabilities of earth-based antenna systems. For example, limb brightening, if any, could be detected. One of the alternate theories to account for the high radiometric measurements of Venus is that these radiations come from a highly active ionosphere. If this theory is correct, then this comparatively close inspection of the disk should show limb brightening in these wavelength regions.

Two infrared radiometers with a 1-degree square window will also scan the surface in conjunction with the microwave radiometers. One of the IR detectors will be sensitive in the 8-to-9-μ and the other in the 10-to-10.8-μ region. The first region corresponds to a window in the CO_2 absorption spectra, and the second covers the weak 10.4-μ absorption band of CO_2.

It is possible that the cloud cover of Venus has breaks in it too small to be resolved by telescopes here on earth. Such breaks might be revealed by inspection from the Mariner R. However, an extremely simple lightweight device must be used, since at the range of Venus the operation of photographic or television equipment is quite beyond the capability of the Mariner R system. This is one of the reasons for the inclusion of the IR radiometers. As the instrument scans over the surface of the planet, the output of the two detectors will be compared. If they should follow each other, always in the same ratio, one would conclude that they are both looking at the top of an unbroken cloud layer, since the absorption band of CO_2 in the 10.4 region is too weak to respond to the amount of CO_2 above the clouds. If, on the other hand, points are noted in which the proportionality between the two detectors suddenly changes and then returns, one would conclude that the 8-to-9-μ detector has seen through a break in the clouds to the surface, unimpeded either by CO_2 or clouds, whereas the 10-to-10.8-μ detector, looking into the same cloud break, has seen only a little farther down to a point at which the optical depth of CO_2 in the Venus atmosphere (at least for the 10.4-μ absorption region) became appreciable.

In addition to the information gained from these comparative readings, the absolute value of the readings themselves will give information on the temperature distribution over the cloud layer to compare with the temperature reading obtained from the microwave radiometers.

The particle detectors and magnetometer operating in the vicinity of Venus should reveal any planet-centered magnetic field and any belts of trapped radiation.

The Mariner B

The Mariner B spacecraft will be a considerable advance over the Mariner R. The Mariner B will be launched with a larger vehicle and will more than two times outweigh the Mariner R. This will permit the inclusion of a larger family of instruments.

Like the Ranger and Mariner R spacecraft, it will rely on panels of solar batteries for its electric power and will communicate with the earth by a parabolic reflecting antenna. The possibility that future flights might carry a capsule for penetration into the atmosphere of either Venus or Mars is being investigated. Such a capsule could be detached at a considerable distance away from the target planet while both spacecraft and capsule were on an impact course. Thereafter the remaining spacecraft might be redirected onto a fly-by course by a maneuver rocket. The capsule would then enter the atmosphere of the planet and decelerate by aerodynamic drag to a point at which it could safely deploy a parachute for continued descent to the surface. During this final descent phase and after landing on the surface the capsule might communicate either directly with the earth or by relay through the parent spacecraft on its fly-by trajectory.

The increased size and weight of the Mariner B spacecraft makes

Figure 6-9 Prototypes of an infrared interferometer (*left*) and grating spectro-photometer of the Ebert type designed for possible inclusion in the Mariner B type of planetary spacecraft.

possible a considerable increase in the bandwidth of its communication system; it will also have the ability to store and process data on board for conservation of the bandwidth. Thus it will be possible to take television photographs of the planet from the comparatively close range of the fly-by. For Mars this capability is of primary importance.

Infrared and ultraviolet spectrometers now under development for spacecraft of the Mariner B series (Figures 6-9 and 6-10) can obtain much more detailed and extensive spectroscopic observations than the simple IR radiometers of the Mariner R. In addition, more extensive microwave radiometers have been designed for observation of the Venus surface in several different wavelengths (Figure 6-11). Field experiments can be carried out with Mariner B spacecraft during its flight from earth to the target planet. This will permit an extensive and detailed survey of solar phenomena and their variations with distance from the sun.

Perhaps the most exciting aspect of the Mariner B is the possibility

Figure 6-10 An ultraviolet grating spectrophotometer of the Ebert design under development for possible inclusion in the Mariner B spacecraft series.

of including a landing capsule. If the surface of Venus is, indeed, as hot as the radiometric measurements indicate, then a landing capsule would probably not survive for any useful period of time on or near the Venus surface. Thus primary experiments for such a capsule would be designed to measure the characteristics of the Venus atmosphere during the capsule descent phase.

For Mars, however, the possibilities inherent in the capsule are more promising. One of the primary objectives of the national space program is the discovery and analysis of life on another planet. Certainly, Mars is the most likely prospect for such a discovery. It is this landing capsule that might well make such a discovery. Several ingenious devices are already under development to carry out this search for extraterrestrial life. One such device would collect samples of surface material, distribute them among various nutrient solutions, and then watch for any metabolic changes in the containers of solutions mixed with Mars material. Another device would observe dust particles with a TV-reading microscope. A third device would make use of gas chromatographic techniques to analyze organic molecules found either in the atmosphere or in the surface material.

Of course, one primary problem comes to mind immediately in relation to the search of extraterrestrial life. Regardless of the urgency of the planetary exploration program, we must be quite careful not to contaminate another planet with earthly bacteria or even with earthly viruses. This problem is far from simple. The sterilization of the spacecraft is a difficult and complex operation. It must be carried out in conjunction with all of the other operations concerned with the launching of the nation's largest guided missiles.

Figure 6-11 The microwave radiometer package under development for possible inclusion in the Mariner B planetary spacecraft series. Four receivers operate from feeds collecting energy from three parabolic reflectors. The 4-, 8-, 13-, and 19-mm regions are examined. Receiver electronics are mounted on the rear of the structural support of the antennas.

The problem is made even severer by the nature of the required sterilization. It is not enough simply to remove the disease bacteria that might be harmful to men; all bacteria must be removed. Furthermore, all complex organic molecules that might become viruses must also be removed. And who is to say what kind of organic molecule might be a virus for an unknown life form on the surface of Mars? Thus the determination of the sterilization requirements is almost as difficult as the sterilization operation itself. The scientists involved with this problem have done their best to combine imagination with practicality and have worked with the engineers to evolve a series of heat treatments and gaseous decontamination operations that will, hopefully, reduce to an acceptably small value the likelihood of accidental contamination of Mars life forms. Certainly, it would be a most tragic blunder if we were accidentally to harm or destroy that very extraterrestrial life form whose discovery is so important to us!

The Voyager

In the planetary program the Voyager occupies an analogous position to the Prospector of the lunar program. It is a title applied to a larger class of vehicles than the Mariners, and it is conceived of as involving a landing device including possibly a roving vehicle, at least in the case of Mars. The design of a Voyager class spacecraft for the surface exploration of Venus must, of course, await further measurements of the condition of the surface, particularly its temperature. As for the experiments that might be carried out for the Voyager spacecraft, there is, of course, no real limit that can be placed on it. Mars is a new world. It has one fourth the surface area of the earth, and, since it is likely that no appreciable fraction of it is covered with oceans, the dry-land area of Mars may be just as great as the dry-land area of the earth. Who can place a limit on the problems and possibilities of its exploration?

6-3 CONCLUSIONS

This completes the summary of the present plans for the exploration of the moon, the planets, and the space between them. It represents a first small step into the vast expanse of the solar system, yet it is an impressive step indeed. The equipment that will carry out the unmanned automatic exploration of Mars, for example, will undoubtedly be the most complex, sophisticated, reliable mechanism ever devised by man. In undertaking the conquest of space, we are not only setting out on an exploration program greater than any human beings have ever attempted in their earth-bound existence but we are doing so with the help of more advanced engineering techniques than have ever been employed in our earthly undertakings. It will be interesting to see which of these two facets results in the greater benefit—the natural phenomena that we will discover or the engineering techniques that we will develop to accomplish these discoveries.

REFERENCES

1. Galilei, Galileo, *Dialogue Concerning the Two Chief World Systems,* translated by Stillman Drake, University of California Press, Berkeley and Los Angeles, 1953.
2. Gilbert, G. K., The Moon's Face: A Study of the Origin of Its Features, delivered to the Philosophical Society of Washington, D. C., 1893.
3. Dietz, R. S., Astroblemes, *Scientific American,* **205,** No. 2, 51 (1961).
4. Cohen, A. J., T. E. Bunch, and A. M. Reid, Coesite Discoveries Establish Cryptovolcanics as Fossil Meteorite Craters, *Science,* **134,** No. 3490, 1624–1625 (November 17, 1961).
5. Cohen, A. J., Megashatter Cone Hypothesis of the Origin of Lunar Volcanoes, *Nature (London),* **192,** No. 4800, 346 (1961).
6. Hibbs, A. R., Lunar Arrays of Small Craters, *Planetary Space Sci.,* **8,** No. 2, 121 (November 1961).
7. Neugebauer, Marcia, *Scientific Experiments for Ranger 1 and 2,* Technical Report No. 32-55, Jet Propulsion Laboratory, Pasadena, California, January 3, 1961.
8. Washburn, H. W., *Scientific Experiments for Ranger 3, 4, and 5,* Technical Report No. 32-199, Jet Propulsion Laboratory, Pasadena, California, December 5, 1961.
9. Sinton, W. M., Further Evidence of Vegetation on Mars, *Science,* **130,** 1234–1237 (November 6, 1939).
10. Sinton, W. M., Spectroscopic Evidence for Vegetation on Mars, *Astrophys. J.,* **126,** No. 2, 231–239 (September 1957).

CHAPTER 7

DYNAMICS, COMPOSITION, AND ORIGIN OF GEOMAGNETICALLY TRAPPED RADIATION *

JAMES A. VAN ALLEN

State University of Iowa

One of the most interesting geophysical discoveries of recent years has been that made with the early American satellites Explorer I (Satellite 1958 Alpha) and Explorer III (Satellite 1958 Gamma). It was found (1, 2) that an immense region around the earth is occupied by a high intensity of charged particles (protons and electrons), temporarily "trapped" in the geomagnetic field. Detailed study of this radiation has been a major endeavor of the last few years by a group at the State University of Iowa, various other groups in the United States, and by Soviet IGY workers. Although knowledge of the trapped radiation is still incomplete, substantial progress has been made in observing and interpreting this new phenomenon (3, 4, 5, 6, 7, 8, 9, 10, 11, 12).

Understanding of the dynamics of the trapping of charged particles in the geomagnetic field has also been considerably advanced by the Argus experiments of August–September 1958. These experiments comprised the artificial injection of beta-decay electrons from the fission fragments of high-altitude detonations of small-yield atomic

* Edited by Alan Rosen, Space Technology Laboratories, Inc.

devices and the subsequent observation by Explorer IV (Satellite 1958 Epsilon), by sounding rockets and by other techniques of the geophysical effects produced (13). It is now established beyond all reasonable doubt that the observed radiation consists of charged particles trapped in the earth's magnetic field in the manner visualized by Poincaré, Störmer, and Alfvén in classical theoretical studies. The nature of the particles and their detailed energy spectra are much more difficult to establish conclusively. The purpose of this chapter is to present a historical summary of the experimental and theoretical aspects of the trapped radiation.

7-1 HISTORICAL SUMMARY

With the wisdom of retrospection, it may well be said that since 1905, or thereabouts, it has been clear that it is physically possible for electrically charged particles to be temporarily trapped in the geomagnetic field. Moreover, the well-known phenomena of the aurorae and geomagnetic storms have led various workers, over the years, to conjecture on the existence of trapped particles. The ring-current hypothesis by Chapman and Ferraro (14) was of this general nature, as were the auroral theories of Alfvén (15) and Martyn (16). Large fluxes of electrons having energies in the range of tens of kev were directly observed by the author and his associates in 1952, 1953, 1954, and 1955 by rocket experiments in the arctic (17) at altitudes of 60 to 110 km and in 1957 by further rocket experiments in the arctic and antarctic. A similar but much smaller effect of the same sort was observed by a Geiger tube in Sputnik II in early November 1957 (18). It was later suggested by these workers that the effect was due to low energy corpuscles arriving in bursts, presumably from the sun. Meanwhile Singer (19) had considered the motion of low-energy trapped electrons $(E \sim 10$ ev) and protons $(E \sim 20$ kev) according to the Alfvén theory and had suggested that the longitudinal drifts of these particles provided the microscopic foundation for the Chapman ring current. During late 1957 and early 1958 Christofilos (20) called attention to the fact that the geomagnetic field would act as a temporary trap for the charged decay products of cosmic-ray-produced neutrons emerging from the atmosphere, and he proposed a series of high-altitude atomic bomb bursts for the injection of energetic electrons into the geomagnetic field as an experimental test of this idea. He also gave a detailed theory of the rate of loss of trapped electrons into the atmosphere by multiple scattering. Unhappily all of this work of Christofilos was contained in classified documents and discussion of it was confined to a small segment of the scientific profession. Portions of it were released for publication considerably later (21), after successful conduct of the proposed experiments.

The first conclusive evidence of the existence of significant intensities of geomagnetically trapped particles was obtained by the author and his students by means of Geiger tubes flown in Explorers I and II in early 1958 (1, 2). The data from these two satellites showed the following in the latitude range ±30°:

1. The intensity of radiation up to some 600 km altitude was in good accord with that to be expected for cosmic rays only, when proper account was taken of the increasing opening angles of geomagnetically allowed cones with increasing altitude and of the concurrent shrinking of the solid angle subtended at the observing point by the solid earth (22).

2. Above some 800 km (this transition altitude being longitude- and latitude-dependent) the intensity of radiation increased rapidly with increasing altitude in a way totally inconsistent with cosmic-ray expectations.

3. At the higher altitudes ($\sim$2000 km) the true counting rate of a Geiger tube with a geometric factor of 17.4 cm^2 and with total shielding of about 1.5 gm/cm^2 of stainless steel (extrapolated range for electron of energy 3 Mev or range for protons of 30 Mev or 1/e transmission for 75 kev X rays) exceeded 25,000 counts/sec. Hence the omnidirectional intensity exceeded 1700 (cm^{2}sec)$^{-1}$ if the radiation consisted wholly of penetrating particles; or it exceeded some 10^8 (cm^{2}sec)$^{-1}$ if the radiation consisted wholly of electrons whose range was less than 1.5 gm/cm^2 but whose bremsstrahlung was sufficiently energetic to penetrate the absorber with little attenuation.

These observations were interpreted by the author (1) as conclusive evidence of the existence of large intensities of geomagnetically trapped, electrically charged particles on the following grounds:

1. The amount of atmosphere surmounted in the altitude range, say 600 to 1200 km, was less by many orders of magnitude than the wall thickness of the counter. Hence the great increase in intensity with increasing altitude could not have been due to the progressive decrease of atmospheric absorption but must have been due to mechanical constraint of the radiation—specifically by the geomagnetic field. The primary radiation being detected must have consisted of electrically charged particles.

2. The charged particles in question could not have been coming from a source remote from the earth by direct Störmer trajectories. It would have required an inconceivably well-adjusted particle momentum to have produced this altitude-dependence even at a single latitude; and even if this had been so at, say, the equator, the particles arriving at slightly higher latitudes would have reached down to much lower altitudes—contrary to the observations.

3. It was also regarded as quantitatively inconceivable that the radiation being detected was arriving directly from a distant source (e.g., the sun) and was penetrating so deeply into the geomagnetic field near the equator in the form of neutral, ionized gas; and even if it were that, it would be doing so at a rate that was independent of time.

The general nature of the observed results of the Iowa group was soon confirmed by two types of apparatus in Sputnik III, which was launched on May 15, 1958. One piece of apparatus was a shielded, cylindrical Na I scintillation crystal (40 by 39 mm in size) mounted on a photomultiplier tube. The counting rate of pulses corresponding to energy loss greater than 35 kev was telemetered, as was also the quasi-direct current to the anode and to the seventh dynode of the photomultiplier tube. The second set of apparatus comprised two thin ZnS (Ag activated, thickness 2 mg/cm^2) fluorescent screens covered with aluminum foils of thickness 0.8 and 0.4 mg/cm^2, respectively, and also mounted on photomultiplier tubes (23). The inclination of the orbit of Sputnik III was 65 degrees and the initial altitudes of perigee and apogee were 217 and 1878 km, respectively. The high intensity of radiation in the equatorial region was confirmed, a strip of radiation in excess of the cosmic-ray level was traversed in subauroral latitudes, and absolute intensities of a tentative nature were presented. The first American satellite to carry a system of radiation detectors designed with prior knowledge of the existence and approximate intensity and nature of the trapped radiation was Explorer IV, launched on July 26, 1958, into a 51-degree inclination orbit with initial perigee and apogee altitudes of 262 and 2210 km. The apparatus designed and built by the Iowa group comprised two small Geiger tubes having different shielding, a small disk of plastic scintillator on a photomultiplier tube for pulse counting, and a small Cs I detector covered by a 1 mg/cm^2 foil and also mounted on a photomultiplier tube for energy-flux measurement. This apparatus operated for about 8 weeks and yielded an enormous amount of data recorded on more than 4000 passes by a worldwide network of receiving stations. Many of the data are still under study, though several major papers have been published (3, 24, 25, 26, 27). Subsequent American satellites and space probes, which have been devoted in part at least to study of the geomagnetically trapped radiation, are the following, with launching date in parentheses: Explorer VI (August 7, 1959), Explorer VII (October 13, 1959), Injun (July 29, 1961), Pioneer I (October 11, 1958), Pioneer II (November 8, 1958), Pioneer III (December 6, 1958), Pioneer IV (March 3, 1959), Pioneer V (March 11, 1960); and a variety of smaller rockets and auxiliary scientific packages carried by military test rockets. Packages of emulsions on some of the flights in the final category have been recovered. The longest term series of observation is that by Explorer VII; some 1,500,000 workable data points have been obtained over a 16-month period. Soviet investigators have flown radiation measuring equipment on two deep space probes: Cosmic Rocket I (January 2, 1959) and Cosmic Rocket II (September 12, 1959) but have not reported further satellite measurements in this field since Sputnik III (May 15, 1958).

Thus there is now a large body of observational knowledge concerning energetic corpuscular radiation around the earth, obtained with a diversity of techniques. The following sections give a brief summary of what is known about various aspects.

7-2 THEORETICAL DEDUCTION PRIOR TO THE DISCOVERY OF THE RADIATION BELTS

In 1896 Birkeland (28) undertook the experimental study of the motion of cathode rays under the influence of the magnetic field of a relatively isolated magnetic pole and then of a magnetic dipole. The proper interpretation of the results obtained in the former case was given by Poincaré (29) by integrating the equation of motion of a charged particle in the field of a magnetic unipole. The laboratory phenomena produced by Birkeland in the latter case were of a much more complex character. They were suggestive of the large-scale geophysical phenomena of the polar aurorae and inspired Störmer to undertake the detailed theoretical study of the motion of electrically charged particles in the field of a magnetic dipole. This undertaking occupied much of Störmer's professional career (30).

The equation of motion of an isolated charged particle in a static magnetic field $\mathbf{B}$ is

$$\frac{d}{dt}\left(\frac{\mathbf{p}c}{Ze}\right) = \mathbf{v} \times \mathbf{B} \qquad (7\text{-}1)$$

wherein $\mathbf{p}$ and $\mathbf{v}$ are the vector momentum and velocity, respectively, of the particle, Ze is its electrical charge in esu and may be either positive or negative, and c is the speed of light. The scalar quantity pc/Ze is the magnetic rigidity R of the particle measured in units of electrical potential (ergs per unit charge if B is in gauss, and cgs units are used elsewhere; the value of the magnetic rigidity in volts is found by multiplying its value in cgs units by 300). The scalar magnitudes of $\mathbf{p}$, R, and $\mathbf{v}$ are seen to be constants of the motion.

Thus the differential equation of the spatial trajectory of the particle is

$$\frac{R}{B}\left(\frac{d\mathbf{v}_1}{ds}\right) = \mathbf{v}_1 \times \mathbf{B}_1. \tag{7-2}$$

In equation (7-2) $\mathbf{v}_1$ and $\mathbf{B}_1$ are unit vectors parallel to $\mathbf{v}$ and $\mathbf{B}$, respectively, and s is the arc length measured along the trajectory. All particles having the same magnetic rigidity R and a given $\mathbf{v}_1$ at a specified point in a specified magnetic field have identical spatial trajectories. The time rate of traversal of the trajectory is proportional to v. The general relationship among magnetic rigidity, momentum, velocity and kinetic energy E is

$$R \equiv \frac{pc}{Ze} = \frac{m_0 c^2}{Ze} \frac{\beta}{\sqrt{1 - \beta^2}} \frac{\sqrt{E^2 + 2E m_0 c^2}}{Ze}, \tag{7-3}$$

m_0 being the rest mass, $m_0 c^2$ being the rest energy, and β being equal to v/c.

The field of a magnetic dipole M is given by

$$B = -\operatorname{grad} \Omega = +\operatorname{grad}\left(\frac{M \sin \lambda}{r^2}\right), \tag{7-4}$$

where M is in the direction of the negative polar axis of a system of spherical coordinates, r, λ, ω.

For the motion of a charged particle in such a field, Störmer obtained a first integral of equation (7-2), which may be written

$$\sin A = \frac{\cos \lambda}{(r/b)^2} + \frac{2(\gamma/b)}{(r/b) \cos \lambda}. \tag{7-5}$$

In equation (7-5) A is the angle between the velocity vector of the particle and its projection on the meridian plane through the particle, $b \equiv \sqrt{ZeM/pc}$, and γ is an arbitrary constant of integration.

Equation (7-5) may be rewritten as follows:

$$\left(\frac{r}{b}\right) = \frac{\cos^2 \lambda}{-(\gamma/b) \pm \sqrt{(\gamma/b)^2 + \sin A \cos^3 \lambda}}. \tag{7-6}$$

It is found that bounded motion is dynamically possible if and only if (neglecting special cases of little practical importance)

$$-\infty < \left(\frac{\gamma}{b}\right) < -1.$$

Subject to this condition, there are two unconnected regions of possible motion (i.e., r is positive real):

Region I: $r_1 \le r \le r_2$ (bounded motion).

Region II: $r \ge r_3$ (unbounded motion).

Region I, hereafter referred to as the "trapping region," is bounded by two surfaces of revolution about the axis of the magnetic dipole, viz.:

$$\frac{r_1}{b} = \frac{\cos^2 \lambda}{-(\gamma/b) + \sqrt{(\gamma/b)^2 + \cos^3 \lambda}}, \tag{7-7}$$

$$\frac{r_2}{b} = \frac{\cos^2 \lambda}{-(\gamma/b) + \sqrt{(\gamma/b)^2 - \cos^3 \lambda}}. \tag{7-8}$$

The inner boundary of Region II is the surface of revolution:

$$\frac{r_3}{b} = \frac{\cos^2 \lambda}{-(\gamma/b) - \sqrt{(\gamma/b)^2 - \cos^3 \lambda}}. \tag{7-9}$$

The detailed trajectory of a particle can be found only by numerical integration. Nonetheless, equations (7-7), (7-8), and (7-9), provide essential information of a general nature.

Störmer was primarily interested in trajectories from infinity and devoted only brief attention to those lying in Region I. He has published a numerically calculated case of a bounded trajectory (31). A meridian projection of this trajectory is reproduced in Figure 7-1. It is, of course, understood that there is an accompanying motion in ω which is not discussed here.

For the case of isolated noninteracting charged particles moving in the field of a static magnetic dipole in a vacuum the Störmer theory of trapping has a certain measure of completeness. Given an adequate computational effort, the motion of a particle can be found to any degree of detail desired.

Yet if we enclose the dipole by an impenetrable sphere centered on the dipole in an effort to apply the theory to the real geophysical case, we are immediately confronted by an essential question to which

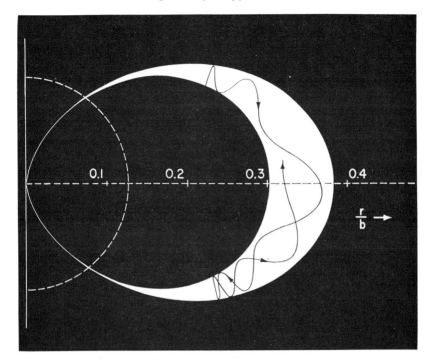

Figure 7-1 A diagram after Störmer (1907), illustrating the meridian projection of the spatial trajectory of an electrically charged particle in the field of a magnetic dipole and the boundaries of the rigorous trapping region.

(to the author's knowledge) no satisfactory theoretical answer has been given. The question is this:

As a given trapped particle performs latitudinal and longitudinal excursions within the trapping region, is there a minimum radial distance of approach to the dipole r_{min} that can be written in terms of the parameters of the problem?

A rigorous answer to this question is, of course, desirable. Even if such does not exist, a quantitative, practical assessment of the matter would be very helpful.

The many published trajectories of Störmer and of others entitle us to the impression, and the hope, that it should be possible to provide an assessment of at least statistical nature—in the form, for example, that a specified particle has a probability of 0.01 of approaching the dipole to a radial distance less than r_{min} in 10^7 latitudinal excursions. There are four evident modes of attack on the matter:

1. Further study of the dynamical problem in the spirit of the work of Störmer (31) and of Lematre and Vallarta (32) on trajectories of particles coming from infinity but with attention to the specific problem of trapped particles.

2. A statistical mechanical study (33).

3. An extensive program of numerical computation using modern techniques.

4. An experimental study.

The early magnetized terella experiments of Birkeland and the more recent ones of Bruche (34), Malmfors (35), Block (36), and Bennett (37) have provided beautiful experimental exhibitions of trajectories leading from and to infinity and of apparently bounded trajectories. Yet, because of gas scattering and other technical limitations, no definitive quantitative answer to the central question at hand has been provided. Among recent experimental techniques in this field perhaps the one that holds the greatest promise is that of Gibson, Jordan, and Lauer (38). These workers have succeeded in confining positrons from the decay of Ne^{19} within a cylindrical "magnetic mirror" machine in the laboratory for times of the order of 10 sec; and, since this trapping time was satisfactorily attributed to multiple scattering on the residual gas, it appears that the trapping time in a perfect vacuum must be at least an order of magnitude greater than 10 sec and might be infinite.

The Alfvén approximation

The tedium of the straightforward application of the Störmer trapping theory has been greatly reduced in many cases of practical importance by an approximate theory due to Alfvén. The Alfvén approximation provides a notably lucid and simple foundation for visualizing the motion of magnetically trapped particles and for discussing many detailed theoretical matters. Moreover, it provides an answer, under certain conditions, to the question posed at the beginning of this section.

The basis of this theory is paraphrased from Alfvén (15) as follows. In the case in which the path of a charged particle makes many loops in the region of a magnetic field that is of interest, the linear dimensions of one loop are small compared to the dimensions of the region; and during a single turn (in many practical cases) the particle is moving in an approximately homogeneous field. The detailed plotting of the trajectory by numerical methods is often beyond practicality. Moreover, such detail may be of little or no interest. Alfvén, therefore, proposes first to calculate the motion in a homogeneous field, then to treat the inhomogeneity as a perturbation.

In an homogeneous field the motion of a charged particle is a helical one, composed of a uniform motion parallel to the field B and a circular motion in a plane perpendicular to B. The center of the instantaneous circle is called the guiding center of the particle's trajectory. Thus the motion of the particle in an homogeneous field may be represented as equivalent of the uniform linear motion of its guiding center parallel to B. In the Alfvén approximation the spiraling particle is regarded as an elementary magnetic dipole (Amperian current loop). The motion of the guiding center is then the motion of this dipole. The scalar value of the dipole moment μ is the product of the area of the particle's loop projected perpendicular to B times the equivalent current flowing in the loop, viz.:

$$\mu = (\pi \rho^2)\left(\frac{Zev}{c}\right),$$

with ρ being the radius of the loop and v, the Larmor frequency. By equation (7-1) the magnetic moment is found to be

$$\mu = \frac{p_\perp^2 \sqrt{1 - \beta^2}}{2mB}. \tag{7-10}$$

In equation (7-10) $p_\perp = p \sin \alpha$, the component of p perpendicular to the magnetic field with α the angle between p and B; $\beta = v/c$ is a constant of the motion; and m is the rest mass of the particle.

In a uniform, time-stationary magnetic field μ is obviously a constant of the motion. Moreover, Alfvén has shown that even in a nonuniform, time-varying magnetic field μ is an adiabatic invariant of the motion provided

$$\rho \left|\frac{\operatorname{grad} \mathbf{B}}{\mathbf{B}}\right| \ll 1 \tag{7-11}$$

and

$$\frac{1}{B\nu} \left|\frac{\partial \mathbf{B}}{\partial t}\right| \ll 1. \tag{7-12}$$

The precise nature of the conservation of μ is important to its application to the discussion of geomagnetic trapping. This subject is under theoretical study, particularly by those engaged in the study of magnetic confinement in proposed controlled-thermonuclear devices. A crucial question is whether departures from constancy are of a nature to lead to loss of particles from a trapped condition within a finite time which may be specified in terms of the parameters of the physical situation. The question is similar to the one posed in the latter portion of section 7-1. This may be seen as follows:

If indeed μ is constant, then it follows from equation (7-10) that

$$\frac{\sin^2 \alpha}{B} = \text{constant.} \tag{7-13}$$

On a given line of force (along which the guiding center of a particle moves) B has its minimum value B_0 in the equatorial plane ($\lambda = 0°$). Hence α also has its minimum value α_0 there. The mirror point (or turning point) of the trajectory of the guiding center occurs at such a value of B that $\alpha = \pi/2$, or

$$B_M = \frac{B_0}{\sin^2 \alpha_0}. \tag{7-14}$$

Hence the motion of the guiding center is seen to be one of an oscillatory nature between two conjugate mirror points in opposite hemispheres, the scalar magnitude of B at the two being identical and given by equation (7-14), a result that is independent of the magnitude of the mass, charge, or energy of the particle provided that conditions (7-11) and (7-12) are met. The guiding center of the particle also undergoes a monotonic, though nonuniform, drift in longitude, which is discussed in a later section.

The rigorous theory of Störmer assures that a particle, once injected into a region in space defined at the beginning of this chapter, will forever execute bounded motion (in the absence of physical perturbation). This condition, of course, continues to apply to the motion discussed under the Alfvén approximation; that is to say, the motion of the particle is bounded between two known surfaces of revolution. Moreover, if μ is strictly conserved, the two loci of conjugate mirror points are small circles formed by the intersection of cones of half angle $\pi/2 \pm \lambda_M$ and having axes parallel to the dipole with the central curved surface of the Störmer trapping region. To the extent that μ is *not* conserved, the following questions arise:

1. Does the mirror latitude $\pm\lambda_M$ merely oscillate in a regular or in an irregular manner over a bounded finite range $\lambda_M' - \lambda_M''$ about a mean value which is obtained from equation (7-14)? If so, can the limits of the range λ_M' and λ_M'' be specified in terms of the parameters of the physical problem?

2. Or does the mirror latitude move progressively or diffuse away from some initial value λ_{M_0} such that after a sufficient number of latitudinal cycles it may have any value between $\pi/2$ and 0? If so, can a function $P(n, \lambda_M, \lambda_{M_0})$ be found which gives the probability that a mirror latitude λ_M will have been reached after n cycles?

As mentioned earlier, the experiments of Gibson et al. (38) and the independent ones of Rodionov (39) appear to provide the best available quantitative answers at present.

Further discussion of this matter is deferred to a later section. Meanwhile it is supposed that μ is conserved.

Characteristic times in geomagnetic trapping

The dynamical motion of geomagnetically trapped particles may be regarded as the composite of three forms of cyclic motion. The first of these, characterized by the Larmor period τ_1, is the circular motion of the particle around its guiding center. The second, with period τ_2, is the cyclic motion of the guiding center between mirror points. The third is the longitudinal drift of the guiding center around the earth with period τ_3.

Visualization of the motion and of the foundations for discussing departures from a simple quiescent state depend in an essential way on a knowledge of the magnitudes of the respective cyclic periods:

$$\tau_1 = \frac{2\pi mc}{ZeB\sqrt{1 - \beta^2}}, \tag{7-15}$$

irrespective of the pitch angle α. At radius r_0 in the plane of the geomagnetic equator, for example,

$$\tau_1 = 1.146 \times 10^{-6} \frac{mr_0^3}{Z\sqrt{1 - \beta^2}} \sec, \tag{7-16}$$

where m is the rest mass of the particle measured in electron masses and r_0 is measured in earth radii. For the present purpose it is sufficient to note that the Larmor periods of trapped electrons are in the general range 1 to 1000 μsec and of trapped protons in the general range 2 to 1000 msec.

$$\tau_2 = 4 \int_0^{\lambda_M} \frac{ds}{v_\parallel} \tag{7-17}$$

with ds the arc length along the line of force followed by the guiding center and $v_\parallel$ the component of velocity of the particle parallel to B. As a consequence of equation (7-13),

$$v_{\parallel} = v\sqrt{1 - (B/B_M)}.$$

Hence

$$\tau_2 = \frac{4}{v} \int_0^{\lambda_M} \frac{ds}{\sqrt{1 - B/B_M}}. \tag{7-18}$$

Hamlin, Karplus, Wik, and Watson (40) have reduced (7-18) to the form

$$\tau_2 = \frac{4r_0}{v} T(\alpha_0). \tag{7-19}$$

The dimensionless function $T(\alpha_0)$ increases monotonically from a value of 0.74 at $\alpha_0 = \pi/2$ to 1.38 at $\alpha_0 = 0$ and is approximated by $\tau(\alpha_0) = 1.30 - 0.56 \sin \alpha_0$. For the geomagnetic field

$$\tau_2 = 0.085 \frac{r_0}{\beta} T(\alpha_0) \text{ sec}, \tag{7-20}$$

with r_0 (in earth radii) being the equatorial radius of the line of force along which the guiding center oscillates.

Some representative values of τ_2 are given in Table 7-1.

In addition to the oscillatory motion of the guiding center from one hemisphere to the other, there is a drift in longitude of the guiding center due to the inhomogeneity of the field and to the centrifugal force on the guiding center as it moves along the curved lines of force. The drift rate is a fluctuating function of time but it is always in

TABLE 7-1

Period of Latitudinal Oscillation, τ_2, and the Radius of
Curvature ρ, for $r_0 = 2.0$ Earth Radii

Particle	Kinetic Energy	β	$\tau_2(\alpha_0 = \pi/2)$	pc	$\rho \begin{pmatrix} \alpha = \pi/2 \\ \lambda = 0 \end{pmatrix}$	
Electron	10 kev	0.195	0.64 sec	0.102 Mev	87	meters
Electron	100 kev	0.548	0.23	0.335	287	
Electron	1 Mev	0.941	0.13	1.422	1.22 km	
Proton	10 kev	4.61×10^{-3}	27.3	4.33 Mev	3.71 km	
Proton	100	1.46×10^{-2}	8.6	13.70	11.7	
Proton	1 Mev	4.61×10^{-2}	2.7	43.3	37.1	
Proton	10	0.146	0.86	137.4	118.0	
Proton	100	0.428	0.29	444.5	381	
Proton	1 Bev	0.875	0.14	1695	1451	

the same sense. The sense is opposite for particles of opposite sign. In the earth's field electrons drift toward the east, protons toward the west.

The drift velocity has been obtained by Alfvén and has been discussed further by Spitzer (41), by Welch and Whitaker (42), by Northrup and Teller (43), by Hamlin, Karplus, Vik, and Watson (40), and by Lew (44). Lew has put the results into particularly convenient form. The time τ_3 required for one complete drift around the earth is given by him

$$\tau_3 = 172.4 \frac{1 + \epsilon}{\epsilon(2 + \epsilon)} \frac{1}{mr_0} \frac{G}{F} \text{ min.} \qquad (7\text{-}21)$$

In equation (7-21) $\epsilon = [1/\sqrt{(1 - \beta^2)} - 1] = $ ratio of kinetic energy of the particle to its energy, m is the rest mass of the particle in units of the rest mass of the electron, r_0 is the equatorial radius of the line of force along which the guiding center is moving in units of the earth's radius, and G/F is the ratio of the drift period of particles mirroring at λ_M to that for particles mirroring at $\lambda_M = 0$. G/F is of the order of unity and is a function of λ_M only. It is tabulated in Table 7-2 and plotted in Figure 7-2.

Figure 7-3 shows the "longitudinal drift function" $r_0\tau_3(F/G)$ as a function of kinetic energy for electrons and protons. As remarked by

TABLE 7-2

(After J. S. Lew)

λM	G/F	λM	G/F
Radians		Radians	
0.0	1.000	1.0	1.366
0.1	1.007	1.1	1.406
0.2	1.028	1.2	1.440
0.3	1.060	1.3	1.467
0.4	1.098	1.4	1.487
0.5	1.141	1.5	1.498
0.6	1.186	$\pi/2$	1.500
0.7	1.232		
0.8	1.278		
0.9	1.323		

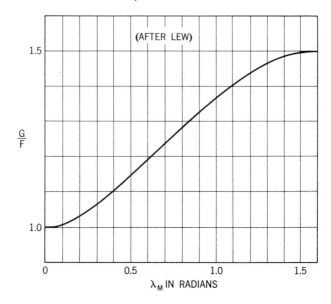

Figure 7-2 The function G/F (after Lew) versus mirror latitude used with Figure 7-3 in finding the longitudinal drift function.

Lew, the longitudinal drift period for an electron is always greater than that for a proton of the same kinetic energy but never more than by a factor of two.

Larmor radii of trapped particles

It is often convenient in considering perturbations of trapped particles to have ready reference to the magnitudes of Larmor radii of protons and electrons of various energies in the earth's field. Hence

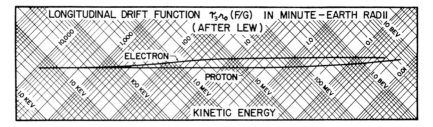

Figure 7-3 A diagram for finding the longitudinal drift period τ_3 for electrons and protons of various energies on magnetic shells cutting the equator at radial distance r_0.

a brief summary is included in this section. It follows from equation (7-1) that

$$\rho = \frac{p_\perp c}{eB} = \frac{pc \sin \alpha}{eB}, \qquad (7\text{-}22)$$

with e in electrostatic units, pc in ergs, ρ in centimeters, and B in gauss. For a given momentum particle, ρ is proportional to $\sin \alpha$.

For the purposes of obtaining representative numerical values, equation (7-22) is specialized to the geomagnetic equator and to $\alpha = \pi/2$:

$$\rho = 107.0 r_0{}^3 \, pc \text{ meters.} \qquad (7\text{-}23)$$

In equation (7-23) r_0 is measured in earth radii and pc in Mev. Sample values are given in Table 7-1.

7-3 THE ROLE OF ADIABATIC INVARIANTS IN GEOMAGNETIC TRAPPING

There are three adiabatic invariants of trapped particle motion associated respectively with the three classes of cyclic motion discussed above.

The first is the Alfvén magnetic moment μ. A special consequence of the conservation of μ is that the locus of the mirror points of a particle's motion lies on a surface of constant scalar $B(= B_M)$.

The second is often called the longitudinal integral invariant. It is the action integral of the oscillating motion of the guiding center between mirror points, viz.:

$$J = \int_M^{M^*} P_\| ds, \qquad (7\text{-}24)$$

the line integral being taken along the magnetic line of force between the mirror point M and its conjugate M^*. The conservation of J was first recognized by Rosenbluth (43). It is convenient to rewrite equation (7-24) as

$$J = P \int_M^{M^*} \sqrt{1 - B/B_M} \, ds$$

and to let

$$I = \frac{J}{P} = \int_M^{M^*} \sqrt{1 - B/B_M} \, ds \qquad (7\text{-}25)$$

The quantity I has the dimensions of length; it is a property of the magnetic field alone and may be attributed to the mirror point M

(or M^*). The Rosenbluth principle for the conservation of I makes possible the identification of a unique sequence of segments of magnetic lines of force that constitute a single-valued, three-dimensional surface (a "magnetic shell") on which the guiding center of a trapped particle will forever lie—to the extent that the conditions for the conservation of μ and I are met—as it moves about in the irregular geomagnetic field.

The conservation of I is essential to the understanding of trapping in the real, irregular geomagnetic field, which does not possess axial symmetry and for which the Störmer first integral does not exist. The argument is illustrated in Figure 7-4. Let the surface $B = $ constant shown there represent the locus of mirror points for a given particle. Let the motion of the particle's guiding center at a chosen time be along the line of force shown in the right-hand side of the figure with the integral I having the value I_0. The question then is: along which of the infinite number of segments of lines of force having values of $I = I_0$, I_1, I_2, etc. (sketched in the left-hand side of Figure 7-4) and having mirror points on the specified surface of constant B will the guiding center of the particle be moving at some later time after a drift in longitude has occurred? The Rosenbluth principle assures that it will be the segment characterized by I_0.

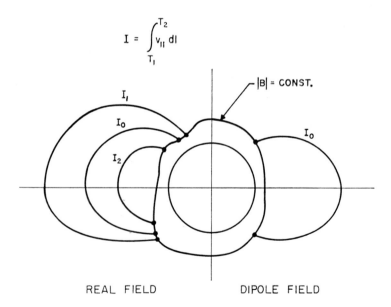

$$I = \int_{T_1}^{T_2} v_{\parallel}\, dl$$

REAL FIELD   DIPOLE FIELD

Figure 7-4 Illustrating the principles of the conservation of the adiabatic invariants μ and I in the geomagnetic field.

It is presumed that I ceases to be conserved when there are perturbations in the guiding magnetic field on a time scale comparable to the period τ_2. Typical pertinent values of τ_2 are of the order of a fraction of second. As in the case of the conservation of μ, there is no satisfactory quantitative foundation for calculating the rate of change of I under specified circumstances.

The third, and weakest, of the adiabatic invariants is the flux invariant Φ (43). Φ is the total flux of B through a surface bounded by a magnetic shell as defined by $I = $ constant. (The computation is made by considering flux in one sense only through the surface.) Northrup and Teller show that $d\Phi/dt = 0$ if the magnetic field within the region in question does not change significantly during τ_3. It is seen from Figure 7-3 that τ_3 varies over a wide range for electrons and protons of typical energies—say from several minutes to several days. Hence under actual geophysical circumstances it will not be surprising if Φ is not conserved, even though both I and μ may be. Moreover, it appears that the nonconservation of Φ is strongly dependent on particle energy.

The magnitude of τ_3 also provides a measure of the extent to which a lack of axial symmetry may be expected under time-varying conditions (42). For example, if a quantity of electrons having various energies of the order of 100 kev are injected into the field at $r_0 = 3$ earth radii, $\tau_3 \approx 3$ hr, a time of the order of one day will be required for the establishment of axial symmetry.

In general summary it is clear that the theory associated with the three adiabatic invariants μ, I, and Φ and the three corresponding cyclic periods τ_1, τ_2, and τ_3 is essential to understanding not only the time-stationary trapping situation but also any proposed time-dependent or spatially dependent perturbation in the real geophysical situation.

7-4 THE NATURAL SYSTEM OF COORDINATES FOR GEOMAGNETICALLY TRAPPED PARTICLES

One of the problems in the study of the energetic particles which are trapped temporarily in the earth's magnetic field is to identify the types of particles present, to measure the absolute energy spectrum of each type, and to make such determinations as a function of positional coordinates, direction, and time.

The problem may be formulated succinctly with the help of the following symbols:

j_i = the undirectional intensity of particles of type i having energies in dE at E;

r, ϕ, θ = the geographic polar coordinates of an arbitrary point in the vicinity of the earth;

l, m, n = the direction cosines of the direction in space being considered;

E = particle kinetic energy;

t = time.

Thus the problem may be said to be the determination of the functions

$$j_i(r, \phi, \theta, l, m, n, E, t),$$

where i denotes successively electrons, protons, alpha particles, etc.

The observational task that corresponds directly to this naïve formulation of the problem is far beyond human capability. Fortunately, in a time-stationary state the application of the foregoing trapping theory simplifies the observational enterprise immensely.

1. At any point the physical situation possesses cylindrical symmetry about the magnetic-field vector **B** and mirror symmetry with respect to the plane perpendicular to **B**. Thus all directions that make an angle α (or $180 - \alpha$) with the magnetic field vector **B** at a specified point are equivalent.

2. Within a given geomagnetic shell, as defined by the integral adiabatic invariant I and as labeled by a single parameter L (see later section), the complete positional and angular dependence of j_i is contained within the dependence of j_i on the angle α_0 to the **B** vector at the position within the shell at which **B** has its minimum value (loosely speaking, on the magnetic equator).

Hence the complete observational problem for the time-stationary state is reduced to that of determining

$$j_i(L, \alpha_0, E).$$

Within the physical limitations of their applicability, the two adiabatic invariants μ and I provide a "natural" system of geomagnetic coordinates which is suitable for the collation and comparison of observational data from a wide variety of geographic positions. This system of coordinates makes feasible the comprehensive study of large masses of data obtained under quiescent conditions; and, by the same token, it provides the proper foundation for studying time fluctuations.

In a quiescent, unperturbed case of magnetic trapping all particles that mirror on a given surface B = constant will always continue to do so; also, the unidirectional intensity within a given magnetic shell $j_i(B, \alpha_0)$ is independent of the magnitude and direction of grad **B**. Moreover, their orbits drift around the earth on such a sequence of lines of force as to conserve I. As mentioned above, this principle defines a unique sequence of lines of force comprising a magnetic shell. The B, I coordinate system is relatively trivial for an idealized dipole. Nonetheless, it is instructive to see the form of the surfaces $B = $ constant and $I = $ constant for a dipole. Several cases are illustrated in Figure 7-5. The $B = $ constant and $I = $ constant surfaces intersect in a system of small circles of various radii with their centers on the dipole axis. Each pair of surfaces intersects in two small circles located, respectively, in opposite hemispheres.

For a dipole field it is readily shown that

$$I_M = L_M \, g(\lambda_M), \tag{7-26}$$

where the subscript M refers to quantities pertaining to a given mirror point, λ_M is the latitude of that mirror point, L_M is the radial distance at which the line of force through the mirror point crosses the equator, I_M is the value of the integral adiabatic invariant corresponding to the mirror point; and g is a function that is known explicitly (numerically but not in closed analytical form).

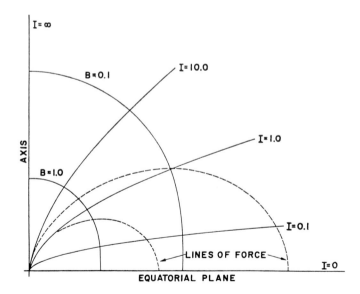

Figure 7-5 The "natural coordinate system" for trapped particles in an idealized dipole field showing contours of $L = $ constant, $B = $ constant and $I = $ constant.

Also

$$\frac{(B_M)}{(B_M)_0} = \frac{\sqrt{4 - 3\cos^2\lambda_M}}{\cos^6\lambda_M}, \tag{7-27}$$

wherein $(B_M)_0$ is the equatorial value of B on the line of force through the mirror point designated by M.

Following McIlwain (27), it is found from equations (7-26) and (7-27) that

$$L_M{}^3 B_M = f(I_M{}^3 B_M). \tag{7-28}$$

In equation (7-28) f is a function that has been calculated numerically.

For the real geomagnetic field Jensen, Murray, and Welch (45), Vestine (46), and Vestine and Sibley (47) have calculated extensive numerical tables of B and I as a function of geographic coordinates around the earth; they have also calculated a large number of lines of force in space. McIlwain (48) and Ray (49) have fitted functions of geographic coordinates to these numerical tables in forms that are convenient for machine computer use in labeling the observations obtained with rocket, satellite, and space-probe equipment.

McIlwain has made a further important advance in the treatment of observation data by utilizing the dipole relation equation (7-28) to define a single parameter L to characterize a specific magnetic shell in its entirety. He has shown by numerical calculation on the real geomagnetic field that the "shell parameter" L, as so defined [using real field quantities in equation (7-28)], not only has the same simple (though approximate) physical meaning as in the dipole case but is indeed very nearly a constant along a given line of force over a large range of B_M and for all longitudes.

Hence there has now been adopted the coordinate system defined by surfaces of constant B and constant L in dealing with the huge body of observations on the geomagnetically trapped radiation. This coordinate system has a sound theoretical foundation, and in the hands of McIlwain, Pennington, Vestine, Forbush, Venkatesan, Ray, Welch, Lin, Pizzella, Van Allen, and others it is proving of great power in the study of trapped radiation in both quiescent and disturbed states. It makes possible the ready comparison of diverse observations at diverse points in space and it provides the foundation for the study of time fluctuations and for the discussion of a variety of theoretical aspects such as the lifetime of trapped particles and the consequences of local acceleration processes.

In an unpublished memorandum Ray (50) has discussed the application of Liouville's theorem on the conservation of density of representative points in phase space to geomagnetically trapped particles. The following two theorems are representative examples of such application:

Theorem 1. If at any point on a particular line of force the directional intensity is isotropic, then along that line of force, in the direction of increasing magnetic field strength, at each point the radiation is isotropic and the omnidirectional intensity is independent of position.

Theorem 2. If, in a magnetic field in which the field strength increases as one goes along a line of force in the direction of decreasing radius r, the intensity has cylindrical symmetry about the line of force and the directional intensity at one point on a particular line of force increases (decreases) monotonically as the angle to the line of force decreases, the omnidirectional intensity increases (decreases) monotonically as one goes to lesser radii along the same line of force.

Ray (26) has also solved the following problem in an explicit form which has general applicability to the interpretation of experimental results:

Given: a complete knowledge of the omnidirectional intensity J_0 of a given type of particle as a function of position (or equivalently as a function of B/B_0) along a given line of force (L = constant).

To find: the angular distribution of the unidirectional intensity j as a function of pitch angle α_0 at the equator $B/B_0 = 1$.

Assuming the conservation of μ, Ray finds

$$j(\sin^2 \alpha_0)$$

$$= \frac{1}{2\pi^2} \frac{d}{d(\sin^2 \alpha_0)} \int_0^{\sin^2 \alpha_0} \sqrt{B_0/B} \left(\sin^2 \alpha_0 - \frac{B_0}{B} \right)^{-\frac{1}{2}} J_0\left(\frac{B_0}{B}\right) d\left(\frac{B_0}{B}\right).$$

$$(7\text{-}29)$$

Figures 7-6 and 7-7 show the relationship of the angular distribution of the unidirectional intensity at the equator to the omnidirectional intensity as a function of B/B_0 for a given magnetic shell.

It is now abundantly clear that the use of the system of "natural coordinates" described above for the real geomagnetic field provides an immense simplification in interpreting experimental observations. In effect, the data for each magnetic shell (as specified by the parameter L) are dealt with separately; and, in fact, since the time-sta-

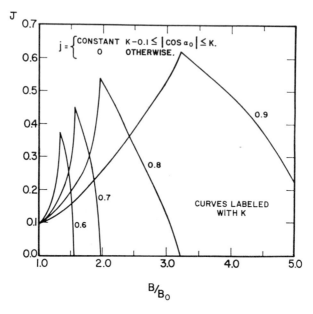

Figure 7-6 Example of the relationship of angular distribution of unidirectional intensity j at the equator $(B = B_0)$ to the omnidirectional intensity as a function of B/B_0 for a given magnetic shell. (After E. C. Ray.)

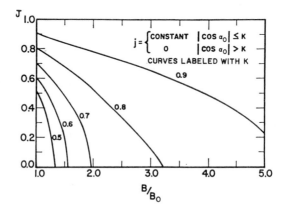

Figure 7-7 Another example. (After E. C. Ray.)

tionary situation has axial symmetry in B, L coordinates, the physical situation along a single line of force of given L is taken to be representative of the entire shell to which it belongs. Within that shell α_0 (or if more convenient B, B/B_0, or $\lambda_N = \text{arc sec}\sqrt{L}$) is the only other parameter necessary for a complete specification of the positional and directional characteristics of the radiation.

In addition to aiding the interpretation of the quiescent state, the "natural coordinates" B and L provide the proper basis for the clear recognition of temporal variations and for study of the detailed features of such variations. The S.U.I. laboratory now routinely converts the geographic ephemeris of its various satellites to B, L coordinates before attempting analysis.

7-5 GEOMETRIC STRUCTURE

For the present purpose, the term "geometric structure" or simply "structure" is taken to mean the spatial distribution of the omnidirectional intensity of a specified component of the trapped radiation. Inasmuch as the radiation is a mixture of protons and electrons (and perhaps other particles) having separate energy spectra that are quite different from each other and are functions of L, α_0, and t, it is necessary to investigate the structure with a variety of detectors of different properties. A priori, it might be thought that the structures for different components might vary; but, in fact, there are certain powerful factors of a general nature which greatly reduce their conceivable variety. The factors are as follows:

1. The dominance of the geomagnetic field in controlling the general form of the structure.

2. The dominance of atmospheric scattering and absorption in determining the form of the inner boundary of the intensity structure near the earth.

3. The nature of the process of injection of solar gas into the outer portion of the geomagnetic field and the nature of the subsequent "local acceleration" processes.

4. The geometric character of the injection of particles from "internal" sources.

In fact a single diagram is found to serve the purpose of a general account of the subject of structure. Such a diagram was constructed by Van Allen and Frank (4) on the basis of the extensive low-altitude satellite observations with the variety of detectors in Explorer IV and with the two traversals through the trapping region by Pioneer III.

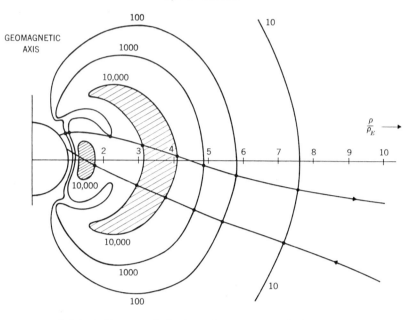

Figure 7-8 Original diagram of the intensity structure of the trapped radiation around the earth. The diagram is a section in a geomagnetic meridian plane of a three-dimensional figure of revolution around the geomagnetic axis. Contours of constant intensity are labeled with numbers, 10, 100, 1000, 10,000. These numbers are the true counting rates of an Anton 302 Geiger tube carried by Explorer IV and Pioneer III. The linear scale of the diagram is relative to the radius of the earth—6371 km. The outbound and inbound legs of the trajectory of Pioneer III are shown by the slanting, undulating lines. (After Van Allen and Frank.)

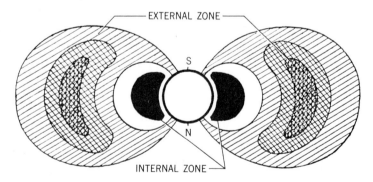

Figure 7-9 A diagram of the same nature as Figure 7-8. (After Vernov and Chudakov.)

It is shown in Figure 7-8. On the basis of more recent data of Explorers VI and VII to be given later, it appears that the form of the outer zone is more nearly like that of a dipole field than shown in Figure 7-8. The radiation region appears to be fundamentally divided into two distinct zones—an inner zone, whose particle population is probably due to internal sources located in the strong region of the geomagnetic field and relatively stable in time, and an outer zone, whose particle population is almost certainly due to external sources located in the outer reaches of the geomagnetic field and having a detailed form and particle content that are strongly dependent on

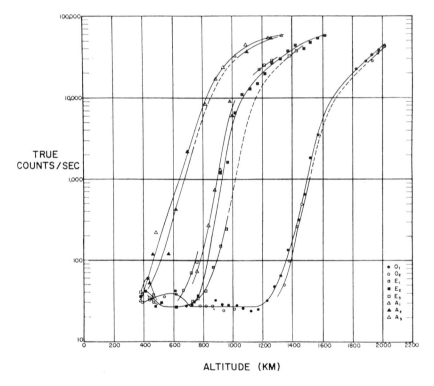

Figure 7-10 True counting rate of the Geiger tube in Explorer I as a function of altitude above sea level for a number of geographic positions, all near the equator but at widely different longitudes. Note the precipitous rise in intensity beginning at an altitude ranging from 400 km over the Central Atlantic (*curve on the left*) to 1300 km over Singapore (*curve on the right*). The effective eccentricity of the magnetic center of the earth is obtained directly from the diagram. (After Yoshida, Ludwig, and Van Allen.)

solar and geomagnetic activity as measured by other means. The region between the two zones has been termed the "slot."

A later version of the same sort of diagram by Vernov and Chudakov is shown in Figure 7-9.

The lower fringe of the inner zone was well determined by a single Geiger tube in Explorer I (51). Figures 7-10, 7-11, and 7-12 summarize the main features of this work. The fact that the intensity data from all longitudes near the equator, for example, fall on a single curve when plotted against scalar B was one of the early successes of the B, L coordinate system described in detail in an earlier section.

The extensive undertaking of replotting in natural coordinates the inner-zone data from the two Geiger tubes in Explorer IV has re-

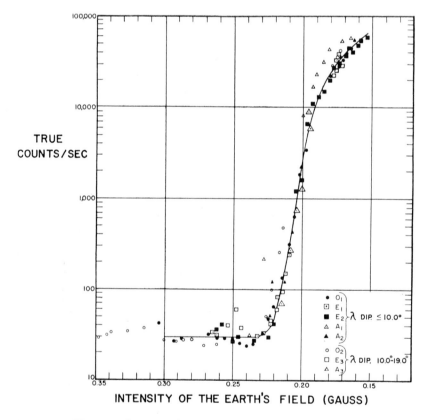

Figure 7-11 The counting rate data of Figure 7-10 replotted as a function of scalar B. This diagram illustrates that the omnidirectional intensity J_0 is a function only of B for $I \approx$ zero. (After Yoshida, Ludwig, and Van Allen.)

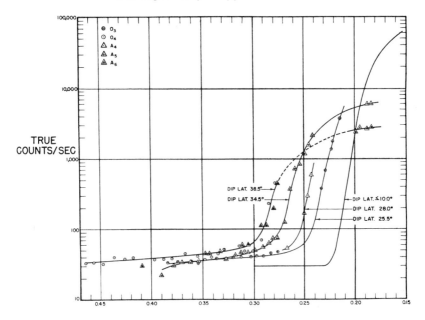

Figure 7-12 Data similar to those in Figure 7-11 but for a variety of dip latitudes or magnetic shells. (After Yoshida, Ludwig, and Van Allen.)

cently been completed by McIlwain (27). Figures 7-13, 7-14, 7-15, and 7-16 show the principal results of this work. In the last two figures the radial and angular coordinates (r_N, λ_N) are defined from the B, L system by the following two relations:

$$\lambda_N = \text{arc sec } \sqrt{L/r_N}, \qquad (7\text{-}30)$$

$$B = \frac{M}{r_N{}^3} \sqrt{4 - 3r_{N/L}}. \qquad (7\text{-}31)$$

(The unit of length is the radius of the earth.)   The subscript N refers to the natural coordinate system and is intended to avoid confusion with any actual geometric coordinates.

The omnidirectional intensity of protons in particles/cm² sec, trustworthy to a factor of two (during the period of the observations July 26–September 21, 1958), can be obtained as follows:

1. Divide the counting rate number given in the figures for the unshielded counter by 0.54 to obtain the omnidirectional intensity of protons having energies exceeding 31 Mev.

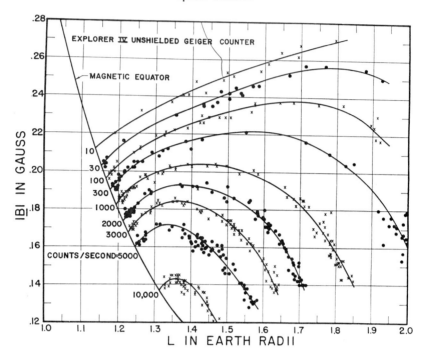

Figure 7-13 Intensity contours on a B, L diagram of data from Explorer IV. Circles and crosses are used alternately to distinguish successive contours. (After McIlwain.)

2. Divide the counting rate number given in the figures for the shielded counter by 0.62 to obtain the omnidirectional intensity of protons having energies exceeding 43 Mev.

A similar analysis is in progress on the observations with the other two detectors in Explorer IV: (1) the directional intensity of electrons of energy greater than 580 kev and (2) the directional energy flux into a thin Cs I crystal covered with a 1 mg/cm² absorber. It is already apparent that the structure of the lower half of the inner zone for energetic electrons is similar to that for protons, though it spreads out to somewhat higher latitudes. The unidirectional intensity of electrons of energy greater than 580 kev in the direction perpendicular to B in the heart of the inner zone is $1 \times 10^7/\text{cm}^2$ sec steradian with an uncertainty of a factor of $2(r_N \sim 1.4$ earth radii).

The altitude-dependence of proton intensity in the lower portion of the inner zone is, generally speaking, as well understood as knowledge of the density and composition of the atmosphere permits. The approximate argument is as follows. In the lower portion of the inner zone the

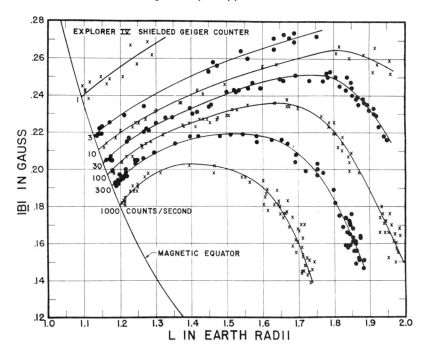

Figure 7-14 Similar to Figure 7-13.

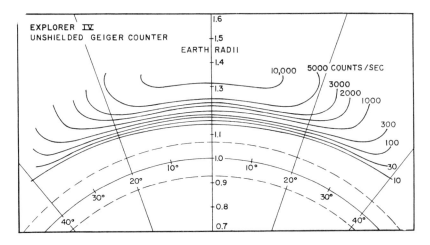

Figure 7-15 Intensity contours of Figure 7-13 transformed to a spherical plot by using the coordinates r_N and λ_N defined from the natural coordinate system of B and L. The dashed arcs of circles represent the limits between which the surface of the solid earth falls at various longitudes. (After McIlwain.)

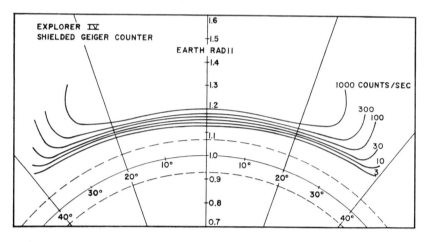

Figure 7-16 Similar to Figure 7-15, showing the transformation of the contours of Figure 7-14.

dominant mechanisms for loss of particles are energy loss and scattering in the high levels of the atmosphere. Hence the intensity at a given value of B_M in a magnetic shell of given L is essentially inversely proportional to the line integral of atmospheric path length (in gm/cm^2) along the trajectory of the particle between B_M and B_M*, provided that the source function of particles is more or less the same over the region in question. This sort of analysis yields a substantially satisfactory understanding of the altitude-dependence of intensity in the lower portion of the inner zone (26).

The fall-off of *both* electron and proton intensity with increasing radius (and the concomitant fall-off with increasing latitude) is not well understood. There is some contribution to the fall-off simply by the geometric dependence of the source function of albedo neutron decay products. But the observed fall-off is considerably more rapid than this.

Singer (52, 53) and Vernov (54) have advocated the "breakdown" of the Alfvén adiabatic invariant as a possible explanation and Singer has calculated the required value of the Alfvén positional discriminant $\rho|\text{grad } B/B|$ to harmonize this line of thought with the observed data of the Iowa and Chicago groups. He finds a value of 0.08 to 0.06 as calculated in the equatorial plane.

The physical process that must be envisioned in the so-called breakdown of the adiabatic invariant is that the mirror point of a particle becomes progressively or randomly lower than that given by equation (7-14):

$$B_M = \frac{B_0}{\sin^2 \alpha_0},$$

or that $p_{\parallel}$ at the equator progressively or randomly increases at the expense of p_1 so that α_0 diminishes (cf. Section 7-2). In the experiments of Gibson et al., previously cited, it was found that the quiescent loss of trapped particles due to breakdown of the adiabatic invariant was unobservably small for more than 10^8 encounters with a magnetic mirror where $\rho | \text{grad } B/B | \sim 0.02$. The number of possible encounters may be greater. It is also of interest to note that for the Störmer case (Figure 7-1) $pc = 966$ Mev, $E = 400$ Mev for a proton, $(r_1 + r_2)/2 = 2.69$ earth radii, and $\rho | \text{grad } B/B | \sim 0.17$ in the vicinity of the mirror point and 0.35 in the equatorial plane.

There is little doubt of the qualitative soundness of the Singer-Vernov suggestion but it is far from clear that the loss of trapped protons from the outer edge of the inner zone is actually dominated by the quiescent loss process proposed. Additional doubt is cast on the proposal by the fact that the inner-zone structure for electrons whose energy exceeds 580 kev is quite similar to that for protons whose energy exceeds 30 Mev, being extended in the equatorial plane by only about 0.3 of an earth's radius. For example, the Alfvén discriminant for an electron of 1 Mev kinetic energy at a radial distance of 2.4 earth radii in the equatorial plane is only 4×10^{-4}.

The present author is inclined to the view that the radial limitation of the inner zone is caused in a dominant way by transient variations both in time and space of the geomagnetic field. The observational evidence for this view is that the low-altitude portion of the inner zone in the equatorial region is quite stable but that temporal variations increase as one goes to higher latitudes; and in the slot variations of more than an order of magnitude are observed, often with sharp spatial and temporal structure.

Specific models of hydromagnetic wave perturbations in the inner zone have been proposed by Welch and Whitaker (42), Dragt and Dessler (55), and by Wentzel (56). The last two authors have developed the theory of the perturbations by hydromagnetic waves in quantitative detail and have demonstrated the plausibility of the observed radial extent of the inner zone for protons. Wentzel has also discussed the question of electrons and has concluded that during strong geomagnetic storms electron orbits may also be significantly

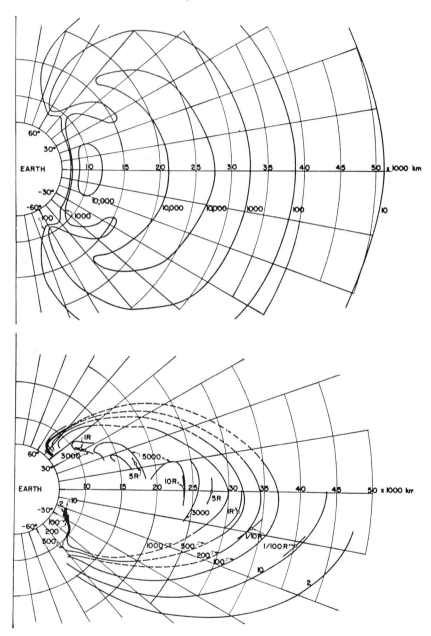

Figure 7-17 Intensity structure of radiation region. (Upper diagram after Van Allen and Frank; lower diagram after Arnoldy, Hoffman, and Winckler.)

perturbed. It is important to keep in mind the fact that the apparent source function for the inner zone is a weak one and that particle lifetimes of the order of 10^8 sec are required in order to permit the development of the observed intensities in the heart of the inner zone.

The structure of the outer zone as sampled by lightly shielded Geiger tubes has been shown in Figure 7-8. A considerably modified structure (57) was observed by an identical detector in Pioneer IV, thus providing a striking example of the great time variability of the structure. This variability had been found in the earlier low-altitude observations with Explorer IV (3).

Many extended studies of the outer-zone variations have been made with the low-altitude data of Explorer VII (58) and the high-altitude data of the very eccentric orbit of Explorer VI (59, 60, 61). Figure 7-17 shows the structure of the outer zone during August and September 1959, as reported by Winckler et al. Figures 7-18 and 7-19 show examples of the time variation as measured in different ways. Forbush et al. have found the geomagnetic ring current parameter of Kertz (62) to be a valuable one in establishing a general connection between outer-zone fluctuation and other geomagnetic effects. Fan et al. have emphasized the bifurcation of the outer zone, as observed by Explorer VI to exist to varying degrees during August and September 1959, and as previously seen in Pioneer III data of December 1958, and have conjectured that this bifurcation is a characteristic feature of the outer zone. The low-altitude data of the Iowa group with Explorer VII show a strongly time-varying structure to the outer zone, including many examples of double and multiple peaks. Hence more extended observations of the outer-zone structure, as found at large radial distances, will be required to determine whether the August–September situation is characteristic or whether it is merely a temporary representation of a large variety of time-variable structural features.

Figure 7-20 shows a large collection of data (63) on the observed position of the peak intensity of the outer zone as found at an approximate 1000-km altitude with Explorer VII. Also shown are the contours of $L = $ constant. All of the data including the contours refer to a sphere of radius 100 km greater than that of the earth. The mean position of the peak of the outer zone lies at an L of about 3.5, which is in remarkably close agreement with its location as found with Pioneer III near the equatorial plane.

Perhaps one of the most striking examples of the validity of present knowledge of the dynamics of geomagnetic trapping was provided by the Explorer IV observations of the artificially produced shells of

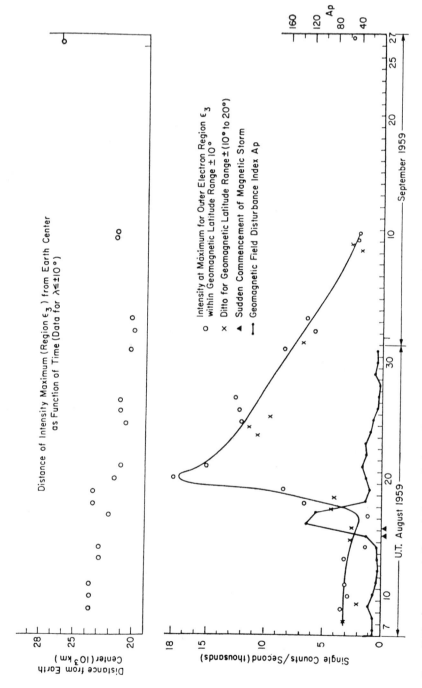

Figure 7-18 A representation of time variations of intensity in the outer zone near the equatorial plane and relationship to magnetic activity. (After Fan, Meyer, and Simpson.)

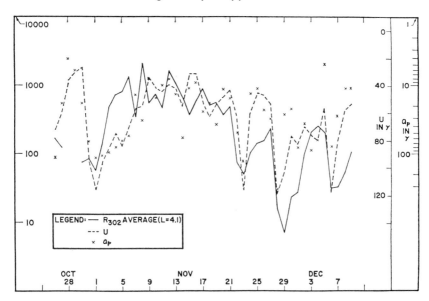

Figure 7-19 A representation of time variations of intensity at about 1000-km altitude in the outer zone and relationship to magnetic activity. (After Forbush, Venkatesan, and McIlwain.)

energetic electrons from the Argus tests in August and September 1958 (64, 3, 27). Figures 7-21 and 7-22 show the remarkable agreement in the form of the three separate Argus shells with magnetic shells defined by L = constant.

7-6 SOURCES OF TRAPPED PARTICLES IN THE INNER ZONE

In consideration of the gross intensity structure of the earth's radiation region (cf. Figure 7-8) and of the quite different level of time variability in the inner and outer zones, it seems reasonable to believe that the two zones originate in different ways.

It is now regarded as likely that the principal source of the particles that are trapped in the inner zone is the neutron component of the cosmic ray albedo arising from nuclear disintegrations produced in the atmosphere by the ordinary cosmic radiation.

The charged particle albedo of the atmosphere has long been recognized as a problem in the determination of the primary cosmic-ray intensity by measurements with rocket equipment above the atmosphere (65, 66, 67, 68), and the neutron component has been discussed

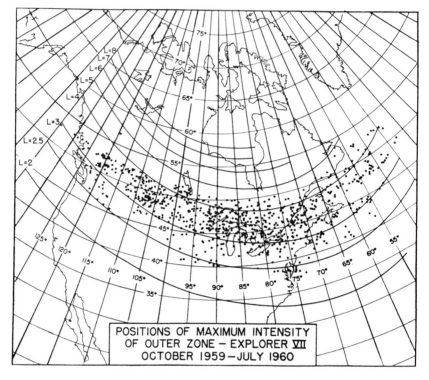

Figure 7-20 Map of the geographic positions of the observed maximum intensity of the outer zone as projected along lines of force onto a sphere of radius 100 km greater than that of the earth and corresponding loci of magnetic shells. $L =$ constant. (After Lin and Van Allen.)

by Rossi (69) as representing one of the losses from the atmosphere in assessing the energy integral of cosmic rays by summing all observable secondary processes.

The possible significance of the albedo neutrons for injecting their charged decay products into trapped orbits within the earth's field was apparently first recognized by Christofilos, whose attention was directed primarily to their decay electrons (beta-ray spectrum with upper limit of 782 kev for a neutron at rest). Later, more quantitative studies of this hypothesis were published by Singer (70), by Vernov and Lebidinsky (10), and by Kellogg (71), after the experimental discovery of the trapped radiation. Singer's treatment of the problem concentrated on the proton-decay products and Kellogg's on the electron-decay products.

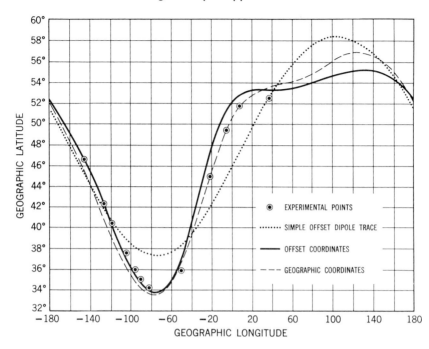

Figure 7-21 Various fits to the Argus III data of Explorer IV showing efficacy of the natural coordinate system. (After Pennington.)

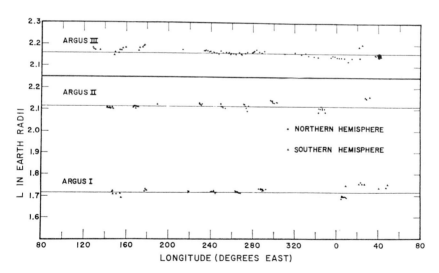

Figure 7-22 The geomagnetic shell coordinate L of the three Argus shells as observed with Explorer IV as a function of geographic longitude. (After McIlwain.)

Later comprehensive treatments of the neutron-albedo theory have come from the work of Hess and others (72, 73, 74, 75).

The data of Explorer IV and of Pioneer IV made it appear likely that the penetrating component in the inner zone was composed of protons (76). The first conclusive identification of this component was by way of recovered nuclear emulsions which had been flown through the lower edge of the inner zone by Freden and White (77). Subsequent work by similar techniques by the same authors (78), by Yagoda (79), by Armstrong, Harrison, and Rosen (80), and by Naugle and Kniffen (81) have provided a good preliminary knowledge of the energy spectrum of protons in the lower portion of the inner zone. The differential number-energy spectrum is given by Freden and White (77) as

$$j(E)\, dE = kE^{-1.8}\, dE$$

for   (7-32)

$$75 < E < 700 \text{ Mev.}$$

The absolute source function for the injection of neutron-decay products into the geomagnetic field (including angular distribution, spatial distribution, and energy distribution of the decay products) is now rather well known, particularly by virtue of the work of Hess and his co-workers.

Also, the theory of the loss of trapped protons from the range of detectability by energy loss and scattering in the tenuous upper atmosphere is as well known as the properties of the exosphere. Hence it is possible to calculate the absolute intensities of trapped protons and their energy spectrum without reference to the experimental data. When this is done, there is a quite plausible measure of agreement with the observed quantities.

The corresponding situation with respect to the electrons in the inner zone is far less satisfactory (71). There are disagreements of orders of magnitude between the observed absolute intensities of electrons and the predicted values. Moreover, the observed spectrum (82) is richer in low-energy electrons than the predicted spectrum; and, as remarked earlier, only the lower altitude (and low-latitude) portion of the structure of the inner zone is properly accounted for by the neutron-albedo theory. Any proper understanding of the outer boundary of the inner zone must rest on other considerations.

It was found by Naugle and Kniffen (81) that the proton spectrum at the northern edge of the inner zone in the energy range 10 to 50 Mev was much steeper than that at a position some 1600 km south of this point, being of the form

$$j(E) \, dE = k'E^{-4.5} \, dE. \tag{7-33}$$

It is perhaps significant that the rocket flight on which these results were obtained was on September 19, 1960, only about two weeks after the prolonged solar-cosmic-ray event of September 3 to 10, 1960. For some time the present author has entertained the thought that solar cosmic rays may make a significant contribution to the trapped proton content of the inner zone by way of neutron albedo secondaries produced in the polar caps. An effect suggestive of this possibility was reported by Armstrong et al. (83). Recently an important new development occurred. Pizzella (84) has found a marked increase in intensity in the inner zone following the early April 1960 solar-cosmic-ray events (85). The effect was much more pronounced at high values of L, being negligible at $L = 1.2$ and a factor of ten at $L = 1.8$. Moreover, the effect was greater for a given L at larger values of B/B_0 (i.e., for lower mirror points). Both of these effects are in qualitative agreement with the basic geometry of particle injection by neutron albedo originating in the polar caps. It is fortunate that there were good satellite observations of the absolute solar-cosmic-ray intensity during the event as well as its latitude dependence (86). Work is now in progress to determine whether quantitative agreement exists.

7-7 SOURCES OF TRAPPED PARTICLES AND/OR KINETIC ENERGY IN THE OUTER ZONE

The outer zone is characterized by an almost complete absence of high-energy protons. An upper limit of $1 \times 10^2/\text{cm}^2$ sec of protons of energy greater than 60 Mev was placed by Pioneer IV (57). The more recent Explorer VI measurements with a lead-shielded coincidence telescope by Fan, Meyer, and Simpson (60) has driven the upper limit of the intensity of protons of $E > 75$ Mev down to $0.1/\text{cm}^2$ sec. There is no information of significance on the intensities of protons of energy less than 30 Mev.

The outer boundary of the outer zone has been observed by means of substantially the same instrument (a single Geiger tube shielded by about 1 gm/cm²) to fluctuate over the radial range 95,000 km (15 earth radii) to about 40,000 km (6.3 earth radii) in the equatorial plane. Figure 7-23 shows a sample of the data obtained from the Geiger counter on Pioneer IV. There is usually a major peak of intensity at a radial distance of about 22,000 km (3.5 earth radii), though the position of the peak varies somewhat, and during some

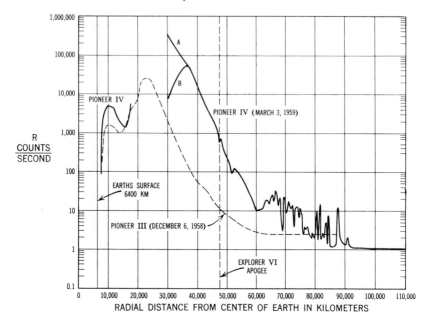

Figure 7-23 A comparative plot of the intensity data of Pioneer III and Pioneer IV on the same scale of radial distance but ignoring differences of latitude and longitude.

periods of time the peak has been observed to be bifurcated into two or more comparable peaks. Among the various measurements over the last three years the magnitude of the intensity in the vicinity of 3.5 earth radii has been observed to vary by nearly two orders of magnitude. Generally speaking, the fluctuations are closely associated with solar and geomagnetic activity, though the association is not of a simple nature (58). The following general pattern has begun to emerge, though it should not be regarded as universal:

1. Within a time of the order of a few hours to a day after the onset of a geomagnetic storm, the content of the outer zone (as measured with a thinly shielded Geiger tube which has an electron-bremsstrahlung threshold of about 20 kev) is markedly depleted. The depletion may be by as much as an order of magnitude or more. On several occasions of large events there have been notable subauroral zone aurorae and red arcs lying along a locus of $L \sim 3.5$ earth radii (59, 87, 88). Also during this "dumping" phase the ring current parameter of Kertz *increases*, apparently signifying an *increase* in the quantity of low-energy protons and electrons (not directly observed

with techniques used thus far) in trapped or quasi-trapped orbits after the manner of Chapman and Ferraro and of Alfvén.

2. Then with a time constant again of the order of one day the observable intensity of electrons undergoes a strong increase and reaches a level equal to or perhaps an order of magnitude greater than its pre-storm value. During this period the ring current declines toward its quiescent value.

3. Finally the intensity of observable electrons in the outer zone relaxes toward its quiescent level with a time constant of the order of a week or more.

One of the best observed and most interesting case histories of an occasion such as that described above occurred during early April 1960. In this period Explorer VII was making a regular patrol of the outer zone at an altitude of about 1000 km and Pioneer V was measuring the particle intensity and the interplanetary magnetic field at a distance of about 0.03 AU (i.e., at a position well outside of the geomagnetic field but in the near-astronomical vicinity of the earth) (85, 89, 59).

Figure 7-24 shows on a common time scale the peak counting rate of the thinly shielded counter in the outer zone (Explorer VII), the magnetic measurements in Pioneer V, and the ground-station record of the geomagnetic field intensity at Iowa City. Also of essential significance are the simultaneous observations of Winckler et al. (also in Pioneer V) of the particle intensity measured with a Geiger tube nearly identical with the one in Explorer VII, in sharp contrast with the Geiger tube rates shown in Figure 7-24. Winckler observed an increase above cosmic-ray rate of at most 1 count/sec during the magnetic peak of Coleman et al.

The following interpretation of this combination of observations is proposed:

1. The magnetometer in Pioneer V recorded the passage of a major burst of ionized, magnetized solar plasma.

2. This plasma contained a negligible intensity of electrons with energies exceeding 20 kev.

3. The arrival of the plasma at the earth (with trivial time lag on the scale shown) produced a major magnetic storm, perturbed the orbits of previously existing trapped electrons of energies in the range of tens of kiloelectron volts, and caused the dumping of a large fraction of the energy of the outer zone into the atmosphere to produce the widespread, brilliant, low-latitude aurora that was observed during this period.

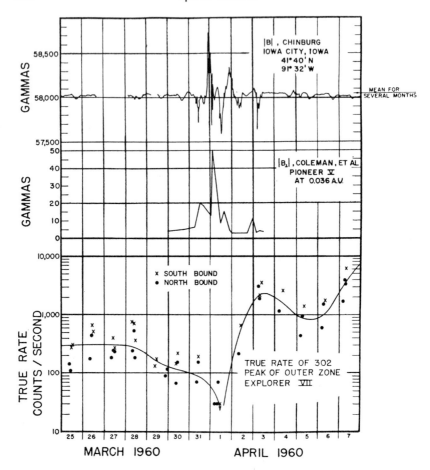

Figure 7-24 The time relationship of the maximum intensity in the low-altitude portion of the outer zone, the interplanetary magnetic field at 0.03 AU, and the ground station record of B. (After Van Allen.)

4. During this process a portion of the low-energy plasma was entrapped by the geomagnetic field.

5. The low-energy particles which thus became a part of the outer zone were subsequently accelerated to a level of observability by magnetic and hydromagnetic process of unknown detailed character.

6. Finally, by virtue of energy loss and other perturbations of more usual character and magnitude, the outer-zone intensity relaxed back to the quiescent level that is presumably maintained by a quiescent solar wind.

On the basis of this type of evidence, the present author feels that there is overwhelming evidence that the outer zone owes its existence to solar plasma and to local accelerating processes of a magnetic nature in the earth's field. Whether the particles being detected are the same ones that arrived in the solar plasma or whether they are those belonging to the earth's system before the arrival of the solar plasma is irrelevant. The essential aspect of the belief is that the energy for producing and maintaining the outer zone is from the sun. Furthermore, there is no significant suggestion that the necessary energy can be delivered to the outer zone in any other form than as kinetic energy of solar plasma.

There remains a wide variety of fascinating problems associated with the origin and dynamics of the outer zone and with the relationship of the outer zone to aurorae, airglow, geomagnetic activity, and atmospheric heating. No attempt to treat these problems has been made in the present paper.

Moreover even direct observational knowledge of the absolute intensities and energy spectra of electrons and protons in the outer zone is in a preliminary state. On the basis of the single assumption that the intensity of electrons of energies exceeding 2.2 Mev does not exceed 10^{-6} of those of lesser energy, the author has given the experimentally based estimate of 10^{11} $(cm^2sec)^{-1}$ as the omnidirectional intensity of electrons of energy exceeding 40 kev in the heart of the outer zone on March 3, 1959 (a date of exceptionally high intensity); and in spite of considerable later evidence, some of a confirmatory and some of a conflicting nature (see, for example, the collection of papers in "Space Research," edited by H. K. Bijl, 1960), he still finds it very difficult to accept a figure less than about 10^{10} $(cm^2sec)^{-1}$ as typifying the intensity of electrons in the tens to hundreds of kiloelectronvolt energy range in the heart of the outer zone.

There remains a pressing need for more decisive experiments in the area. Such experiments are currently underway.

REFERENCES

1. Van Allen, J. A., Special joint meeting of National Academy of Sciences and American Physical Society, Washington, D. C., May 1, 1958. Verbatim transcript of lecture published in IGY Satellite Report Number 13, January 1961, IGY World Data Center A, Rockets and Satellites—National Academy of Sciences, National Research Council, Washington 25, D. C.
2. Van Allen, J. A., G. H. Ludwig, E. C. Ray, and C. E. McIlwain, Observation of High Intensity Radiation by Satellites 1958 Alpha and Gamma, *Jet Propulsion*, **28**, 588–592 (1958).

3. Van Allen, J. A., C. E. McIlwain, and G. H. Ludwig, Radiation Observations with Satellite 1958 Epsilon, *J. Geophys. Res.,* **64,** 271–286 (1959).

4. Van Allen, J. A., and L. A. Frank, Radiation Around the Earth to a Radial Distance of 107,400 Kilometers, *Nature (London),* **183,** 430–434 (1959).

5. Coleman, P. J., Jr., C. P. Sonett, and A. Rosen, Ionizing Radiation at Altitudes of 3500 to 36,000 Km.: Pioneer I. *Bull. Am. Phys. Soc.,* Ser. II, **4,** No. 4, 223 (1959); also *J. Geophys. Res.,* **64,** 709–712 (1959).

6. Rosen, A., C. P. Sonett, and P. J. Coleman, Jr., Ionizing Radiation Detected by Pioneer II. *Bull. Am. Phys. Soc.,* Ser. II, **4,** No. 4, 223 (1959); also *Planetary Space Sci.,* **1,** 343–346 (1959).

7. Singer, S. F., Radiation Belt and Trapped Cosmic Ray Albedo, *Phys. Rev. Letters,* **1,** 171–173 (1958).

8. Vernov, S. N., A. Ye. Chudakov, P. V. Vakulov, and Yu. I. Logachev, Study of Terrestrial Corpuscular Radiation and Cosmic Rays by the Flight of a Cosmic Rocket, *Dokl. Akad. Nauk SSSR,* **125,** 304–307 (1959).

9. Singer, S. F., Trapped Albedo Theory of the Radiation Belt, *Phys. Rev. Letters,* **1,** 181–183 (1958).

10. Vernov, S. N. (and A. I. Lebedinsky), Special Lecture, Fifth General Assembly of CSAGI in Moscow, July 30–August 9, 1958; also *The New York Times,* Friday, August 1, 1958.

11. McIlwain, C. E., and P. Rothwell, Spatial Dependence of the Intensity of Charged Particles Trapped in the Earth's Field Between 50°N and 50°S Geographic Latitude, and 300- to 2000-km Altitude, *J. Geophys. Res.,* **65,** 2508–2509 (1960) (abstract).

12. Kellogg, P. J., Possible Explanation of the Radiation Observed by Van Allen at High Altitudes in Satellites, *Nuovo Cimento,* Series X, **11,** 48–66 (January 1959).

13. National Academy of Sciences, April 29, 1959, Washington, D. C. Symposium on Scientific Effects of Artificially Introduced Radiations at High Altitudes
   (a) R. W. Porter, Introduction.
   (b) N. Christofilos, The Argus Experiment.
   (c) J. A. Van Allen, C. E. McIlwain, and G. H. Ludwig, Satellite Observations of Radiation Artificially Injected into the Geomagnetic Field.
   (d) L. Allen, Jr., Measurement of Trapped Electrons from a Nuclear Device by Sounding Rockets.
   (e) J. A. Welsch, Jr., Theory of Geomagnetically Trapped Electrons from an Artificial Source.
   (f) P. Newman, Optical, Electromagnetic, and Satellite Observations of High-Altitude Nuclear Detonations—Part I.
   (g) A. M. Peterson, Optical, Electromagnetic, and Satellite Observations of High-Altitude Nuclear Detonations—Part II.

14. Chapman, S., and J. Bartels, *Geomagnetism,* Vols. I and II, Oxford at the Clarendon Press, 1940.

15. Alfvén, H., *Cosmical Electrodynamics,* Oxford at the Clarendon Press, 1950.

16. Martyn, D. F., The Theory of Magnetic Storms and Auroras, *Nature (London),* **167,** 92–94 (1951).

17. Van Allen, J. A., Direct Detection of Auroral Radiation with Rocket Equipment, *Proc. Natl. Acad. Sci., U. S.,* **43,** 57–92 (1957).

18. Vernov, S. N., N. I. Grigorov, Yu. I. Logachev, and A. Ye. Chudakov, Artificial Satellite Measurements of Cosmic Radiation, *Dokl. Akad. Nauk SSSR,* **120,** 1231–1233 (1958).

19. Singer, S. F., A New Model of Magnetic Storms and Aurorae, *Trans. Am. Geophys. Union*, **38**, 175–190 (1957).
20. Christofilos, N. C., Various classified memoranda, U. S. Atomic Energy Commission, 1958.
21. Christofilos, N. C., The Argus Experiment, *J. Geophys. Res.*, **64**, 869–875 (1959).
22. Kasper, J. E., Geomagnetic Effects on Cosmic Radiation for Observation Points Above the Earth, *J. Geophys. Res.*, **65**, 39–53 (1960).
23. Vernov, S. N., and A. E. Chudakov, Terrestrial Corpuscular Radiation and Cosmic Rays, pp. 751–796 of *Space Research*, Proceedings of the First International Space Science Symposium, ed. H. K. Kallmann-Bijl, North Holland, Amsterdam, 1960.
24. Rothwell, P., and C. E. McIlwain, Magnetic Storms and the Van Allen Radiation Belts: Observation with Satellite 1958 (Explorer IV), *J. Geophys. Res.*, **65**, 799–806 (1960).
25. Van Allen, J. A., C. E. McIlwain, and G. H. Ludwig, Satellite Observations of Electrons Artifically Injected into the Geomagnetic Field, *J. Geophys. Res.*, **64**, 877–891 (1959).
26. Ray, E. C., On the Theory of Protons Trapped in the Earth's Magnetic Field, *J. Geophys. Res.*, **65**, 1125–1134 (1960).
27. McIlwain, C. E., Coordinates for Mapping the Distribution of Magnetically Trapped Particles, *J. Geophys. Res.*, **66**, 3681–3691 (1961).
28. Birkeland, K., The Norwegian Aurora Polaris Expedition, Volume I, *On the Cause of Magnetic Storms and the Origin of Terrestrial Magnetism.* First section, pp. 1–315, Plates I–XXI, 1908; second section, pp. 319–801, Plates XXII–XLII, H. Aschehong and Co., Christiania, Norway, 1913 (English).
29. Poincaré, H., Remarques sur une experience de M. Birkeland, *G. R. Acad. Sci., Paris*, **123**, 930 (1896).
30. Störmer, C., *The Polar Aurora*, Oxford at the Clarendon Press, 1955.
31. Störmer, C., Sur les Trajectoires des corpuscles electrises dans l'espace sous l'action du magnetisme terrestre, Chapitre IV, *Arch. Sci. Phys. Naturelles (Geneva)*, **24**, 317–364 (1907).
32. Vallarta, M. S., *An Outline of the Theory of the Allowed Cone of Cosmic Radiation*, University of Toronto Studies, Applied Mathematics Series No. 3, University of Toronto Press, Toronto, 1938.
33. Dresden, M., private communication, 1961.
34. Brüche, E., Some New Theoretical and Experimental Results of the Aurora Polaris, *Terrestrial Magnetism and Atmospheric Electricity*, **36**, 41–52 (1931).
35. Malmfors, K. G., Determination of Orbits in the Field of a Magnetic Dipole with Applications to the Theory of the Diurnal Variation of Cosmic Radiation, *Arkiv Matematik, Astronomi, Fysik*, **32A**, No. 8, 64 (1945).
36. Block, L., Model Experiments on Aurorae and Magnetic Storms, *Tellus*, **7**, 65–86 (1955).
37. Bennett, W. H., Solar Proton Stream Forms with a Laboratory Model, *Rev. Sci. Instr.*, **30**, 63–69 (1959).
38. Gibson, G., W. C. Jordan, and E. J. Lauer, Containment of Positrons in a Mirror Machine, *Phys. Rev. Letters*, **5**, 141–144 (1960).
39. Rodionov, S. N., An Experimental Test of the Behavior of Charged Particles in an Adiabatic Trap, *J. Nucl. Energy, Part C, Plasma Physics*, **1**, 247–252 (1960).

40. Hamlin, D. A., R. Karplus, R. C. Vik, and K. M. Watson, Mirror and Azimuthal Drift Frequencies for Geomagnetically Trapped Particles, *J. Geophys. Res.*, **66**, 1–4 (1961).

41. Spitzer, L., Jr., Physics of Fully Ionized Gases, Interscience Publishers, New York, 1956.

42. Welch, J. A., Jr., and W. A. Whitaker, Theory of Geomagnetically Trapped Electrons from an Artificial Source, *J. Geophys. Res.*, **64**, 909–922 (1959).

43. Northrop, T. G., and E. Teller, Stability of the Adiabatic Motion of Charged Particles in the Earth's Field, *Phys. Rev.*, **117**, 215–225 (1960).

44. Lew, J. S., *Drift Rate in a Dipole Field*, Air Force Special Weapons Center, Kirtland Air Force Base, New Mexico (unpublished), 1960.

45. Jensen, D. C., R. W. Murray, and J. A. Welch, Jr., Tables of Adiabatic Invariants for the Geomagnetic Field 1955.0, AFSWC-TN-60-8, April 1960; AFSWC-TN-60-19, 77 pp., August 1960 (unpublished). Air Force Special Weapons Center, Kirtland Air Force Base, New Mexico.

46. Vestine, E. H., Note on Conjugate Points of Geomagnetic Field Lines for Some Selected Auroral and Whistler Stations of the I.G.Y., *J. Geophys. Res.*, **64**, 1411–1414 (1959).

47. Vestine, E. H., and W. L. Sibley, The Geomagnetic Field in Space, Ring Currents, and Auroral Isochasms, *J. Geophys. Res.*, **65**, 1967–1979 (1960).

48. McIlwain, C. E., private communication, 1960.

49. Ray, E. C., private communication, 1960.

50. Ray, E. C., *On the Application of Liouville's Theorem to the Intensity of Radiation Trapped in the Geomagnetic Field*, State University of Iowa Research Report 59-21, 1959 (unpublished).

51. Yoshida, S., G. H. Ludwig, and J. A. Van Allen, Distribution of Trapped Radiation in the Geomagnetic Field, *J. Geophys. Res.*, **65**, 807–813 (1960).

52. Singer, S. F., Cause of the Minimum in the Earth's Radiation Belt, *Phys. Rev. Letters*, **3**, 188–190 (1959).

53. Singer, S. F., Latitude and Altitude Distribution of Geomagnetically Trapped Protons, *Phys. Rev. Letters*, **5**, 300–303 (1960).

54. Vernov, S. N., and A. E. Chudakov, Investigation of Radiation in Outer Space, pp. 19–29 of Proceedings of the Moscow Cosmic Ray Conference, Vol. III, ed. S. I. Syrovatsky, International Union of Pure and Applied Physics, Moscow, 1960.

55. Dragt, A. J., Effect of Hydromagnetic Waves on the Lifetime of Van Allen Radiation Protons, *J. Geophys. Res.*, **66**, 1641–1649 (1961).

56. Wentzel, D. G., Hydromagnetic Waves and the Trapped Radiation, Part 1. Breakdown of the Adiabatic Invariance, Part 2. Displacements of the Mirror Points, *J. Geophys. Res.*, **66**, 359–362 and 363–369 (1961).

57. Van Allen, J. A., and L. A. Frank, Radiation Measurements to 658,300 Km. with Pioneer IV, *Nature (London)*, **184**, 219–224 (1959).

58. Forbush, S. E., D. Venkatesan, and C. E. McIlwain, Intensity Variations in Outer Van Allen Radiation Belt, *J. Geophys. Res.*, **66**, 2275–2287 (1961).

59. Arnoldy, R. L., R. A. Hoffman, and J. R. Winckler, Observations of the Van Allen Radiation Regions during August and September 1959, Part I, *J. Geophys. Res.*, **65**, 1361–1375 (1960).

60. Fan, C. Y., P. Meyer, and J. A. Simpson, Trapped and Cosmic Radiation Measurements from Explorer VI, *Space Research*, Proceedings of the First International Space Science Symposium, ed. H. K. Kallmann-Bijl, North Holland, Amsterdam, 1960, pp. 951–966.

61. Rosen, A., T. A. Farley, and C. P. Sonett, Soft Radiation Measurements on Explorer VI Earth Satellite, *Space Research,* Proceedings of the First International Space Science Symposium, ed. H. K. Kallmann-Bijl, North Holland, Amsterdam, 1960, pp. 938–950.

62. Kertz, W., Ein neues Mass fur die Feldstärke der erdmagnetischen agnatorialen Ringstrom Abhandlungen, Akademie der Wissenschaften in Göttingen, mathematisch-physikalische Klasse, Beiträge zum internationalen geophysikalischen Jahr, No. 2, Göttingen: Vandenhoeck and Ruprecht, 1958.

63. Lin, W. C., and J. A. Van Allen, private communication, 1960.

64. Pennington, R. H., Equation of a Charged Particle Shell in a Perturbed Dipole Field, *J. Geophys. Res.,* **66,** 709–712 (1961).

65. Van Allen, J. A., and H. E. Tatel, The Cosmic-Ray Counting Rate of a Single Geiger Counter from Ground Level to 161 Kilometers Altitude, *Phys. Rev.,* **73,** 245–251 (1948).

66. Gangnes, A. V., J. F. Jenkins, Jr., and J. A. Van Allen, The Cosmic-Ray Intensity Above the Atmosphere, *Phys. Rev.,* **75,** 57–69 (1949).

67. Kulenkampf, H., Bemerkung zum Intensitätsverlauf der Ultrastrahlung in grossen Höhen, *Naturwissenschaften,* **21,** 25–26 (1933).

68. Van Allen, J. A., and S. F. Singer, On the Primary Cosmic-Ray Spectrum, *Phys. Rev.,* **78,** 819, and **80,** 116 (1950).

69. Rossi, B., Interpretation of Cosmic-Ray Phenomena, *Rev. Mod. Phys.,* **20,** 537–583 (1948).

70. Singer, S. F., On the Nature and Origin of the Earth's Radiation Belts, pp. 797–820 of *Space Research,* Proceedings of the First International Space Science Symposium, ed. H. K. Kallmann-Bijl, North Holland, Amsterdam, 1960.

71. Kellogg, P. J., Electrons of the Van Allen Radiation, *J. Geophys. Res.,* **65,** 2705–2713 (1960).

72. Hess, W. N., Van Allen Belt Protons from Cosmic-Ray Neutron Leakage, *Phys. Rev. Letters,* **3,** 11–13 (1959); *ibid.,* **3,** 145 (1959).

73. Hess, W. N., H. W. Patterson, R. Wallace, and E. L. Chupp, Cosmic-Ray Neutron Energy Spectrum, *Phys. Rev.,* **116,** 445–457 (1959).

74. Hess, W. N., and A. J. Starnes, Measurement of the Neutron Flux in Space, *Phys. Rev. Letters,* **5,** 48–50 (1960).

75. Hess, W. N., E. H. Canfield, and R. E. Lingenfelter, Cosmic-Ray Neutron Demography, *J. Geophys. Res.,* **66,** 665–677 (1961).

76. Van Allen, J. A., The Geomagnetically Trapped Corpuscular Radiation, *J. Geophys. Res.,* **64,** 1683–1689 (1959).

77. Freden, S. C., and R. S. White, Protons in the Earth's Magnetic Field, *Phys. Rev. Letters,* **3,** 9–10, 1959; *ibid.,* **3,** 145 (1959).

78. Freden, S. C., and R. S. White, Particle Fluxes in the Inner Radiation Belt, *J. Geophys. Res.,* **65,** 1377–1383 (1960).

79. Yagoda, H., Star Production by Trapped Protons in the Inner Radiation Belt, *Phys. Rev. Letters,* **5,** 17–18 (1960).

80. Armstrong, A. H., F. B. Harrison, and L. Rosen, Flux and Energy of Charged Particles at 300- and 600-mile Altitude, *Bull. Am. Phys. Soc.,* **4,** 360 (1959).

81. Naugle, J. E., and D. A. Kniffen, Flux and Energy Spectrum of the Protons in the Inner Van Allen Belt, *Phys. Rev. Letters,* **7,** 3–6 (1961).

82. Holly, F. E., and R. G. Johnson, Measurement of Radiation in the Lower Van Allen Belt, *J. Geophys. Res.,* **65,** 771–772 (1960).

83. Armstrong, A. H., F. B. Harrison, H. H. Heckman, and L. Rosen, Charged Particles in the Inner Van Allen Radiation Belt, *J. Geophys. Res.*, **66**, 351–357 (1961).
84. Pizzella, G., private communication, 1961.
85. Van Allen, J. A., and W. C. Lin, Outer Radiation Belt and Solar Proton Observations with Explorer VII during March–April 1960, *J. Geophys. Res.*, **65**, 2998–3003 (1960).
86. Lin, W. C., Observation of Galactic and Solar Cosmic Rays from October 13, 1959, to February 17, 1961 with Explorer VII (Satellite 1959 Iota), State University of Iowa Research Report 61-16, August 1961 (unpublished).
87. O'Brien, B. J., J. A. Van Allen, F. E. Roach, and C. W. Gartlein, Correlation of an Auroral Arc and a Subvisible Monochromatic 6300A. Arc with Outer-Zone Radiation on November 28, 1959, *J. Geophys. Res.*, **65**, 2759–2766 (1960).
88. O'Brien, B. J., and G. H. Ludwig, Development of Multiple Radiation Zones on October 18, 1959, *J. Geophys. Res.*, **65**, 2696–2699 (1960).
89. Coleman, P. J., Jr., C. P. Sonett, and D. L. Judge, Some Preliminary Results of the Pioneer V Magnetometer Experiment, *J. Geophys. Res.*, **65**, 1856–1857 (1960).

CHAPTER 8

THE DYNAMICS OF THE
OUTER RADIATION ZONE

ALAN ROSEN

Space Technology Laboratories, Inc.

Recent advances in rocketry, satellites, and space probes have opened up a new area of study which represents an application of the established fields of physics and engineering to a single discipline, namely, space physics. Astronomy, magnetohydrodynamics, plasma physics, and geophysics are necessary ingredients for the study of space physics. On the other hand, these individual disciplines have received, and will continue to receive, immense impetus as a result of space-physics investigations. Although the most glamorous experiments of space physics are done in the space environment, it is important to realize that earth-bound laboratory experiments, balloon and sounding rocket experiments, as well as theoretical studies relating to the extraterrestrial space environment have been in progress for decades.

This chapter singles out one aspect of space physics in discussing experimental observation and interpretation of dynamic mechanisms active in the earth's trapped radiation zones. Charged particles trapped in quasi-stable orbits by the geomagnetic field comprise the terrestrial radiation belt. The motions of these particles are affected by interactions of solar magnetic fields, plasmas, and hydromagnetic waves with the quiescent geomagnetic field. In order to discuss dynamic mechanisms in the radiation zones, it will be necessary to review the properties of the motion of particles trapped by the geomagnetic field. It will then be possible to consider injection, depletion, and lifetime of particles in the radiation belt. We shall begin by considering the fundamental formulation governing the behavior of particles trapped in the geomagnetic field and then take advantage of the recent observations from rockets, satellites, and space probes in order to discuss the interpretation of experimental observations relating to dynamic mechanisms active in the trapped radiation zones.

8-1   THE RADIATION BELTS

The intensity of the trapped radiation, its composition, and the energy spectrum of each component as a function of position in space, direction, and time have not been established conclusively. J. A. Van Allen, in Chapter 7, discusses the evidence relating to the composition and intensity of the trapped radiation as a function of position and time.   For the purpose of relating the present discussion to the experimental observations in the radiation belt, the following hypothetical model, which approximates the radiation environment as well as it is known, will be used.   We shall assume that the radiation belt consists of energetic electrons and protons trapped in the geomagnetic

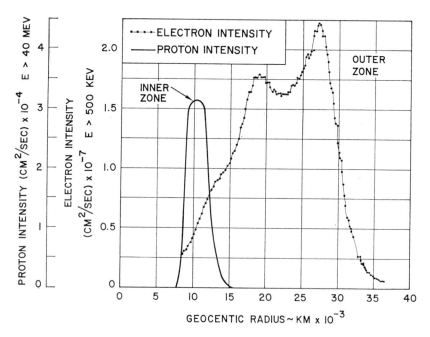

Figure 8-1 Intensity of electrons and protons in the inner and outer zone as a function of radial distance (in an equatorial plane).

field. The demarcation of the radiation into an inner and outer zone results from an energetic proton component found in the altitude range of 600 to 10,000 km. An electron component makes up the outer zone, but the spatial extent of the outer zone is such that it permeates through the inner-zone proton component (see Figure 8-1).

The inner zone

The inner zone is temporally stable in that it is not grossly affected by solar activity. In the equatorial plane it begins at an altitude of 600 km and extends to an altitude of 10,000 km. The boundary of the inner zone, in a meridian plane, is a magnetic line of force which emerges from the earth at approximately 37.5 degrees geomagnetic latitude.

This zone consists of energetic protons ($E > 10$ Mev), with the maximum intensity centered at an altitude of 3600 km in the equatorial plane. The intensity and energy spectrum of electrons and protons in the heart of the inner zone is shown in Table 8-1. Figure 8-2 shows electron and proton isointensity contours. In the energy range of 45 kev to 5 Mev the inner zone integral electron spectral flux distribution may be approximated by the outer zone electron spectrum shown in Figure 8-3. The proton spectrum may be approximated by $kE^{-0.8}$, with $J(E > 75$ Mev$) = 1400$ proton/cm^2 sec at the low altitude edge of the inner radiation zone. $J(E > 75$ Mev$)$ is the omnidirectional intensity of protons with energy greater than 75 Mev. At the heart of the inner zone, $J(E > 40$ Mev$) = 2 \times 10^4$ protons/cm^2 sec. As the high-altitude edge of the inner zone is approached, the average energy of the trapped protons decreases so that $J(E > 75$ Mev$) = 100$ protons/cm^2 sec and $J(E > 10$ Mev$) = 10^5$ protons/cm^2 sec. Figure 8-4 shows the proton-energy spectrum at various radial distances.

The outer zone

The outer zone begins at an altitude of about 10,000 km in an equatorial plane and extends to 70,000 km. In a meridian plane the outer radiation zone boundary dips down to lower altitudes with increasing latitude. In the interval of geomagnetic latitude 55 to 70 degrees the outer zone covers an altitude range 300 to 1500 km.

The particles comprising the outer zone are electrons in the energy range 50 to 5000 kev and soft protons with energy less than 10 Mev. Measurements with the Explorer VI earth satellite show that the outer zone consists of two regions separated by a relative minimum at about 15,000-km altitude in an equatorial plane. With the experimental data on hand, a completely satisfactory explanation for this

TABLE 8-1

Radiation Intensity and Energy Distribution of Radiation Belt Particles

Intensity	Spectrum

Heart of the Inner Zone

Protons		Proton Spectra
$E > 40$ Mev	2×10^4/cm² sec	$\dfrac{dJ}{dE} = kE^{-1.8}$ $E > 20$ Mev
		$\dfrac{dJ}{dE} = kE^{-4.5}$ $20 > E > 5$
Electrons		Electron Spectra *
$E > 45$ kev	3×10^8/cm² sec	See Figure 8-3
$E > 500$ kev	2×10^7/cm² sec	

Heart of the Outer Zone †

Electrons		Electron Spectra
$E > 45$ kev	3×10^8/cm² sec	See Figure 8-3
$E > 500$ kev	2×10^7/cm² sec	
Protons		Proton Spectra
$E > 100$ Mev	< 10/cm² sec	See Figure 8-4
$E > 30$	< 10/cm² sec	

* Electron spectral data in the heart of the inner zone is lacking. The most reasonable assumption is that outer-zone electrons permeate through the inner zone, which is defined by the energetic proton component found in the vicinity of the earth.

† The outer zone is temporally unstable, and factors of 20 variations in intensity have been observed in this region. The numbers shown in the table are representative of a situation of average intensity.

gap is not yet possible. It may be an instrumental effect arising from the energy-response characteristics of the detecting instruments, or it may be a region of space in which the trapped particle energy density is abnormally low. The existence of low magnetic-field strength in that region, known as the Capetown anomaly, may account for the observed depression.

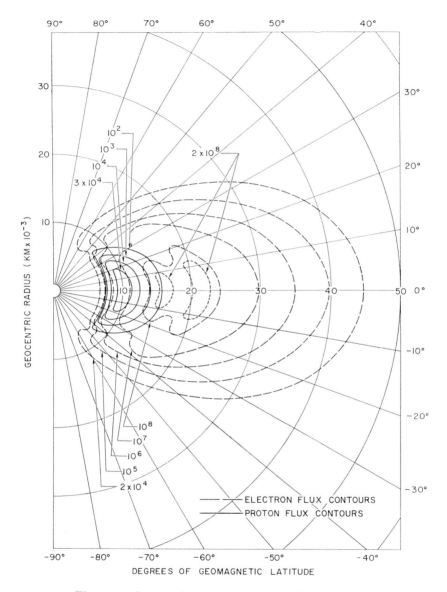

Figure 8-2 Electron and proton isointensity contours. Omnidirectional intensities of electrons and protons given for $E > 45$ kev and $E > 40$ Mev, respectively.

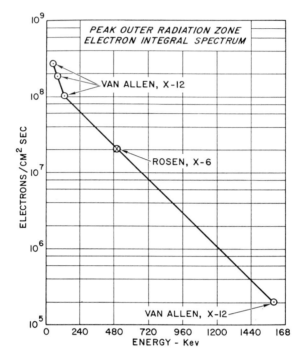

Figure 8-3 The electron integral spectrum at the peak of the outer radiation zone.

Figure 8-3 shows the spectral flux distribution of electrons in the outer zone.

8-2　BASIC DEFINITIONS

The omnidirectional flux J_0 is defined at any point in space as the number of particles of a particular type (e.g., electrons), with kinetic energy greater than some value E_0 which arrive uniformly from all directions and traverse a small test sphere whose cross-sectional area is 1 cm^2.

The unidirectional flux $j = J_0/4\pi$ is that portion of the omnidirectional flux which arrives at the test sphere per unit solid angle from a particular direction. Thus $(J_0/4\pi)\,d\Omega$ is the number of particles arriving at the test sphere within a solid angle $d\Omega$. The number of particles incident on a plane of cross-sectional area dA oriented at an angle θ with respect to the direction of incidence is given by

$$dn = \frac{J_0}{4\pi} d\Omega \, (dA \cos \theta) = \frac{J_0}{4\pi} (2\pi \sin \theta \, d\theta) \, dA \cos \theta, \qquad (8\text{-}1)$$

where $d\Omega = 2\pi \sin \theta \, d\theta$. Integrating this expression from $-\pi/2$ to $+\pi/2$ yields

$$n = \frac{J_0}{2} \Delta A. \qquad (8\text{-}2)$$

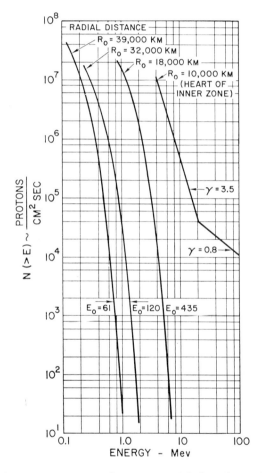

Figure 8-4 Proton energy spectrum in an equatorial plane for various radial distances. γ and E_0 are defined, respectively,

$$N \, (>E) = kE^{-\gamma} \quad \text{and} \quad N \, (>E) = ke^{-E/E_0}.$$

Since $n/\Delta A = J_{\ominus}$, the omnidirectional intensity referred to a plane of unit cross-sectional area (particles incident on the plane from the top and bottom), the omnidirectional intensity is related to $J_{\ominus}$ by

$$J_{\ominus} = \frac{J_0}{2}. \tag{8-3}$$

The omnidirectional intensity referred to a plane of unit cross-sectional area is one half the omnidirectional intensity referred to a sphere of unit cross-sectional area. If we consider radiation incident on the top surface only, then $n/\Delta A = J_0/4$. Whenever omnidirectional intensity data is given without reference to whether it refers to a plane, sphere, or other geometry, it is generally understood that the intensity is to be referred to a sphere of unit cross-sectional area.

In a space experiment designed to determine the intensity of radiation the observed count rate C is related to the intensity J_0 by the omnidirectional geometrical factor G which is defined by

$$G = \frac{C}{J_0}. \tag{8-4}$$

The omnidirectional geometrical factor depends on the counter-surface area ΔA, the solid angle through which radiation can reach the counter, $\Delta\Omega$, and the detection efficiency ϵ of the counter for the radiation in question, that is, $G = (\epsilon/4\pi)\,\Delta\Omega\,\Delta A$. Since $J_0 = C/G$, it is clear that the omnidirectional geometrical factor must have the following characteristics in order that the omnidirectional intensity can be unambiguously deduced from the count rate.

1. Since J_0 is defined for particles of a particular specie with energy greater than E, it is necessary that the geometrical factor G be known as a function of energy. The omnidirectional intensity is then related to the omnidirectional count rate C by

$$J(>E) = \int_0^{\infty} G(E)\,\frac{dC}{dE}\,dE. \tag{8-5}$$

2. The omnidirectional geometrical factor must be large for one type of particle (electron or protons) and zero for all others.

It is difficult to satisfy the first condition because the spacecraft itself and the miscellany of equipment around the detector make it impossible for the detector to be truly omnidirectional. Thus the area of the detector and the solid angle through which radiation arrives at

the detector are energy-dependent, with the higher energy particles
coming through a larger solid angle and impinging on a larger area.
It is difficult to satisfy the second condition because particle detectors
generally respond to all charged particles, regardless of species.
Furthermore, some detectors respond efficiently to secondary radiation
produced in the walls of the detector.

The difference between an elegant and a nonelegant radiation-belt
space experiment is determined by the care with which the experiment
is designed to yield an unambiguous deduction of the omnidirectional
or unidirectional intensity from the observed count rate. Furthermore, it is precisely because the first few radiation-belt space experiments were simple, nonelegant packages that the structure of the radiation zones has been ambiguous for the few years following the first
space-probe launch.

8-3 EQUATIONS OF MOTION

A more quantitative understanding of the motion of a trapped
particle may be obtained by considering the equation of motion of a
charged particle in a magnetic field B.

$$m \frac{d\mathbf{v}}{dt} = q\mathbf{v} \times \mathbf{B} + \mathbf{F}, \tag{8-6}$$

where m and q are the mass and charge of the particle, respectively, $\mathbf{B}$
is the magnetic field vector, $\mathbf{F}$ is any additional force which may be exerted on the particle (e.g., electric field or gravitational force), and $d\mathbf{v}/dt$
is the acceleration.

Three special cases, each representing simplifying assumptions imposed on equation (8-6), will be considered in order to break down the
motion of a particle in a dipole field into its simplest components. In
the first case we shall set $\mathbf{B}$ = constant and $\mathbf{F}$ = 0 and find that the
particle executes small-scale cyclotron oscillations about the line of force,
with its guiding center moving very nearly along the field line (see upper
portion of Figure 8-5). In the second case we shall remove the restriction that B = constant and assume that the magnetic field is in the configuration of a mirror geometry (see Figure 8-5). In such a configuration
the magnetic-field intensity is high at the boundaries of the region in
which the particle moves and low in the interior of the region. Furthermore, in this case we shall constrain the magnetic moment M of the
particle to be a constant of the motion. It will be shown that the particle
executes small-scale cyclotron oscillations about the lines of force and

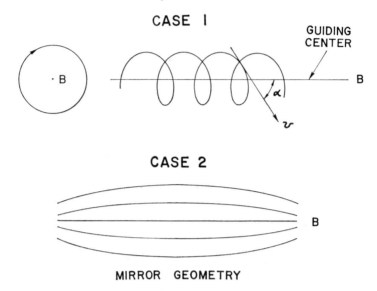

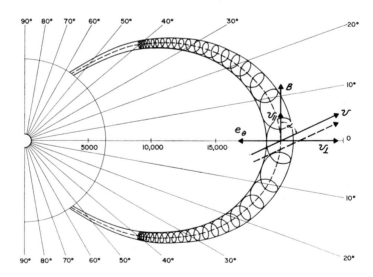

Figure 8-5 Case 1 shows the trajectory of a charged particle in a uniform, constant magnetic field. The angle α is known as the pitch angle of the particle. Case 2 illustrates a possible magnetic field configuration in a mirror geometry. Case 3 shows the bounce motion of a particle in a dipole field.

its guiding center moves very nearly along a field line, bouncing back and forth between the boundary regions where the field intensity is high. The point in space where the particle reverses its direction of motion is known as the mirror point of the particle. Finally, in Case III we shall remove the constraint that $\mathbf{F} = 0$; however, we shall set $\mathbf{B}$ and $\mathbf{F}$ equal to a constant, with B perpendicular to F. We shall find that the particle drifts in a direction perpendicular to both B and F. If we refer this motion to the dipole field of the earth, then the guiding center of the particle drifts in longitude.

Case I. $\mathbf{F} = 0$; $\mathbf{B} = $ constant. The angle α in Figure 8-5 between the magnetic field vector and the velocity of the particle is known as the pitch angle. In this case equation (8-6) reduces to

$$m\frac{dv_\parallel}{dt} = 0 \quad \text{and} \quad m\frac{dv_\perp}{dt} = qv_\perp B, \tag{8-7}$$

so that

$$v_\parallel = \text{constant} \quad \text{and} \quad qv_\perp B = \frac{mv_\perp^2}{a}.$$

The component of the velocity parallel to the magnetic field $v_\parallel$ is undeviated, for the force $\mathbf{v}_\parallel \times \mathbf{B}$ is zero. Thus $v_\parallel$ is constant. The component of velocity perpendicular to the magnetic-field vector $v_\perp$ is effective in producing circular motion of the particle about the magnetic line of force.

Thus one component of the motion may be described approximately as a gyration around a point that is moving in the direction of the magnetic line of force with constant velocity $v_\parallel$. The circular motion of the particle will be of radius $mv_\perp/qB$ and angular velocity qB/m. The instantaneous center of gyration is called the guiding center of the particle.

In the geomagnetic field, as the guiding center of the particle approaches higher latitudes, the increasing field strength results in an increasing gyro-frequency. Figure 8-6 shows the gyro-frequency of electrons and protons trapped along the line of force crossing the equator at a radial distance of 3 Re (3 earth radii measured from earth's center, 1 Re = 6370 km).

Case II. $M = $ constant; $F = 0$; field B in a mirror geometry.

The magnetic moment M of a particle moving in a magnetic field is given by

$$M = q\frac{\omega}{2\pi} = \frac{\frac{1}{2}mv_\perp^2}{B}, \tag{8-8}$$

where $\omega/2\pi$ is the frequency of oscillation of the particle.

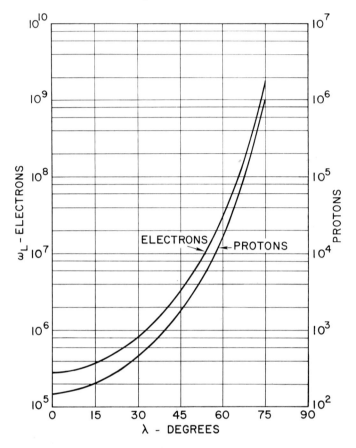

Figure 8-6 The gyro frequency in radians per second of electrons and protons trapped along the line of force crossing the geomagnetic equator at a radial distance of 3 Re, as a function of geomagnetic latitude. The scale on the left is to be read with the curve labeled electrons. The scale on the right is to be read with the curve labeled protons.

M is an adiabatic invariant whenever the radius of gyration of the particle is small in comparison to the fractional change in the gradient of the field, that is, $a \ll \partial B/B \, \partial r$, and the temporal variations in the geomagnetic field are long in comparison to the period of gyration of the particle $\omega \gg \partial B/B \, \partial t$. For proof of this relation, the reader is referred to Alfvén's book, *Cosmical Electrodynamics* (1). If it is assumed that the magnetic moment of a particle in the geomagnetic field is an adiabatic invariant, it is clear that as a particle moves toward higher B-field values the perpendicular component of the energy $\frac{1}{2}mv_\perp^2$

must increase to maintain a constant M. This result is based on the fact that the total velocity of the particle is a constant of the motion. In equation (8-6), if $F = 0$, note that $\mathbf{v} \times \mathbf{B}$ is perpendicular to $\mathbf{v}$, so that the magnetic field does no work on the particle and the energy or velocity of a nonrelativistic particle is indeed a constant of the motion. The particle is thus constrained to remain in a region $B \leq B_m$, where $B_m = E_{tot}/M$. The point where $B = B_m$ is known as the mirror point of the particle. If we write $\sin \alpha = v_\perp/v$, the magnetic moment equation reduces to $B = B_m \sin^2 \alpha$. This is known as the mirror point equation of Alfvén. In a dipole field (see Figure 8-5) the perpendicular component of the particle velocity gives rise to a gyration about the line of force, whereas the parallel component of the velocity gives rise to a displacement of the guiding center along the line of force. As the particle moves toward higher latitudes along the line of force, the pitch angle increases until the particle reaches the mirror point where the pitch angle is 90 degrees. It is then reflected back along the line until it reaches a conjugate point $B_m{}^* = B_m$, where it is again reflected. The time required to travel from B_m to $B_m{}^*$ and back is called the bounce period of the particle. It is given by

$$ T = 2 \int_B^{B^*} \frac{dl}{v_\parallel}, \tag{8-9} $$

where dl is an arc length measured along the magnetic line of force. The bounce period of relativistic electron trapped in the geomagnetic field (approximated by a dipole field) is shown in Figure 8-7. An approximate expression for the bounce period is $T = 0.14 r_0/c$. For a relativistic particle, T varies linearly with r_0 (the radial distance of the particle when it crosses the equatorial plane) (2).

The restoring force responsible for the harmonic-type motion of the particle arises from the gradient in the field along the geomagnetic line of force $M \nabla B$, which always acts to oppose v.

Case III. $\mathbf{F} \perp \mathbf{B}$; $\mathbf{B}$ and $\mathbf{F}$ constant.

If we transform equation (8-6) to a coordinate system moving in a direction perpendicular to both B and F with a velocity $\mathbf{v}_b = (\mathbf{F} \times \mathbf{B})/qB^2$, then equation (8-1) reduces to

$$ m \frac{d\mathbf{v}}{dt} = q(\mathbf{v} + \mathbf{v}_b) \times \mathbf{B} + \mathbf{F} = q\mathbf{v} \times \mathbf{B}. \tag{8-10} $$

In this coordinate system the particle motion is reduced to a gyration about a line of force, similar to Case I. Thus the motion of the particle

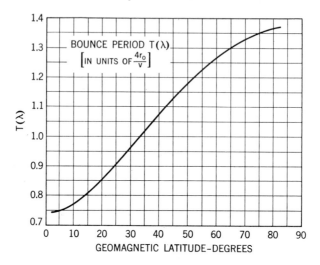

Figure 8-7 The bounce period of particles trapped in a dipole field plotted as a function of the geomagnetic latitude at which the particle mirrors. r_0 is the geocentric radius of the line of force in the equatorial plane and v is the particle velocity.

consists of a drift motion perpendicular to both F and B, and a gyration about the line of force.

Two particular forces are of interest in the case of the geomagnetic field. The first arises because the guiding center of the particle follows the curved path of the geomagnetic line of force (see Figure 8-5) and gives rise to a centripetal force, $m(v_{\parallel}^2/R)$, where R is the radius of curvature of the line of force. The drift velocity in this case is

$$v_b = \frac{mv_{\parallel}^2}{RqB}. \tag{8-11}$$

The second type of force F is one arising from the gradient in the magnetic field B. The force in this case is $M \nabla B$, and the drift velocity is given by $M \nabla B/qB$, where M is the magnetic moment of the particle. The total drift velocity in the geomagnetic field is then equal to

$$v_b = \tfrac{1}{2}a\frac{v_\perp \nabla B}{B} B + \frac{mv_{\parallel}^2}{RqB}. \tag{8-12}$$

Thus as a particle bounces between mirror points in the geomagnetic field it drifts in longitude around the earth; positively charged particles drift to the west, whereas negatively charged particles drift to the east.

The time required for electrons or protons to drift around the world as a function of particle energy is shown in Figure 8-8. Since the drift period depends on the mirror point of the particle, upper and lower curves for mirror points of 90 and 45 degrees, respectively, are shown in Figure 8-8.

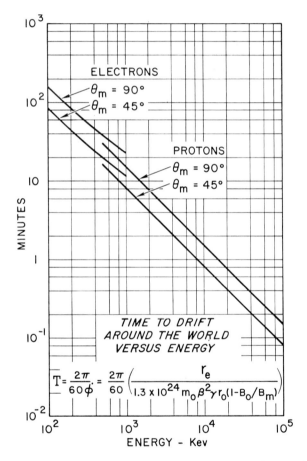

Figure 8-8 The time required for electrons and protons to drift around the world as a function of particle energy. The data shown in this figure applies to particles trapped along a line of force crossing the equator at a radial distance of 3 Re ($r_0/R_e = 3$). Since the drift periods also depend on the mirror points of the particles, upper and lower curves, for mirror points of $\theta_m = 90°$ and $\theta_m = 45°$, respectively, are shown in the figure.

The foregoing three cases may be summarized by stating that a particle trapped by the geomagnetic field executes the following motions:

1. It undergoes small-scale cyclotron oscillations about a line of force.

2. Its guiding center moves very nearly along a field line and bounces back and forth between northern and southern hemisphere mirror points.

3. Its guiding center slowly drifts in longitude.

The conservation of the magnetic moment M is known as the first integral invariant of the motion of a charged particle trapped in the magnetic field. There are two other invariants of the motion which aid in describing the behavior of trapped particles. The second invariant, known as the longitudinal invariant, defined by

$$2 \int_B^{B^*} v_\parallel \, dl, \qquad (8\text{-}13)$$

places an additional constraint on the drift motion of the particle (dl is an element of length along the line of force). If the first and second invariants are constant, the particle must drift in longitude in such a way that it eventually returns to the same field line from which it started. As long as temporal variation in the magnetic field is slower than the transit time of a particle between mirror points, the longitudinal invariance condition may be used to describe the motion of a particle. Thus, if the first and second invariants are constant as a particle drifts around the earth, the guiding center of the particle path defines a surface known as a magnetic shell. A parameter L, characterizing this shell, has been defined by McIlwain (3). In the case of a dipole field, the L parameter reduces to the radial distance of the particle guiding center when it crosses the geomagnetic equator.

The third invariant, the flux invariant, requires that the magnetic flux inside a surface A bounded by the magnetic shell be constant.

$$\Phi = \int_A B \, dA \; = \text{constant.} \qquad (8\text{-}14)$$

Thus, if the field contracts or expands, the magnetic shell must change its size in such a manner that Φ will remain constant.

The third integral invariant is a useful parameter as long as temporal variations in the magnetic field $1 \; \partial B/B \; \partial t$ are small compared to the angular velocity with which a particle circles the earth.

Additional parameters useful for describing properties of the trapped radiation zones are the particle density, the mirror-point density $w(r)$, the injection density $n(r)$, and the pitch angle distribution $p(r_0, \alpha)$. These parameters refer to the distribution of particles along a particular line of force, characterized by r_0, the geocentric radius in the equatorial plane. If r is the geocentric radius to any point on the line of force, then $w(r)$ is the number density of particles mirroring at r and $n(r)$ is the time rate at which particles are injected into a unit volume at r; $p(r_0, \alpha)$ is the rate at which particles cross a sphere of unit cross-sectional area, located at the geomagnetic equator, per unit solid angle centered about the direction defined by the angle α.

8-4 MOTION OF PARTICLES IN THE RADIATION BELT

The objective of experimental observation in the radiation belt is to gain sufficient data relating to trapped particle phenomena to be able to deduce theoretically the intensity of the trapped radiation, its composition, and the energy spectrum of each component as a function of position in space, direction, and time. Even though it has not yet been possible to achieve this goal, some general properties of the structure of the radiation belt are readily apparent from the fundamental equations governing the motion of particles in the radiation belt. For example, if we consider the distribution of mirror points along a line of force, we note that no trapped particle may mirror in the earth's atmosphere. This imposes a constraint on the equatorial pitch-angle distribution, since particles mirroring deeper in the atmosphere have a lesser equatorial pitch angle. The minimal equatorial pitch angle that a trapped particle may have is thus determined by the pitch angle of a particle that mirrors at the top of the atmosphere.

Figure 8-9 shows the minimum equatorial pitch angle that trapped particles may have as a function of the radial distances of a line of force as it crosses the geomagnetic equator. Particles trapped at lower altitudes should show a unidirectionality, since they are restricted to a narrow cone with axis perpendicular to the line of force. The cone angle opens up with increasing altitude until at the outer zone the intensity may become omnidirectional.

The gross features of the geomagnetic field are similar to those of a uniformly magnetized sphere, but it is important to recognize the limitations of such a model. Two major shortcomings are (1) there are many deviations from the dipole approximation that necessitate spherical harmonic analysis of the static field parameters, and (2) the magnetization vector of the earth does not pass through the geo-

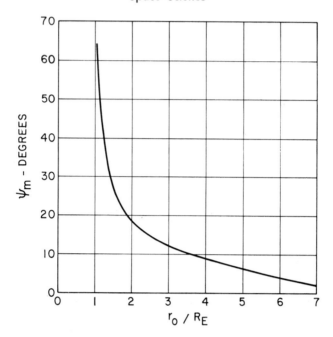

Figure 8-9 The minimum equatorial pitch angle that a trapped particle may have as a function of the radial distance of the particle as it crosses the geomagnetic equator. r_0/R_E is given in units of earth radii.

center, but is eccentric. If we consider the deviation of the time-constant geomagnetic field from a dipole field, it is possible to determine a variety of properties of the structure of the radiation belt. For example, Figure 8-10 shows contours of constant B as a function of altitude and a longitude for the Northern and Southern Hemisphere of the earth (4). A particle mirroring at a field $B = 0.3$ gauss would always remain at an altitude above 1000 km in the Northern Hemisphere as it drifted around the earth. In the Southern Hemisphere, however, its mirror point would dip down to an altitude of about 200 km as it drifted past a longitude of about 15°E. At that point, the particle would be over Capetown, South Africa, and it is quite likely that it would interact with the earth's atmosphere and be scattered out of the radiation belt. Thus, if most of the particles trapped in the radiation belt had mirror points close to the top of the atmosphere, we should expect a depletion of particles from the line of force intersecting the earth at Capetown. If the intensity of radiation were plotted in an equatorial plane as a function of altitude, this effect would produce a dip in the intensity of radiation at the altitude at which the line of force crosses the equator. The existence of a low magnetic-field strength in the region of Capetown is known as the Capetown anomaly. Dessler (5) has proposed that the Capetown anomaly affects the structure of the radiation belt.

Measurements with the Explorer VI earth satellite show that the outer zone consists of two regions separated by a relative minimum at about 15,000-km altitude in an equatorial plane. With the experimental data on hand, a completely satisfactory explanation for this gap is not yet possible, for the gap does not coincide exactly with the Capetown anomaly and the position varies slightly for different measurements. This disagreement may be an instrumental effect arising from the energy-response characteristics of the detecting instruments.

The foregoing brief review of the subject of motion of a charged particle in the geomagnetic field is important to an understanding of the structure of the radiation belt. However, in order to gain further insight at this point, it is necessary to consider how charged particles are injected into the field and the mechanism for scattering particles out of the trapping region.

At any point in space the time average change in particle density $\rho(r)$ is given by

$$\Delta \rho(r) = n(r) - \rho/\tau, \tag{8-15}$$

where $n(r)$ is the injection density and ρ/τ is the leakage per unit volume. The leakage is proportional to the particle density ρ and inversely pro-

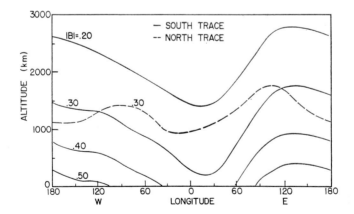

Figure 8-10 Contours of constant $|B|$ as a function of altitude and longitude for the northern and southern hemisphere of the earth. $|B|$ is shown in units of gauss.

portional to the trapping lifetime τ of the particles, i.e., if the change in density due to leakage is given by $d\rho = \rho\, dt$, then $\rho/\rho_0 = e^{-t}$ and, when $\rho = \rho_0/e$, $t = \tau$. When $\Delta\,\rho(r) = 0$, a quasi-stationary state in the radiation belt will result, and the rate of injection will balance the rate of loss.

$$n(r) = \frac{\rho}{\tau}. \tag{8-16}$$

The mean lifetime for electrons in the radiation belt is determined predominantly by small angle scattering of electrons by the air. The effective loss of protons, on the other hand, is dominated by scattering off the ambient electron plasma and possibly by scattering by hydromagnetic waves propagating along lines of force.

8-5 INJECTION AND TRAPPING OF PARTICLES

It is well known that charged particles which impinge on the geomagnetic field are not trapped in the field but are either reflected or, if the particle is sufficiently energetic, penetrate to the atmosphere where nuclear reactions occur (6). Speaking broadly, there are two possible injection mechanisms for populating the radiation zones. The first is a mechanism by which an unstable particle decays in the geomagnetic field and the charged decay products have a sufficiently high mirror altitude so that they are trapped. The second mechanism, solar injection, is associated with magnetic storms arising from the ejection of dense plasma clouds from the sun. It is now generally accepted that the primary mechanism representative of the first category, and most effective in populating the inner radiation zone, is neutron albedo. In this case primary cosmic rays interacting with the earth's atmosphere produce energetic neutrons that penetrate into the geomagnetic field and there decay into an electron and proton that may be trapped. In contrast to the neutron-albedo theory, a quantitative solar injection hypothesis has not been presented. It has been suggested that solar plasma clouds interacting with the geomagnetic field produce instabilities in the magnetic field at the interface between the plasma cloud front and the geomagnetic field. The hypothesis is that because of these instabilities particles are somehow injected into the radiation belt.

8-6 EXPERIMENTAL DATA

The dynamic character of the trapped radiation zone is exemplified by fluctuations in the intensity of the geomagnetically trapped par-

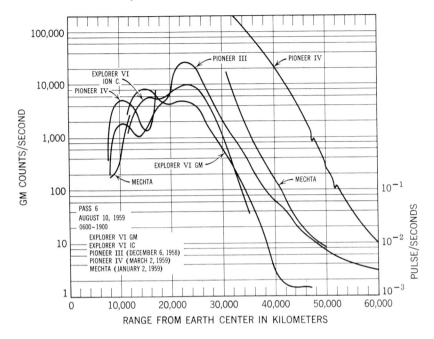

Figure 8-11   Radiation intensities observed at different times in traversing the outer Van Allen zones.

ticles. These fluctuations may be divided into two classes. Long-term, secular variations and daily variations in the structure of the radiation belts may be grouped into one class; intense, unusual fluctuations, rising and falling by a few orders of magnitude within a few minutes, form the second class. In the following sections examples of some of the early satellite and space-probe data illustrating these two classes of fluctuations are presented.

Figure 8-11 illustrates the relative intensities observed at different times for instruments traversing the outer regions of the radiation zones. The plot shows data obtained from Geiger tubes on Pioneer III, Pioneer IV, Explorer VI, and the Russian rocket Mechta. The curves labeled Explorer VI GM and Explorer VI Ion. C. were obtained with a Geiger tube and an ionization chamber, respectively. The difference in the trajectories of the vehicles is slight and does not account for the difference in the observed intensities.

The structure of the Van Allen radiation regions, as determined with a Geiger counter in August 1959, is shown in the lower portion of Figure 8-12. The upper portion of Figure 8-12 shows isointensity contours that were previously observed by Van Allen (7) with the

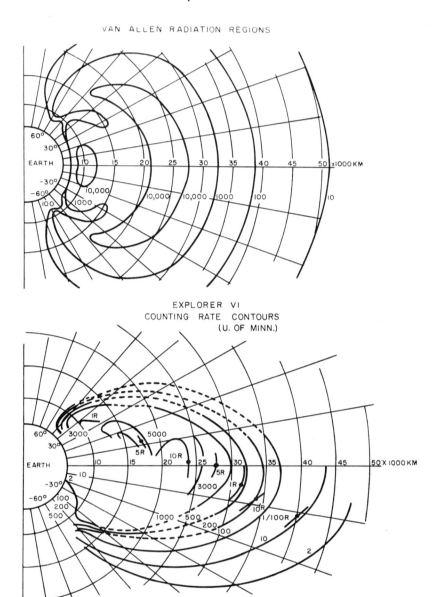

Figure 8-12 Isointensity contours as determined by means of a Geiger counter. The upper portion of the figure shows the contours deduced by Van Allen from the Pioneer III data (December 1958). The lower figure shows the contours deduced from the Explorer VI Geiger counter data (August 1959).

Pioneer III deep space probe. The same instrument was used in both spacecraft in order to facilitate a comparison of the data. It is to be noted that the radiation zones have shrunk considerably during the interval between the Pioneer III flight (December 1958) and the time that the Explorer VI data were taken (August 1959). Furthermore, the University of Minnesota Geiger counter on Explorer VI shows structure in the outer Van Allen zone (lower portion of Figure 8-12) (8).

The isointensity contours, as observed by a scintillation counter on Explorer VI, are shown in Figure 8-13.

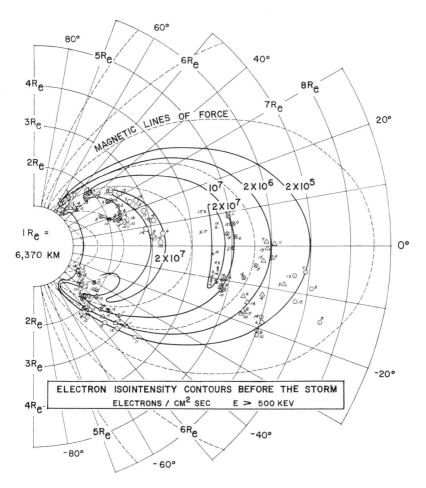

Figure 8-13 Isointensity contours determined from the Explorer VI scintillation counter data.

The scintillation counter experiment (9) consisted of a plastic scintillator that was cemented to a Dumont 6467 photomultiplier tube. This is the only instrument on Explorer VI that responded to electrons directly rather than through bremsstrahlung.

Output pulses of the photomultiplier tube were amplified and fed into a 20-bit binary register, three of which were used to modulate a subcarrier oscillator, so that transitions between these states could be used to determine the counting rates. The minimum energy of detectable particles was determined by the mass distribution around the crystal and an adjusted electronic bias of 100 kev. The purpose of the scintillation counter experiment on the Explorer VI earth satellite was to make direct observations of electrons in both the inner and outer radiation zones with a detector relatively insensitive to bremsstrahlung.

During the operation of the analog transmitter which broadcast the scintillator data, the satellite completed more than 60 circuits around its trajectory. However, because there were gross fluctuations in the outer zone associated with enhanced solar activity and magnetic storms, the isointensity plot shown in Figure 8-13 includes only data from the period between August 7 and 15, 1959, when there was a minimum of such activity. In spite of this selection, there are daily variations in the outer zone, and the isointensity lines in this region may be broadened into bands to include the daily variation of the contours. The number beside each point represents the revolution of the satellite during which the data were taken, with orbits numbered consecutively from launch. The innermost region in space shows the two-peak structure, and the lines represent decreasing intensity levels, as shown. The location of the lines where no points are available has been estimated from symmetry considerations. Data points at 10^7 electrons/cm^{2}sec at northern latitudes and a radial distance of 10,000 to 17,000 km were obtained in a region where the isointensity contour defines a "slot" (see Figure 8-13). The data illustrate the stability of this feature when compared with the spread of points at radial distances greater than 30,000 km. Data point Number 3, for example, is consistent with the other data points defining the boundary of the slot. At radial distances greater than 30,000 km, however, the points of the third revolution are a few thousand kilometers removed from the other points defining the contours. Evidently the outer zone contained more particles or the average energy of the particles increased during the third revolution on August 9 (a mildly disturbed day), although the inner zone remained essentially unchanged.

Consideration of the foregoing data shows that the structure of the outer Van Allen zone varied markedly with time. In addition to long-term, secular variations, there are violent changes associated with magnetic storms. There is evidence also of daily fluctuations. The scintillation counter which detected particles directly also revealed most noticeably the occurrence of short-term fluctuations.

Traversals of the outer radiation zone by the Soviet space rockets I and II (10) were made on January 2, 1959, and September 12, 1959. The upper portion of Figure 8-14 shows the space probes' trajectories relative to the geomagnetic lines of force. These lines of force intersect the earth's surface at 50, 55, 60, 65, and 70 degrees geomagnetic latitude. The trajectories labeled 2.1.59 and 12.9.59 correspond to the January 2 and September 12 flights, respectively. Superposed on these trajectories are the relative intensities observed during these two flights. The shift in the maximum, almost 9000 km closer to the earth on September 12 than on January 2, could not be accounted for by the difference in trajectory and lends further evidence for temporal variation in intensity in the outer zone. The September 12 flight occurred after a period of intense solar activity and strong magnetic storms, whereas a relatively quiet period preceeded the January 2 flight. It is interesting to note that the shoulder in the radiation intensity at the location of the inner radiation zone observed on January 2 had completely disappeared by September 12. The shaded areas in the upper portion of Figure 8-14 denote the approximate boundaries of the inner and outer radiation zones. The first Soviet space rocket was instrumented with a scintillation counter biased at various levels to sort out those pulses denoting energy losses in the scintillating crystal of 45, 450, and 4500 kev. Electrons of energy greater than 2 Mev or protons of energy greater than 30 Mev could penetrate the hull of 1 gm/cm^2 areal density and reach the scintillating crystal. Bremsstrahlung of electrons absorbed by the hull of the space probe could also contribute to the observed count rates. The lower portion of Figure 8-14 shows the radiation intensity measured by the various detectors on the first Soviet space rocket as a function of radial distance in thousands of kilometers from earth center. Curves labeled I, II, and III represent the omnidirectional intensity observed with the scintillation counter biased at 45 kev, 450 kev, and 4.5 Mev, respectively. Curve IV shows the energy flux, the total amount of energy released within the crystal per unit time, and curve V is the intensity obtained by means of a Geiger counter. The ratio of the Geiger counter rate to the ionization in the crystal at 40,000 to 50,000 km is consistent with bremsstrahlung created by electrons of energy of the order 50 kev. Since the ratio increases with

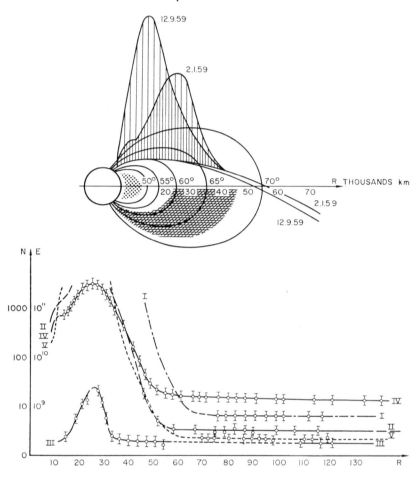

Figure 8-14 The upper curve shows the trajectories of the Soviet Space Rockets I (1/2/59) and II (9/12/59). Superposed on these trajectories are the relative intensities observed during the flights. The ordinate N is the omnidirectional intensity (particles per square centimeter second) for curves labeled I, II, and III with thresholds at 45 kev, 450 kev and 4500 kev, respectively. The ordinate E in ergs per second is the total energy released in a crystal and refers to the curve labeled IV. The abscissa R is the radial distance expressed in thousands of kilometers.

increasing energy, Figure 8-14 indicates that the radiation hardens at the position of peak intensity and softens at altitudes below and above the peak.

Long-term, temporal fluctuations are characteristic of the structure of the outer radiation belt. In the following sections intense and unusual short-term fluctuations associated with a geomagnetic storm are discussed in order to evaluate the degree to which solar injection and neutron albedo contribute to the population of the trapped radiation.

8-7 LIFETIME OF TRAPPED PARTICLES

The trapping lifetime of charged particles gives a measure of the amount of time a particle will spend in the radiation zones from the time it is injected to the time it is scattered out of the radiation zone. The most obvious process for the removal of particles from trapped orbits is by scattering by the ambient particles in the exosphere. It is believed that well above the earth's atmosphere, space is filled with a neutral plasma consisting of ionized hydrogen and electrons with a density of about 1000 particles/cm^3. An effective mechanism for scattering electrons is by interaction with the ionized proton component. The lifetime for scattering of electrons through an angle of the order of 90 degrees is given by (11)

$$\tau_\rho = \frac{1}{8\pi N v \left(\dfrac{e^2}{2E}\right)^2 \ln\left(2E/e^2 N^{1/3}\right)}. \tag{8-17}$$

N is the number of scattering centers/cm^3, E is the energy, and v is the velocity of the particle.

Ford (12) has shown that scattering by the ambient plasma electrons is a more effective mechanism for removing protons from the trapped radiation zone than scattering by the ambient plasma ions. The lifetime for this process is given by

$$\tau_e = \frac{mMv^3}{8\pi N e^4 \ln 2mv/q_c}. \tag{8-18}$$

M and m are the proton and electron mass, respectively, and q_c is the minimum momentum transfer in a collision. The first and second columns of Table 8-2 show the lifetime of electrons and protons in this medium as a function of energy. It is interesting to compare proton lifetimes resulting from scattering by the ambient plasma electrons to the lifetimes resulting from scattering by the ambient plasma protons. Column 3 of Table 8-2 shows the lifetime of protons resulting from scattering by the ionized hydrogen atoms in the exosphere.

Other mechanisms for scattering particles out of the radiation zone involve the violation of the first, second, and third invariants of motion

TABLE 8-2

The Lifetimes of Particles in the Radiation Zones
for Scattering by the Ambient Particles

Electron Lifetimes		Proton Lifetimes			
Energy (kev)	Lifetimes for Scattering from Ions (sec)	Energy (Mev)	Lifetimes for Scattering from Electrons (sec)	Energy (Mev)	Lifetimes for Scattering from Ions (sec)
0.1	7.0×10^3	1	1.2×10^8	1	2.0×10^{11}
1.0	2.0×10^5	10	3.2×10^9	10	6.0×10^{12}
10	5.5×10^6	20	1.0×10^{10}	20	1.6×10^{13}
100	1.7×10^8	30	1.7×10^{10}	30	2.9×10^{13}
200	5.5×10^8	40	2.5×10^{10}	40	4.2×10^{13}
500	2.7×10^9	50	3.3×10^{10}	50	6.1×10^{13}
1000	9.5×10^9	75	5.5×10^{10}	75	1.1×10^{14}
1500	2.0×10^{10}	100	8.0×10^{10}	100	1.9×10^{14}

of the charged particles in the geomagnetic field. A breakdown of the first invariant of the motion has been proposed by Singer (13) as a possible explanation of the decrease in the intensity of the high-energy ($E > 10$ Mev) proton component with increasing altitude. It is to be recalled that the magnetic moment of a particle is adiabatically invariant if the gradient of the magnetic field is small compared to the gyro radius of the particle, $[a(|\Delta B|/B) \ll 1]$. For a 1-Mev proton at 2 earth radii, this condition is certainly fulfilled. However, for a 100-Mev proton at 6 earth radii, the gyro radius becomes comparable to the gradient in the field, $1/B |\partial B/\partial r|$. In this case the mirror point is no longer well defined but changes randomly during each bounce of the particle in its reciprocal motion. The particle thus performs a random walk up and down the magnetic-field line, and since there is a sink at low mirror points the particle will eventually diffuse out of the trapped orbit. It should be noted that the magnetic moment of electrons in the range of 10 kev to a few Mev is an adiabatic invariant to extremely high altitudes.

The most likely source of temporal fluctuations, and of possible breakdown of the adiabatic invariants of the motion of particles in the geomagnetic field, is the existence of hydromagnetic waves in the exosphere. These low-frequency waves are possibly generated by the interaction of the solar wind with the geomagnetic field in the neighborhood of 10 earth radii. Hydromagnetic waves are observed as pulsations in the surface geomagnetic field. If the temporal changes in the field are fast in comparison to the gyro period of the particle, then the first adiabatic invariant will again be violated. Dragt (14) considered the effect of hydromagnetic waves in the frequency range of 0 to 4 cps on the trapped proton component of the radiation. These waves are effective in scattering protons from the radiation belt and lead to extremely short trapping lifetimes compared to the scattering mechanism previously considered. For a 100-Mev proton, for example, Dragt obtains a lifetime of approximately ½ day (43,200 seconds) at a radial distance of 6 Re.

The problem of scattering of particles from the radiation zone resulting from a breakdown of the second invariant of the motion has been considered by Parker (15). It was shown that if the relative amplitude $\Delta B/B$ of the hydromagnetic wave is maintained throughout the mirror field particles will soon diffuse through the mirror and be lost. High-energy electrons (~ 0.1 kev) in the outer Van Allen radiation zone would diffuse along the line of force with a characteristic time of about 4 months when acted on by waves with a 1-cps frequency and an amplitude of 10 gamma. Hydromagnetic diffusion appears to be more important than collisions in determining the electron lifetime and distribution in the outer Van Allen radiation zone. The effects of a breakdown of the third invariant of the motion have also been considered by Parker (16). This breakdown leads to diffusion and particle loss from the trapped region at a rate greater than that resulting from the compression and rarification of the magnetic field. The total energy of the particles remaining in the field decreases as a result of hydromagnetic disturbances. It is important to point out that in order to be effective in scattering particles from the radiation belt all of these mechanisms depend on the existence of a rather high flux of hydromagnetic waves in the exosphere. Such fluxes, although reasonable, have not yet been observed.

8-8   NEUTRON ALBEDO INJECTION

A neutron albedo hypothesis has been proposed for populating the radiation zones with particles (17). This hypothesis assumes that primary cosmic radiation impinging on the upper atmosphere of the earth interacts with oxygen and nitrogen molecules. Some of these interactions result in spallation reactions in which neutrons and protons are emitted in all directions. The protons moving radially away from the center of the earth are not likely to be trapped by the geomagnetic field. The neutrons, on the other hand, have a lifetime of approximately 12 minutes before they decay into electrons and protons. During this 12-minute interval some neutrons can escape from the upper regions of the atmosphere into the region of the radiation belts. There they decay and produce a characteristic proton spectrum and an electron spectrum with an end point at approximately 780 kev. Because of the requirement of conservation of momentum, the proton will carry off nearly all of the neutron kinetic energy, and the end point of the electron spectrum at 780 kev will be essentially independent of the neutron kinetic energy. A comprehensive treatment of the cosmic-ray, neutron-albedo theory has been given by Hess, Canfield, and Lengenfelter (18). Ford (12) has adopted their results to show the number of decay neutrons/cm³ sec Mev versus energy for radial distances of 2, 4, and 8 earth radii. This is shown in Figure 8-15. Since the energy of a proton resulting from beta decay is nearly the same as that of the neutron, this graph can also be interpreted

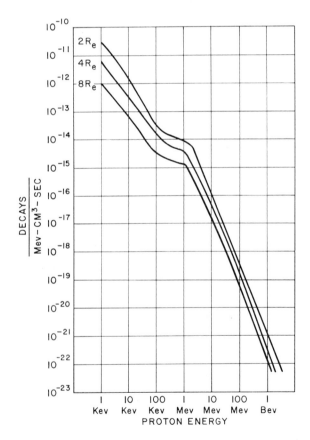

Figure 8-15   Energy spectrum of neutrons decaying at altitudes of 2 Re, 4 Re, and 8 Re.

as giving the spectral rate of injection of protons at these altitudes. In order to calculate the equilibrium intensity of protons in the heart of the inner zone for energies greater than 40 Mev, it is necessary to integrate the 2 Re curve from 40 Mev to infinity. The total number of protons injected per unit volume per second with energies greater than 40 Mev is 10^{-16} protons/cm^3 sec. From equation (8-16), the equilibrium density of protons is given by $\rho = n(r)\tau$. Since $J = \rho v$,

$$J = n(r)v\tau = 10^{-16} \times 5 \times 10^9 \times 10^{10} = 5 \times 10^3 \text{ protons/cm}^2 \text{ sec,}$$

where an average velocity of 5×10^9 cm/sec was assumed for protons of energy greater than 40 Mev, and the lifetime τ was taken from Table 8-2. The calculated intensity is in good agreement with the observed intensity as tabulated in Table 8-1.

From the neutron decay curve (Figure 8-15) it is also possible to determine the electron intensity in the outer radiation zone. By integrating the 4 Re curve from zero to infinity, the total number of decay neutrons/cm^2 sec is obtained. This number may also be interpreted as the rate of injection of electrons in the energy range 0–800 kev into the outer radiation zone. The rate of injection is $n(r) < 10^{-12}$ electrons/ cm^3 sec, the average velocity $v \sim 10^9$ cm/sec, and the lifetime (from Table 8-2) $\tau \sim 10^9$ sec. Thus

$$J = n(r)v\tau = 10^{-12} \times 10^9 \times 10^9 = 10^6 \text{ electrons/cm}^2 \text{ sec.}$$

In this case the calculated intensity is almost 3 orders of magnitude lower than the observed values tabulated in Table 8-2. The neutron-albedo injection mechanism successfully accounts for the intensity of the energetic proton component found in the inner radiation zone; however, it does not account for the electron intensities observed in the outer radiation zone.

If the neutron-albedo mechanism were the only one active in populating the radiation zones, then the structure of the zones would have the following distinctive characteristics. First, the energy spectrum of the electron component would be characteristic of the neutron-decay beta spectrum, with an end point at approximately 780 kev. Second, since the primary cosmic flux is constant in time, the intensity of particles in the radiation belt should also be roughly constant with time if the geomagnetic field does not undergo great fluctuations in magnetic intensity. Third, the electron pitch-angle distribution should be characteristic of the neutron injection mechanism. In this case, since particles mirroring at high latitudes are affected by the upper atmosphere (or the model chosen to describe the upper atmosphere), the pitch-angle distribution curve near pitch angles of 90 degrees is most representative of neutron albedo. In the following sections some experimental observations in conflict with these characteristics are presented.

As previously pointed out in the discussion of various experimental observations of intensities in the radiation belt, long-range temporal variations are commonly observed in the outer radiation zone. It is possible to explain these observations in terms of slowly varying fields and the properties of the detecting instruments. If the geomagnetic field is compressed and then rarified, as it would be during a geomagnetic storm, the particles trapped in the field would be accelerated and decelerated by a betatron-type mechanism. Furthermore, the density of particles should increase with compression and decrease with rarification of the magnetic field. Since the efficiency of detection of most instruments increases with increasing particle energy, both factors would give rise to fluctuations in particle intensity, correlated with the compression and rarification of the magnetic field. Thus, if a neutron-albedo mechanism populated the outer radiation zone and no other injection mechanism were active, then, neglecting

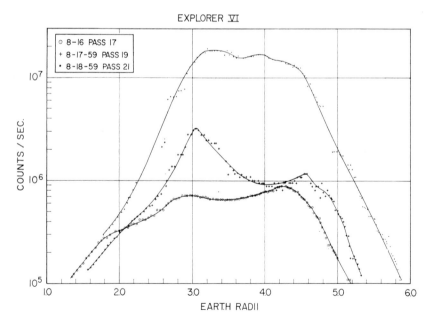

Figure 8-16 The count rates from the Explorer VI scintillation counter for three traversals of the outer Van Allen zone at approximately 24-hr intervals during a geomagnetic storm, showing a continuous increase in count rate.

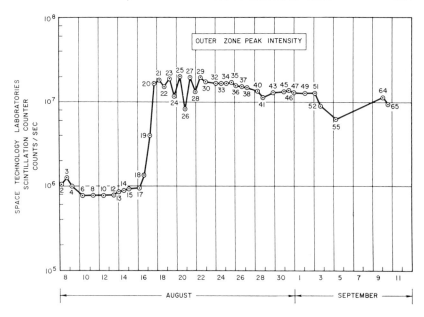

Figure 8-17 Approximate maximum count rate of the scintillation counter determined twice daily as the satellite traversed the outer radiation zone.

for a moment the existence of acceleration mechanisms other than betatron acceleration, we should expect to observe a correlation between the geomagnetic field intensity and the intensity of radiation trapped in the outer zone. An unusual opportunity to observe just such an effect resulted from the data obtained from the radiation instruments on Explorer VI (19). On August 16, 1959, a geomagnetic storm occurred while the instruments on Explorer VI were gathering data in the radiation belt. Figure 8-16 shows the intensity observed with a scintillation counter before and after the geomagnetic storm. The lower graph of Figure 8-16 is the intensity of radiation in the radiation belt prior to the geomagnetic storm. Twelve hours after the sudden commencement a continual buildup in peak intensity was observed until on the twenty-first pass the intensity was 20 times the prestorm value. Since the magnetic field is compressed during the main phase of the storm and approaches its prestorm value during the recovery phase, it would be expected that the peak intensity of radiation would increase with a time constant comparable to the period of the geomagnetic storm. Figure 8-17 shows the peak intensity observed by the scintillation counter on successive passes before and after the geomagnetic storm. Note that the peak intensity remains fairly constant for many days after the sudden commencement of the geomagnetic storm and does not seem to decrease, even when the field has returned back to its normal value. This observation indicates that it is not possible to explain the injection of particles into the radiation belt by a neutron-albedo theory alone. The greatest success of the neutron-albedo theory is in its prediction of proton intensities in the inner radiation zone of the same order of magnitude as actually observed.

It has recently been proposed that the fluctuations observed in the radiation belt may be accounted for by a modified neutron-albedo mechanism. In this hypothesis solar flare protons striking the atmosphere at high latitudes give rise to the albedo neutrons. Thus it may be possible to produce long-range fluctuations in intensity over a period of a few days.

8-9 PITCH-ANGLE DISTRIBUTION AND THE NEUTRON-ALBEDO THEORY

The pitch-angle distribution $p(\alpha_0)$ is defined as the number of particles/cm^2 sec ster in an equatorial plane with pitch angles between α_0 and $\alpha_0 + d\alpha_0$. (The subscript refers to values of the variables at the geomagnetic equator.) Thus the pitch-angle distribution function $p(\alpha_0)$ is the unidirectional intensity $j(\alpha_0)$ of particles in an equatorial plane. If the omnidirectional intensity along a geomagnetic line of force is known, it is possible to determine the pitch-angle distribution and mirror-point density of particles trapped along a tube of force including the given line. The importance of the pitch-angle distribution and mirror-point density arises not only because they characterize the trapped particles but also because given an injection mechanism, such as neutron albedo, it is possible to determine a theoretical pitch-angle distribution and mirror-point density. Thus it should be possible to compare a theoretical pitch-angle distribution with the one observed in the radiation belt. The purpose of this section is to present one such comparison. It will be shown that although the observed pitch-angle distributions are in good agreement with the theoretical pitch-angle distributions for particles that mirror at latitudes removed from the equator, there is great deviation between the two distributions in the equatorial region.

The omnidirectional intensity at any point along a line of force is related to the unidirectional intensity at the point $j(\alpha, r)$ by the integral of $j(\alpha, r)$ over the total solid angle.

$$J(r) = 4\pi \int_{\alpha \min}^{\pi/2} j(\alpha, r) \sin \alpha \, d\alpha = 4\pi \int_{\alpha \min}^{\pi/2} j(\cos \alpha, r) \, d(\cos \alpha), \quad (8\text{-}19)$$

where $2\pi \sin \alpha \, d\alpha = d\Omega$.

The solution of equation (8-19) has been carried out by Farley and Sanders (2). They show that the unidirectional intensity at α_0 at the geomagnetic equator is equal to the unidirectional intensity at α at any point along the line of force if α is related to α_0 by the mirror-point equation $B(r) \sin^2 \alpha_0 = B_0 \sin^2 \alpha$. Substituting $j(r, \cos \alpha) = p(\cos \alpha_0)$ into equation (8-19), it is possible, by changing the variable of integration and making the proper substitution (2), to reduce the equation to the form of Abel's integral equation. The solution to this equation is found in most standard mathematics textbooks on integral equations [e.g., Courant (20)]. The general solution gives $p(\cos \alpha_0)$ when the omnidirectional intensity $J(r)$ is known along the line of force. If the pitch-angle distribution is plotted against $\cos \alpha_0$, rather than α_0 itself, then the area under the $p(\cos \alpha_0)$ versus $\cos \alpha_0$ curve represents the omnidirectional intensity in the equatorial plane. Thus it is customary to plot the pitch-angle distribution against $\cos \alpha$ and to regard the pitch-angle distribution as a function of $\cos \alpha$, that is, $p(\cos \alpha)$.

In order to illustrate the data from which pitch-angle distributions have been calculated, the count rates of the Explorer VI scintillation counter at the time that the satellite crossed the geomagnetic field line intersecting the equator at 21,000 km are shown in Figure 8-18. It was assumed in the calculation that these count rates are proportional to the omnidirectional particle intensity at the point in space at which the data was taken. The apparent absence of particles with pitch angle near 90 degrees during magnetically quiet periods is an interesting aspect of the data. The analysis by Farley and Sanders of similar data for the period immediately following a geomagnetic storm, August 18 to 22, 1959, showed that the "dip" in count rate at the geomagnetic equator was replaced by a sharply rising peak. Figure 8-19 shows the pitch-angle distributions calculated from the data presented in Figure 8-18 (August 8 to 16) and similar data obtained between August 18 and 22, during the recovery phase of a geomagnetic storm. The dotted line is the pitch-angle distribution calculated from omnidirectional intensities given by Hess et al. (21) for neutron-decay electrons. It is clear from the data that the pitch-angle distribution of electrons in the outer radiation zone is incompatible with the existence of an unmodified neutron-decay electron-energy spectrum. Indeed, other data indicate the existence of a substantial flux of electrons of energies greater than 1 Mev and that the flux of these particles increases markedly after a geomagnetic storm (19). It is, of course, quite possible that the neutron decay is the source mechanism for electrons in the outer zone and that the pitch-angle distribution and energy of these particles is subsequently modified by some unknown time-dependent mechanism.

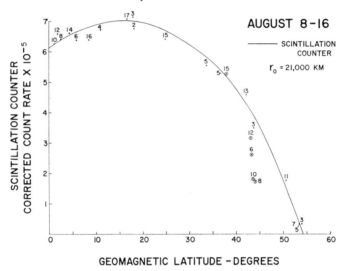

Figure 8-18 Scintillation counter count rate as a function of geomagnetic latitude taken along the line of force crossing the geomagnetic equator at 21,000 km.

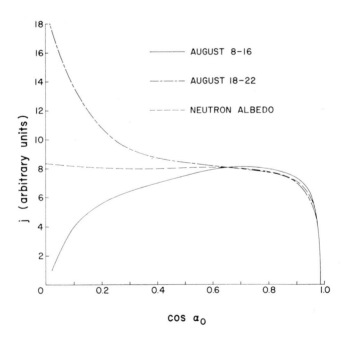

Figure 8-19 Comparison of the August 8–16 and August 18–22 pitch-angle distributions with that calculated from the omnidirectional intensities for neutron decay electrons.

8-10 SOLAR INJECTION

A solar injection hypothesis to account for the population of the radiation zone is appealing because the sun is the only known source of particles with energies comparable to those found in the radiation belt. Furthermore, the sun is known to emit immense plasma clouds during magnetic storms occurring on its surface. These plasma clouds have sufficient energy to cause severe perturbations of the geomagnetic field. Unfortunately, it is very difficult to explain how particles can be injected into a convex field geometry such as the geomagnetic field, and a quantitative theory which can be tested against experimental observations has not yet been evolved. Most of the ideas relating to solar injection involve instabilities that somehow develop in the interface region between a plasma cloud ejected from the sun and the geomagnetic field. Moreover, experimental evidence for violent fluctuations in both particle intensities and magnetic-field measurements is common. The geomagnetic storm of August 16, 1959, produced intense and unusual fluctuations in the particle intensity measured by the Explorer VI scintillation counter. Figure 8-20 shows the fluctuations that were first observed during pass 17 at about 0600 Greenwich Mean Time (GMT) some 2 hr after the storm's sudden commencement. These fluctuations, rising and falling by as much as three orders of magnitude within a few minutes, were observed while the vehicle was traveling at a speed of less than 1.5 km/sec with respect to the earth.

The direct intrusion of a diamagnetic gas cloud containing energetic electrons ($E > 200$ kev) was inferred from the data gathered during the storm of August 16 (22). The observed data consist of the magnetic-field strength deduced from a magnetometer onboard the Explorer VI earth satellite and correlated scintillation-counter intensity measurements. Figure 8-21 shows a portion of the detailed correlations made at 44,000 km on August 16, 1959 (pass 18). The scintillation-counter intensity fluctuations are observed to be 180 degrees out of phase with the magnetometer fluctuation. These observations indicate that there is a magnetic field associated with the particles seen by the scintillation counter, which is capable of substantially reducing the geomagnetic field at that distance. This magnetic-field depression may possibly be the result of an intrusion of diamagnetic gas clouds into the geomagnetic field caused by the increased pressure of the storm-day solar wind or by the arrival of a cloud of solar gas in the vicinity of the earth. The particles in these ragged gas clouds may have disordered internal motions which become

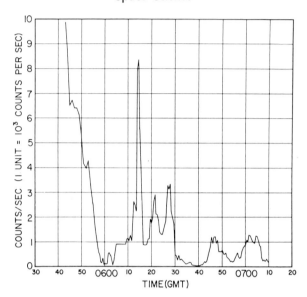

TIME(GMT)

Figure 8-20 Rapid variations in particle intensity during the geomagnetic storm of August 16, 1959.

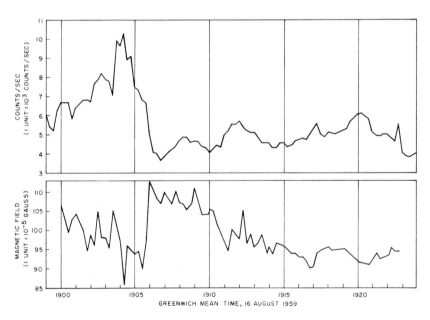

GREENWICH MEAN TIME, 16 AUGUST 1959

Figure 8-21 Simultaneous particle count rates and magnetic field measurements at 44,000 km during a geomagnetic storm. The upper graph shows the scintillation counter count rates and the lower curve shows the magnitude of one component of the geomagnetic field.

ordered as the particles take up internal orbits that will exclude the geomagnetic field. The field outside the clouds is increased because some lines of force are excluded from the interior of the bubbles. The field inside the clouds is not zero, since the geomagnetic field lines are not completely excluded or because the clouds have some internal fields of their own.

The local time on Explorer VI at 7 earth radii was about 7 P.M., and the satellite therefore was on the side of the earth away from the sun at this distance. Whether these gas clouds ever penetrate to distances less than 7 earth radii on the dark side of the earth has not yet been determined. The particles seen by the scintillation counter at this time may be either electrons or protons. If they are electrons above 500 kev, which seems likely, and if the particle flux is isotropic, a count rate of 10^4/sec corresponds to a flux of approximately 3×10^5 electrons/cm^2 sec. This flux of 500-kev electrons has an energy density of about 10^{-11} ergs/cm^3. The magnetic energy density in a field of 100 gamma (10^{-3} gauss) is 4×10^{-8} ergs/cm^3. Even if the particles are protons, the particle fluxes measured by the scintillation counter are inadequate to cause the observed variations in the magnetic field, and there must be large numbers of low-energy particles associated with the particles seen by the scintillation counter.

An effect not directly related to enhanced solar activity, and involving a betatron acceleration of particles by a time-varying field, has also been observed. Figure 8-22 shows a comparison of the Ex-

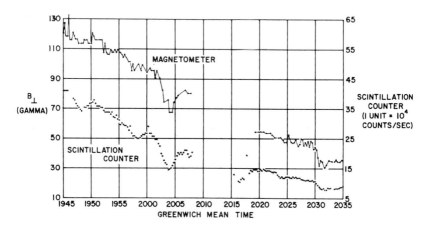

Figure 8-22   Betatron acceleration: simultaneous particle count rates and magnetic field measurements. The upper curve shows the magnitude of one component of the magnetic field and the lower curve shows the scintillation counter count rates.

plorer VI magnetometer and scintillation counter on August 9, 1959. The in-phase correlation between the two instruments has been interpreted as an acceleration and deceleration of particles above and below the scintillation counter bias level by a time-varying geomagnetic field. Calculations to determine the exponent γ in an $E^{-\gamma}$ energy spectrum and a detailed study of this phenomenon have been undertaken by Judge and Coleman (23). The correlations illustrated by Figure 8-22 may be compared to the anticorrelations observed during the geomagnetic storm. In a betatron acceleration mechanism the geomagnetic field is in control of the particles, whereas in the case of anticorrelations the opposite situation exists.

8-11 CONCLUSIONS

It is clear that the fluctuating nature of phenomena in the exosphere is quite similar to meteorological conditions on earth. Whether a neutron-albedo-type mechanism could predominate in such an environment has still not been resolved. Nevertheless, a neutron-albedo-type mechanism can explain only a small segment of the experimental observations. On the other hand, a satisfactory solar injection theory is still not in existence. Observations in interplanetary space by means of a Geiger counter on Pioneer V indicate that solar injection of particles of the same energy as observed in the radiation zone does not occur. It is still possible that particles of energy appreciably lower than those observed in the radiation belt are injected. Thus it is necessary that the solar injection mechanism be somehow coupled with a local acceleration mechanism to account for the structure of the radiation belt. The quest into what these mechanisms may be is the goal of research for the coming years.

REFERENCES

1. Alfvén, H., *Cosmical Electrodynamics*, Oxford University Press, London, 1953.
2. Farley, T. A., and N. L. Sanders, Pitch Angle Distribution and Mirror Point Densities in the Outer Radiation Zone, *J. Geophys. Res.*, **67**, 2159–2168 (June 1962).
3. McIlwain, Carl E., Coordinates for Mapping the Distribution of Magnetically Trapped Particles, *J. Geophys. Res.*, **66**, 3681–3691 (1961).
4. Welch, J. A., and W. A. Whitaker, Theory of Geomagnetically Trapped Electrons from an Artificial Source, *J. Geophys. Res.*, **64**, 909–922 (1959).
5. Dessler, A. J., Effects of Magnetic Anomaly on Particle Radiation Trapped in Geomagnetic Field, *J. Geophys. Res.*, **64**, 713–715 (1959).

6. Janossy, L., *Cosmic Rays*, Second Edition, Oxford University Press, London, 1950, pp. 22–26.

7. Van Allen, J. A., and L. Frank, Radiation Around the Earth to a Radial Distance of 107,400 km, *Nature*, **183**, 430–434 (1959).

8. Arnoldy, R. L., R. A. Hoffman, and J. R. Winckler, Observations of the Van Allen Radiation Regions during August and September 1959, Part 1, *J. Geophys. Res.*, **65**, 1361–1376 (1960).

9. Rosen, A., T. A. Farley, and C. P. Sonett, Soft Radiation Measurements on Explorer VI Earth Satellite, *Space Research*, Proceedings of the First International Space Science Symposium, ed. H. K. Kallmann-Bijl, North Holland, Amsterdam, 1960, pp. 938–950.

10. Vernov, S. N., and A. E. Chadakov, Terrestrial Corpuscular Radiation and Cosmic Rays, *Space Research*, Proceedings of the First International Space Science Symposium, ed. H. K. Kallmann-Bijl, North Holland, Amsterdam, 1960, p. 751.

11. Kellogg, P. J., Possible Explanation of the Radiation Observed by Van Allen at High Altitudes in Satellites, *Nuovo Cimento*, Series X, **II**, 48–66 (1959). See also L. Spitzer, *Physics of Fully Ionized Gases*, Interscience Publishers, 1956, equations 5-5 and 5-13.

12. Ford, G. W., *Estimation of the Flux of Energetic Protons Above the Lower Radiation Belt*, Space Technology Laboratories, Inc., Theoretical Physics Report STL/5101-0040-RV-000, November 1961.

13. Singer, S. F., Latitude and Altitude Distribution of Geomagnetically Trapped Protons, *Phys. Rev. Letters*, **5**, 300 (1960).

14. Dragt, A. J., Effect of Hydromagnetic Waves on the Lifetime of Van Allen Radiation Protons, *J. Geophys. Res.*, **66**, 1641–1650 (1961).

15. Parker, E. N., Effects of Hydromagnetic Waves in a Dipole Field on the Longitudinal Invariant, *J. Geophys. Res.*, **66**, 693–788 (1961).

16. Parker, E. N., Geomagnetic Fluctuations and the Form of the Outer Zone of the Van Allen Radiation Belt, *J. Geophys. Res.*, **65**, 3117–3130 (1960).

17. Singer, S. F., Trapped Albedo Theory of the Radiation Belt, *Phys. Rev. Letters*, **1**, 525 (1958).

18. Hess, W. N., E. Canfield, and R. E. Lengenfelter, Cosmic-Ray Neutron Demography, *J. Geophys. Res.*, **66**, 665–677 (1961).

19. Rosen, A., and T. A. Farley, Characteristics of the Van Allen Radiation Zones as Measured by the Scintillation Counter on Explorer VI, *J. Geophys. Res.*, **66**, 2013–2028 (1961).

20. Courant, R., *Differential and Integral Calculus*, Interscience Publishers, 1956, p. 340.

21. Hess, W. N., and J. Killeen, Spatial Distribution of Electrons from Neutron Decay in the Outer Radiation Belt, *J. Geophys. Res.*, **66**, 3671–3680 (1961).

22. Farley, T. A., and A. Rosen, Charged Particle Variations in the Outer Van Allen Zones during a Geomagnetic Storm, *J. Geophys. Res.*, **65**, 3494–3496 (1960).

23. Judge, D. J., and P. J. Coleman, *Evidence for Acceleration of Geomagnetically Trapped Particles by Hydromagnetic Waves; Explorer VI*, to be submitted for publication.

CHAPTER 9

THEORETICAL AND EXPERIMENTAL ASPECTS OF RING CURRENTS

EDWARD J. SMITH

Jet Propulsion Laboratory
California Institute of Technology

Throughout most of this century scientific interest in the possible existence of a geomagnetic ring current has been persistent. A ring current is a toroidal current concentric with the earth and lying in the equatorial plane. It is expected to be a westward current of several million amperes and is typically placed at a geocentric altitude of 5 to 10 R_E (R_E = earth radii), that is, in the tenuous outer fringes of the earth's atmosphere. A ring current is a convenient source of a large-scale, quasi-uniform magnetic field. The existence of such a field surrounding the earth may account for certain geophysical phenomena associated with magnetic storms and aurorae.

A ring current is one of a class of large-scale currents that deform or perturb the geomagnetic field. Presently accepted theories, which are supported by the available experimental evidence, suggest that the earth's field is confined to a cavity inside the interplanetary medium (1, 2). The cavity contains the geomagnetic field and the ionized outer atmosphere of the earth, including the Van Allen radiation zones. The magnetic energy inside the cavity exceeds the kinetic energies of the plasma (ionized gas) and the trapped, high-energy particles. For this reason the cavity is called "the magnetosphere."

The boundary, or "magnetopause," consists of the compressed geomagnetic field on one side and the perfectly conducting, interplanetary gas on the other. The containment of the geomagnetic field implies that currents flow along the inner surface of the cavity. Thus, there is a large-scale current system at the termination of the geomagnetic field. The best estimates, based on data from space probes, place these currents at 15 R_E on the side of the earth facing the sun. The interplanetary plasma may not be stationary; it may be flowing outward from the sun. This streaming gas is frequently referred to as the "solar wind." Because of this flow, the magnetosphere may be deformed into the shape of a tear drop with a tail pointing away from the sun (3).

The magnetosphere is bounded on its interior by the ionosphere (altitude, 100 to 300 km) and the insulating air layer lying below it. There are large-scale current systems in the ionosphere that cause regular, daily variations in the magnitude and direction of the geomagnetic field (4). Large perturbations of the geomagnetic field are associated with ionospheric currents located near the auroral zones.

The possible existence of a ring current is important because it is related to many fundamental problems concerning the earth's outer atmosphere and its interaction with the interplanetary medium. (1) It may play a crucial role in magnetic storms. The growth and subsidence of a ring current could be responsible for certain characteristic features of the storms observed at the earth's surface. (2) It may be intimately related to the aurorae. The charged particles in a ring current may either cause the aurorae or so perturb the distant geomagnetic field that particles which might not do so otherwise can reach the polar atmosphere. (3) The properties and dynamics of the earth's outer atmosphere could be strongly influenced by the presence of a ring current. If magnetic storm and auroral effects are indeed the result, then the charged particles which cause the current are an important constituent of the outer atmosphere. The origin and characteristics of these particles would represent important information. The existence of the ring current and its dynamic, or time-dependent, variations may imply that trapping and loss mechanisms are operating in the magnetosphere or that modes of energy exchange exist for a collisionless plasma.

Our discussion of ring currents consists of two major sections. One is a theoretical discussion of how a ring current can originate and be maintained; in the second the experimental evidence concerning its existence is presented and discussed. Measurements made on earth satellites and space probes are emphasized.

9-1 THEORY

The following discussion traces the historical development of ring-current theory. This approach is employed because the fairly sophisticated modern theory can be most readily understood by seeing how it evolved from simpler, and more naïve, concepts. Furthermore, this approach gives dramatic emphasis to an important difference between the modern theory and the earlier explanations. The older theories, though based on simple concepts and simple mathematical models, involved *ad hoc* assumptions and unnatural, or artificial, physical situations. On the other hand, in the modern theory the ring current arises in a natural way, with a minimum number of assumptions, even though the physical concepts and mathematics are more complicated. This combination of history and theory is intended to be an accurate record, although the writer has gone beyond some of the original works in an attempt to recreate the motivation for each.

Historically, the primary goal of ring-current theory has been to solve the steady-state problem. The basic question has been: how can such a current system be maintained? This preoccupation with the steady state is adhered to in the following discussion, except for a few comments on the origin and decay of the ring current.

Störmer's theory

In 1911 the famous mathematical physicist Carl Störmer postulated that a ring current encircled the earth at very great altitudes (5). This postulate was part of Störmer's attempt to explain the aurorae. He was an advocate of an explanation proposed by Birkeland shortly before the turn of the century, which is still given serious consideration. The basic concept is that the auroral emissions (electromagnetic radiation from gases in the upper atmosphere) are excited by the bombardment of particles from interplanetary space. According to this explanation, charged particles emitted by the sun, which arrive in the vicinity of the earth, are deflected toward the poles by the geomagnetic field. Störmer undertook a theoretical study of the motion of a charged particle in a magnetic-dipole field.

One of the most important results of his analysis was that for particles entering the earth's field from outside there are regions of space into which the particles cannot enter, the so-called "forbidden zones." In order for particles to penetrate close to the earth's surface, a certain minimum kinetic energy is required. It is known that approximately 1½ days elapse between a solar flare and the associated magnetic storm and aurorae. Thus the time required for the particles to propagate from the sun to the earth implies an average velocity of 1000 km/sec. Since the sun is composed primarily of hydrogen, it is likely that such particles are protons. These two pieces of information provide an estimate of the kinetic energy of the incoming particles (~20 kev). It was clear from Störmer's analysis that such low-energy particles could reach the earth only in the immediate vicinity of the magnetic poles. However, the auroral zones, that is, the range of latitudes inside which auroral activity is most common, are located at a geomagnetic latitude of approximately 68 degrees, or 22 degrees from the poles. This paradox represented a fundamental obstacle to the acceptance of the auroral theory.

In an attempt to resolve this dilemma, Störmer invoked a westward ring current. Such a current would produce a large-scale magnetic field directed southward interior to itself. (This can be seen most simply by employing the right-hand rule.) Since the geomagnetic field is directed northward (the north magnetic pole is located near the south geographic pole), the ring-current field would oppose, or "weaken," the geomagnetic field. The reduced strength of the field surrounding the earth could permit low-energy particles to reach the earth at lower latitudes, that is, in the vicinity of the auroral zones.

In addition to postulating the existence of a ring current, Störmer attempted to explain how such a current could arise, that is, what sort of orbits the charge particles would move in which produced the current. The force exerted on a charged particle moving in a magnetic field is given by the Lorentz force law (in MKS units):

$$\mathbf{F} = e\mathbf{v} \times \mathbf{B}, \tag{9-1}$$

where e is the charge on the particle, $\mathbf{v}$ is the particle velocity, and $\mathbf{B}$ is the magnetic field. Since the force is transverse to both $\mathbf{v}$ and $\mathbf{B}$, no work is done on the particle by the field (its kinetic energy is constant) and the effect of the field is merely to cause the particle to circle about the field lines. In the simple orbit proposed by Störmer the particles moved in equatorial circular orbits about the earth (Figure 9-1). The centrifugal reaction mv^2/R (m is the particle mass and R is the location of the orbit from the center of the earth) was exactly compensated by the centripetal Lorentz force. Thus

$$\frac{mv^2}{R} = evB. \tag{9-2}$$

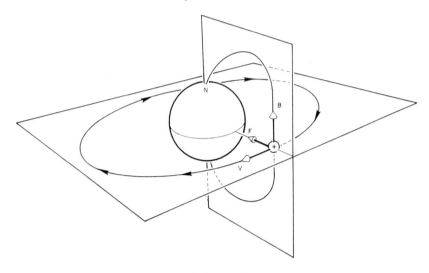

Figure 9-1   Störmer ring current.

The magnitude of the geomagnetic field in the equatorial plane is given by

$$B = \frac{\mu_0}{4\pi} \frac{M_E}{R^3},\tag{9-3}$$

where M_E is the earth's magnetic dipole moment. By combining these equations, the radius can be found at which this condition is fulfilled, namely

$$R = \left(\frac{\mu_0 M_E e}{4\pi m v}\right)^{\frac{1}{2}}.\tag{9-4}$$

(This distance is frequently written c_{st} and called the Störmer unit.)

If representative values of m and v are substituted in equation (9-4), for example, protons with a velocity of 1000 km/sec, then $R = 150\ R_E$. Since the distance from the earth to the moon is approximately 60 R_E, the ring current proposed by Störmer would be located far outside the orbit of the moon!

Störmer's ring-current theory is primarily of historical interest. Criticisms which the theory could not overcome were very quickly raised. The fundamental problem of both the ring-current theory and this particular version of auroral theory was that only particles of one sign were involved. In the case of a ring current, for example, the mutual electrostatic repulsion between the positively charged particles would quickly dispel the current, provided the particles were able to get into these rather peculiar and special orbits in the first place. The large-scale neutrality of ionized gases, such as those emitted by the sun, is now a well-established principle of cosmic electrodynamics.

Störmer was unable to develop a satisfactory ring-current theory. Furthermore, it may be that his auroral theory is incorrect; it appears now that the particles that cause the aurorae may be stored in the magnetosphere before being "dumped" into the high-latitude auroral zone. However, Störmer's suggestions and analysis are still of great value. His analysis of the motion of individual particles in the geomagnetic field has been applied successfully to cosmic rays and to high-energy solar protons. His analysis of the effect a ring current would have on the trajectories of particles is still valid. It is a fact that the auroral zones move toward lower latitudes during the main phase of magnetic storms (6). The creation or intensification of a ring current could be responsible. Furthermore, variations in the intensity of solar protons arriving at a normally forbidden latitude as a function of magnetic storm phase are also consistent with the effects caused by a ring current (7).

Historically, the effect of a ring current on the aurorae has been of secondary interest. The primary motive in ring current theory has been to explain certain aspects of magnetic storms. Subsequent ring-current theories are closely related to magnetic storm effects, although it has been common to try to explain both magnetic storms and aurorae with a single theory.

The Chapman-Ferraro theory

The steady geomagnetic field is subject to "storms" at an average rate of 3 or 4 days per month. The characteristic feature of magnetic storms is the occurrence of fluctuations in the field elements (horizontal intensity, declination, dip, etc.) (4, 8). The typical period of these fluctuations can range from an hour to less than a second. The corresponding magnitude changes may vary between several hundred or a thousand gamma to a fraction of one gamma. (1 gamma = 10^{-5} gauss, approximately one fifty-thousandth of the earth's field at the surface.) This *irregular* component of the storm field is strongly latitude-dependent and the maximum amplitude occurs in the auroral zone.

In addition to these rapid changes in the storm field, there is a *regular*, long-period component (hours to days) that exhibits a characteristic behavior during magnetic storms. Changes in the horizontal field intensity provide the simplest and most direct evidence of this tendency of the gross features of magnetic storms to be reproducible. The typical time-dependent behavior of the horizontal component (Figure 9-2) is as follows:

1. The beginning of the storm (the *initial phase*) is accompanied by an increase in average field intensity. A typical value for the peak of the initial phase is ~20γ. This phase usually lasts several hours, after which the average horizontal intensity has returned to its prestorm value.

2. The average intensity continues to decrease to a value less than prestorm value (the *main phase*). It reaches a minimum value in perhaps 1 day. A typical value of the average field change during the main phase is 100γ.

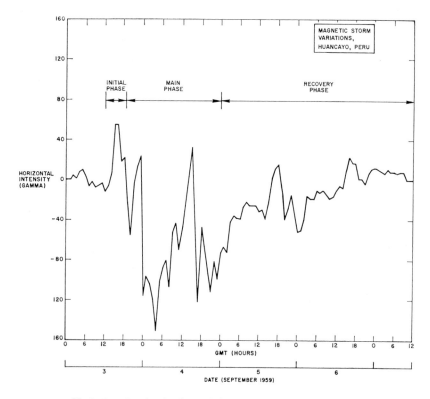

Figure 9-2 Variation in the horizontal intensity of the earth's field during a magnetic storm.

3. There is a gradual recovery to the quiescent prestorm value requiring 1 to 2 days (the *recovery phase*).

In 1916 Adolph Schmidt attempted to explain the "main phase decrease." From a study of magnetograms made at the earth's surface, he postulated the existence of a ring current (9). He also suggested that the current died away so slowly that it was a common feature of the region of space surrounding the earth.

Beginning in 1931, Chapman and Ferraro developed a comprehensive theory of magnetic storms (10). Their theory involved many concepts that are still widely accepted, although somewhat modified. The starting point of the Chapman-Ferraro storm theory is the emission by the sun of a neutral ionized gas cloud. This plasma cloud travels toward the earth, and the magnetic storm is initiated by a collision between the ionized gas and the distant geomagnetic field. The plasma cloud is diamagnetic, that is, it tends to exclude magnetic fields from its interior. As a result, it compresses the geomagnetic field into a hollow inside the cloud. This feature, which was used by Chapman and Ferraro to explain the initial phase of magnetic storms, has since been extended to nonstorm conditions. The cavity discussed at the beginning of this chapter is frequently referred to as the Chapman-Ferraro cavity.

Chapman and Ferraro were able to relate the magnitude of the initial phase of the storm to the distance from the center of the earth to the ionized cloud. For a typical value of 20γ, the corresponding distance was approximately 10 R_E.

In order to explain the main phase decrease, Chapman and Ferraro also invoked a ring current. Obviously, such a current should lie inside the cavity containing the geomagnetic field. To be consistent with the predictions of the theory regarding the initial phase, this implied that the ring current was located within 10 R_E of the earth's center.

The basic problem confronting Chapman and Ferraro was to establish such a current system at an altitude of 10 R_E or less. As we have seen, Störmer's theory had particles moving in circular orbits, but the orbits were located at great distances (150 R_E). The fundamental difficulty can be stated another way. The centrifugal reaction of a particle moving in a circular orbit of radius 10 R_E is approximately 10^{-18} dyne (for 20-kev protons, as above). On the other hand, the magnitude of the geomagnetic field at 10 R_E is 100γ and the corresponding Lorentz force, evB, is 10^{-15} dyne. Clearly, another force was required in order to compensate for the large Lorentz force.

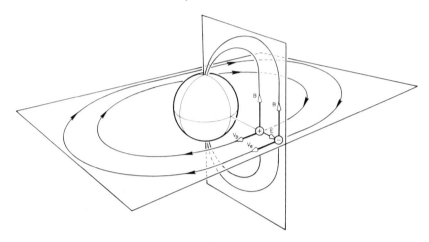

Figure 9-3 Chapman-Ferraro ring current.

Chapman and Ferraro suggested that the compensating force was provided by an electric field. The electric field was caused by the separation of positive and negative charges.

The Chapman-Ferraro ring current is shown in Figure 9-3. The positive charges (protons) move toward the west with velocity V_p, provided the Lorentz force exceeds the outward electrostatic force. Hence,

$$\frac{m_p V_p{}^2}{R} = Be V_p - eE. \tag{9-5}$$

The negative charges (electrons), on the other hand, have a *centripetal* force exerted on them by the electric field. Hence the Lorentz force must be oppositely directed, or outward. This implies that the electrons also move toward the west (with velocity V_e), so that

$$\frac{m_e V_e{}^2}{R} = eE - eBV_e. \tag{9-6}$$

The westward moving electrons represent an eastward current that tends to compensate the westward current associated with the protons. However, adding the two equations above,

$$\frac{m_p V_p{}^2}{R} + \frac{m_e V_e{}^2}{R} = eB(V_p - V_e). \tag{9-7}$$

Since the left-hand side of the equation is positive, $V_p > V_e$ and the net current flow is westward. This is required by the observed direction of the large-scale, main-phase storm field.

This rather ingenious mechanism for maintaining a ring current was subject to several serious criticisms. Although Chapman and Ferraro suggested that a current might be established by a discharge across the cavity by particles of opposite sign, there was really no mechanism to establish such a curious physical situation. Furthermore, Alfvén questioned the stability of this current, assuming it were possible to place the particles in these unique orbits (11). He attempted to show that any perturbation would quickly lead to a disruption of the current flow. The Chapman-Ferraro ring-current theory was given serious consideration as late as 1957; however, it has since been abandoned in favor of the modern ring-current theory to be discussed below. Chapman has accepted the modern explanation and is presently involved in detailed calculations of the associated magnetic field.

Alfvén's electric field theory

Beginning in 1939, H. O. Alfvén attempted to show that both magnetic storms and aurorae are caused by the interaction between the geomagnetic field and incident solar plasma (12). Alfvén studied the trajectories of the plasma particles in interplanetary space and in the geomagnetic field. His theory indicates that as the solar cloud passes near the earth the particle motions include a component which, in effect, represents a ring current. This ring current gives rise to the main phase decrease, as in the Chapman-Ferraro theory; however, the origin of the current is quite different in the two theories. In Alfvén's theory the ring-current particles are not trapped inside the geomagnetic field.

Alfvén's theory is more sophisticated than either of the theories discussed above. It involves many subtleties that have been incorporated into the modern ring-current theory. Therefore, it will be helpful to review the general aspects of the storm theory before becoming involved in the physical and mathematical details.

The starting point of Alfvén's theory is the physical state of the solar plasma as it travels through interplanetary space toward the earth. Alfvén postulated that a regular interplanetary magnetic field exists (presumably a solar field). As the conducting plasma moves through the interplanetary field, a large-scale electric field is generated. The charged particles in the plasma cloud move in spirals about the interplanetary magnetic field and represent tiny magnetic dipoles. As the gyrating particles near the earth, a repulsive force is exerted on them by the inhomogeneous, geomagnetic, dipole field. The earth's field gradient deflects the positive and negative charges toward opposite sides of the earth.

The field gradient also causes an ion-electron velocity difference. This causes westward currents on both sides of the earth that are *equivalent* to a ring current. Because of the lateral displacement of the particles, they extract energy from the large-scale electric field surrounding the earth. The increased kinetic energy allows them to enter the geomagnetic field, although there are certain forbidden regions concentric with the earth into which the particles cannot penetrate. The magnetic storm field at the earth's surface is due not only to the ring current but also to a field component associated with the spiral motion of the particles, which represent an aggregate of tiny magnetic dipoles. The particles pass around the earth and continue on into interplanetary space. The magnetic storm terminates when all the plasma passes beyond the earth's orbit.

The mathematical details of Alfvén's theory involve (1) the character of the electric field inside the plasma, (2) the velocities of the particles as they pass the earth, and (3) the equation of motion, or the trajectories, of the particles.

1. The electric field. It is well known that if a solid conductor is transported through a magnetic field the conductor will become electrically polarized (13). Positive and negative charges appear on opposite faces of the conductor, transverse to the magnetic field. The polarization is caused by the Lorentz force which deflects charges of opposite sign in opposite directions. Charge separation continues until an electric field which compensates the Lorentz force per unit charge is produced.

In the case of a *plasma* moving through a magnetic field, the basic motion of the particles is a spiraling about the magnetic field caused by the Lorentz force. Consider the equation of motion of a particle in combined electric and magnetic fields:

$$m\dot{\mathbf{V}} = e\mathbf{E} + e\mathbf{V} \times \mathbf{B}. \tag{9-8}$$

In many physical situations the motion of the particle can be separated into two components: (1) motion about an instantaneous center of rotation, called the *guiding center*, and (2) a translation. For example, let

$$\mathbf{V} = \mathbf{V}_G + \mathbf{V}_D \tag{9-9}$$

$$m\dot{\mathbf{V}}_G = e\mathbf{V}_G \times \mathbf{B} + e(\mathbf{E} + \mathbf{V}_D \times \mathbf{B} - \frac{m}{e}\dot{\mathbf{V}}_D). \tag{9-10}$$

There is a steady-state solution ($d\mathbf{V}/dt = \dot{\mathbf{V}} = 0$) in which the term inside the bracket vanishes so that

$$m\dot{\mathbf{V}}_G = e\mathbf{V}_G \times \mathbf{B} \qquad (9\text{-}11)$$

$$\mathbf{V}_D \times \mathbf{B} = -\mathbf{E}. \qquad (9\text{-}12)$$

Equation (9-11) is the equation of motion of a particle in a magnetic field. Taking the cross product of $\mathbf{B}$ with equation (9-12), one obtains

$$\mathbf{V}_D = \frac{\mathbf{E} \times \mathbf{B}}{B^2}. \qquad (9\text{-}13)$$

Thus, under the action of crossed electric and magnetic fields, particles drift in a direction transverse to both (Figure 9-4). Alternatively, plasma transported through a field with velocity $\mathbf{V}_D$ will give rise to an electric field $\mathbf{E} = -\mathbf{V}_D \times \mathbf{B}$. Note that the direction and magnitude of the drift velocity are the same for both positive and negative particles so that in a neutral plasma there is no net current.

The separation of the particle motion into a spiral motion superposed on a steady drift is an important feature of modern ring-current and plasma theory. The drift velocity V_D is typically several orders of magnitude smaller than the velocity associated with the gyration V_G (corresponding to the kinetic energy). This condition is essential, since the so-called *guiding center approximation* is valid only when there is a small change in B due to the drift during one gyro period.

2. Particle velocity inside the geomagnetic field. The spiral motion of the particle gives rise to a magnetic dipole moment of magnitude, μ. The circular motion of the particle is equivalent to a current, $i = e/T$, T being

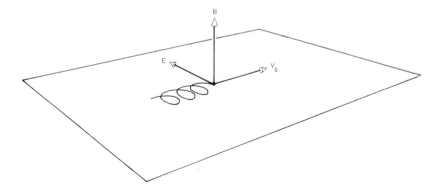

Figure 9-4 Motion of a charged particle in crossed electric and magnetic fields.

the gyro period. The magnetic moment of the equivalent current loop is iA, where A is the area enclosed. Since $A = \pi\rho^2$, $\rho = mv_\perp/eB$, and $2\pi/T = (e/m)B$,

$$\mu = \frac{\frac{1}{2}mv_\perp{}^2}{B} = \frac{w_\perp}{B}. \tag{9-14}$$

The Lorentz force is transverse to $v_\perp$ and cannot increase the transverse kinetic energy of the particle; hence μ is a constant. The direction of the magnetic moment is the same for both ions and electrons, that is, antiparallel to the magnetic field.

A plasma in a magnetic field represents an aggregate of magnetic dipoles rather than a simple collection of charged particles. Hence the bulk motion of the plasma depends on the forces that can be exerted on the magnetic dipoles. When such a force occurs, the dipoles begin to drift. This gives rise to a secondary Lorentz force, $e\mathbf{V}_D \times \mathbf{B}$, since the motion of the dipole involves the transport of charge through a magnetic field. In equilibrium the secondary Lorentz force must just compensate the force acting on the elementary dipole. Thus

$$e\mathbf{V}_D \times \mathbf{B} + \mathbf{F} = 0 \tag{9-15}$$

Since

$$e\mathbf{V}_D \times \mathbf{B} \times \mathbf{B} = -e\mathbf{V}_D B^2 \tag{9-16}$$

$$\mathbf{V}_D = \frac{\mathbf{F} \times \mathbf{B}}{eB^2}. \tag{9-17}$$

[If F is caused by an electric field we recover equation (9-13) above.]

As long as F is independent of the sign of the charge, a current will result. Thus currents inside neutral plasmas are caused by forces and not by electric fields. This result is contrary to our normal everyday experience with conductors, in which an electric field is almost always the cause of a current

The Alfvén storm theory is based on the force exerted on the magnetic dipoles by the inhomogeneous geomagnetic field. A magnetic dipole placed in a field gradient will experience a force

$$\mathbf{F} = \nabla(\mathbf{\mu} \cdot \mathbf{B}). \tag{9-18}$$

Thus

$$\mathbf{V}_D = \frac{1}{eB^2}\nabla(\mathbf{\mu} \cdot \mathbf{B}) \times \mathbf{B} = -\frac{\mu}{eB^2}\nabla B \times \mathbf{B}. \tag{9-19}$$

Since the gradient of the geomagnetic field is directed toward the earth and B is northward on the geomagnetic equator, ions will drift

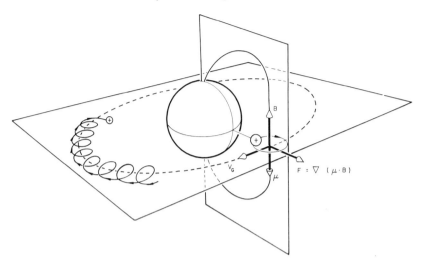

Figure 9-5 Alfvén drift velocity for a particle in the inhomogeneous geomagnetic field.

toward the west and electrons toward the east (Figure 9-5). The resulting current density is given by

$$\mathbf{J} = en(\mathbf{V}_D{}^+ - \mathbf{V}_D{}^-), \tag{9-20}$$

where the superscript plus and minus refer to the sign of the charge on the particle. Since

$$\mathbf{V}_D{}^+ = \frac{\mathbf{E} \times \mathbf{B}}{B^2} - \frac{w_\perp{}^+}{eB^2} \nabla B \tag{9-21}$$

and

$$\mathbf{V}_D{}^- = \frac{\mathbf{E} \times \mathbf{B}}{B^2} + \frac{w_\perp{}^-}{eB^2} \nabla B, \tag{9-22}$$

$$J = -n(w_\perp{}^+ + w_\perp{}^-) \frac{\nabla B}{B^2}. \tag{9-23}$$

The negative sign implies that the current due to both ions and electrons is westward. The deflection of the electrons toward the east produces a westward current because of their negative charge.

The major contribution to the storm field comes from this westward current. Alfvén also called attention to another component of the storm field. The resultant field, obtained by summing fields from each of the elementary dipoles, increases the magnitude of the geo-magnetic field at the earth's surface and diminishes it inside the plasma. This fundamental property of plasmas is called *diamag-netism* (see p. 336). Alfvén showed that at the earth's surface the diamagnetic component is only one third of the field magnitude asso-ciated with the drift current. Therefore, the dominant westward current causes a decreased field at the surface (the main phase).

3. Equation of motion of the plasma. The foregoing discussions have provided a description of the physical state of the solar plasma in interplanetary space and the currents inside a plasma in the geo-magnetic field. Alfvén's theory also relates the characteristics of the particles in the two regions of space. Alfvén shows how the particles are able to enter the geomagnetic field, and he derives the equation of motion of the guiding centers. For simplicity, he assumes that the motion of the particles is confined to the equatorial plane as in equations (9-20) to (9-23).

In the guiding center approximation all field changes are slow compared to the gyro period of the particles, and the magnetic mo-ment of the particles is a constant of motion. The magnetic moment in the approaching plasma cloud is given by

$$\mu = \frac{W_0}{B_0}, \tag{9-24}$$

where W_0 is the transverse kinetic energy of the particle and B_0 is the magnitude of the interplanetary magnetic field.

If a particle enters the geomagnetic field, B_0 is augmented by G, the magnitude of the geomagnetic field. Since μ must remain constant, the kinetic energy of the particles must increase in order that they may penetrate into the geomagnetic field. But the particles are in a large-scale electric field and can gain kinetic energy by developing a lateral component of motion. A component of motion parallel to E will result in a decreased electric potential and an increased kinetic energy. As we have seen, because of the inhomogeneity of the earth's field, forces are actually exerted on the particles which cause them to drift laterally. Hence

$$\mu = \frac{W_0}{B_0} = \frac{\frac{1}{2}mv^2 + eE\,\Delta X}{B_0 + G(X,\,Y)}. \tag{9-25}$$

X and Y are the coordinates of a guiding center in the equatorial plane and ΔX is the lateral displacement of the guiding center in the electric field.

This is essentially an expression for X as a function of Y, that is, the equation of motion of the particles. Alfvén used equation (9-25) to compute the trajectories of the guiding centers. The motion of the electron guiding centers is shown in Figure 9-6. The motions of the ions are essentially the mirror images of the electron trajectories.

Mathematically, solutions of the foregoing equation exist only outside certain zones that are inaccessible to the particles. The physical basis for the existence of forbidden regions is that there is a maximum amount of energy that a particle can extract from the electric field. There are forbidden zones for both electrons and ions. In general, the boundaries of the forbidden zones will not coincide.

The validity of Alfvén's storm theory is still a controversial subject. Alfvén has persisted in his views. New information, which has been forthcoming since Alfvén proposed his theory, has produced concepts of magnetic storm phenomena different from those employed by Alfvén. The differences apply to many aspects of Alfvén's theory: the initial conditions in interplanetary space before the solar plasma arrives that causes the storm, the physical state of the solar plasma as it approaches the earth, and the interaction between the plasma and the geomagnetic field.

In all three theories discussed above it was assumed that interplanetary space, and the space surrounding the earth, was a vacuum. The solar plasma was assumed to propagate into regions containing vacuum magnetic fields. However, there is now experimental evidence that both interplanetary space and the earth's magnetosphere contain plasma (14, 15, 16). The plasma number density in both regions is estimated at 10 to 1000 particles cm^{-3}, a density that may

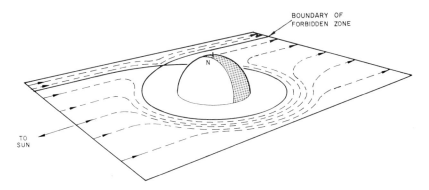

Figure 9-6 Motion of the electron guiding centers according to Alfvén's theory.

be greater than the density of the plasma associated with a solar disturbance. Furthermore, the ambient, interplanetary plasma may be streaming outward from the sun (17). If an interplanetary magnetic field does exist, its configuration could be quite different than it would be in a vacuum. For example, solar magnetic field lines might be strongly spiraled or the fields could be nonuniform and irregular (18). Neither of these conditions were anticipated by Alfvén's theory.

It is now commonly thought that the plasma emitted by the sun causes a hydromagnetic shock wave as it propagates toward the earth (19, 20, 21). The physics of a collisionless shock differs from the behavior of an aggregate of individual particles in a strong magnetic field.

The modern views of the interaction between the solar plasma and the geomagnetic field are strongly conditioned by the expectation that there is an interface between the earth's magnetosphere and interplanetary space. If the space were actually a vacuum, an interplanetary field might simply merge with the geomagnetic field, as assumed by Alfvén. However, the present theoretical view is that a complex, hydromagnetic, boundary-value problem is involved, in which the ionized, interplanetary gas confines the geomagnetic field, and the associated terrestrial plasma, to a rather well-defined volume of space. Thus injection mechanisms are required in order to transfer particles from interplanetary space into the magnetosphere. Alfvén is virtually alone in arguing that the plasma can enter the magnetosphere directly.

From the standpoint of ring-current theory, the most important feature of Alfvén's storm theory was his use of the guiding center approximation. Störmer and Chapman and Ferraro proposed ring-current models in which charged particles move in large, circular orbits concentric with the earth. Alfvén showed that particles can spiral about magnetic lines of force in small circular orbits that are not concentric with the earth but that give rise to a current because of a slow drift of the guiding center. This concept overcomes the handicaps of the earlier theories because the Lorentz force that causes the particles to spiral can be orders of magnitude larger than the forces that cause the guiding center to drift. This fundamental result is the basis of the modern ring-current theory. Alfvén also recognized that there were diamagnetic effects associated with the plasma, and these are also an important feature of modern ring-current theory.

The modern ring-current theory

In 1957 S. F. Singer set forth a hypothesis which provided the basis for what we may call the modern ring-current theory (20). His hypothesis was directly related to Störmer's analysis of the trajectories of particles that enter the geomagnetic field. Störmer established that there were forbidden zones into which an incident particle could not penetrate. Similarly, particles inside the forbidden zone are trapped by the geomagnetic field and move in captive orbits from which they cannot escape.

The trajectory of a trapped particle consists of a helical path which tends to follow geomagnetic field lines but has an azimuthal component. The representation of the complex particle motion was simplified by Alfvén, who used a perturbation technique, namely, the guiding center approximation discussed above (12). Alfvén showed that the guiding center of the trapped particle travels up and down in the magnetic field while drifting around the earth, somewhat like the horses on a carousel.

Singer suggested that during a magnetic storm solar particles were trapped in Störmer's forbidden regions. This was a direct violation of Störmer's results for incident particles. Singer showed, however, that the motion of the trapped particles is equivalent to a westward current, which he identified with the main-phase ring current. The strength of Singer's hypothesis is that it is necessary only to make a single assumption in order to establish a ring current, that is, there are particles in trapped orbits.

This assumption is reasonable if one allows any one of a fairly large number of trapping mechanisms to operate, so that Störmer's analysis is invalidated. Singer, for example, suggested that a bubble of gas containing many particles can deform the geomagnetic field locally so that it is no longer dipolar. It has also been suggested that small irregularities in the solar plasma can diffuse into the earth's field or that solar particles can be scattered into the trapped orbits by hydromagnetic shock waves (22, 23).

Irrespective of a detailed understanding of injection mechanisms, we know that particles are actually trapped in these captive orbits. The high-energy particles of the Van Allen radiation zones move along the trajectories studied by Störmer, Alfvén, and Singer. There appears to be an adequate injection mechanism to explain the high-energy protons found in the inner zone, namely, the decay of neutrons caused by cosmic rays (24, 25, 26). However, at the present time the origin of the outer zone is unknown.

When the radiation zones were first discovered, it was thought that the radiation particles might be responsible for the ring current. However, subsequent investigations have shown that the radiation particles do not cause a current system of sufficient magnitude to account for the geophysical effects (such as the main-phase decrease) usually attributed to a ring current. It is likely that there is a current system associated with the radiation particles; however, it is apparently a weak current.

The ring current may be caused by trapped particles other than the radiation particles. If the average kinetic energy of such particles is much less than the average kinetic energy of the radiation particles, their presence would not be detected by the radiation particle detectors. Such detectors respond only to the high-energy particles. Although the average kinetic energy per ring current particle may be much less than the average kinetic energy per Van Allen particle, there are, presumably, many more of them. Thus the kinetic-energy density, total kinetic energy, and current associated with the ring-current particles could be large. *The ring-current particles would have orbits that are essentially the same as the orbits of the radiation particles.* The trapped particles spiral about the magnetic lines of force while traveling back and forth between "mirror points" in the Northern and Southern Hemispheres.

How do trapped particles cause a ring current? As in Alfvén's theory, each spiraling particle has a magnetic moment. The repulsive force exerted on this moment by the geomagnetic field gradient causes the guiding center to drift and a westward current is the result.

The guiding center also will drift because of the curvature of the geomagnetic lines of force. Singer used some numerical results worked out by Alfvén to describe the motion of particles in the Störmer orbits. Singer's results implicitly contained this component of the drift, which was not included in Alfvén's storm theory. Subsequently, Dessler and Parker derived an explicit expression for the current density associated with the curvature drift (22).

Dessler and Parker also called attention to a third current component associated with the diamagnetism of the plasma. Diamagnetism causes virtual, or fictitious, currents to flow. Diamagnetic currents are not associated with forces exerted on individual particles but arise in an aggregate of particles.

To summarize the present theoretical view, a diamagnetic ring current is caused by trapped plasma. The ring current is actually the sum of three ring currents associated with (1) gradient drift, (2) curvature drift, and (3) diamagnetism.

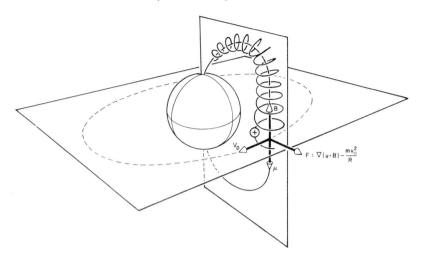

Figure 9-7 Drift velocity of a particle trapped in the geomagnetic field.

1. Gradient drift. The basic physics of the two drift currents is the same as that in the Alfvén storm theory (Figure 9-7). Under the action of a force, the guiding center drifts with a velocity given by equation (9-17).

$$\mathbf{V}_D = \frac{\mathbf{F} \times \mathbf{B}}{eB^2}.$$

When **F** is the force exerted by the earth's field gradient, the drift velocity is

$$\mathbf{V}_\mu = -\frac{w_\perp}{eB^3} \nabla B \times \mathbf{B}. \tag{9-26}$$

The corresponding current density is

$$\mathbf{J}_\mu = ne\mathbf{V}_\mu = -\frac{W_\perp}{B^3} \nabla B \times \mathbf{B}; \tag{9-27}$$

n is the particle number density and $W_\perp = \frac{1}{2}nmV_\perp^2$ is the total transverse kinetic energy density. The current is westward for both protons and electrons. On the equator the magnitude of the current density is

$$J_\mu = \frac{W_\perp}{B^2} \nabla B \tag{9-28}$$

2. Curvature drift. A centripetal force is required to keep a trapped particle moving along the curved geomagnetic field lines. The centripetal force is provided by a secondary Lorentz force $e\mathbf{V}_R \times \mathbf{B}$ which just compensates for the centrifugal reaction of the particle. The reaction is equivalent to a force

$$\mathbf{F} = -\frac{mv_\parallel^2}{R}\,\hat{e}_R. \tag{9-29}$$

V_R is the drift velocity due to the curvature, R is the radius of curvature of the field line having a direction, $\hat{e}_R$ (a unit vector). Substituting in the fundamental equation (9-17),

$$\mathbf{V}_R = -\frac{mv_\parallel^2}{eRB^2}\,\hat{e}_R \times \mathbf{B}. \tag{9-30}$$

If there are n particles per unit volume with a total longitudinal kinetic-energy density $W_\parallel$,

$$\mathbf{J}_R = -\frac{2W_\parallel}{RB^2}\,\hat{e}_R \times \mathbf{B}. \tag{9-31}$$

On the equator the magnitude of the curvature drift-current density becomes simply

$$J_R = \frac{2W_\parallel}{RB}. \tag{9-32}$$

Since $\hat{e}_R$ is directed toward the earth, and $\mathbf{B}$ is northward, the guiding center of a positive particle will drift toward the west and the guiding center of a negative particle will drift toward the east. A westward current results in either case.

3. Diamagnetism. If a plasma is embedded in a magnetic field, the spiraling particles reduce the magnitude of the field locally. Consider the direction of motion of the charged particles. The Lorentz force produces tiny current loops whose field, interior to the loop, is opposed to the primary field. This is merely an application of Lenz's law. The orientation of all current loops, each of magnetic moment μ, causes the plasma to acquire a dipole moment per unit volume, $n\mu$. The magnetization of the plasma produces a macroscopic magnetic field which alters the field that was present in the absence of the plasma. In fact, the plasma tends to expel the field lines from its interior, a general property of magnetic materials called *diamagnetism*. Although diamagnetism is caused by the induced alignment of the dipole moments of the constituents, it is often convenient to describe the induced field in terms of equivalent fictitious macroscopic currents. This is a common procedure in studying the properties of magnetic materials in classical electromagnetic theory.

Inside a magnetic medium the equation relating the magnetic induction B and magnetic intensity H is generalized:

$$\mathbf{B} = \mu_m\mathbf{H} = \mu_0(\mathbf{H} + \mathbf{M}). \tag{9-33}$$

$\mathbf{M}$ is the magnetization, the dipole moment per unit volume of the material. Hence

$$\mathbf{M} = n\boldsymbol{\mu}. \tag{9-34}$$

The magnetostatic form of Ampère's law is

$$\nabla \times \mathbf{H} = \mathbf{J}. \tag{9-35}$$

Since

$$\mathbf{H} = \frac{\mathbf{B}}{\mu_0} - \mathbf{M}, \tag{9-36}$$

by (9-33)

$$\nabla \times \mathbf{B} = \mu_0(\mathbf{J} + \nabla \times \mathbf{M}). \tag{9-37}$$

According to this equation, the origin of the B-field is not only a real current but a spatial distribution of magnetization. Since $\nabla \times \mathbf{M}$ is equivalent to a current, we may introduce a fictitious current density J_M, called the amperian current density, in which

$$\mathbf{J}_M = \nabla \times \mathbf{M} = \nabla \times (n\boldsymbol{\mu}) = -\nabla \times \frac{W_\perp}{B}\hat{e}_B. \tag{9-38}$$

Two simple examples may help to clarify these concepts. An example that occurs frequently in treatises on electromagnetism is the case of the homogeneous cylinder of circular cross section placed in a uniform field. Figure 9-8 shows a cross section through the rod. The elementary current loops are oriented with their axes along the direction of the applied field. The effect of the magnetization can be studied heuristically without resorting to equations. If one sums the currents in the interior of the rod, the result is $J_M = 0$, since adjacent to each element of a given current loop there is an oppositely directed current element. Thus the *volume current density* is zero. However, on the surface of the rod the current elements add constructively to produce an equivalent *surface current*. The magnetic effects of the rod can be determined, both inside and outside, from the field of the Amperian surface current.

A closely related example, which is more pertinent to the present

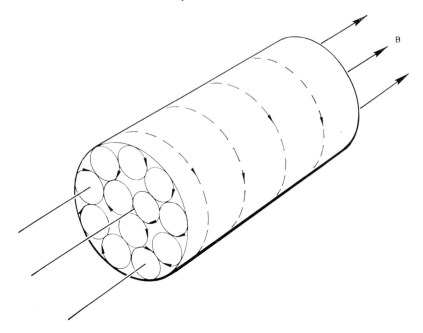

Figure 9-8 Diamagnetic currents on the surface of a magnetic cylinder in an external field.

discussion, is the case of a cylindrical slab of plasma in a magnetic field. For simplicity, we assume that the field is uniform and that the plasma is a uniform cylindrical shell, sharply bounded on both sides (Figure 9-9). Then

$$\mathbf{J}_M = \frac{\frac{1}{2}mv^2}{B} \frac{\partial n(r)}{\partial r} \hat{e}\phi. \tag{9-39}$$

J_M vanishes inside the plasma, since n is constant. However, near the boundaries neither $\partial n/\partial r$ nor J_M is zero. In effect, there are two oppositely directed current sheets on the surfaces of the plasma.

If the direction of the field is north, then the innermost surface current is eastward and the current on the outer surface is westward. Thus the magnetization currents cause fields that reduce the primary field interior to the plasma and increase the primary field exterior to the plasma. The field lines have, in effect, been partially expelled by the diamagnetic plasma.

Since this example is related to the problem of the geomagnetic ring current, two additional comments are worth making. If the surface currents are equal in magnitude, as in this example, the resultant field interior to the plasma ring will be increased above its value in the absence of the plasma. Consider two elements of each surface current, that is, two filamentary current loops. The field at the center of each loop is given by

$$\Delta B = \frac{\mu_0 i}{2a}, \tag{9-40}$$

where i is the current and a is the radius of the ring. If $i_1 = i_2$, the field on the inner boundary will dominate, since $a_1 < a_2$. Hence, to produce the main-phase decrease, the westward component of the ring current must be dominant, although eastward currents may occur locally. The second comment is that contrary to this special case J_M will not vanish, in general, inside the plasma and *volume diamagnetic currents* will also flow.

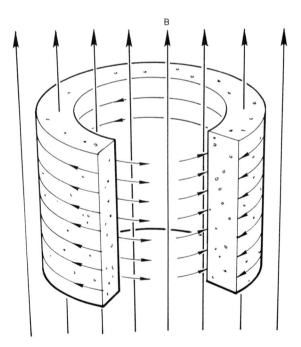

Figure 9-9 Diamagnetic currents on the surfaces of a cylindrical plasma slab in an external field.

The current density of the ring current is the algebraic sum of these three toroidal components. Hence

$$\mathbf{J} = \mathbf{J}_\mu + \mathbf{J}_R + \mathbf{J}_M = -\frac{W_\perp}{B^2} \nabla B \times \hat{e}_B - \frac{2W_\parallel}{RB^2} \hat{e}_R \times \mathbf{B} - \nabla \times \frac{W_\perp}{B} \hat{e}_B.$$

$$(9\text{-}41)$$

The production of the main-phase decrease by a diamagnetic ring current raises questions concerning the possible trapping of solar particles in the geomagnetic field. Modern ring-current theory also has important consequences associated with the recovery phase of a magnetic storm. Presumably the recovery phase is due to the gradual dissipation of the ring current, which implies a diminished particle energy. (Note that all three components of the current density depend essentially on the energy of the trapped particles.) Dessler and Parker suggested that the ring-current particles are protons and are removed by exchanging their charge with neutral hydrogen atoms (22). This process (charge exchange) transforms an energetic proton and a thermal (low-energy) hydrogen atom into an energetic hydrogen atom and a low-energy proton. Hence energy is removed from the ring current. There is some evidence that neutral hydrogen is an important constituent of the outer atmosphere. The time required to remove a significant fraction of the energy in the ring current, based on the charge-exchange interaction cross section and theoretical density distribution of neutral hydrogen, appears to be consistent with the 1-to-2-day recovery period of storm. Originally Singer had suggested that protons responsible for the storm ring current are removed from trapped orbits by interaction with the earth's atmosphere near their "mirror points" (20). Normally only particles with a narrow range of pitch angles penetrate deeply enough into the atmosphere to lie inside such a "loss cone." In order to remove particles continuously, Singer postulated that some mechanism exists, such as scattering by charged particles or hydromagnetic waves, which leads to a steady redistribution of particle pitch angles.

At the present time, modern ring-current theory seems to be based on sound physical principles. The modern theory explains the maintenance of the ring current in a satisfactory way and with a minimum number of assumptions. If plasma becomes trapped in the geomagnetic field, a ring current must exist. The theory relates the current density of the ring current to the properties of the trapped plasma. The same equations have also been derived recently in connection with thermonuclear research. Thus they represent general results of modern plasma physics (27).

4. Numerical results. There have been several theoretical investigations of the ring current associated with an assumed density distribution function of trapped particles n. Given n, and the characteristics of the geomagnetic field, the total current density can be derived from equation (9-35). The perturbation field, ΔB, produced by the current distribution, can be computed from J by using the Biot-Savart law. Determination of the perturbation field involves an integration over the entire volume of the current for each point of observation. The integrals have been evaluated numerically with electronic computers. Akasofu and Chapman and Apel, Singer, and Wentworth, have carried out this type of calculation (28, 29). The theoretical disturbance field ΔB and resultant field $G + \Delta B$ were computed for points of observation in the magnetosphere as well as at the surface of the earth. The calculations can be compared with magnetic field measurements made by spacecraft magnetometers. Since the results of such measurements are presented and discussed in Section 9-2, it will be helpful to review briefly the most pertinent results of these calculations before proceeding to a study of the data.

In general, the density-distribution function n will depend on (a) position, such as geomagnetic latitude and geocentric distance, (b) the pitch angle of the particles, usually specified by its value as the particle crosses the equatorial plane (the pitch angle is the inverse tangent of $V_\perp/V_\parallel$), and (c) the kinetic energy of the particles. In the models to be discussed the expression for n was simplified by assuming (a) that all particles have the same average energy, E_0, and (b) that n can be represented as the product of two functions, a term, $N(r_e)$, which specifies the radial dependence along the equatorial plane, and a term that essentially determines the pitch-angle distribution. The results appear to depend primarily on the radial dependence of n, and to a lesser extent on the pitch angle distribution. Hence in the following we characterize n by $N(r_e)$. The interested reader is referred to the literature for the exact details of the mathematical description.

Figure 9-10 contains the results of the Akasofu-Chapman and the Apel-Singer-Wentworth calculations. The numerical calculations were carried out for points of observation in the equatorial plane because of the simplifications associated with latitudinal symmetry. The radial density-distribution functions appear in Figure 9-10a. Figure 9-10b shows the current-density function corresponding to each. Negative values correspond to eastward currents and positive values to westward currents. Figure 9-10c shows the perturbation field on

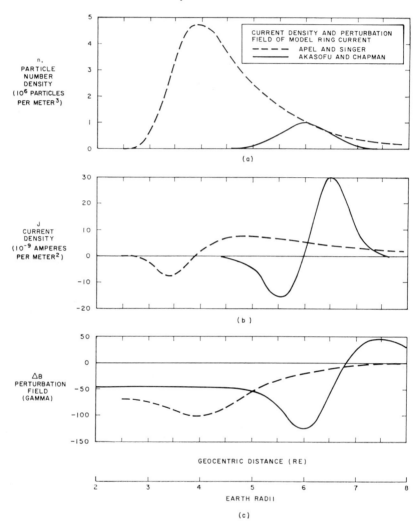

Figure 9-10 The ring current and perturbation field of a model trapped particle distribution.

the equatorial plane as a function of geocentric distance. The perturbation field is southward inside the ring current in spite of the contribution from the diamagnetic, eastward current component. The field minimum occurs at the peak in the particle distribution function. This illustrates the basic diamagnetism of the plasma. Exterior to the ring current the field is northward and increases the field magnitude above that of the unperturbed dipole field. Figure 9-11 is a plot of the total magnitude of the resultant field on the equatorial plane. The earth's dipole field is also shown for comparison.

Figure 9-11 reveals an important difference between the Apel-Singer-Wentworth and Akasofu-Chapman calculations. The perturbation field derived by the former does not lead to a reversal of the earth's field gradient. In the Akasofu-Chapman results, however, there is a region, just beyond 6 R_E, where the earth's field increases rather than decreases. It is doubtful that a ring current, which is caused in part by the gradient and curvature of the geomagnetic field, could actually produce such a field configuration. Apel, Singer, and Wentworth have shown that the reversal of the gradient implies that the kinetic energy density of the particles, $\frac{1}{2}nmv^2$, exceeds the energy density of the field, $B^2/2\mu_0$. Under these circumstances, it is difficult to see how the particles could remain trapped, since they should be

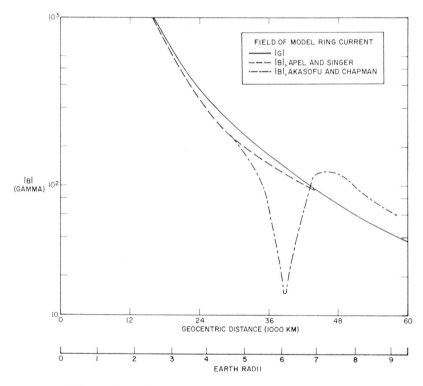

Figure 9-11 The resultant field of a model ring current compared with the geomagnetic field.

able to disrupt the field. It is possible to obtain a result that contradicts some of the fundamental premises because this type of calculation is not self-consistent. Obviously the ring-current field can significantly perturb the geomagnetic field so that it is not legitimate to determine J solely from the characteristics of the dipole field. This approach can provide only a first approximation to the exact solution. The Akasofu-Chapman result may imply the following. If a storm main-phase decrease of 100γ is caused by a ring current associated with trapped particles, then either the peak in the particle distribution is located at geocentric distances of less than 6 R_E, or the current and particles occupy a larger volume than was assumed by Akasofu and Chapman.

9-2 EXPERIMENTAL EVIDENCE OF THE EXISTENCE OF THE RING CURRENT

Evidence based on surface observations

Particle and field measurements at the earth's surface provide indirect evidence for the existence of a ring current. The evidence is based on (1) the harmonic analysis of the main-phase storm field, (2) the changes in the geographic location of aurora during magnetic storms, (3) the arrival of solar protons at "forbidden" latitudes during storms, and (4) the observation of a cosmic-ray "latitude knee."

The geographic dependence of the magnetic storm field has been studied extensively. These studies show that the storm field can be divided into two parts. One component, S_D, the disturbance daily variation, is a function of local time. The other component, D_{st}, the storm time variation (see Figure 9-2 and the description of the storm phases), is independent of longitude, or local time. The D_{st} variations are a world-wide effect and occur simultaneously over the entire surface of the earth. Simultaneous observations at ground stations which are well distributed in latitude and longitude makes it possible to expand the D_{st} field into a series of spherical harmonic functions. Harmonic analysis has shown that the source of the D_{st} field must be an overhead current system, that is, above the earth's surface. The altitude at which the current system is located is not uniquely established by such an analysis. Chapman derived a possible current system consisting of concentric current loops lying on a spherical surface just above, and completely enclosing, the earth (30). However, as Chapman pointed out, a toroidal ring current at much greater altitudes could produce the same D_{st} field at the earth's surface.

During magnetic storms the location of the polar aurora shifts to lower geomagnetic latitudes (i.e., <68 degrees). Bless, Gartlein, Kimball, and Sprague have derived an empirical relation between the latitude of the auroral maximum and the magnetic K index (6). As we have seen, Störmer proposed that such observations were caused by the effect of an extraterrestrial ring current on the trajectories of solar particles incident on the earth from interplanetary space. Even if the origin of the auroral particles should turn out to be the radiation zones, or some other reservoir of trapped particles, the shifting of the aurorae is likely to be the result of a large-scale deformation of the distant geomagnetic field, which could be caused by a ring current.

Another observation appears to be explainable by Störmer's analysis. Kellogg and Winckler have recently discussed observations of solar protons by balloon-borne equipment flown near Minneapolis, Minnesota (7). The balloon data shows that 75-Mev protons emitted by the sun are able to enter the atmosphere during the beginning of the main phase of magnetic storms. Protons in this energy range would normally be forbidden at such latitudes. Kellogg and Winckler suggest that this effect is due to the formation of the main-phase ring current.

Certain characteristics of cosmic radiation are also consistent with the existence of the ring current. The experimental measurements of cosmic-ray intensity exhibit a latitude dependence. Beginning at low latitudes, the intensity increases with increasing latitude. This result is predicted by Störmer's theory, since the low-energy cosmic rays are able to reach the earth's surface only at the higher latitudes. However, a latitude is reached at which the intensity ceases to increase. Cosmic-ray physicists have chosen to call this feature the "knee" in the intensity versus latitude curve. This observation could imply that the primary cosmic radiation has a low-energy cutoff. However, Ray has shown that the observations are consistent with the effects of a ring current, located at 7.5 R_E, with a magnetic moment equal to that of the earth (31). He also showed that an apparent variation in the latitude of the "knee" with the solar cycle is consistent with a diminution of the ring current during the solar minimum.

Although the foregoing observations are consistent with the existence of a ring current, all that surface observations really imply is that the earth is immersed in a large-scale disturbance field. The origin of such a field is difficult, if not impossible, to ascertain from surface observations alone. This explains the importance of investigating the nature of the disturbance field above the earth's surface, using satellites and space probes.

Evidence from spacecraft: magnetic field measurements

Because of the recent development of rocket technology, it is now possible to make direct measurements of the distant geomagnetic field. Magnetic-field measurements, or simultaneous field and particle measurements, should definitely establish the presence or absence of the geomagnetic ring current. The following discussion is a summary of the measurements carried out on spacecraft as they pertain to this question of the existence of the ring current.

At the present time, seven spacecraft have carried magnetometers into the distant geomagnetic field. Table 9-1 contains the spacecraft name, or designation, and the respective launch dates. The table also indicates whether the spacecraft was a probe or satellite—an important distinction, since a space probe obviously makes a single traversal of the earth's field, whereas a satellite makes periodic measurements under a variety of magnetic conditions. Finally, Table 9-1 indicates the magnetic conditions at the earth's surface during the measurements. (An international organization tabulates the 5 quietest, 10 quietest, and 5 most disturbed days of each month.) Figure 9-12 shows the essential orientation of the probe trajectory or satellite orbit with respect to the earth-sun direction. The orientation of Pioneers III and IV are also included, since these spacecraft are referred to in connection with charged particle measurements.

1. Pioneer I (Sonett, Judge, Sims, and Kelso). Pioneer I contained a search-coil magnetometer consisting of a solenoid wound on a high-permeability core and a voltage amplifier tuned to the rotation frequency of the spin-stabilized spacecraft. The output voltage from the search-coil amplifier is a sinusoid whose amplitude is proportional to the ambi-

TABLE 9-1

Spacecraft Containing Magnetometers

Spacecraft Designation	Date	Type of Spacecraft	Magnetic Conditions at the Earth's Surface
Pioneer I	October 11 and 12, 1958	Space probe	One of 5 quiet days
Lunik I	January 2, 1959	Space probe	One of 5 quiet days
Explorer VI	August 7 to September 16, 1959	Earth satellite	Magnetic storms: August 16 and Sept. 3
Lunik II	September 12, 1959	Lunar impacter	One of 10 quiet days
Vanguard III	September 18 to November 12, 1959	Earth satellite	Magnetic storms: September 19 to 21
Pioneer V	March 11, 1960	Space probe	One of 5 disturbed days
Explorer X	March 25 to 27, 1961	Earth satellite	Quiet until storm: March 27

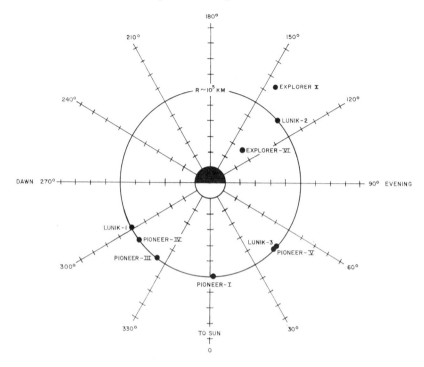

Figure 9-12   Spacecraft orientation referred to the earth-sun direction.

ent magnetic field projected into the equatorial plane of the spacecraft, that is, perpendicular to the spin axis. The projected field magnitude is called $B_\perp$.

Figure 9-13 is a plot of the Pioneer I measurements of $B_\perp$ as a function of geocentric altitude (32). A latitude dependence is also implicit, since the trajectory was not confined to an equatorial plane. (This condition is also characteristic of the trajectories of all satellites and space probes discussed below.) Also shown in Figure 9-13 is $G_\perp$, the corresponding value of the geomagnetic field extrapolated from the surface to the position of the spacecraft. The extrapolation is based on a spherical harmonic expansion of the surface field. The geomagnetic field, rotated into the spacecraft frame of reference, has a component perpendicular to the spin axis $G_\perp$. The observed field can be compared with the theoretical value of the geomagnetic field at great altitudes. A large-scale departure between the two could indicate the presence of a ring current.

Pioneer I data was obtained in the region from 3.7 to 7 R_E. Because of instrumental difficulties, which led to an uncertainty in the calibration

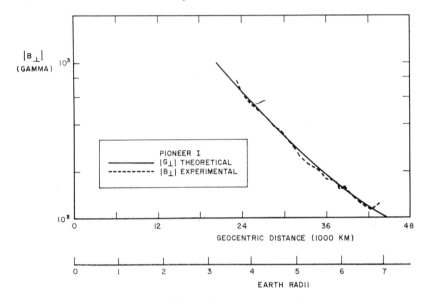

Figure 9-13 Pioneer I magnetometer data.

of the magnetometer, it was necessary to normalize the data. $B_\perp$ was made to equal $G_\perp$ at 3.7 R_E. The rest of the data points were then found to agree quite well with the earth's dipole field. The Pioneer I data were obtained during an interval of quiet magnetic conditions at the surface.

2. Luniks I, II (Dolganov and Pushkov). The Lunik I magnetometer was a triaxial fluxgate magnetometer. It was oriented by servomechanisms so that two of the magnetometer sensors were normal to the ambient field. The signal from the third sensor, which was parallel to the field so that it measured the total magnitude, was telemetered. Data were obtained between 2 and 6 R_E while the spacecraft was moving from 30°N magnetic latitude to 15° north latitude. The data (B) are shown in Figure 9-14 (33). G, the scalar magnitude of the extrapolated geomagnetic field, is also shown as a function of geocentric altitude. There are two features of particular interest: (a) there is a general depression of the observed field such that $B < G$ everywhere; and (b) there is an anomaly, located between 3 and 4 R_E, superposed on the general field depression. The anomaly has the approximate shape of a single cycle of a sinusoid with a peak-to-peak amplitude of 400 γ.

The Lunik I data were received with a great deal of interest, particularly the large-scale anomaly at 3 to 4 R_E. The radiation zones

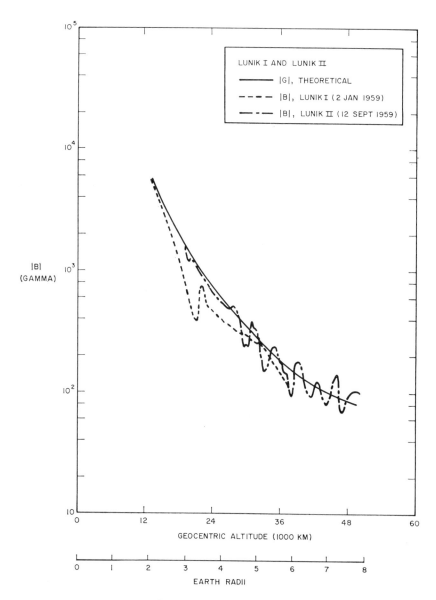

Figure 9-14 Lunik I-Lunik II magnetometer data.

had been discovered only a short time before, and it was known that the peak in the outer zone was located at approximately the same altitude. It was speculated that a ring current associated with the radiation particles had been observed.

Antsilevich and Shevnin attempted to support the hypothesis that a ring current was responsible for the anomaly by comparing the Lunik I data with ground-station magnetograms (34). There was a small magnetic storm on the launch date, beginning at 1120 GMT and exhibiting a main-phase decrease of 20 γ at 1400 GMT. (However, the Lunik I measurements were made at 1800 GMT.) At the altitude for which the field lines passing through the anomaly cross the equator, a 20 γ decrease in the surface field implied a ring current of 6×10^5 amp. Antsilevich and Shevnin computed the magnitude of the current required to produce a 400 γ change on the assumption that the spacecraft passed directly through the current. The result was 5×10^5 amp. Therefore they concluded that the results did not contradict the hypothesis that there was a ring current at 3 to 4 R_E when the measurements were made.

However, critics of this interpretation were quick to point out that the data show a reversal of the earth's field gradient. According to the generally accepted theoretical view, such a feature could not exist as a steady state. It has been suggested that the generalized depression could be the result of a ring current and that the anomaly could be a time-dependent transient phenomenon (35). Subsequent magnetometer flights, discussed below, have failed to reproduce the anomaly. It does not appear to be a permanent feature of the distant field, nor is it associated with the outer radiation zone.

Lunik II also contained a triaxial fluxgate magnetometer. The signals from each of the three axes were telemetered and the field magnitude was computed from the three components. The Lunik II data are also shown in Figure 9-14 (36). There is no evidence of either the large-scale depression or the anomaly that appeared in the Lunik I data, at least neither is present in anywhere near the same magnitude. The Lunik II data show a succession of large field fluctuations between 4 and 8 R_E. Apparently no one has offered an explanation of these fluctuations. There is no evidence of a ring current in the Lunik II data, although the large variations from 4 to 8 R_E could have obscured a moderate large-scale departure from the extrapolated geomagnetic field.

3. Explorer VI and Pioneer V (Sonett, Judge, Coleman, and Smith). Explorer VI contained a search-coil magnetometer similar to the one flown on Pioneer I. However, in addition to the magnitude of the field component perpendicular to the spin axis $(B_\perp)$, the Explorer VI magnetometer also measured its direction. The direction of $B_\perp$ was determined by a magnetic-field aspect indicator which measured the time delay between the zero-voltage crossing of the search-coil sinusoid and a pulse received from a photodiode, attached to the shell of the spacecraft, when it was illuminated by solar radiation. The phase comparator measures the *phase angle* ϕ between $B_\perp$ and $S_\perp$, $S_\perp$ being the projection into the equatorial plane of the spacecraft of a unit vector pointing in the direction of the sun (see Figure 9-15). Thus ϕ is essentially the declination of the magnetic field measured with respect to the earth-sun direction.

The Explorer VI orbit was highly eccentric (apogee = 48,800 km; perigee = 6740 km). The orbit plane was nonequatorial, being inclined at an angle of 47 degrees with respect to the geographic equator. The major axis of the orbit made an angle of 20 degrees with the equatorial plane and was turned through an angle of approximately 135 degrees with respect to the earth-sun direction; that is, apogee was located on the side of the earth opposite the sun at approximately 2100 local time (see Figure 9-12). The Explorer VI orbital period was $12\frac{3}{4}$ hr, so that the distant geomagnetic field was traversed twice a day. Scientific data were obtained almost continuously (18 hr a day on the average) for 40 days. During that interval several magnetic storms as well as several periods of magnetic quiet occurred at the earth's surface. The experi-

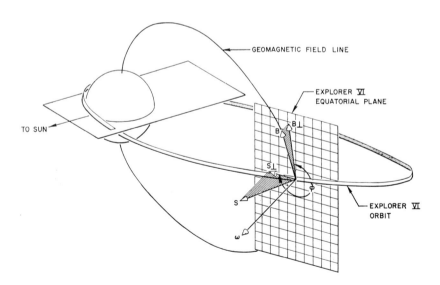

Figure 9-15   Explorer VI spacecraft coordinates.

mental results obtained under magnetically quiet and magnetically disturbed conditions are reviewed separately.

Explorer VI data obtained on nonstorm days (Figure 9-16) reveal discrepancies between $B_\perp$ and $G_\perp$ throughout most of the trajectory (37, 38). At altitudes below approximately 5 R_E (the actual altitude is time-dependent); the observed field magnitude exhibits the same general altitude dependence as the geomagnetic field but tends to have a somewhat larger magnitude. Beyond 5 R_E, $B_\perp$ differs from $G_\perp$ in both magnitude and altitude dependence. The phase data indicate close agreement between ϕ and ϕ_G out to 5 R_E, where, again, a deviation of ϕ from ϕ_G typically occurs.

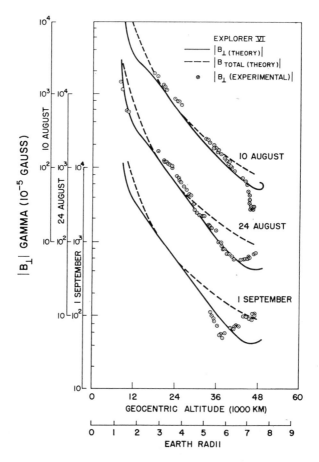

Figure 9-16 Explorer VI magnetometer data.

The Explorer VI data indicate that the extraterrestrial field is essentially dipolar out to 5 R_E but that there is a large-scale deviation that becomes progressively larger at greater altitudes. The existence of the deviation is evidence of a large-scale current system in the magnetosphere.

An attempt was made to determine the characteristics of the current responsible for the observed deviation. The shapes of the magnitude difference, $B_\perp - G_\perp$, and phase difference, $\phi - \phi_G$, are strongly dependent on the geometry of the experiment, particularly the spacecraft trajectory and spin axis orientation. Model calculations were employed to overcome the geometrical effects as well as to investigate the characteristics of the current. A simple mathematical model of the current was used, that is, a longitudinal current with a finite circular cross-sectional area. The field due to the current was computed at points along the trajectory and added vectorially to the geomagnetic field and a coordinate transformation was performed to yield $B_\perp$ and ϕ. Figure 9-17 shows a comparison of the data and the results of the model calculation (39). Reasonable agreement was obtained for a westward current of 5.10^6 amp located at 10 R_E. According to the model calculations, Explorer VI did not penetrate into the current, which implied that the cross-sectional radius of the current had a value less than 3 R_E.

At the time these results were obtained, magnetometer data became available from Pioneer V, which contained a search-coil magnetometer similar to the one flown on Explorer VI. (However, no phase data were available.) While the Explorer VI orbit was directed away from the sun, Pioneer V passed through the distant geomagnetic field on the sunward side of the earth. The same mathematical model was applied to the Pioneer V data, which were digitized before being telemetered (Figure 9-18). Reasonable agreement was obtained between the data and the model calculations for a westward current of 5.10^6 amp, located between 5 and 11 R_E (39). The similar current characteristics in the two regions of space suggests that the deviation is caused by a ring current. This result is of particular interest because the data were obtained during nonstorm intervals. August 9, 1959 (Explorer VI), was somewhat disturbed but was not actually a storm day. March 11, 1960 (Pioneer VI), contained a moderate magnetic storm from which the earth's field had recovered before the time of launch.

Explorer VI data obtained during magnetic storms are now discussed (40). Figure 9-19a shows the time variation of the field magnitude in the outer radiation zone for points of observation near the geomagnetic equatorial plane. Each datum is obtained from the average field mag-

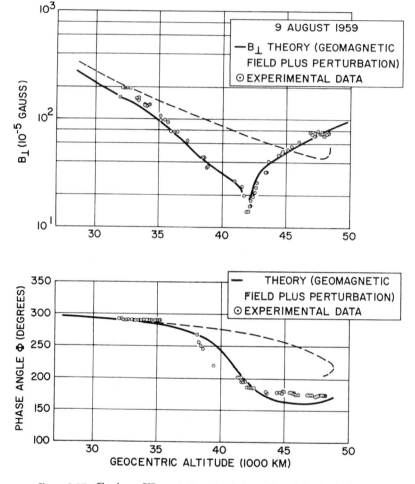

Figure 9-17 Explorer VI magnetometer data and model calculations.

nitude $B_\perp$ at an altitude of approximately 24,000 km (3.75 R_E) during a single orbital pass. Figure 9-19a is a plot of $B = B_\perp - G_\perp$ during the first 2 weeks of Explorer VI observations.

This time interval contained the severe magnetic storm of August 16. Figure 9-19b shows the time variation of the horizontal component of the earth's field at the surface. Each datum is the variation in the daily mean value of the horizontal intensity at Huancayo, Peru (geomagnetic latitude, −0.6 degrees) normalized to the 2 quiet days, August 11 and 12. The Huancayo data show the effect of three superimposed magnetic storms between August 15 and 20. Figure 9-19c is a smoothed D_{st} curve and shows the characteristics of the severe sudden-commencement storm of August 16 in greater detail (41).

The orientation of the Explorer VI spin axis was such that $G_\perp$ was approximately equal to G at the particular altitude 4 R_E. If the storm perturbation field is (a) symmetric above and below the equatorial plane and (b) confined to magnetic meridian planes defined by the dipole field lines and the center of the earth, then B should represent the time dependence of the disturbance field on the equatorial plane. The latter point of observation is important because only the magnitude of the geomagnetic field would be affected by a ring current without a corresponding change in direction. (The storm field is antiparallel to G on the equator.) Furthermore, most of the theoretical calculations involving diamagnetic ring currents have been restricted to the equatorial plane.

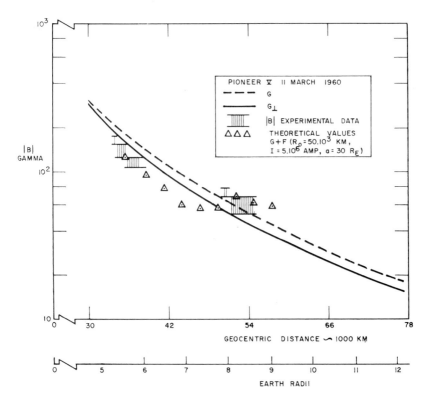

Figure 9-18 Pioneer V magnetometer data and model calculations.

Figure 9-19 shows that the long-period variation of the storm field at the surface (D_{st}) is reproduced at an altitude of 4 R_E. There is a main-phase decrease and recovery phase at 4 R_E which is coincident with D_{st}. The magnitude of the main-phase decrease is 360 γ at 4 R_E and 140 γ at the surface, that is, it is approximately $2\frac{1}{2}$ times larger. Furthermore, the direction of the storm field is the same at 1 and 4 R_E, that is, opposed to the geomagnetic field.

The interpretation of the experimental data is simplest for points of observation located on the geomagnetic equatorial plane. At non-

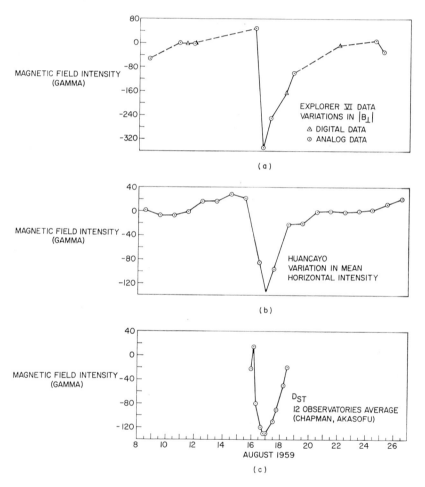

Figure 9-19 Magnetic storm variation in the field magnitude near 4 R_E and at the earth's surface.

EXPLORER VI
MAGNETOMETER PHASE ANGLE

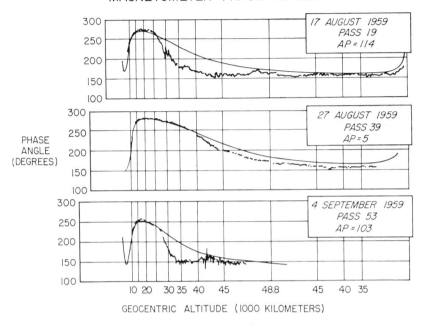

Figure 9-20   Field direction during two storm days and a quiet day.

zero latitudes the vector sum of the disturbance field and the geomagnetic field will cause changes in the direction of the distant field
as well as in magnitude.   Changes in direction can be studied by
considering the phase-angle data.

Figure 9-20 shows the departure of the observed field direction (ϕ)
from the direction of the extrapolated geomagnetic field (ϕ_G) and
contrasts the departure on storm days and days that are magnetically
quiet.   There were magnetic storms on August 17 and September 4,
but August 27 was the quietest day of the month.

When the variation in ϕ is studied throughout a given magnetic
storm, it is found that there is a progressive enhancement of $\Delta\phi$ during the storm, and a subsequent gradual return to the prestorm values.
Figure 9-21a shows the variation in $\Delta\phi$ at an altitude of 40,000 km
during the August 16 storm.   Figure 9-21b contains the simultaneous
variation in the horizontal intensity at the earth's surface (hourly
mean values at Huancayo), and Figure 9-21c is a plot of the corresponding 3-hr K index (which is a measure of the magnitude of the

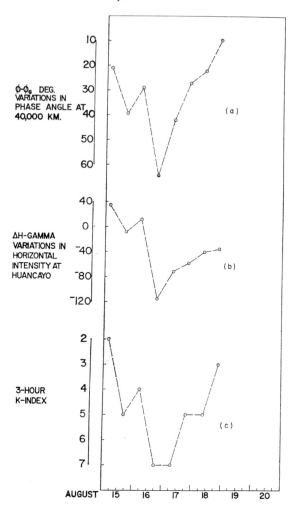

Figure 9-21 Magnetic storm variation in field direction at 6.25 R_E compared with variations in the surface field.

field fluctuations at the surface). The direction of the distant field is correlated with both the variations in the horizontal component and the degree of the magnetic agitation of the surface field.

The Explorer VI storm data imply that the main-phase decrease is only one manifestation of a large-scale magnetic field that surrounds the earth. This much of the original speculation, out of which the concept of the ring current evolved, appears to be true. Furthermore, the storm field seems to represent an enhancement of a large-scale disturbance field which can exist during quiet intervals.

The Explorer VI data also imply that the geomagnetic field dominates the storm field out to at least 8 R_E. The evidence is the following: (a) the gradual time variation from quiet to disturbed conditions and the subsequent recovery, (b) the correlation with the slow storm variations of the surface field, and (c) the existence during the storm main phase of trapped radiation particles on lines of force that cross the equator near this altitude (42). The dominance of the geomagnetic field is an important condition, if the large-scale field is to be explained by a diamagnetic ring current of the type discussed. Since G is 60 γ at 8 R_E on the equatorial plane, it follows that D, the disturbance field, must be less than 60 γ. Since the disturbance field is -100 γ at the earth's surface and -360 γ at 4 R_E, a rather strong variation of the disturbance field with altitude is implied (see Figure 9-22).

In general, it has not been possible so far to get good quantitative agreement between the storm data and simple current models (e.g., the longitudinal current with finite circular cross section or a circular loop). Good agreement has been obtained for specific orbits. However, the currents required to fit the data at 5 to 8 R_E do not account

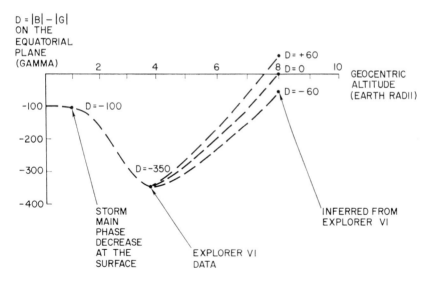

Figure 9-22 Magnitude of the storm field near the equatorial plane inferred from surface and Explorer VI measurements.

for all of the main-phase decrease at the surface. In spite of such ambiguities, which may reflect the inadequacies of the simple models, the storm data is clearly qualitatively consistent with the existence of a ring current. Model calculations had previously demonstrated this for nonstorm days.

4. Vanguard III (Heppner, Stolarik, Shapiro, and Cain). The earth satellite, Vanguard III, contained a proton-precession magnetometer that measured the total scalar magnitude of the geomagnetic field G. Vanguard III was placed in a low-altitude orbit (perigee 6880 km and apogee 10,120 km), which was chosen in order to carry out an extensive mapping of the earth's field above the ionosphere. Data were obtained once per orbit for a period of nearly 2 months. The data indicated that the field magnitude was systematically less by 100γ than anticipated on the basis of extrapolated spherical harmonic expansions (43). Taken at face value, this implies that either (a) the usual field expansions are incorrect, or (b) there is a current system above the satellite orbit. Data obtained during several moderate magnetic storms showed that the field magnitude above the ionosphere tended to be reduced during the storm main phase. This result agrees with the Explorer VI data and is consistent with a westward storm current above the satellite orbit.

5. Explorer X (Heppner, Ness, Skillman, and Scearce). Explorer X was placed in a highly eccentric orbit (apogee 37.5 R_E). Technically, it was an earth satellite. However, data could be obtained only on the outward portion of the first orbit during 53 hr of equipment operation. Therefore, the information it provided is similar to that obtained with space probes. The spacecraft contained both a fluxgate and a rubidium magnetometer. The rubidium magnetometer was used to measure the total magnitude of the geomagnetic field near the earth $(R \leqq 7\ R_E)$ and to calibrate the fluxgate magnetometers at higher altitudes.

The data obtained below 7 R_E are shown in Figure 9-23 (44). There is a discrepancy of only tens of gamma between B and G, which apparently cannot be attributed to uncertainties in the spacecraft trajectory. The depressed value of the field $(\Delta B < 0)$ agrees with the Vanguard III results. The experimenters suggest that a current, which causes these discrepancies, is located in the slot between the inner and outer radiation zones. The surface field before and during launch was magnetically quiet.

At altitudes beyond 7 R_E the fluxgate magnetometers gave both the magnitude and direction of the distant field. The direction is ex-

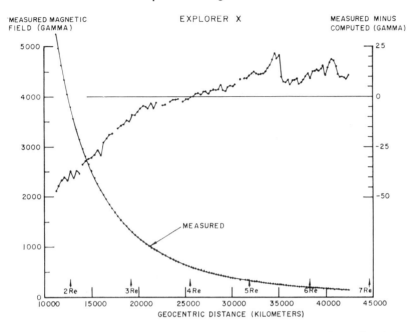

EXPLORER X

MEASURED MINUS
COMPUTED (GAMMA)

Figure 9-23 Explorer X magnetometer data at radial distances of less than 7 R_E. [Taken from a figure by Heppner, Ness, Skillman, and Scearce (44).]

pressed in terms of two angles: ψ, the sun-phase angle discussed in connection with Explorer VI, and α, the angle between B and the spacecraft spin axis.

Figures 9-24 and 9-25 present B, α, and ψ as a function of geocentric distance over the range from 4 to 20 R_E. The geomagnetic field is strongly deformed throughout this region. B is greater than the earth's dipole field and shows a clockwise rotation of field direction. (The spacecraft was located at southern magnetic latitudes.) These observations are qualitatively consistent with the Explorer VI data, particularly the sense and magnitude of the field rotation. Apogee for both Explorer VI and Explorer X occurred at an angle of approximately 135 degrees with respect to the earth-sun direction at southern latitudes, so that the orbits bear a certain resemblance to one another. Similarly, Pioneer I and Pioneer V showed a region of increased field magnitude at large distances (approximately 15 R_E). However, they passed through the earth's field on the sunward side, and the magnitude of the increase nowhere appeared to be more than double the value of unperturbed geomagnetic field.

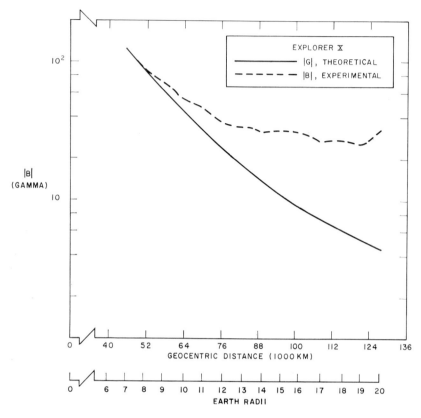

Figure 9-24   Explorer X magnetometer data (field magnitude) between 7 and 20 R_E.

(The Chapman-Ferraro theory predicts that the field magnitude will be double in the vicinity of the magneto pause.)

In their preliminary analysis of the data the experimenters state that the field has the character of a superposition of the earth's field and the solar-interplanetary field, although it could be the result of the geomagnetic field being swept around to the dark side of the earth by solar wind. They do not favor an explanation involving a ring current near or beyond 10 R_E (cf. Explorer VI).

Evidence from spacecraft: particle measurements

According to modern ring-current theory, the question of the possible existence of a ring current in the magnetosphere is also a question whether plasma is trapped in the geomagnetic field. Conclusive

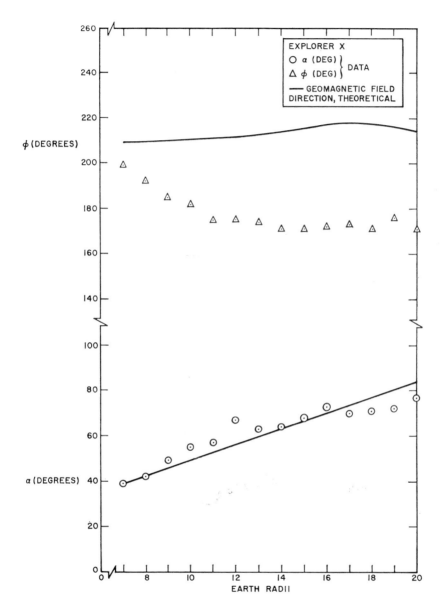

Figure 9-25 Explorer X magnetometer data (field directions) between 7 and 20 R_E.

evidence for the existence of the ring current probably requires the simultaneous observation of (1) a characteristic deformation of the geomagnetic field and (2) a distribution of charged particles having sufficient total energy to produce the observed field deformation consistent with the theory. The question of particle trapping is crucial, since the Störmer theory indicates that individual particles cannot be trapped unless an injection mechanism exists.

There are particles in the magnetosphere that are trapped in Störmer orbits, namely, the radiation particles that constitute the Van Allen zones. Although it follows that there must be a current associated with these particles, there is evidence to indicate that the radiation particles are not responsible for a current system of sufficient magnitude to account for the geophysical effects attributed to the ring current. First, recent evidence indicates that the radiation particles are high-energy particles (1 Mev) so few in number (much less than 1/cm³) that their energy density, and total energy, is too small to deform the geomagnetic field substantially (45, 46, 47). Second, observations of the behavior of the outer zone during magnetic storms is contrary to what would be expected if the radiation particles were responsible for the ring current. The high-energy particle count rates decrease during the main phase of the storm and show large increases only during the recovery phase (48, 49, 50). This observation is contrary to the requirements of an enhanced ring current during the main phase, which subsequently decays during the recovery phase of the storm.

If the high-energy particle component of the magnetosphere does not cause the ring current, it follows that low-energy plasma might be responsible. If the plasma is of solar origin, it might be anticipated that the kinetic energy of the ions and electrons would correspond to the average velocity of propagation of disturbances from sun to earth. A velocity of 1000 km/sec implies protons of 10-kev average energy and electrons with a kinetic energy of 10 ev. Only two spacecraft so far have contained detectors capable of investigating such low-energy protons and electrons. The Luniks contained ion traps capable of detecting both ions and electrons with energies above 200 volts. Explorer X contained a plasma probe able to detect protons with energies in the range of 5 to 2300 volts.

1. Lunik I, II (Gringauz, Kurt, Moroz, and Shklovsky). The results of the ion trap measurements can be summarized as follows (46):

(a) Low-energy plasma was observed out to geocentric distances of 22,000 km. Presumably, this low-energy plasma originates in the earth's atmosphere at lower levels.

(b) No plasma was observed between 22,000 and 55,000 km. The charged particles in this region are predominantly, or entirely, radiation particles. (The propagation of audiofrequency electromagnetic radiation through this region of space ("whistlers") implies the presence of low-energy, thermal plasma, which is not inconsistent with these measurements.)

(c) Low-energy electrons ($E > 200$ volts) were observed in the region 7 to 13 R_E. Gringauz and Rytov compared these measurements with the parameters of the Explorer VI–Pioneer V model calculations (51). They concluded that the particle characteristics could be reconciled with the characteristics of the ring current suggested by the model calculations. They interpreted the empirical results as indicating the presence of a third particle zone consisting of trapped, low-energy electrons. The Pioneer IV Geiger counter had previously detected particles at the same distances from the earth [Figure 9-12 (52)]. The particle count rate was characterized by persistent, rapid fluctuations. However, measurements with the same equipment on the earlier Pioneer III flight gave no such results (53).

2. Explorer X (Bridge, Dilworth, Lazarus, Lyon, Rossi, and Scherb). The results of these measurements may be summarized as follows (54):

(a) Low-energy plasma was observed between 1.3 and 2.9 R_E. This observation is consistent with the ion trap measurements above.

(b) There was a complete absence of plasma between 2.9 and 21.5 R_E.

(c) Plasma was observed intermittently beyond 21.5 R_E.

The absence of plasma beyond 2.9 R_E, and while the Explorer X was inside the geomagnetic field, is an important result. As indicated above, the magnetometer data from Explorer X in the region out to approximately 10 R_E agrees qualitatively with the Explorer VI results. Both magnetometers indicate that the distant geomagnetic field is strongly deformed. The deformation can be visualized as a stretching of the geomagnetic field lines to produce a change in the field magnitude and direction. Since the trajectories of the two spacecraft were similar, it appears likely that the deformation seen by both is characteristic of magnetically quiet periods. The absence of low-energy protons during the Explorer X flight suggests that none was present during the Explorer VI measurements. This important conclusion does not, however, rule out the possibility that trapped electrons are responsible for a quiet-day ring current or that there may be protons trapped in the magnetosphere during magnetic storms.

Summary: present status of evidence concerning the existence of the ring current

The theoretical and experimental aspects of ring currents represent a half-century of scientific endeavor. A detailed and well-founded theory has evolved. Although precise details in the application of the theory to the magnetosphere remain to be worked out, ring-current theory is one of the major accomplishments of geophysics. Very few theories of geophysical phenomena may represent so close an approximation to an actual geophysical situation. There is indirect evidence for the existence of the ring current based on surface measurements. Rocket technology makes particle and field measurements possible within the region of space in which the ring current should exist. The results of the preliminary exploration of the magnetosphere has been described above. In view of these developments, can we, at last, say whether the ring current really exists?

The answer is that we still do not know. The following discussion explores the reasons why we do not. Such a discussion is valuable because, first, a review of the present status reveals the remaining obstacles and suggests how and when we can expect a breakthrough; second, this discussion represents an aspect of science that is not normally encountered in textbooks—science as it is practiced rather than science as a body of classified knowledge.

There is sufficient evidence from spacecraft field measurements to establish that the distant geomagnetic field is deformed. At a geocentric distance of 2 to 3 R_E the Vanguard III and Explorer X data indicate that the geomagnetic field magnitude is depressed by approximately 10 to 100 γ. From 3 to 6 R_E, Lunik I and Pioneer V found $B < G$, whereas the Pioneer I, Lunik II, and Explorer X measurements agree with the extrapolated earth's field in magnitude or radial dependence.

Most of the measurements discussed above were made during relatively quiet magnetic conditions. The Explorer VI storm data show a large perturbation of the geomagnetic field at 4 R_E. Thus we are really considering two closely related problems, the possible existence of a ring current during nonstorm as well as storm periods. If the deformation during quiet conditions turns out to have a cause other than a ring current, the question of the existence of the main-phase ring current might still be unanswered.

Beyond 6 R_E the Explorer VI, Pioneer V, and Explorer X magnetometer data all show a deviation between B and G. A difference in the direction of the observed and extrapolated geomagnetic fields is, perhaps, the most notable feature.

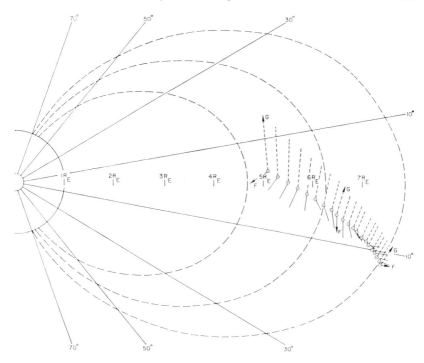

Figure 9-26   Disturbance field in geomagnetic coordinates: Explorer VI.

The Explorer VI and Explorer X vector field measurements have been transformed into geomagnetic coordinates (radial distance R, geomagnetic latitude δ_M, and longitude λ_M) and compared (55). Figure 9-26 shows the disturbance field in geomagnetic coordinates measured by Explorer VI. The disturbance field F is equal to $B - G$. B is obtained by transforming the measured field parameters $B_\perp$ and ϕ into geomagnetic coordinates, assuming that there is no component of F perpendicular to the magnetic meridian plane (the plane containing the earth's dipole field line and the center of the earth). F is shown at several positions on the Explorer VI trajectory, viewed from a direction perpendicular to the local magnetic meridian plane. The data were obtained on August 9, 1959 (during a moderately disturbed interval), and were used in conjunction with the model calculations discussed above.

Figure 9-27 is the corresponding result for the disturbance field measured by Explorer X (during a quiet interval). Figures 9-26 and 9-27 show a southward-directed disturbance field vector **F**, which rotates counterclockwise with increasing radial distance. The qualita-

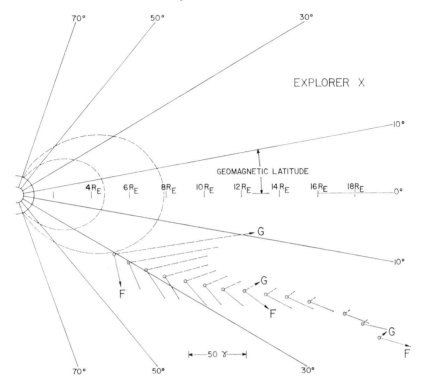

Figure 9-27   Disturbance field in geomagnetic coordinates: Explorer X.

tive agreement between the two sets of data confirms that a large-scale deformation of the geomagnetic field is present beyond 6 R_E even on nonstorm days.   The disturbance field is such that the dipole field lines are "stretched out" but tend to remain inside magnetic meridian planes.

The fact that the distant geomagnetic field is deformed does not establish the existence of a ring current.   Persistent interest in the ring current can probably be explained by (1) the basic simplicity of such a current system and (2) the assumption that most of the geomagnetic field occupied a vacuum.   It is difficult to imagine a current system, capable of producing a quasi-uniform field surrounding the earth, that can be described as simply as a ring current (although the modern ring current is considerably more complicated than its original concept).   The recognition that both the outer atmosphere and interplanetary space are hydromagnetic media has been a comparatively recent development.   The additional complexity in the composition and dynamics of both provides other possible explanations for a deformation of the geomagnetic field.

One of the most promising alternatives appears to be a theory proposed by Piddington (56, 57), who suggested another mechanism for producing a large-scale reduction of the geomagnetic field that involves the interaction between the distant geomagnetic field and the streaming solar plasma. In common with many other theorists, Piddington initially adopts the Chapman-Ferraro view, in which the earth's field is confined to a cavity inside the plasma. Small-scale irregularities enable geomagnetic field lines to diffuse into the plasma. The field lines, which are embedded in the streaming solar plasma, are transported around to the side of the earth opposite the sun to form a magnetic "tail" (see Figure 9-28). As field lines diffuse outward, the magnitude of the geomagnetic field inside the cavity is reduced, for there are now fewer field lines inside the magnetosphere. Since the magnetosphere contains plasma and is a hydromagnetic medium, the stresses that are set up could cause a redistribution of the field such that the deformation would be symmetric near the earth (58). Thus, according to the theory, the main-phase decrease is a characteristic deformation of the magnetosphere caused by solar plasma. This is presumably accomplished without the necessity of trapping plasma in the geomagnetic field. The arguments apply as

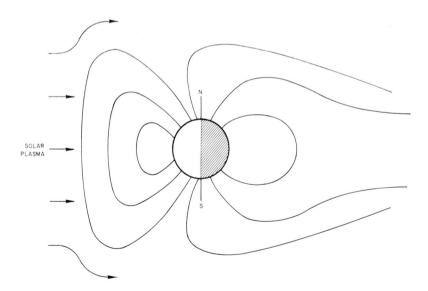

Figure 9-28 The deformation of the geomagnetic field by the solar wind.

well to nonstorm conditions, the only difference being the kinetic-energy density of the solar plasma and the magnitude of the effect in the magnetosphere (3).

These two alternatives, the ring current and magnetic tail, are not necessarily mutually exclusive. There appears to be no reason to exclude the simultaneous occurrence of a magnetic tail and a ring current. If there is unstable equilibrium at the magnetopause between the field-energy density and the particle-energy density, perhaps both trapping of particles and transport of the geomagnetic field can occur. A recent storm theory due to Axford and Hines deals with the deformed magnetosphere and has plasma being convected into the geomagnetic field from the magnetic tail to cause a storm-time ring current (59).

At the present time we cannot decide between these two alternatives by a comparison between observation and theory. The experimental measurements do not yield a clear-cut description of the deformation, and theoretical calculations involving the ring current cannot be compared with the data in a definitive way. The theoretical calculations have been based on a few restricted-particle-distribution functions. This was necessary in order to simplify the mathematics and because the particles which are presumably responsible for the ring current have not been observed; therefore, their distribution function is unknown. Furthermore, most calculations have been restricted to points of observation on the magnetic equatorial plane. On the other hand, the spacecraft orbits were not confined to equatorial planes, but involved latitude variations. A rudimentary comparison was carried out by Apel, Singer, and Wentworth, using the Lunik I and Explorer VI data (29), and by Akasofu and Chapman, who used the Explorer VI data (28). Both comparisons suffered from the limitations mentioned above. Model currents have also been invoked to determine whether the data are consistent with the existence of a field caused by a ring current. Such calculations have provided some agreement with the observed field. However, it is not always possible to get satisfactory agreement by using simple models, for when agreement has been obtained there are ambiguities associated with the reversal of the earth's field gradient. It has not been possible to compare the data with the magnetic tail theory, which at present is completely qualitative.

Presumably, simultaneous particle and field observations could resolve this problem. If we knew the particle characteristics and the nature of the field deformation, the ring-current theory could establish whether the two observations were mutually consistent. Moreover, the presence or absence of trapped particles, with a kinetic-energy density large enough to deform the geomagnetic field strongly, is a fundamental distinction between theories involving the ring current and the magnetic tail. Actually, it has been customary to make simultaneous particle and field measurements on spacecraft. The spacecraft discussed above (Table 9-1) carried particle detectors as well as magnetometers. However, simple particle detectors were included and were intended to investigate the presence of high-energy particles. The description of the particles that have been observed, for example, in the radiation zones, appears to be quite complicated. The data involve ambiguities about the sign of the particles (both protons and electrons appear to be present) and their energies. In any case, the particles responsible for the outer radiation zone apparently do not cause the ring current. The radiation zones seem to be controlled by the field changes rather than the converse. Observations of low-energy particles have been attempted (e.g., Explorer X), but they were restricted to a single-particle species and a limited energy range.

The situation at the present time may be summarized as follows. Although we have learned a great deal from experimental space science, we still do not possess much of the basic knowledge about the magnetosphere. In order to settle the question of the existence of the ring current, we will need more and better experimental data. Required are (1) simultaneous field and particle measurements in which particles of both signs and all energies are differentiated, (2) a better understanding of the extent of the magnetosphere and its shape, and (3) theoretical calculations that are less restricted and that apply more nearly to the actual measurements. This seems to imply a future effort of considerable magnitude. Of course, there is an element of chance involved, and we could be lucky enough to settle this question in the near future with measurements carried out on a single spacecraft. Irrespective of how and when the problem of the geomagnetic ring current is finally resolved, knowledge of the theoretical and experimental aspects of ring currents discussed above will be required in order to understand and appreciate the answer.

REFERENCES

1. Dungey, J. W., *Cosmic Electrodynamics,* Cambridge University Press, Cambridge, 1958.
2. Beard, D. B., *J. Geophys. Res.,* **65,** 3559 (1960).
3. Johnson, F. S., *J. Geophys. Res.,* **65,** 3049 (1960).

4. Chapman, S., and J. Bartels, *Geomagnetism*, Vols. 1 and 2, Oxford University Press, New York, 1949.
5. Stoermer, C., *The Polar Aurora*, Oxford at the Clarendon Press, 1955.
6. Bless, R. C., C. W. Gartlein, D. S. Kimball, and G. Sprague, *J. Geophys. Res.*, **64**, 949 (1959).
7. Kellogg, P. J., and J. R. Winckler, *J. Geophys. Res.*, **66**, 3991 (1961).
8. Vestine, E. H., in *Physics of the Upper Atmosphere*, ed. J. A. Ratcliffe, Academic Press, New York, 1960, p. 471.
9. Schmidt, A., *Abhandl. Kgl. Pr. Met. Inst.*, **5**, 37 (1916); also *Encyclopedia der Math. Wiss.*, **6**, 334.
10. Chapman, S., and V. C. A. Ferraro, *Terr. Magn.*, **36**, 77, 171 (1931); *Terr. Magn.*, **37**, 147, 421 (1932); *Terr. Magn.*, **38**, 79 (1933); *Terr. Magn.*, **45**, 245 (1940); *Terr. Magn.*, **46**, 1 (1941).
11. Alfvén, H., *Tellus*, **7**, 50 (1955).
12. Alfvén, H., *Cosmical Electrodynamics*, Oxford at the Clarendon Press, 1950.
13. Panofsky, W. K. H., and M. Phillips, *Classical Electricity and Magnetism*, Addison-Wesley, Reading, 1955, p. 149.
14. Behr, A., H. Siedentopf, and H. Elsasser, *Nature (London)*, **171**, 1066 (1953).
15. Blackwell, D. E., *Observatory*, **77**, 187 (1957).
16. Storey, L. R. O., *Phil. Trans. Roy. Soc. (London)*, **A246**, 113 (1953).
17. Biermann, L., *Observatory*, **77**, 109 (1957).
18. Parker, E. N., in *Plasma Physics*, ed. F. H. Clauser, Addison-Wesley, Reading, 1960, p. 233.
19. Gold, T., in *Dynamics of Cosmic Clouds*, ed. J. M. Burgers and H. C. Van de Hulst, Interscience Publishers, New York, 1955, p. 103.
20. Singer, S. F., *Trans. Am. Geophys. Union*, **38**, 175 (1957).
21. Parker, E. N., *Astrophys. J.*, **129**, 217 (1959).
22. Dessler, A. J., and E. N. Parker, *J. Geophys. Res.*, **64**, 2239 (1959).
23. Sonett, C. P., *J. Geophys. Res.*, to be published (1962).
24. Singer, S. F., *Phys. Rev. Letters*, **1**, 171 (1958); also S. F. Singer and A. M. Lenchek in *Progress in Cosmic Ray Physics*, **6**, Interscience Publishers, New York, 1962.
25. Kellogg, P. J., *Nuovo Cimento*, **11**, 48 (1959).
26. Hess, W., *Phys. Rev. Letters*, **3**, 11 (1959).
27. Chandrasekhar, S., *Plasma Physics*, ed. S. K. Trehan, University of Chicago Press, Chicago, 1960.
28. Akasofu, S. I., and S. Chapman, *J. Geophys. Res.*, **66**, 1321 (1961).
29. Apel, J., S. F. Singer, and R. C. Wentworth, *Advances in Geophysics*, ed. H. E. Landsberg and J. V. Mieghem, Vol. IX, Academic Press, New York, 1962.
30. Mitra, S. K., *The Upper Atmosphere*, The Asiatic Society, Calcutta, 1952.
31. Ray, E. C., *Phys. Rev.*, **101**, 1142 (1956).
32. Sonett, C. P., D. L. Judge, A. R. Sims, and J. M. Kelso, *J. Geophys. Res.*, **65**, 55 (1960).
33. Dolganov, S., and N. Pushkov, *Dokl. Akad. Nauk SSSR*, **129**, 1 (1959).
34. Antsilevich, M. G., and A. D. Shevnin, *Dokl. Akad. Nauk SSSR*, **135**, 298 (1960).
35. Apel, J. R., M.S. Thesis, University of Maryland (1960).
36. Krassovsky, V. I., *Astronaut. Acta*, **6**, 32 (1960).

37. Sonett, C. P., E. J. Smith, D. L. Judge, and P. J. Coleman, *Phys. Rev. Letters*, **4**, 161 (1960).

38. Sonett, C. P., E. J. Smith, and A. R. Sims, *Space Research*, Proceedings of First International Space Science Symposium, ed. H. K. Kallmann-Bijl, North Holland, Amsterdam, 1960, p. 982.

39. Smith, E. J., P. J. Coleman, D. L. Judge, and C. P. Sonett, *J. Geophys. Res.*, **65**, 1858 (1960).

40. Smith, E. J., and C. P. Sonett, Proceedings of International Conference on Cosmic Rays and the Earth Storm (Kyoto, September 1961) (1962).

41. Arnoldy, R. L., R. A. Hoffman, and J. R. Winckler, *J. Geophys. Res.*, **65**, 3004 (1960).

42. Rosen, A., T. A. Farley, and C. P. Sonett, *Space Research,* ed. H. K. Kallmann-Bijl, North Holland, Amsterdam, 1960, p. 938.

43. Heppner, J. P., J. D. Stolarik, I. R. Shapiro, and J. C. Cain, *Space Research,* ed. H. K. Kallmann-Bijl, North Holland, Amsterdam, 1960, p. 982.

44. Heppner, J. P., N. F. Ness, T. L. Skillman, and C. S. Scearce, Proceedings of International Conference on Cosmic Rays and the Earth Storm (Kyoto, September 1961) (1962).

45. Rosen, A., and T. A. Farley, *J. Geophys. Res.*, **66**, 2013 (1961).

46. Gringauz, K. I., V. G. Kurt, V. I. Moroz, and I. S. Shklovsky, *Astron. Zh.* (*Soviet Astron.—AJ*), **37** (1960).

47. O'Brien, B. J., J. A. Van Allen, C. D. Laughlin, and L. A. Frank, *J. Geophys. Res.*, **67**, 397 (1962).

48. Arnoldy, R., R. Hoffman, and J. R. Winckler, *Space Research,* ed. H. K. Kallmann-Bijl, North Holland, Amsterdam, 1960, p. 877.

49. Fan, C. Y., P. Meyer, and J. A. Simpson, *Space Research,* ed. H. K. Kallmann-Bijl, North Holland, Amsterdam, 1960, p. 951.

50. Rothwell, P., and C. E. McIlwain, *Space Research,* ed. H. K. Kallman-Bijl, North Holland, Amsterdam, 1960, p. 897.

51. Gringauz, K. I., and S. M. Rytov, *Dokl. Akad. Nauk SSSR*, **135**, 48 (1960).

52. Van Allen, J. A., and L. A. Frank, *Nature* (*London*), **184**, 219 (1959).

53. Van Allen, J. A., and L. A. Frank, *Nature* (*London*), **183**, 430 (1959).

54. Bridge, H. S., C. Dilworth, A. Lazarus, E. F. Lyon, B. Rossi, and F. Scherb, Proceedings of International Conference on Cosmic Rays and the Earth Storm (Kyoto, September 1961) (1962).

55. Smith, E. J., *J. Geophys. Res.* (1962).

56. Piddington, J. H., *Geophys. J.*, **2**, 173 (1959).

57. Piddington, J. H., *J. Geophys. Res.*, **65**, 93 (1960).

58. Parker, E. N., *Phys. Fluids*, **1**, 171 (1958).

59. Axford, W. I., and C. O. Hines, *Can. J. Phys.*, **39**, 1433 (1961).

CHAPTER 10

ROCKET EXPERIMENTS
IN COSMIC MAGNETISM
AND THEIR SIGNIFICANCE

CHARLES P. SONETT *

National Aeronautics and Space Administration

With the exception of the sensible planetary atmospheres and perhaps the regions far from stars, much of the gaseous matter of the universe is thought to exist in a partially ionized state. It is believed that hydrogen, constituting the bulk of this matter, provides the primary ingredient from which this ionized medium is formed. In the case of the earth and, presumably, other planets containing a supply of hydrogenous material of sufficiently low vapor pressure, the far atmosphere, being bathed in the solar far ultraviolet, also would consist primarily of ionized hydrogen.

Such regions of ionized gas, called plasmas, have properties sufficiently different from those of gases obeying conventional equations of state to suggest that they be considered a fourth state of matter. One fundamental distinction is that the existence of many free electrons and ions makes coulomb interactions important. Since these interactions are long range, the dynamical behavior of this medium is considerably different from either the ideal or Van der Waals gas. Linhart (1) has pointed out that by extrapolating the energy domain of existence of plasmas to extreme values a counterpart nuclear plasma, or "nugas," and even a highly relativistic free meson-nucleon-electron plasma should exist. It seems reasonable, in fact, to consider

* Formerly with Space Technology Laboratories, Inc.

the primary cosmic radiation over a sufficiently great distance scale as constituting this relativistic plasma.

It has often been argued that plasmas of astrophysical scale can be shown to be electrically neutral over distances large enough to average out fluctuations (2). The electrical neutrality, or what is equivalent, the approximate inequality of free charge, implies that $\nabla \cdot D$ is small and $\rho E \ll J \times B$, that is, electrical forces are small in comparison to magnetic forces. This condition is violated for frequencies in which displacement currents are important and radiation fields exist. For the subject of hydromagnetics, the frequencies are taken so low that $\partial D/\partial t \sim 0$. Violation of this condition may be considered as the transition from the discipline of hydromagnetics to that of radio astronomy.

Because of the physically important implications when magnetic fields and plasmas are mixed, their combined existence is a fundamental subject in the field of astrophysics. Until 1908 the only large-scale natural magnetic field known was that of the earth. In that year Hale demonstrated spectroscopically the existence of fields of some thousands of gauss associated with sunspots. In 1946 Babcock at Mt. Wilson Observatory reported a 1500-gauss field component about the star 78 Virginis, and today the list of such stars is much extended. Indeed, radio astronomical observations of the galactic halo strongly support the idea that the continuum radiation noted at radio frequencies is from synchrotron emission that requires a magnetic field for its generation (3).

The discovery of the polarization of starlight by Hiltner, Hall, and Mikesell (4, 5) in 1949 has lent support to the notion of a spiral arm field in the Galaxy, a mechanism of polarization having been supplied by a theory of Davis and Greenstein (6) that involves alignment of interstellar dust grains.

Recent years have seen the development of interplanetary models; for example, those of Parker (7), Elliot (8), Lüst and Schlüter (9), and Block (10), all invoking fields for their completeness. The existence of large-scale fields on the sun in regions away from spots and some characteristics of their behavior have also been established by Babcock and Babcock (11).

Today, on the scale of the earth's magnetosphere, in interplanetary space and in interstellar space beyond, there are compelling arguments for the existence of magnetic fields and for their importance in the dynamic makeup and history of the universe.

Looked at from the standpoint of astrophysics, rockets are a new tool available for the direct study of problems in astronomy unencumbered by the body or atmosphere of the earth. The opacity of the earth's atmosphere to the far-ultraviolet is a well-known and non-trivial constraint on optical astronomy. The high atmosphere, or exosphere, of the earth with its magnetic field is a qualitatively similar barricade to propagating interplanetary phenomena, although here transmission, albeit highly modified, does occur.

This chapter deals with some of the principal results of the experimental complement to cosmic electrodynamics, the direct observation of magnetic fields and plasmas in space, which have been made since the first lunar orbiter attempt some 4 years ago. This research program is in its infancy; observations bearing on the structure of the outer gaseous mantle of the earth have been made, but the number of unsolved problems appears to have increased since the first experiment on Pioneer I. Experiments carried on Pioneer V (Figure 10-1) contributed considerable scientific knowledge about deep space.

The discussion considers some measurements of the interplanetary field and their relation to theoretical models and the interaction of the earth with both the undisturbed and storm-time interplanetary medium. Certain aspects of the interplanetary medium as well as of certain phases of the geophysical resultant of interplanetary storm-earth interaction, such as ring currents, are covered in Chapter 9.

The breadth of the fields of geophysical and interplanetary hydromagnetics is so great that no claim for completeness can be made for this review, which is necessarily limited to material directly relevant to certain experiments. A strong case is made for consideration of plasma data as well as magnetometer data, and so comments are included on both.

In this country the principal efforts to the time of this writing have been in magnetic fields, although interest is increasing in the area of plasmas. These efforts have been conducted by the author and co-workers at Space Technology Laboratories, Inc., and by Heppner and associates at Goddard Space Flight Center. Plasma measurements have been made by Bridge and colleagues at Massachusetts Institute of Technology and by Bader at Ames Research Center; experiments unfortunately terminated by rocket failure have been attempted by Snyder and Neugebauer at the Jet Propulsion Laboratory of California Institute of Technology. Russian magnetometer data is considered, although spacecraft fields in these instances have high thresholds so that interplanetary measurements generally provide only upper bounds. Plasma-probe data are more complete and, indeed, a large portion of available information seems to have come from the USSR.

Figure 10-1 The launching of Pioneer V on March 11, 1960. This spacecraft achieved the deepest penetration of interplanetary space to this time and provided a number of new scientific observations. (NASA photo.)

10-1 SOME CONDITIONS ON ASTROPHYSICAL PLASMAS

There are certain characteristics of cosmic plasmas that make them distinctive from laboratory plasmas. These are charge neutrality and the collisionless condition, except, perhaps, in the interior or neighborhood of stars. Thus, to some extent, even long-range coulomb interactions are secondary in importance compared to the effect of the magnetic field. The latter replaces electrostatic interactions, and one finds that the dominant length is the Larmor radius. Collisional rearrangements leading to the establishment of well-behaved Boltzmann distributions become inoperative, and dynamical perturbations do not necessarily lead to equilibrium states; that is, the velocity distributions are anisotropic, and electron and proton energies may be non-Maxwellian.

The most important forces that operate on a cosmic plasma are those provided by electric fields, magnetic fields, pressure gradients, and inertial accelerations (including gravity). Particle collisional effects are, as already discussed, usually ignorable in interplanetary and interstellar space and often in planetary exospheres. The equation of motion (Newton's second law) then becomes (12)

$$m\left(\frac{d\mathbf{v}}{dt}\right) = e(\mathbf{E} + \mathbf{v} \times \mathbf{B}) - \nabla \cdot \chi - m\mathbf{g}, \qquad (10\text{-}1)$$

where m is the particle mass,

$$\frac{d}{dt} \text{ means } \frac{\partial}{\partial t} + \mathbf{v} \cdot \nabla,$$

$\nabla \cdot \chi$ is the divergence of the stress tensor (the pressure gradient for zero shear), and $\mathbf{g}$ is the net acceleration due to gravity forces.

Together with the equation of continuity $\nabla \cdot (\rho v) = 0$ and Maxwell's equations taken with the special conditions that free charge and displacement currents are zero, equation (10-1) forms the framework in which much of the subject is cast. A more formal approach, using the Boltzmann equation reduced to Liouville's theorem (invariance of the distribution function in phase space for no collisions), is often employed. Equation (10-1) is obtained from it by integrating the Boltzmann equation over velocity space, having first multiplied through by the momentum.

Of importance in nonrelativistic cosmic electrodynamics is the velocity transformation of fields. When $v/c \ll 1$, the magnetic field transforms into itself. As a consequence of the high conductivity for the observer moving with a cosmic plasma, no electric field is seen. In coordinate systems having relative motion with respect to the plasma an electric field is displayed, given by $E = -V \times B$, where V is the relative velocity with respect to the plasma. More generally, that is, for large but finite conductivity (σ) and under the foregoing conditions, an electric field of reduced value is seen. The "freezing in" of lines of force to the plasma for the case of infinite conductivity (in effect a consequence of Lenz's law) is modified in the case of $\sigma < \infty$ by diffusion of the field through the plasma. This is seen as follows: assume a gyrotropic plasma having associated with it a velocity field (with respect to a frame 0), given by v, where $v/c \ll 1$, and an electromagnetic field, $\mathbf{E}$, $\mathbf{H}$, where $\mathbf{E}$, $\mathbf{H}$ is measured in the frame of reference in which the plasma displays the velocity field $\mathbf{v}$ (namely 0). Further, for simplicity, assume a finite scalar (13) conductivity. Then, in the frame of the plasma the field vectors transform into $(\mathbf{E} + \mathbf{v} \times \mathbf{B}, \mathbf{B})$ and any current that flows is given by

$$\mathbf{j} = \sigma(\mathbf{E} + \mathbf{v} \times \mathbf{B}). \tag{10-2}$$

Since Maxwell's equations are invariant to this transformation, in the plasma frame

$$-\frac{\partial B}{\partial t} = \nabla \times \mathbf{v} \times \mathbf{B} - \frac{1}{\sigma} \nabla \times j. \tag{10-3}$$

In the limit of low frequencies $j = \nabla \times \mathbf{H}$ and making use of the appropriate vector calculus equation (10-3) reduces to

$$\frac{\partial \mathbf{H}}{\partial t} = \nabla \times \mathbf{v} \times \mathbf{H} + \frac{1}{\mu\sigma} \nabla^2 \mathbf{H}, \tag{10-4}$$

a result given by Cowling (14). For illustrative purposes, the two limiting cases of $\sigma \to \infty$ and $\sigma \to 0$ can be examined. Consider the case in which $\sigma \to \infty$; the leading term dominates. This corresponds to the condition of extreme conductivity, in which the velocity field for the plasma is pointwise isomorphic with the velocity field of $\mathbf{H}$, and to the geophysically and astrophysically important situation in which the field is "frozen" into the plasma. Proof of this is direct. Consider a tube of force forming the cylinder defined by a bundle of lines of force, the end sections being pointwise normal to the lines. Then everywhere on the side surfaces * of the tube $\mathbf{B} \cdot d\mathbf{s} = 0$ the two ends sum to zero, and it follows that

$$\frac{\partial}{\partial t} \int \mathbf{B} \cdot d\mathbf{s} = 0 \tag{10-5}$$

* By side surface is meant the generatrix of the conic.

everywhere on the surface of the tube. [Equation (10-5) is, incidentally, also true for any subsidiary tube of force.] Application of Stokes's theorem to equation (10-3) under the restriction of equation (10-5) then demands that

$$\int \mathbf{v} \times \mathbf{B} \cdot d\mathbf{l} = 0, \tag{10-6}$$

where $\mathbf{v}$ is measured in the plasma frame. Since $d\mathbf{l}$ and $\mathbf{B}$ are nonzero, $\mathbf{v} = 0$ in this limit.

The situation in which the second term of equation (10-4) dominates provides an equation of diffusion, for if

$$\frac{1}{\mu\sigma} \nabla^2 \mathbf{H} \gg \nabla \times \mathbf{v} \times \mathbf{H},$$

then

$$\frac{\partial \mathbf{H}}{\partial t} \sim \frac{1}{\mu\sigma} \nabla^2 \mathbf{H}. \tag{10-7}$$

Dimensionally, one can associate a characteristic time and length from equation (10-7), where

$$\tau \sim \mu\sigma L^2. \tag{10-8}$$

This expression is of fundamental importance in cosmic electrodynamics, since it relates the diffusion time of a field out of a region to a characteristic length. For example, Cowling estimates for the earth that the field would decay in $\sim 10^4$ years if sources of energy were not present (15). Thus the annihilation of a primordial field should have occurred early in the history of the earth. Also, say, for an interstellar gas cloud in which $L \sim 3 \times 10^{19}$ cm, the decay time is $\sim 10^{23}$ years (16). It is important to recognize that σ need not actually be comparable to laboratory values. The enormous scale of distance normally suffices to make the apparent conductivity high. Since this discussion is applicable to continuous media, for dimensions comparable to Larmor radii, the theory breaks down. This means, then, that a sharp corner in a field might well diffuse faster than given by equation (10-8). Also, the presence of large amplitude waves or turbulence of scale comparable to the Larmor radius might reduce the time scale of diffusion appreciably (17). Alternatively, one might consider that the conductivity was lower than calculable by equation (10-8). Nevertheless, the continuum theory has enormous importance, for it enables one to show that for many cases of interest cosmic fields are a feature of extreme lifetime astrophysically.

The geometry of a tube of force has deeper meaning than the line of force, since one can discuss energy in a manner useful to an understanding of field stability and dynamic properties. It is not hard to show, directly, from the Maxwell stress tensor for an electromagnetic field (18) that the magnetic-energy density is given by $(\mathbf{B \cdot H})/8\pi$, and that this energy density is equivalent to a pressure tending to distend the field much as if it were a gas. This pressure is anisotropic; that is, it is dependent on direction with respect to the field. A convenient model shown in Figure 10-2 provides an isotropic pressure of $H^2/8\pi$ and a tension along the lines of force tending to shrink the tube length by $H^2/4\pi$. Simple magnetic configurations such as tubes of force and closed tubes (toroids) that are not twisted in a special manner are unstable and have no potential minimum.

Plasmas normally exhibit a multitude of oscillatory modes. Spitzer (19) has described those in an electron gas. Without magnetic field, the low-frequency transmission cutoff is given by the plasma frequency $\omega_p = (4\pi ne^2/m)^{1/2}$. When a one-component plasma is immersed in a magnetic field, other modes appear. First, the plasma is birefringent and exhibits an ordinary and extraordinary mode. There will be a mode propagated below the plasma frequency (circularly polarized, extraordinary mode). Electrostatic waves are also allowed; for binary plasmas, both ion and electron waves are present. Binary plasmas exhibit modes of propagation to $\omega = 0$. The hydromagnetic mode is popularly used to signify a

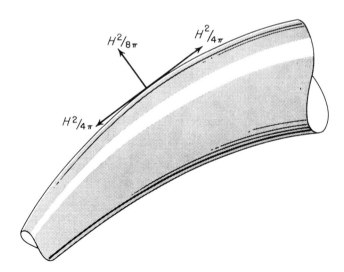

Figure 10-2   Idealized tube of force, showing the forces exerted by the field. Plasma forces are not shown.

group that exists below the ion gyro cutoff. The transverse mode was discovered by Alfvén (20) and bears his name. This mode is in reality two: circularly polarized, right- and left-handed, and in the low frequency limit the medium becomes monorefringent. Åstrom (21) has discussed the multicomponent plasma in a magnetic field and analyzes the allowed modes. Figure 10-3 shows the simplest case of transverse waves to illustrate the many stop bands in a polytropic plasma.

Finally, the problem of hydromagnetic turbulence appears occasionally in the data. For the purposes here, a detailed definition of this phenomenon, seemingly unresolved, is not needed. What is of importance are the energy densities of gas and field; that is to say, which is in dynamic control? If it is the former, we would expect that the field would "wrinkle" and become disordered in direction as a result of motions in the gas. The lifetime of magnetic eddies resulting from annihilation of opposed tubes of force is now unknown. For the case of field control, the consequences seem more straightforward, for plasma motion is then governed by the dominant field and follows the usual rules for charged particles in fields.

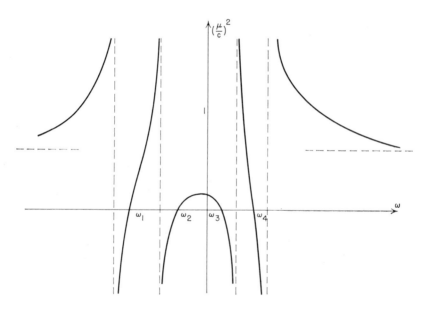

Figure 10-3 Passbands and stopbands in a multicomponent gyrotropic plasma for the transverse mode. The vertical asymptotes correspond to the Larmor frequencies, $+\omega$ corresponding to positive particles and $-\omega$ to negative. The lower half-plane corresponds only to evanescent propagation since $(\mu/c)^2 < 0$, where μ is the phase velocity. [From E. Åstrom (21). Courtesy of the Royal Swedish Academy of Science.]

10-2 THE OUTER ATMOSPHERE OF THE EARTH

Before Storey's analysis (22) of some unusual radio signals of a type first observed by Barkhausen in World War I, it was generally held that the earth had an exosphere, a region beyond the ionosphere, in which collisional effects were so sparse because of the low density that gas molecules executed free ballistic motion. This was in keeping with an escape rate dependent on temperature. In one sense, this model was not even fluid dynamical; in any event, it provided no coupling to the geomagnetic field, for the total gas body was taken to be nonionized. Storey's analysis profoundly modified exospheric models, since he demonstrated that the propagation characteristics of the signals he analyzed demanded an electron gas of 10^2 to $10^3/\text{cm}^3$ density. An immediate consequence, as recognized by Dungey (23), was that the usual requirement of cosmic electrodynamics of no free charge, that is, $\nabla \cdot D = 0$, required an ion-electron atmosphere of pointwise charge neutrality. Today we recognize the exosphere, or, as it has more recently been called, the magnetosphere (24), as a body of gas bounded on its interior surface by the nonconducting atmosphere and on its exterior surface by electrodynamic coupling between it and the interplanetary gas in some manner not well understood. The general shape of the magnetosphere may approximate the dipolar field equatorially; there is presently some evidence that a solar-antisolar asymmetry exists because of unequal pressure gradients. The polar field at extreme altitudes is the subject of conjecture; the connectivity to the interplanetary field is unknown. An apparent surface current singularity might exist where the polar axis intersects the boundary of the magnetosphere.

The connectivity of the geomagnetic field to the interplanetary volume has suggested that exchange of angular momentum might have braked the rotational velocity of the earth appreciably in geological times. However, paleomagnetic evidence of magnetic polar wander, accompanied, perhaps, by spin pole wander, makes any surmises hypothetical. The extent of geopolar-interplanetary field tangling as a primary means of exchange of angular momentum with "frictionless" slipping in nonpolar regions remains to be investigated.

Current systems

Quite generally, the magnetosphere is an electrodynamic medium, both inhomogeneous and anisotropic, containing the Van Allen belts, large-scale currents, and perhaps other still uncovered phenomena. This body of gas, in effect, provides us with an earth-centered astrophysical gas cloud, having primarily magnetofluid behavior, close at hand, which can be studied with broad-band telemetry and high-information-rate instruments for a better understanding of astrophysical behavior as it takes place in the universe at large. The physical behavior of the magnetosphere is governed by the distribution of plasma, consisting primarily of protons and electrons, the configuration of the magnetic field, both that generated in the core of the earth and locally generated fields in the high atmosphere, and motions introduced, for example, by solar plasma outbursts and by the rotation of the earth. The boundary conditions discussed before, both at the interior and exterior boundaries of the magnetosphere, require consideration when discussing the dynamics, for as Gold (25) has pointed out, on the interior boundary the insulating atmosphere provides a "disconnecting" mechanism between the solid earth and the magnetosphere allowing free exchange of field lines. Indeed, such a mechanism may obviate the question of spin damping raised before.

It is generally thought that the magnetosphere shows a high order of regularity out to some 5 R_e (R_e = geocentric radii) (26, 27). The large-scale dipolar field order * provides a setting in which the magnetic energy density exceeds the gas kinetic-energy density by a sufficient amount so that hydromagnetic turbulence probably does not exist, and the Alfvén signal velocity can, for many purposes, be assumed isotropic. It is in this region of space that the Van Allen belts exist and that ring current effects may be important. The actual geomagnetic-interplanetary interface (the outer boundary of the exosphere) possibly has a variable distance from the earth, depending on the longitude with respect to the earth-sun line and perhaps also on the state of solar activity. Present indications from space probes are that the magnetosphere may be divisible into two regions of fundamentally different hydromagnetic behavior. These are the magnetosphere proper, characterized by a magnetic pressure much greater than the gas pressure, or $H^2/8\pi nkt \gg 1$ out to perhaps 5 to 7 R_e, and what may be termed the magnetopause, where more nearly $H^2/8\pi nkt \sim 1$; in the magnetopause the field appears to be subjected at times to shock waves, disorder, and perhaps other species of hydromagnetic activity (27, 28). (These correspond to low and high β cases of laboratory plasma physics.)

Although a considerable literature now exists on the physics of the magnetosphere, much of this work is still of a theoretical nature and has little supportive evidence experimentally. It does, however, form the groundwork against which the reduction and analysis of

---

* Large-scale order is not intended to imply the absence of currents but rather "mixing," turbulence, or large waves.

experimental data from satellites can be examined. The magneto-sphere demands consideration in the context of a closed volume sur-rounding the earth so that any solar phenomena propagated earth-ward must pass through it; it acts essentially as a transmission medium. These characteristics must be understood in order to develop the relationship between interplanetary phenomena and resultant geo-physical effects seen on the surface of the earth.

Ring currents far antedate the discovery of the magnetosphere. They were first proposed by Birkeland and by Störmer to explain the latitude of the auroral zones. Later, others, including Chapman and Ferraro, invoked the concept of a ring current to explain the apparent symmetry of the main-phase decrease of magnetic storms. With the discovery of the magnetosphere, it became important to fold into it the hypothesis of a ring current. One of the first to attack this problem was Singer (29), who proposed that the drift of positive and negative particles in the inhomogeneous field of the earth in itself constituted a ring current which existed all the time and depressed the field at the surface below that of normal dipolar value. Following this work of Singer came the discovery by Van Allen of trapped particles at very high energy (30). Attempts were then made to fit the Van Allen radiation belts into the ring-current concept, most of which centered around the idea of drift currents of charged particles in the inhomogeneous field. Dessler and Parker (31) then proposed that diamagnetic effects were important. Their model of the ring current placed the center at the peak of the second Van Allen radia-tion belt at approximately 4 R_e. At about the same time the mag-netometer experiment on Explorer VI by Sonett and co-workers (32) showed distinctly that large-scale currents were flowing in the far exosphere of the earth because of the large anomalies that were seen on most days during the 6 weeks in which the magnetometer was operating. Neither the Pioneer I, the Explorer VI (27) nor the Ex-plorer X experiments noted large-scale field deviations at geocentric distances of less than 5 R_e (26, 32), whereas Lunik I (33) reported a large anomaly in the field at $\sim$2 R_e. (See Figure 10-4 for Pioneer I.) The Lunik I experiment suggests the existence of a large ring current in the region between the two Van Allen belts. The regular variations in the field beyond 5 R_e noted on the Explorer VI experi-ment were seen again on Explorer X and seemed to extend out to much greater distances.

The Lunik data is somewhat difficult to interpret because the anomaly is about one half the quiescent field, making, for example, any linear drift-current theory difficult to apply. Strong pressure

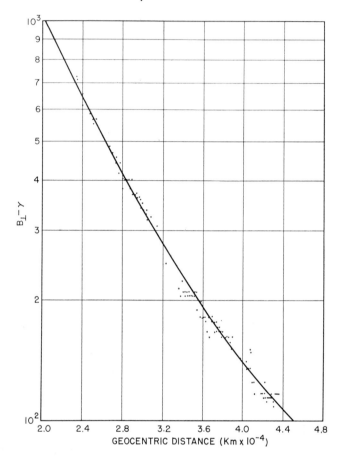

Figure 10-4   Radial traverse in the geomagnetic field from $3.7 \leqq R_e \leqq 7$ taken on Pioneer I. [From C. P. Sonett et al. (26). Courtesy *J. Geophys. Res.*]

gradients are required to sustain this variation. Possible evidence is afforded by Lunik II plasma data when a steep gradient is observed in this region. An additional difficulty is the fact that the field is depressed everywhere, which would seem to violate the need to conserve the field energy (and, therefore, amplitude) over such a large volume; this, in turn, requires positive excursions. [This result is also arrived at directly by consideration of diamagnetic effects (34).] The reversed gradient offers additional difficulties in any interpretation involving conventional drift-current theories. These data are shown in Figure 10-5 with Lunik II, which, interestingly, does not show the same anomaly.

The deformation of the field first seen on Explorer VI, again on Pioneer V, and much extended on Explorer X is a separate problem. The Explorer X indicates a persistent deviation out of 21.5 R_e, mostly positive. A small negative deviation was noted at $\sim$7.5 R_e of a few gammas. There was no evidence of any obvious similarity to Explorer VI in field amplitude. The angular rotation of the field, however, is quite similar, the Explorer VI case being more involved because of the complication of the apogee turnaround at $\sim$8 R_e, with attendant changes in geomagnetic attitude of the spacecraft.

Currently, two explanations for the far-disturbances are the existence of a current system closing axisymmetrically about the earth in the far field (35) and a field deformation caused by a solar wind

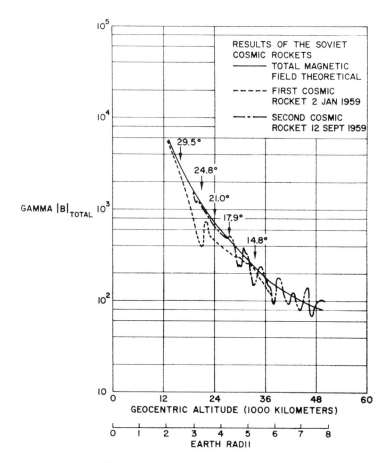

Figure 10-5   Radial geomagnetic traverse from Lunik I and Lunik II.

(36, 37). Analysis is presently insufficient to decide between these alternatives or whether both are correct. In any event, the deformation or geomagnetic tail implies the existence of a current system defined by $\nabla \times H \neq 0$, so that in either case a nonzero curl is indicated in the magnetopause. This is an important result of space probes, for it means that the electrodynamics of the magnetosphere and the magnetopause require a modified dipole.

Analysis of data from Explorer VI and Explorer X is complicated by the need to study all 6 degrees of freedom of the spacecraft before completing the magnetic-field analysis. Many of the data for both spacecraft are still being processed.

The storm-time field may be related to the often-seen field anomalies of Explorer VI. Recent analysis of storm data for the period around August 16, 1959, indicates a generalized D_{st} westward current over possibly a broad region of the magnetosphere (38). There appears to be a main-phase decrease and recovery at 4 R_e, which coincides with the surface storm effects. Furthermore, the 4 R_e decrease is larger by a factor of 3.6. This provides definite evidence for a general magnetospheric current source for the storm-time (D_{st}) field. Antsilevich (39) has recently examined surface magnetograms for the time during which Explorer VI was in flight and finds some correspondence between surface and satellite measurements.

Limited information of a preliminary sort has just become available from Explorer XII. Cahill (40) reports no evidence of magnetospheric currents but finds evidence of a termination at ~ 10 R_e. The negative finding is accurate to about 20γ, since this is the limit of digitization of the data. Rotation of the field was not available because the expected dipolar direction as seen by the spacecraft was not available. If the digitization transitions are read, they are probably precise to something like 0.1 to 1γ (better than the flux-gate magnetometer zero). However, an unknown $\pm 20\gamma$ variation could exist and not be detected. If the data pass through two adjacent digitization transitions, the 20γ separation of levels is resolved, but two new ambiguities totaling 40γ are introduced. The effect of this on the angular accuracy can be calculated easily by the reader and depends partly on the resolution of the field in spacecraft coordinates.

Since the curl of **H** is a tensor whose components are given by $\partial H_i/\partial x_j$, it is clear that definitive study of the currents associated with field distortions requires s program using earth satellites with a high degree of sophistication. Single traversals by probes and other limited arrangements will not, in the long sense, provide the components of the curl. The time variance of field perturbations, particularly in the magnetopause, must also be folded into a proper field description. Even with the assumption of ignorable displacement currents, the extreme difficulty of ever obtaining a complete description of $\nabla \times H$ suggests that a microscopic (individual-particle) analysis is needed. It is important to recognize that the self-consistent theory required when large deformations of the field are encountered will require extensive study before the magnetospheric field can be specified with completeness. Dessler and Karplus (41) have presented strong arguments for a storm-time current at about 4 R_e. The results of Apel (42), used by them, show that a diamagnetic pair of currents may produce a decrease at the surface in spite of the lower altitude of the eastward component. This, together with energy considerations, makes the likelihood of broad, diffuse currents centered perhaps at 3 to 5 R_e quite attractive and is consistent with the recent analysis of Explorer VI data (38).

The rotation of the earth may be important in the balance of forces in the magnetosphere. This problem was considered in the corotation of the interplanetary field with the sun by Lüst and Schlüter, though their interest was generated by the question of magnetic spin damping in stars (9). The same general problem has been treated by Block (10). In the earth's magnetosphere, beyond the distance of synchronous rotation defined by

$$R_0{}^3 = \frac{GM}{\omega^2},$$
(10-9)

the magnetic field becomes the constraining agent. In short, the equilibrium condition is hydromagnetic [equation (10-1)] and is governed by the equation of motion of a rarefied plasma in the presence of pressure (∇p) gradients and gravity. A uniquely magnetic constraint is applicable at distances beyond which these quantities are important.

Plasma experiments

To understand the properties of ring currents which appear to flow in the magnetosphere requires detailed information on the plasma and density gradients, for the flow of currents is governed by the equations of bulk hydromagnetics that contain, in addition to the gravity potential, the pressure gradient and body forces.

There are some data available from satellites at the present time on the question of density and density gradients. Table 10-1 lists the principal plasma experiments which have been conducted on space probes and high-altitude satellites. The lower altitude Sputniks and Explorer VIII have not been included. Principally, three types of instruments have been used, the USSR favoring the ion trap of hemispherical design. Gringauz et al. (43) have provided a description of this equipment. On Lunik II it consisted of a hemispherical

TABLE 10-1

High Satellite and Space Probe Plasma Data (Part One)

Name	IGY Designation	Launch Date	Instrument
Lunik I (Mechta)		1-2-59	Three-electrode trap
Lunik II		9-12-59	Four 3-electrode traps
Venus Probe	1961 Gamma	2-12-61	Equipment "similar" to above
Explorer X	1961 Kappa	3-25-61	Faraday cage
Explorer XII	1961 Epsilon	8-15-61	Curved plate electrostatic analyzer

High Satellite and Space Probe Plasma Data (Part Two)

Range	Current Range	Stationary Plasmas
Unknown	Unknown	Consistent with Lunik II
Electrons >200 ev; potentials of -10, -5, 0, $+15$ volts to spacecraft body	10^{-10} to 5×10^{-9} amp for ions; 10^{-10} to 1.5×10^{-10} for electrons; threshold $\sim 2 \times 10^7/\mathrm{cm}^2$-sec	From $1 < R_e < 4.7$ plasma ($T < 5 \times 10^4$ °K); beyond $1.5\,R_e$ no current on $+15$-volt trap; negative currents to 4.7 R_e less than 10^{-10} amp; fluctuations from vehicle rotation imply "low"-temperature plasma
By inference one trap biased to $+25$ volts Automatically programmed stepped bias 0 to 2300 volts; no provision for negative currents	$5 \times 10^6/\mathrm{cm}^2$-sec of singly charged ions	Sporadic between streams; $N_i \leq 1/\mathrm{cm}^3$ in free space "Cold" plasma, i.e., ions of velocity comparable to spacecraft velocity from 1.3 to 2.9 R_e; density data not available; below threshold from $2.9 \leq R_e$ ≤ 21.5
0.2 to 20 kv positive ions only	4×10^{-14} amp or $4 \times 10^5/\mathrm{cm}^2$-sec	Not observed to date; data reduction in progress

TABLE 10-1 (*Continued*)

High Satellite and Space Probe Plasma Data (Part Three)

Streams	Reference
Consistent with Lunik II	K. I. Gringauz et al. (43)
Electron flux $\lesssim 2 \times 10^8/cm^2$-sec at $8.3 < R_e < 12.5$	K. I. Gringauz et al. (43) E. R. Mustel (101)
Ion (probably proton) flux $\sim 2 \times 10/cm^2$-sec; $E > 15$ ev at 3.3×10^5 km $\leq R \leq$ moon impact	K. I. Gringauz and S. M. Rytov (44)
Ion flux $\sim 2 \times 10^8/cm^2$-sec at $R \sim$ 1.25×10^5 km or 1.5×10^5 km correlated with K index	
Ion flux $\sim 10^9/cm^2$-sec^1 (Mustel); $N_i \sim 20/cm^3$ for $V \sim 500$ km/sec (timed from storm)	E. R. Mustel (100)
Irregular density streams from solar direction beyond 21.5 R_e; mean energy ~ 500 ev shifted higher after SC; indicated velocity ~ 300 km/sec; out of phase correlation with magnetometer amplitude	H. Bridge et al. (47, 48) J. P. Heppner et al. (27)

N_i screen enclosing a flat N_i collector which was itself covered by a tungsten photoelectric suppressor grid. There were four traps on Lunik II, and the vehicle performed attitude maneuvers * so that at all times one trap was shielded from the sun, providing a test for photoelectric currents. An important adjunct to the arrangement was the ordering of potentials with respect to the spacecraft body: internal collectors 60 to 90 volts negative, photosuppressor grids 200 volts negative, and outer cover screens -10, -5, 0, and $+15$ volts. Incomplete information is available to this writer on the equipment aboard Lunik I and the Venus probe; the comments of Gringauz et al. indicate at least a qualitative similarity to Lunik II. One difference is that on the Venus probe the maximum positive potential was increased to $+25$ volts.

* It is not clear from the available translation whether these were controlled maneuvers or tumbling; either suffices for the photoelectric tests.

There appear to be two primary results within the confines of the magnetosphere. First, a relatively cold plasma (in contrast to the Van Allen radiation) was noted to 2.8×10^4 km, although the apparent concentration of $\sim 500/cm^3$ began to droop just past 2.1×10^4 km. The density was "hydrostatic" to 2.1×10^4 km. The temperature is estimated from current modulation on the negatively biased traps as having an upper bound of $\sim 5 \times 10^{4}$°K. It is important to note that in this interval electron currents were small or zero, even on the $+15$ volt trap.

From 2.8×10^4 to 5×10^4 km negative currents varying from zero to 6×10^{-10} amp were noted on all traps, indicating, it would seem, electron bursts of energy ≥ 15 volts.

From 5×10^4 to 7×10^4 km simultaneous electron currents were seen on all four traps. Gringauz and Rytov (44) have compared these results with the computations of Smith et al. for the magnetometer data of Explorer VI and Pioneer V, and find the plasma and field measurements to be consistent for the assumption of a large ring current. It must be remembered that Dessler and Karplus (41) have pointed out that consistency is obtained by postulating a body of electrons not actually seen by Gringauz et al. As they show, there may be serious problems in trying to reconcile the Explorer VI and Lunik II data. Furthermore, the question whether the Explorer VI quiet-time perturbation was a drawn-out tail or a ringlike current is not resolved. This question is certainly intensified by the Explorer X data.

The results during passage through the second Van Allen belt are particularly puzzling. The latest available information taken by Rosen and Farley (45) from Explorer VI indicates that the outer belt flux, if in electrons, is $2 \times 10^7/cm^2$-sec^1 for 500 kv * and $2.7 \times 10^9/cm^2$-sec above 200 ev. This would imply that the experiment by Rosen and Farley saw much of the radiation and that the commonly postulated low, that is, 20 kv, sea of electrons, is nonexistent. This is in strong contrast to the deductions of previous observers who estimate fluxes many orders of magnitude higher.

The electron stream results at 5×10^4 to 7×10^4 km are believed by Gringauz et al. to imply a flux of 1 to 2×10^8 electrons/cm^2-sec with energies above 200 volts, leading them to postulate a third outermost belt (46). It is of specific interest to consider the relation of their measurements to those of Sonett and co-workers, for Gringauz and Rytov claim to show a quantitative consistency between their electron-stream measurements and the simple, nondiamagnetic, ring-current model as previously mentioned.

* This is from the relatively bremsstrahlung-insensitive, organic-phosphor detector. The two values quoted are for satellite penetration and nonpenetration, respectively.

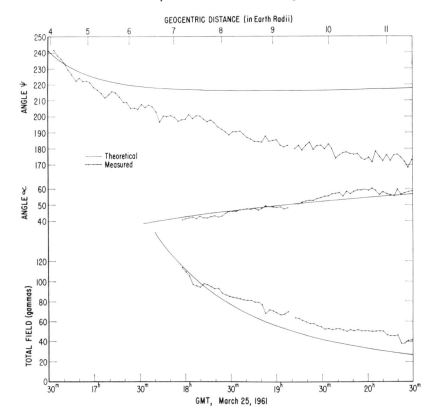

Figure 10-6 Data from Explorer X from 4 to 11 R_e, showing the trend in field magnitude as well as the rotation in direction. The angles are the same as those used in Explorer VI and are defined in the text. [From J. P. Heppner et al. (27)]

The highly diamagnetic ring current, primarily protonic, as proposed by Dessler and Parker (31) and studied by Apel (42), shows a drift maximum at 4 R_e, the combination of drift current and diamagnetism providing a general field depression from the surface of the earth to out past 4 R_e.* The electron stream of Gringauz et al. leads them to suppose a volume density $\sim 600/cm^3$ in the region of their observation. Clearly, the general importance of density gradients, along with field gradients, in establishing the pattern of ring currents, points to the need for comprehensive plasma-pressure-gradient data.

Explorer X (see Figure 10-6) was equipped with a variable, integrally biased Faraday cup with photoelectric suppression (47). A

---

* These results presuppose an *ad hoc* distribution of volume density and temperature for the plasma.

schematic diagram of the cup is shown in Figure 10-7. The bias gates were discretely variable from 0 to 2300 volts in eight steps. Preliminary findings from this experiment indicate that cold plasma was encountered from 1.3 R_e to 2.9 R_e (48). The vehicle velocity can be estimated at about 10^6 cm/sec at injection. The electrometer current was spin modulated in this interval. From the velocity, then, one estimates a maximum proton energy in this region of space of $\sim$1 ev. (Electrons were not sensed by this probe.) Beyond 2.9 R_e, no ion current was registered until the vehicle had ascended to 21.5 R_e. The results are discussed later, together with field results. Threshold for this instrument was $\sim$5 $\times$ 10^6/cm²-sec. Therefore a 25,000°K proton temperature, say, would indicate a volume-density threshold of $\sim$10/cm³.

Explorer XII's initial apogee was approximately in the subsolar direction, which is to be compared to Explorer X, where apogee was at about midnight. The plasma probe was a curved plate analyzer of quadrispherical design (Figure 10-8). The operation of this device is differential in contrast to the integral design for the instrument by Bridge et al. A detailed description of the operation of the plasma probe in Figure 10-9 is given by Bader et al. (49).

Some preliminary data are now available from this experiment. Throughout the orbit, there was a low level of 0.02 $\mu\mu$a, corresponding

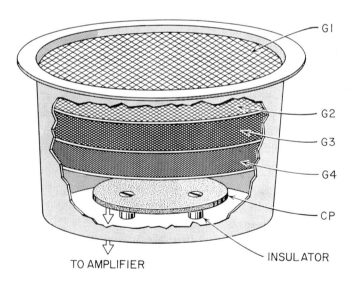

Figure 10-7 View of Faraday cup of Bridge et al., as used on Explorer X. G1 is the ground screen; G2 is a repeller grid to eliminate electrons; G3 is the stepped bias grid; G4 is the photoelectric suppression grid; and CP is the collector plate.

Figure 10-8   The differential quadrispherical electrostatic analyzer of Bader, showing the geometry and electronics. (NASA photo.)

to approximately 5.6×10^{-3} particle/cm^3, assuming 10-kev protons. The readings fluctuated at times, indicating "wisps" at all distances from the earth for radii $\geq \sim 3\ R_e$. The proton densities are quoted by the experimenters as ranging from 0.8 to 10^2 particles/cm^3, with the majority lying between 1 and 10 particles/cm^3. These "wisps" of enhanced density were found at all measurable energies. In addition, what appear to be proton clouds with densities of ~ 1/cm^3 were seen in the outer regions of the orbit. The analysis of this experiment is still in a preliminary state, and quoted figures are subject to change.

In summary, the available data from Lunik I, Lunik II, and Explorer X concerning the inner magnetosphere are qualitatively consistent, although quantitative Explorer X data for the inner field are not available. Since Explorer X was not equipped to study electrons, direct comparison from 4.7 to 21.5 R_e could not be made. It is curious that the inner magnetospheric cold plasma disappeared at 2.9 R_e on Explorer X, even though the sensitivity appears to be higher than Lunik II by a factor of 20.*

* This is arrived at from a quoted figure (Explorer X) and a threshold inferred from Gringauz et al.

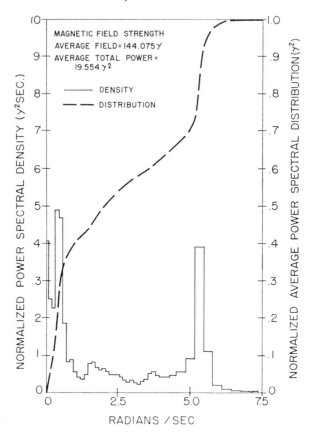

Figure 10-9 The differential and integral spectra of hydromagnetic disturbances in the amplitude of the field in the magnetosphere on October 11, 1958. [From C. P. Sonett et al. (58). Courtesy *J. Geophys. Res.*]

Another source of data concerning the thermal plasma density in the magnetosphere is obtained from whistler echoes. The study of time delay echoes of whistler-mode propagation in the magnetosphere has the advantage of inherently including the thermal component of the plasma. However, it suffers the disadvantage of obtaining a weighted mean value of plasma density along a tube of force.* Although satellites are beset by the problem of electric charge in determining the low-energy component of the plasma, they can, on the other hand, map the field of plasma to obtain the spatial distribution and thereby provide information on pressure gradients.

* The mean is weighted to the equatorial plasma density since the velocity is a minimum in this region yielding a maximum in transit time.

Waves

Although propagation in the magnetosphere is characterized by the many allowed modes of a binary gyrotropic plasma with passbands and stopbands reminiscent of a polyrefringent crystal, there are the important additions that the magnetic field is curved and that finite amplitude waves can exist. It is both convenient and physically important to consider separately the modes that propagate below the local gyro frequency. In particular, the modes that propagate below the ion gyro frequency are loosely termed hydromagnetic. It is these modes that appear to characterize many of the interesting properties of the magnetosphere. They are, for example, connected with at least some types of micropulsations (50) and the propagation of geomagnetic storm transients and may well be connected with acceleration and dissipation of the Van Allen radiation (51 to 55). They are chiefly the transverse, or Alfvén, mode that propagates two circularly polarized waves in the direction of the field at the phase velocity $v = H/\sqrt{4\pi\rho}$, where ρ is the particle density in gm/cm^3, and a longitudinal mode that propagates across the field * in a manner somewhat analogous to an acoustic wave for which the velocity is modified by the presence of the magnetic field.† In the magnetosphere proper ρ is a slowly varying function of position and velocity is regulated primarily by the field. In the ionosphere decoupling occurs and the propagation becomes more complex (56).

The Argus experiment provides what appears to be the first direct evidence of transmission via hydromagnetic modes. Additional evidence has been found from the fine structure analysis of the field for Pioneer I and Explorer VI data (58, 59).

The geometry of a satellite in a geomagnetic coordinate system allows specification of the various wave modes which are possible. An example of the separation of wave modes in the detection of hydromagnetic phenomena in the magnetosphere has been given for the case of Pioneer I, where a study of the amplitude and phase of the magnetometer signal allowed a partial separation of the transverse Alfvén and the compressional or magnetoacoustic modes to be affected. In that experiment, hydromagnetic activity was demonstrated in the region of 3.7 to 7 R_E in the sunlit hemisphere. Details of the procedure for decoupling modes are given by Sonett et al. (58).

---

*Propagation along the field can, of course, take place for an acoustic wave, although for infinitesimal waves it is decoupled from field effects.

† MacDonald has recently characterized the hydromagnetic modes in terms of a propagating vorticity and divergence of the velocity field associated with the magnetic effects (57).

Typical power spectra for amplitude and phase are shown in Figures 10-9 and 10-10. There are, in certain instances, pure magnetoacoustic modes, pure transverse modes, and a third instance shows a coupling of the two modes. Typical hydromagnetic-wave energy densities varied from 10^{-13} to 10^{-12} erg/cm^3 from 0 to 1 cps. The finite line widths found provide a measure of broadening, possibly due to positive ion Landau damping. In general, these spectra suggest excitation of the far magnetosphere, perhaps at the boundary. On the assump-

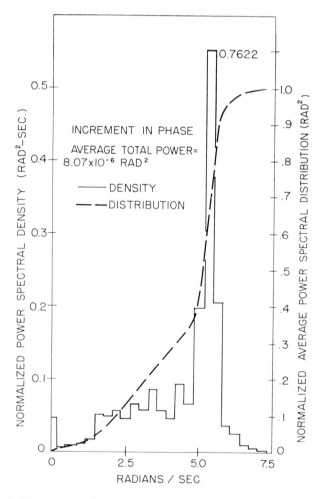

Figure 10-10 The differential and integral spectra of transverse disturbances simultaneous with those of Figure 10-9. [From C. P. Sonett et al. (58). Courtesy *J. Geophys. Res.*]

tion that the available sample was representative of the magneto-spheric volume to ~7 R_e, the hydromagnetic energy appeared to be of order 10^{18} ergs over 1 cps. In contrast to magnetic storm activity, this is trivial over short time spans, and its importance must be assessed over periods of months.

Data from Explorer VI show that combined magnetic and particle effects attributable to the occurrence of magnetoacoustic waves with attendant adiabatic particle acceleration can occur at certain times. An example of an out-of-phase correlation between magnetometer and scintillation counter on Explorer VI is given by Farley and Rosen (60). This type of disturbance, as well as quiet-time field oscillations, has been studied in detail by Judge and Coleman (59). Coleman (61) has made a relativistically correct calculation of the spectral changes to be expected in the Van Allen belts, assuming a power law, when the field is subject to adiabatic compressional variations. Application of these to the Explorer VI data yields an integral spectrum with exponent -1. The waves used were observed to have periods of 100 and 500 sec with amplitudes as high as 30γ in a base field of $\sim100\gamma$. The presence of Alfvén waves was also indicated, since the sun scanner showed angular changes of approximately 15 degrees. A most interesting additional effect was the sporadic presence of damped trains with decay of approximately 500 sec. These are consistent with Suguira's (62) observations in polar regions of the circularly polarized transverse mode. The lines of force on which Judge and Coleman made their studies were those that end in or near the auroral zones.

The magnetopause

Until recently it was held that the geomagnetic field extended to some 5 R_e (geocentric radii) and was terminated on the solar side by the pressure of a solar wind. Parker (63) has pointed out that during storms the wind pressure might increase from a quiet-time value of perhaps 10^{-8} dyne/cm^2 to perhaps 10^{-6} dyne/cm^2, thus collapsing the field on the solar side to some 2 to 3 R_e. These concepts were an outgrowth of the Chapman-Ferraro theory of the earth storm published in 1931 (64 to 66). Dungey later elaborated on some possible results of a wind interacting with the geomagnetic field with emphasis on quiet times (67).

The details of any interaction model between a wind and the field generally follow Chapman and Ferraro. The results from the major storm sequence observed by Pioneer V indicate that magnetic pressures of 10^{-8} dyne/cm^2 can accompany a storm plasma (68). This means that field momentum may be important in this problem, and the impingement of a field-free plasma on a plasma-free geomagnetic field, as assumed by Chapman and Ferraro and others, may bear re-examination. Nevertheless, some form of cavity satisfying both Maxwell and mechanical boundary conditions seems to follow from the limited analyses that have so far been made.

The model of the magnetopause involving a mechanically deformed tail should be dependent on the status of the solar wind on any particular day. The findings of Pioneer V would indicate that at the time of flight about 50 percent of the time the interplanetary field was in a quiescent condition (69). Hultqvist (70) indicates that perhaps 25 to 30 percent of the time the auroral magnetic field does not display severe variations. On this basis, it seems reasonable to suggest that the orientation of a geomagnetic tail would be determined by the wind velocity, vectorially modified by the aberration introduced by the earth's motion. This assumes that any stationary plasma with velocity equal to that of the earth's orbital speed does not coexist with the wind (71). Otherwise, the pressure vectors of the two plasmas would define the tail direction which would then not necessarily be aligned along the apparent (aberrated) wind-velocity vector. In any event, the tail should swing through directions bounded, at most, by dusk and the antisolar direction, the former obtaining in the event of an extremely weak wind velocity. There is presently little experimental data available to use in exploring this question, although the data of Explorer X do appear to satisfy the model of a swept-out tail.

The data of Explorer X (27, 48) in its traverse of the distant magnetosphere or magnetopause are particularly interesting. Generally, any plasma to 21.5 R_e was below threshold, which was four times lower than Lunik II for ions. However, electrons could not be sensed, and so a confirmation of the Lunik II electron stream results could not be made. The sudden appearance of disordered field and sporadic plasma at 21.5 R_e argues for a geomagnetic field termination. This is shown in Figure 10-11, where for $\lesssim 21.5$ R_e the field is nearly radial from the sun * and suddenly displays rapid variations as large as $\pm\pi/2$ and the plasma is peaked well above zero energy. A peculiarity of the data is the out-of-phase correlation of plasma and field much as was noted on Explorer VI during a magnetic storm. It is stated by the experimenters that plasma streams were seen emanating from the general vicinity of the sun and

---

* The normal geomagnetic field direction may be ambiguously close to the solar direction at the time of these measurements.

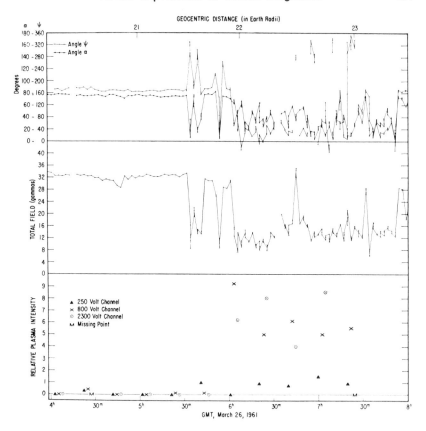

Figure 10-11 Apparent termination of the geomagnetic field on the night hemisphere of the magnetopause from Explorer X. This data shows the abrupt transition starting at 21.5 R_e concurrent with the appearance of plasma. [From J. P. Heppner et al. (27)]

only when field values were depressed. Reference to Figure 10-11 shows the sudden onset of disorder, but it also shows a tendency for the field direction to be along the spacecraft spin axis ($\alpha = 0$ degree) and at 45 degrees to the sun * in contrast to normal to the spin axis and in the antisolar direction before the appearance of the instabilities. Rossi (72) has also pointed out that the "turbulence" would indicate equipartition of gas kinetic- and magnetic-energy densities. Typically, a region of $\sim 10^{11}$ cm scale and of $\sim 10/cm^3$ density would be followed by another

---

* The angles used are the same as those previously discussed in the various papers on Explorer VI, being the spin-axis field angle (α) and the azimuth in the spacecraft equator (ψ).

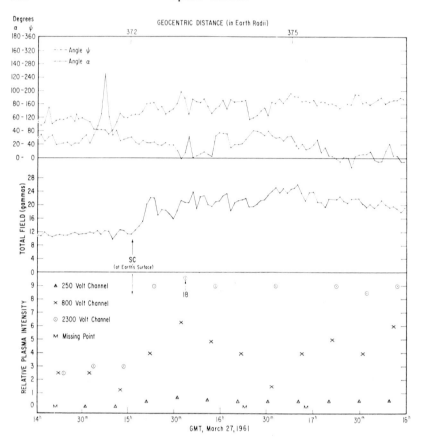

Figure 10-12 Sudden commencement on Explorer X.

cell where $n_p \sim 0.2$ cm^3 with the same scale size. The ordered plasma-energy density was $\sim 8 \times 10^{-9}$ erg/cm^3 when the magnetic-energy density was $\sim 4 \times 10^{-10}$ erg/cm^3. From this it appears that the thermal or disordered gas kinetic-energy density was $\sim 4 \times 10^{-10}$ erg/cm^3, indicating for $n_p \sim 10$ cm^3 a particle thermal energy of ~ 25 ev or some 2 to 3×10^5°K corresponding * more, say, to a coronal than a chromospheric temperature.

A striking phenomenon noted was a sudden commencement while in this region (Figure 10-12). The field magnitude doubled and the relatively flat plasma spectrum peaked in the 2300-volt channel. The field direction reversed in the sense that the angle α went from approximately

* Assuming protons.

30 to 120 degrees and returned. This event, however, preceded the sudden commencement by about $\frac{1}{4}$ hr. The richness of these phenomena preclude any detailed interpretation at the time of this writing. If the field increase were assumed shocklike, then its thickness (assuming a passage not too oblique and $\sim$300 km/sec) seems to indicate a preponderance of high-energy gas, for it took about 10 min to rise, indicating a breadth of $\sim$2 × 10^5 km. (In a 10γ field the gyro radius of protons would correspond to an energy of $\sim 10^5$ ev.) It is difficult to accept this as indeed a collisionless shock, for there is no substantiating evidence that particles of such high energy carry the bulk of the plasma momentum. Furthermore, the character of the disturbance shown in Figure 10-12 is not that of a shock, since the downstream field stays high.

The geomagnetic boundary

Beard (73), Spreiter (74), and others (75 to 78) have examined the form of the boundary with the assumption of a field-free, zero-temperature plasma incident on a plasma-free magnetosphere. This type of model displays a complex sheet of currents over the boundary having an approximate resemblance to an eastward flowing current in the region of the equatorial subsolar point. Nonequatorially, the currents deviate from this simple picture. In general, they close about the null lines which represent the axis of the geomagnetic dipole deformed somewhat toward the solar direction. The closure of the boundary currents on the night side becomes somewhat more difficult to discuss. Johnson's (37) topology shows lines from the sunlit hemisphere folding over to the dark side. Indeed, the dipolar axis closes on itself, coupling the polar regions to supply a winter polar ionosphere. This field, however, does not provide the auroral entrability of other models which provide O-type nulls facing the solar wind.

The dynamics of the impact phenomena of a solar wind having a thermal energy density 0.1 that of its ordered energy density, as indicated by Explorer X, on the geomagnetic field is presently an intractable mathematical problems. Numerous suggestions have been made concerning the generation of surface waves, torsional waves, shock waves, hydromagnetic analogs of Rayleigh-Taylor instabilities, and other effects such as particle acceleration. In addition to Explorer X, data available on two flights, Pioneers I and V, show intense hydromagnetic activity out to some 14 R_e on the solar side of the field (28). Both a geomagnetic termination (Figure 10-13) and the appearance of shocklike disturbances (Figure 10-14) suggest that a complex interaction is taking place. One result of the Pioneer I

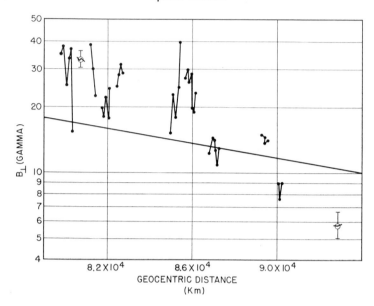

Figure 10-13 Suggested termination of the geomagnetic field near the subsolar point seen on Pioneer I at approximately 14 R_e. [From C. P. Sonett et al. (26). Courtesy *J. Geophys. Res.*]

data is the difficulty of making a momentum balance across the boundary unless the bulk of the incident wind momentum presumed present is convected into the field by these waves (79). These hyperwaves have front-rear slope asymmetries with oscillating rear-slope structures indicative of the collisionless hydromagnetic pulses studied theoretically by a number of investigators (80). The frequent association of these pulses with field zeros on their upstream sides suggests the penetration of the field by a rain of hypersonic plasma bubbles (81). Particle acceleration is strongly suggested by theoretical studies of collisionless pulses and is consistent with the magnetic observations. Strong support for electron acceleration * in this region (the magnetopause) comes from Pioneer IV, which order of magnitude fluctuations in electron count rate were observed in essentially the same region of the magnetopause as Pioneer I (82) (see Figure 10-15). Its bearing on the local acceleration hypothesis for the Van Allen radiation is apparent. The implication of this shock excitation mechanism would seem to encompass other situations in which magnetoionic gas clouds collide, a process of reasonable prob-

* A reversed role implying electron acceleration has been intimated by Gardner et al.

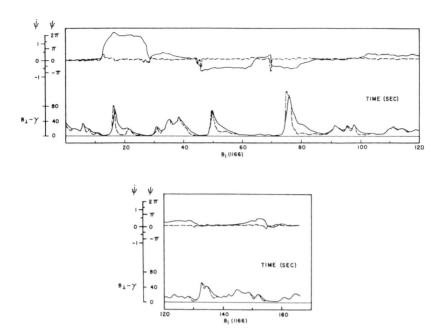

Figure 10-14 Fine-scale structure of the magnetopause near termination at the subsolar point, suggesting finite amplitude collisionless waves and X-type nulls. ψ shows a number of field rotations through large angle. [From C. P. Sonett (81)]

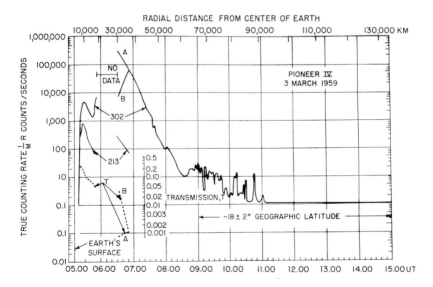

Figure 10-15 The subsolar geomagnetic termination as seen on Pioneer IV, indicating a magnetopause some 4 R_e in thickness on this day and terminating at 14 R_e as on Pioneer I. This figure is a cosmic-ray view of the termination. [From J. A. Van Allen and L. A. Frank (82). Courtesy *J. Geophys. Res.*]

ability in the galaxy at large. The energy density of the field of hyperwaves seen on Pioneer I is also of correct value to be consistent with the recent theory of Axford and Hines (83) which requires a convection of energy from the solar to antisolar regions of the magnetosphere to account for a number of interesting geophysical phenomena.

Mention should be made here of the terminal data of Explorer XII as reported by Cahill (40), where large angular reversals in the region of 8 to 10 R_e have been observed without accompanying magnitude charges over distances of ~ 100 km. It is tempting to think of these as X-type nulls, although the data analysis is still in a formative stage and strong conclusions are perhaps not yet warranted.

10-3 THE INTERPLANETARY CAVITY

Introduction

A sufficient and necessary model of the interplanetary cavity must explain certain cosmic-ray phenomena seen on earth, such as the modulation of the galactic cosmic radiation, the Forbush decreases, the diurnal, 27-day, and 11-year cycles, and the propagation of solar cosmic rays and other debris of solar-flare explosions. Phenomena other than cosmic-ray variations, for example, long-term changes in the character of micropulsations, the magnetic moment of ring currents, and the density of plasma in the magnetosphere may turn out to be related to solar activity. In this vein, the transparency of the medium between sun and earth, as well as its physical effects, may be important, though it is perhaps too early to dwell on it.

There is little direct rocket data in this region. Most of the model structure has been laboriously constructed from earth-surface studies of cosmic-ray variations and solar-terrestrial magnetic-storm phenomena. Some additional information has come from investigations of comet-tail-plasma interactions and from investigations of the properties of the zodiacal light. The results of these studies are subject to some controversy; factors of 5 to 10 difference in plasma density appear in the literature, though there appears to be substantial evidence of an interplanetary medium.

Two primary problems have been identified in the physics of this region. The first is the quiet-time behavior, composed of the extension of the solar corona, the breakdown of corotation, the coupling of the interplanetary and galactic fields, and hydrodynamics of the gas flow. The second outstanding problem today is that of solar-terrestrial relations. It may seem surprising that this subject is more than 100 years old; since it was first established in 1855 by Carrington and Hodgson that a conspicuous brightening on a small region of the sun was followed almost immediately (~ 8 min) by a minor geomagnetic disturbance and about a day later by a severe magnetic storm. This fortuitous observation might well be considered as the beginning of the study of the field of solar-geophysical phenomena, for it was then that the existence of a flow of corporeal matter or electromagnetic energy, or their combination, from the sun to the earth across the intervening stretches of space, was recognized. From that time on developments in this field were slow because of the lack of modern observational techniques. However, even as long ago as 1896 Birkeland proposed that geomagnetic storms were the result of particle streams emitted from the sun. It was he and Störmer, as well as others, who proposed that the aurora was in some way connected with the flow of matter from the sun and that a large-scale ring current, that is, a current situated axisymmetrically about the earth in the form of a torus, with a radius variously hypothesized between 5 and 100 R_E in distance, was responsible for the fact that auroral particles were seen to enter the earth's atmosphere maximally at some 67 degrees geomagnetic latitude rather than at the poles, where dipolar entrance is most allowed. The combination of the earth's dipole and this ring current then provided a path such that the threshold for entrance of charged particles would occur at 67 degrees magnetic.

Reference is made in this section to data taken directly in interplanetary space by the use of space probes; there is also some discussion of comets because of their history in the development of the solar wind hypothesis. The extent of theoretical study is large, and it is not intended to cover this area in any detail.

Models

The general magnetic field on the sun, as observed by Babcock, is thought to be distended somewhat by the outward evaporative flow of gas from the solar surface, modified at times by explosive outbursts. The configuration of this field and its connection with the solar corona has not been established. The extent of the distension of the solar magnetic field into space may be governed by the flow of plasma outward as well as by the magnetic and particulate conditions in interplanetary space itself. Observations by Hewish have indicated that the solar field appears to have a radial component to distances of some 50 solar radii from the sun, this being obtained from the polarization of radio signals during occultations of the crab nebula behind the solar corona.

According to various authors, notably Biermann (71) and Parker (63), a solar plasma wind during solar quiet exists, and the streaming plasma distends the solar field so that it is propagated outward in the plane of the ecliptic to distances of perhaps 1.5 AU. At this distance the anisotropic velocity distribution in the plasma is such that the transverse velocity components have an energy density comparable to the distended magnetic field and the field breaks up into a kind of turbulent pattern in the form of a disordered halo. It is this halo of disordered field that is supposed to move in and out with the solar cycle and to be responsible, at least in part, for the 11-year cycle of flux variations in the galactic component in cosmic rays (84). Other models of the interplanetary magnetic field, including the usual tacit assumption that the field is essentially zero, a model requiring the interstellar magnetic field to have been swept aside by a solar wind (85), have been postulated from time to time. Clouds of plasma containing disordered fields moving in interplanetary space have also been considered as another source of gas and field by Cocconi et al. (86). Elliot (8) has proposed, on the basis of cosmic-ray studies, a dipolar interplanetary field of 3 to 8×10^{-5} gauss at earth, generated, perhaps, by ringlike currents flowing in the solar corona. This model, which necessarily does violence to a steady solar wind, seems to fit many of the cosmic-ray data. To be sure, it is entirely heuristic from the standpoint of interplanetary hydromagnetics. Nevertheless, it is in accord with some of the data presently available.

The solar wind hypothesis, which was first proposed as a quiet-time phenomenon, owes its development primarily to the study of the motion of comet tails, discussed in a later section. Today, in addition to the school of thought that holds that a quiet-time solar wind exists, others suggest, at most, a slow and perhaps steady outflow of gas from the sun, moving at some few kilometers per second (87).[*] Although one might be tempted to reconcile the Parker-Biermann hypersonic model of the quiet-time solar wind with the slow-moving case, the physical requirements on which these two cases are developed are somewhat different. MacDonald (88) has made the suggestion that the outflow of gas from the sun is controlled not by hydrodynamic flow due to expansion of the solar corona, which would

---

[*] Some models, for example, Elliot's, do not discuss a wind. By inference it must be small; otherwise the field would disrupt.

apply to the Parker-Biermann or the Chamberlain model, but rather to the propagation of hydromagnetic waves which in turn slowly convect plasma outward. The present state of plasma observations is not in complete agreement with the Parker-Biermann solar wind but is consistent, at least qualitatively, with Chamberlain's study.

Although the magnetometer experiment of Sonett and co-workers on Pioneer V did not provide a unique and unambiguous resolution of the properties of the interplanetary field, the evidence of this experiment is in possible conflict with a hypersonic quiet-time solar-plasma wind. Russian plasma-probe data, taken in interplanetary space, seem to support models of interplanetary dynamics developed by Chamberlain, Alfvén, Block, and others (89), to form a generally consistent pattern not showing gross inconsistency with the magnetometer results.

Consideration of a solar wind, in particular the resultant radiality of any magnetic field, is implied by the energy density of a wind of protons of velocity $\sim 3 \times 10^7$ cm/sec and density $\sim 30/cm^3 (\sim 10^{-9}$ erg/cm^3). Thus any reasonable interplanetary field (H $\sim 2 \times 10^{-5}$ gauss) at 1 AU should be swept out. Such a model also provides a halo of disordered field at ~ 1.5 AU or more, depending exactly on where the thermal-energy density in the plasma becomes comparable with the magnetic-energy density, and is designed to account for the 11-year cycle in the galactic cosmic-ray low-energy cutoff. There are, however, uncomfortable features of this hypersonic flow. In particular, Davis (90) has pointed out that an outward transport of field from the sun should provide regions of opposed polarity. In the simplest example of a uniform sweeping out of a large-scale solar field a null plane congruent with the plane of symmetry of gas flow should exist. Propagation of a "spotty" solar field should still provide null regions. Such regions should tend to collapse because of body forces and to lead to a disordering of field and feeding of field energy into the plasma. These processes have been studied by Parker (91). A possible example is given by Sonett et al. (92) during the observation of a magnetic storm-flare sequence observed on Pioneer V.

It seems reasonable, on the basis of all evidence, to suppose that an outward convection of coronal gas takes place during quiet times. The conflict between the models of Parker and Chamberlain is intensified by the need of an *ad hoc* coronal plasma accelerator for the Parker model,* whereas the velocities required by Chamberlain are much more modest (a few kilometers per second). The dynamical

---

*Schlüter has suggested that plasma clouds could be accelerated outward in the solar field by the reaction between cloud diamagnetism and the field gradient.

consequences of which model is correct are, to be sure, far reaching; a limitation of the Chamberlain model is its purely hydrodynamic basis, whereas for such a case it seems reasonable to suppose comparable field- and plasma-energy densities, thereby demanding a hydromagnetic process.

Measurements of electron density in the corona, the zodiacal light, and observation of the scattered Fraunhofer spectrum in the zodiacal light have yielded values of which the most current is $\sim 10^2/\text{cm}^3$. The assumption of charge neutrality would then imply an equal density of protons. (The question of the contribution of ions of $Z > 1$ has not been explored in detail. A reasonable assumption is that the interplanetary plasma displays the coronal abundances during solar minimum and tends to solar atmospheric abundances during solar maximum as the result of debris accumulated from flare activity.) The detailed balance between plasma and nonionized hydrogen has been studied by Brandt (93), who considers recombination, collisional and photoionization and diffusion resulting from charge exchange. He finds a density of a few tenths of a particle per cubic centimeter. His examination of the balance of ionization and recombination provides a means of studying the plasma density by optical examination of L_α resonance radiation.

Comet observations

An indirect approach to the problem of interplanetary gas is afforded by the work of Biermann (94) and his group. Briefly, the photoionization rate of cometary nuclei is too low to account for some rapid changes observed optically. For example, the photo cross section for CO is $\sim 1.5 \times 10^{-17}$ cm^2 between 400 and 700 Å. From this they estimate a 60-day ionization time scale using Johnson's (95) estimate of the solar flux in this wavelength interval. It is postulated by Biermann and co-workers that charge exchange principally between CO, N_2, and incident protons is much more likely ($\sim 10^{-15}$ cm^2). They estimate that a subsequent exchange of momentum between the resultant cometary ions and the incident electron stream, which he suggests must accompany the incident protons, produces the observed accelerations in comet tails of Type I.* These accelerations reach 10^2 to 10^3 times solar gravity at times, a value far too large to be accounted for by radiation pressure alone. Schlüter (96) has suggested that if the corpuscular radiation carried with it entrained fields they would provide an additional mechanism for momentum exchange

---

* Type I comet tails are ionized according to the classification of Bredichin, whereas Types II and III are un-ionized CN, C_2, and /or dust.

between convected matter and the comet tail. In summary, the study of comet tails has shown that interactions other than radiation pressure must be invoked between plasma injected into the interplanetary medium and certain types of comet tails. Many of the details, in particular, charge exchange reactions which excite radiation in the vacuum ultraviolet (unstudied, to date, because of optical inaccessibility) and the contribution of field-plasma interactions to the total momentum balance, remain unanswered and would reduce the upper bound on interplanetary gas momentum obtained by these means to values nearer those obtained by plasma probes.

The variation in plasma flow outward from the sun is usually treated two dimensionally, yet the symmetry of the flow might well be expected to be nonspherical. Some evidence of heliocentric latitude dependence is suggested by studies by Beyer (97), which show a marked dependence of brightness of Comet 1948a over 50 degrees latitude. For this comet, a variation of 3 magnitudes was noted after correction for both distance from earth and sun. If the visual brightness is proportional, say, to the incident momentum of gas and field impinging on the comet, this represents a factor of 15 in activity.

Rhea Lust (98) has examined comet tails during times of low solar activity and geomagnetic calm. She finds cases in which small bursts of activity correlate with cometary brightness increases and correlate best for an assumed transit velocity of 350 km/sec. Finally, a conclusion by Biermann from comet observations is that any stationary interplanetary gas would be expected to interact with a solar wind in a manner analogous to that apparently existing for comet tails. It might be expected, in this case, that because the hydrogen-proton charge exchange cross section is almost inversely proportional to velocity of more than 0.2 to 20 kv and $\sim 10^{15}$ cm^2 at 5 kv any static gas would be rapidly removed (71). The general conclusion from these comet studies supports the idea of a steady outward flow of interplanetary plasma from the sun during quiet times having a flux of $\sim 10^9$/cm^2-sec corresponding to a volume density of ~ 30/cm^3.

Magnetometer data

So far, magnetometer flights have been made into the interplanetary cavity by a number of vehicles. These include Pioneer V, Luniks I and II, and the Russian Venus probe. In the Russian flights (99) the equipment threshold quoted was $\sim 50\gamma$ and thus possibly of limited use in discussing the quiescent interplanetary field, or, at least, so present data from Pioneer V suggest.

Pioneer V was in operation for some 60 days; it moved radially toward

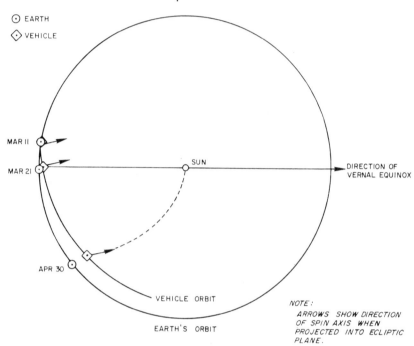

Figure 10-16 Orbit of Pioneer V about the sun. The obliquity of the spin axis to the ecliptic (plane of the paper) is 2 degrees. [From P. J. Coleman et al. (69). Courtesy *J. Geophys. Res.*]

the sun about 0.1 AU and traveled some 1.25×10^8 km in orbit during its active life, as shown in Figure 10-16. The sun was in a declining state of activity with respect to the 11-year cycle, yet displayed many flares. The data of this experiment (69) indicate that perhaps 50 percent of the samples taken were representative of a quiet field and that the remaining time was occupied by disturbed conditions. It seems reasonable, then, to infer that two fundamentally different types of data were obtained by the spacecraft. It is important to point out, also, that the magnetometer makes a two-dimensional cut in the field and that this cut is oriented in a fixed direction with respect to the stars. Specifically, the spin axis lay nearly in the ecliptic. Consider a coordinate system with origin in the sun and a basis set ($\mathbf{r}$, $\boldsymbol{\theta}$, $\mathbf{z}$) which is cylindrical, $\mathbf{r}$ being the unit vector positive outward from the sun, $\boldsymbol{\theta}$ positive in the clockwise direction looking down on the ecliptic, and $\mathbf{z}$ positive upward. Then field components H_r and H_θ should, if $\mathbf{H}$ is time-invariant, show a semiannual * periodicity, the two components having a $\pi/2$ phase dif-

---

* "Semiannual" is defined as one half the spacecraft year, which was 311 days.

ference. H_z is time-invariant, since it was always contained in the plane of the spacecraft equator. Thus the data of the experiment were representable by

$$H_\perp = [|H_z|^2 + (|H_r| \cos \omega t)^2 + (|H_\theta| \sin \omega t)^2]^{1/2},$$

where $H_\perp$ is the measured component in the plane of the spacecraft equator. The orientation of the spin axis was such that any appreciable component, H_r, in the quiescent field should have been detected during the 60 days as a sinusoidal variation of the steady field. The same argument applies to H_θ, although here the experimental geometry was such that if a combination of H_r and H_θ existed in the plane of the ecliptic and was spiraled to be nearly normal to $\mathbf{r}$ a sinusoid having insufficient amplitude to have been detected might have resulted. The most reasonable deduction is that the field had a large component, H_z. One is then faced with an inconsistency with a quiet-time solar wind, for a wind of the energy density suggested by Biermann and by Parker should transport outward any solar field so that the net field would have only $\mathbf{r}$ and $\mathbf{\theta}$ components, the relative components depending on the wind velocity.

What is now left are the alternatives of a field spiraled nearly 90 degrees or the abandonment of a quiet-time wind of appreciable energy density. It is important to point out that a field spiraled by such a large angle implies wind velocities so low that they void the basic premise of a hypersonic velocity anyway.

During disturbed time the interplanetary field displayed rapid rises in intensity. Indeed, on three occasions (Figure 10-17) the geomagnetic field showed synchronous disturbances larger by a factor of about 3. The most noteworthy of the numerous disturbances studied has been reported by Coleman, Sonett, and Davis (68). On this occasion the maximum field was at least 50γ. A higher value, between telemetry transmissions, was possible. Further, the value measured was of $(H_\theta^2 + H_z^2)^{1/2}$, the spacecraft spin orientation being in the solar direction at the time. So an actual field 50 to 100 percent larger was possible. From these data it can be concluded that a curved beam model is tenable for the fortuitous occurrence of solar cosmic rays which were emitted from the sun during this flare sequence.

Finally, the importance of electric fields in the galactic (Forbush) modulation seems to require investigation. Clearly, the motional electric fields, estimated to be some 5×10^{-9} volt/cm for the events of Pioneer V, can be alternatively considered from the standpoint of a moving magnetic scatterer. However, this leaves open the importance of time-dependent fields in the plasma cloud frame of reference, due to

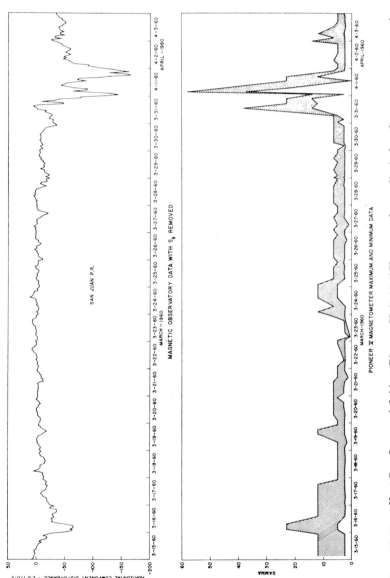

Figure 10-17. ΔH at San Juan and field at Pioneer V (0.95 AU on earth-sun line) for three concurrent earth-space disturbances. The space disturbances not seen in ΔH are simultaneous with cosmic ray data of C. Y. Fan et al., on Pioneer V. The field values are maxima and minima during a particular transmission. [See Figure 10-20. (From P. J. Coleman et al. (69). Courtesy *Phys. Rev. Letters.*]

field annihilation, a point which cannot presently be explored in an empirical manner. There is evidence of fine structure in the interplanetary field which consists of periods of quiet steady field alternating with what appears to be periodic types of fluctuations. These are presently under investigation. Of particular interest is a null in the field noted in conjunction with the flare sequence of March 13 to April 1. At that time the field generally was $\geq 10\gamma$, with wavelike variations. On April 1 a decrease to magnetometer threshold ($\sim 0.5\gamma$), lasting for several minutes, was noted. Arguments have been made by Sonett, Davis, and Coleman (93) to show how this structure appears to be consistent with a null-surface on the axis of symmetry of the plasma which must have been emitted with the large fields noted in space. Models of a solar flare gas cloud with regions of opposed field within the core have particular correspondence to this observation.

We now turn to the Russian magnetometer data. Information is tabulated in Table 10-2. Data and technique are sparse from these experiments. An upper bound of 50γ has been established for the lunar field by Lunik II. Neugebauer has pointed out that since the impact was on the solar side of the moon a solar wind might have collapsed the field to a point at which the last measurement before impact would have been exterior to the boundary. Evidence from the far-atmosphere of earth indicates that the compression might be more complex than describable by a simple elastic process, leaving this question somewhat open. In any event, the results of Pioneer V indicate the need for magnetometers with thresholds far less than 50γ for quiescent field measurements.

TABLE 10-2

Magnetometer Experiments (Part One)

Name	Designation	Launch Date
Venus Probe	—	2-12-61
Pioneer I	—	10-11-58
Explorer VI	1959 Delta	8-9-59
Pioneer V	1960 Alpha	3-11-60
Vanguard III	1959 Eta	9-18-59
Lunik I	—	1-2-59
Lunik II	—	9-12-59
Explorer X	1961 Kappa	3-25-61
Explorer XII	1961 Epsilon	8-15-61

TABLE 10-2 (Continued)

Magnetometer Experiments (Part Two)

Threshold Range	Instrument
—	Variometers
Threshold <1γ at bottom of range; range <1 to 10⁴γ; nonlinear amplifier	Search coil
Threshold <1γ at bottom of range; range <1 to 3 × 10³γ; nonlinear amplifier; angle threshold ∼1 degree	Search coil Sun scanner
Threshold <0.5γ; sensitivity determined by digitization windows 0.05γ to 5γ, depending on window and log response of amplifier	Search coil
Threshold ∼0.1 gauss; accuracy at least 1:10⁵ determined in part by ground oscillator reference	Proton precession magnetometer
Quoted threshold ∼100γ; may be due to spacecraft fields	Field-aligned flux gates
Quoted threshold ∼50γ; may be due to spacecraft fields	Field-aligned flux gates
Rb magnetometer accuracy determined by orbit data, still being considered; flux gates calibrated by Rb; self-consistent shift of 7γ	Rb magnetometer flux gates sun scanner
May be dependent on digitization windows whose width ∼20γ	Flux gates

Magnetometer Experiments (Part Three)

Range	Reference
—	Mustel, E. R. (100)
{3.7–7 R_e {12.6–14.3 R_e	Sonett et al. (26, 28)
1–8 R_e	Sonett et al. (32) Smith et al. (38)
0.9–1.0 AU	Coleman et al. (68, 69)
—	Heppner et al. (27)
Lunar impact	Dolginov and Pushkov (33)
Lunar impact	Dolginov and Pushkov (33)
1–37.5 R_e	Heppner et al. (27)
∼1–8 R_e	Cahill (40)

Mustel (100) has provided some data on the Russian Venus probe. Here the instruments were "variometers"; design data were not provided. The sensitivity was quoted as 2γ, with range of 50γ. During the flight of the Venus probe, on February 12, a 4γ "bump" in the field with a period of 3 to 5 min was noted. Mustel implies that this was a wave, since no associated Forbush decrease was noted. Further information is not available to this author. Finally, in regard to waves, there is a large body of data from Pioneer V that show field variations in the range of minutes. This material is still being processed and detailed results are pending.

Cosmic rays

Discussed below are some of the observational cosmic-ray data from Pioneer V. The three cosmic-ray instruments and their characteristics are listed in Table 10-3. The proportional counter telescope of Fan et al. (101) was of 2π geometry. The concentric construction allowed single-triple coincidence events to be registered, the singles corresponding to protons of $E \geq 17$ Mev and to electron Bremsstrahlung and photons. The usual steep-energy spectra for solar cosmic rays made demonstra-

TABLE 10-3

Cosmic-Ray Detectors on Pioneer V

Device	Shielding	Geometry	Remarks
Triple coincidence telescope	1 gm/cm² brass counter walls; 5 gm/cm² Pb	$\sim 2\pi$	Triples threshold ~ 75 Mev for protons; ~ 13 Mev for electrons; counter dead time $\sim 0.5\mu$ sec; filling methane-argon
Geiger tube	~ 1 gm/cm²	$\sim 4\pi$	Halogen-filled Anton 302
Ionization chamber	~ 1 gm/cm²	4π	Argon-filled; Neher-Millikan quartz fiber

Note: None of the shielding values is accurate, since the spacecraft data have not been published; the addition of absorber from the body of the spacecraft is probably not serious for the 75 Mev threshold and tends to increase the Bremsstrahlung yield for the singles events in the telescope. For the Geiger tube and ion chamber the effects may be substantial; some idea may be gained by reference to the Explorer VI case [R. H. Hoffman, R. L. Arnoldy, and J. R. Winckler, *J. Geophys. Research*, **67**, 1 (1962)].

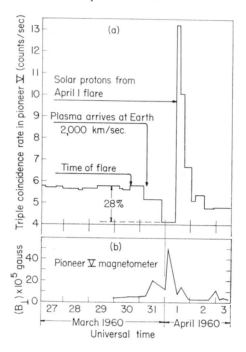

Figure 10-18   The detailed timing of events for the interplanetary-geomagnetic storm and solar cosmic ray outburst of March 30–April 1, 1960. [From C. Y. Fan et al. (102). Courtesy *Phys. Rev. Letters.*]

tion of high-energy electrons concurrent with the cosmic-ray outburst difficult to detect, although it was originally suspected by Fan et al. that relativistic electrons were noted in the storm of March 31 to April 1 (102).

The simultaneity of the cosmic-ray and magnetometer data from Pioneer V provides insight into the play of phenomena in space. Considered here is the flare sequence of March 30 to April 1 for which the magnetometer data were discussed earlier. Figure 10-18 displays the simultaneity of Forbush decrease given by the initial decline in the steady galactic count rate shown by the triples plot and the enhanced field (both indicating the arrival of plasma at the spacecraft, followed by an intense burst of solar protons). The Forbush decrease at the spacecraft was 1.3 ± 0.15 times that at the top of the atmosphere, using extrapolated neutron monitor data. This is attributed to the lower threshold in the spacecraft (75 Mev versus 2.4 bev). An energy-dependent return to the prestorm level was noted at the spacecraft. More than 30 days ensued before recovery. (Neutron monitor data for relativistic particles showed a faster recovery.)

Evidently the Forbush decrease "prepared" the interplanetary cavity for the April 1 solar proton event, the transit time being ≥ 1 hr. Since the high magnetic-field values preceded the solar protons, that is to say, the high values were recorded near earth in the plane normal to the propagation direction at the time of emission of protons, it is safe to say that the solar protons must have been guided by the field. More detailed arguments are given by Coleman, Sonett, and Davis (75). Cosmic-ray data are shown in Figure 10-19 and should be compared with Figure 10-17, which shows the field changes. It is worth noting that the field *normal* to the sun was ∼50γ. Therefore, if the field were primarily radial, say 5 degrees to the solar direction, it would have to be ∼500γ, a value high for numerous reasons. Thus we conclude that rotation occurred and that the field at the spacecraft had an appreciable angle to the sun. Finally, for a mean energy, say, of 300 Mev, the rectilinear flight time would have been somewhat less than the actual time of 1 hr, arguing for a curved field.

The solar proton decay law was t^{-1} for the 75-Mev cutoff, whereas

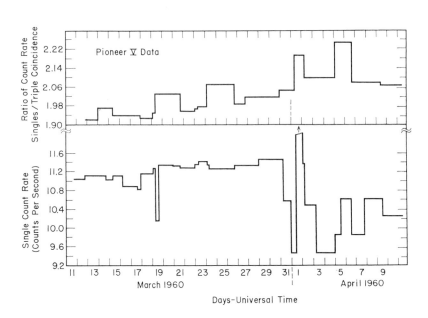

Figure 10-19 Cosmic-ray data from Pioneer V. The upper plot shows the energy dependence of the Forbush decrease as the singles-triple ratio increases at each magnetic disturbance. (See Figure 10-17.) The lower plot shows the singles count alone. Here, the statistics are insufficient to show Forbush effects prior to March 30. The large increase immediately following is a solar cosmic ray event. [From C. Y. Fan et al. (102). Courtesy *J. Geophys. Res.*]

for the counter arrangement of Winckler et al. the decay was as $t^{-1.9}$. This would be consistent with a faster decay for the lower energy particle seen by Winckler et al. (103).

Summary

In summary, the interplanetary field making a substantial angle with the ecliptic is consistent with some avenues of theory, with the Russian plasma-probe data, and with Pioneer V. To complete this limited and incomplete discussion, it would be necessary to establish the origin of the field seen by Pioneer V. The consequences of the conservation of the angular momentum in a rotating interplanetary field also would require consideration.

During time of solar disturbance geomagnetic storms and the Forbush decrease have for many years suggested a profound modification of the quiet-time field configuration. That this is indeed so is seen by examination of the storm-time profile of the Pioneer V magnetometer data, which, for each major disturbance during the first month of orbit, also displayed a Forbush decrease at the spacecraft. Briefly, enhanced fields lying in a plane approximately orthogonal to the earth-sun line were noted rising on one occasion to at least $\sim 50\gamma$. The data of March 30 to April 1 is consistent with the model of a large tongue or blast of gas escaping from the sun, transporting outword an extended field and propagating solar cosmic rays as well as occluding the galactic cosmic rays. In some respects the model suggested is consistent with that of Cocconi et al. (86) and Gold (24).

The solar-terrestrial process, whose understanding began a century ago with the recognition of solar flares and subsequent magnetic storms, now has further experimental verification. Solar emission is observed, the plasma-driven field is seen in space complete with a solar cosmic-ray event, and the multitudinous geophysical effects are observed in the magnetosphere and surface of the earth.

Future research in the field of cosmic electrodynamics hinges partly on the energy availability of large boosters. It does not seem too remote to consider that some one to two decades hence it will be possible to approach the sun to something less than 0.1 AU and to escape the solar nebula. Penetration into the galactic arm would permit direct observation of the magnitude of the interstellar field in the neighborhood of the sun. This would permit a direct estimate to be made of the magnetic pressure in the local arm of the Galaxy. The relativistic cosmic-ray flux would contribute to the gas pressure. Thus, on the assumption of static equilibrium, the gravitational contractive force could be estimated. The isotropy of cosmic rays would determine the leakage rate from the Galaxy. The origin of cosmic rays and the processes of acceleration are subjects about which direct evidence could be obtained even with a crude spectrum, for information of this type would determine the rate of production and acceleration of cosmic rays.

Until such time that penetration of the solar-interstellar boundary and direct examination of the magnetic-field structure and the relativistic cosmic-ray gas in the local arm of our Galaxy can be made, rocket technology limits experimental hydromagnetics to a band in the solar system extending from 0.7 to 1.2 AU in the plane of the ecliptic.

REFERENCES

1. Linhart, J. G., *Plasma Physics,* Interscience Publishers, New York, 1960.
2. Alfvén, H., *Cosmical Electrodynamics,* Oxford University Press, London, 1953.
3. Shklovsky, I. S., *Cosmic Radio Waves,* Harvard University Press, Cambridge, 1960, p. 191.
4. Hiltner, W. A., On the Presence of Polarization in the Continuous Radiation of Stars, *Ap. J.,* **109,** 471 (1949).
5. Hall, J. S., and A. H. Mikesell, Observations of Polarized Light from Stars, *Ap. J.,* **54,** 187 (1949).
6. Davis, L., Jr., and Jesse L. Greenstein, The Polarization of Starlight by Aligned Dust Grains, *Ap. J.,* **114,** 206 (1951).
7. Parker, E. N., Solar, Planetary, and Interplanetary Magnetohydrodynamics, Chapter 8 in *Plasma Dynamics,* F. H. Clauser, ed., Addison-Wesley, Reading, 1960.
8. Elliot, H., Cosmic Ray Intensity Variations and the Interplanetary Magnetic Field, *Phil. Mag.,* **5,** 601 (1960) .
9. Lüst, R., and A. Schlüter, Kraftfreie Magnetfelder, *Z. Astrophys.,* **34,** 263 (1954); also Drehimpulstransport durch Magnetfelderund die Abbremsung rotierender Sterne, *ibid.,* **38,** 110 (1955).
10. Block, L., On the Interplanetary Gas and Its Magnetic Field, *Arkiv Fysik,* **14,** 179 (1958).
11. Babcock, H. W., and H. D. Babcock, The Sun's Magnetic Field, 1952–1954, *Ap. J.,* **121,** 349 (1955).
12. Spitzer, L., *The Physics of Fully Ionized Gases,* Interscience Publishers, New York, 1956, p. 18.
13. Biermann, L., Stellar Atmospheres as Plasmas, *Nuovo Cimento,* **13,** Ser. X, 189 (1959).
14. Cowling, T. G., *Magnetohydrodynamics,* Interscience Publishers, New York, 1957.
15. *Ibid.,* p. 5.

16. Shklovsky, I. S., *ibid.*, p. 182.
17. Fishman, F. J., A. R. Kantrowitz, and H. E. Petschek, Magnetohydro-dynamic Shock Wave in a Collision-Free Plasma, *Rev. Mod. Phys.*, **32**, 959 (1960).
18. Stratton, J. A., *Electromagnetic Theory*, McGraw-Hill, New York, 1941, p. 97.
19. Spitzer, L., Jr., *ibid.*, Chapter 4.
20. Alfvén, H., *ibid.*
21. Åstrom, E., On Waves in an Ionized Medium, *Archiv Fysik*, **2**, 443 (1950).
22. Storey, L. R. O., An Investigation of Whisting Atmospherics, *Phil. Trans. Roy. Soc.*, **246**, 113 (1953).
23. Dungey, J. W., Electrodynamics in the Outer Atmosphere, Physics of the Ionosphere, *Phys. Soc. London*, 229–236 (1955).
24. Gold, T., Plasmas and Magnetic Fields in the Solar System, *J. Geophys. Res.*, **64**, 1665 (1959).
25. Gold, T., Motions in Magnetosphere of the Earth, *J. Geophys. Res.*, **64**, 1219 (1959).
26. Sonett, C. P., D. L. Judge, A. R. Sims, and J. M. Kelso, A Radial Rocket Survey of the Distant Geomagnetic Field, *J. Geophys. Res.*, **65**, 55 (1960).
27. Heppner, J. P., N. F. Ness, T. L. Skillman, and C. S. Scearce, Magnetic Field Measurements with the Explorer X Satellite; Proceedings of the International Conference on Cosmic Rays and the Earth Storm (Kyoto, September 1961), *J. Phys. Soc. Japan*, **17**, Supp. II-A, 546 (1962).
28. Sonett, C. P., E. J. Smith, and A. R. Sims, Rocket Surveys of the Distant Geo-Magnetic Field, *Space Science*, ed. H. K. Kallmann-Bijl, North Holland, Amsterdam, 1960.
29. Singer, F. S., A New Model of Magnetic Storms and Aurorae, *Trans. Am. Geophys. Union*, **38**, 175 (1957).
30. For example, J. A. Van Allen, C. E. McIlwain, G. H. Ludwig, Jr., Radiation Observations with Satellite 1958 Epsilon, *J. Geophys. Res.*, **64**, 271 (1959).
31. Dessler, A. J., and E. N. Parker, Hydromagnetic Theory of Geomagnetic Storms, *J. Geophys. Res.*, **64**, 2239 (1959).
32. Sonett, C. P., E. J. Smith, D. L. Judge, and P. J. Coleman, Jr., Current Systems in the Vestigial Geomagnetic Field, *Phys. Rev. Letters*, **4**, 1961 (1960).
33. Dolginov, S. Sh., and N. V. Pushkov, Magnetic Field of the Outer Cor-puscular Region, *Proc. Moscow Cosmic Ray Conf., Moscow*, **3**, 30 (1960).
34. Dessler, A. J., private communication.
35. Smith, E. J., P. J. Coleman, Jr., D. L. Judge, and C. P. Sonett, Character-istics of the Extraterrestrial Current System: Explorer VI and Pioneer V, *J. Geophys. Res.*, **665**, 1858 (1960).
36. Piddington, J. H., Geomagnetic Storm Theory, *J. Geophys. Res.* **65**, 93 (1960).
37. Johnson, F. S., The Gross Character of the Geomagnetic Field in the Solar Wind, *J. Geophys. Res.*, **65**, 3049 (1960).
38. Smith, E. J., and C. P. Sonett, Satellite Observations of the Distant Field during Magnetic Storms: Explorer VI, Proceedings of the International Conference on Cosmic Rays and the Earth Storm (Kyoto, September 1961), *J. Phys. Soc. Japan*, **17**, Supp. II-A, 17 (1962).

39. Antsilevich, M. G., Geomagnetic Field Variations on 9, 10, 24, 25 August, 1–2 September 1959, and 11 March 1960, *Geomagnetism and Aeronomics,* **1**, 320 (1961).

40. Cahill, L. J., Preliminary Magnetic Results of Explorer XII, Explorer XII Symposium, Goddard Space Flight Center, Greenbelt, Md., January 18, 1962.

41. Dessler, A. J., and R. Karplus, Some Effects of Diamagnetic Ring Currents on Van Allen Radiation, *J. Geophys. Res.,* **66**, 2289 (1961).

42. Apel, J. R., Geomagnetic Field Perturbations Due to Trapped Particles, M. S. Thesis, University of Maryland, 1961.

43. Gringauz, K. I., V. V. Bezrukikh, V. D. Ozerov, and R. Ye. Rybchinskiy, Study of the Interplanetary Ionized Gas, High Energy Electrons, and Solar Corpuscular Radiation by Means of Three Electrode Traps for Charged Particles on the Second Soviet Cosmic Rocket, Artificial Earth Satellites, #6 Moscow (1961).

44. Gringauz, K. I., and S. M. Rytov, On the Relationship between the Magnetic Field Measurements Obtained by Soviet Cosmic Rockets with Charged Particle Traps and Those Obtained by U.S.A. Explorer VI and Pioneer V, *Proc. Acad. Sci., USSR,* **135**, 48 (1960).

45. Rosen, A., and T. A. Farley, Characteristics of the Van Allen Radiation Zones as Measured by the Scintillation Counter on Explorer VI, *J. Geophys. Res.,* **66**, 2013 (1961).

46. Gringauz, K. I., V. G. Kurt, V. I. Moroz, and I. S. Shklovsky, Ionized Gas and High Speed Electrons in the Vicinity of the Earth and in Interplanetary Space, *Proc. Acad. Sci., USSR,* **132**, 1062 (1960).

47. Bridge, H. S., C. Dilworth, B. Rossi, and F. Scherb, An Instrument for the Investigation of Interplanetary Plasma, *J. Geophys. Res.,* **65**, 3053 (1960).

48. Bridge, H. S., C. Dilworth, A. Lazarus, E. F. Lyon, B. Rossi, and F. Scherb, Direct Observation of the Interplanetary Plasma; Proceedings of the International Conference on Cosmic Rays and the Earth Storm (Kyoto, September 1961), *J. Phys. Soc. Japan,* **17**, Supp. II-A, 553 (1962).

49. Bader, M., T. B. Fryer, and F. C. Witteborn, Two Instruments for Measuring Distributions of Low-Energy Charged Particles in Space, NASA Technical Note D-1035.

50. Troitskaya, V., Pulsations of the Earth's Electromagnetic Field and Their Connection with Phenomena in the High Atmosphere, *J. Geophys. Res.,* **66**, 5 (1961).

51. Welch, J. A., Jr., and W. A. Whitacker, Theory of Geomagnetically Trapped Electrons from an Artificial Source, *J. Geophys. Res.,* **64**, 909 (1959).

52. Dragt, A. J., Effect of Hydromagnetic Waves on the Lifetime of Van Allen Radiation Protons, *J. Geophys. Res.,* **66**, 1641 (1961).

53. Parker, E. N., Geomagnetic Fluctuations and the Form of the Outer Zone the Van Allen Radiation Belt, *J. Geophys. Res.,* **65**, 3117 (1960).

54. Parker, E. N., Effect of Hydromagnetic Waves in a Dipole on the Longitudinal Invariant, *J. Geophys. Res.,* **66**, 693 (1961).

55. Davis, L., Jr., and David B. J. Chang, On the Effect of Fluctuations on Trapped Particles, presented at AGU Natl. Meeting, Los Angeles, December 1961.

56. Francis, W. E., and R. Karplus, Hydromagnetic Waves in the Ionosphere, *J. Geophys. Res.,* **65**, 3593 (1960).

57. MacDonald, G. J. F., Spectrum of Hydromagnetic Waves in the Exosphere, *J. Geophys. Res.,* **666,** 639 (1961).
58. Sonett, C. P., A. R. Sims, and I. J. Abrams, The Distant Geomagnetic Field, I: Infinitesimal Hydromagnetic Waves, *J. Geophys. Res.,* **67,** 1191 (1962).
59. Judge, D. L., and P. J. Coleman, Jr., Observations of Low Frequency Hydromagnetic Waves in the Distant Geomagnetic Field; Explorer VI (in draft).
60. Farley, T. A., and A. Rosen, Charged Particle Variations in the Outer Van Allen Zone during a Geomagnetic Storm, *J. Geophys. Res.,* **65,** 3494 (1960).
61. Coleman, P. J., Jr., The Effects of Betation Accelerations upon the Intensity and Energy Spectrum of Magnetically Trapped Particles, *J. Geophys. Res.,* **66,** 1351 (1961).
62. Suguira, M., Evidence of Low Frequency Hydromagnetic Waves in the Exosphere, *J. Geophys. Res.,* **66,** 4087 (1961).
63. Parker, E. N., Interaction of the Solar Wind with the Geomagnetic Field, *Phys. Fluids,* **1,** 171 (1958).
64. Chapman, S., and V. C. H. Ferraro, A New Theory of Magnetic Storms, *Terr. Mag. Atm. Elect.,* **36,** 77 and 171 (1931).
65. *Ibid.,* **38,** 79 (1933).
66. *Ibid.,* **45,** 245 (1940).
67. Dungey, J. W., *Cosmical Electrodynamics,* Chapter 8, Cambridge University Press, Cambridge, 1958.
68. Coleman, P. J., Jr., C. P. Sonett, and L. Davis, Jr., On the Interplanetary Magnetic Storm: Pioneer V, *J. Geophys. Res.,* **66,** 2043 (1961).
69. Coleman, P. J., Jr., L. Davis, Jr., and C. P. Sonett, The Steady Component of the Interplanetary Magnetic Field, *Phys. Rev. Letters,* **5,** 43 (1960).
70. Hultqvist, private communication.
71. Biermann, L., Solar Corpuscular Radiation and the Interplanetary Gas, *Observatory,* **77,** 109 (1957).
72. Rossi, B., Discussion at International Conference on Cosmic Rays and the Earth Storm (Kyoto, September 1961).
73. Beard, D. B., The Interaction of the Terrestrial Magnetic Field with the Solar Corpuscular Radiation, *J. Geophys. Res.,* **65,** 3559 (1960).
74. Spreiter, J. R., and A. Y. Alksne, On the Effect of a Ring Current on the Terminal Shape of the Geomagnetic Field, *J. Geophys. Res.* (in press).
75. Midgeley, J. E., and L. Davis, Jr., Computation of the Bounding Surface of a Dipole Field in a Plasma by a Moment Techniques, AGU Natl. Meeting, Los Angeles, December 1961.
76. Dungey, J. W., The Steady State of the Chapman-Ferraro Problem in Two Dimensions, *J. Geophys. Res.,* **66,** 1043 (1961).
77. Ferraro, V. C. A., An Approximate Method of Estimating the Size and Shape of the Stationary Hollow Carved Out on a Neutral Ionized Stream of Corpuscular Impinging on the Geomagnetic Field, *J. Geophys. Res.,* **65,** 3951 (1960).
78. Hurley, J., Interaction between the Solar Wind and the Geomagnetic Field, N.Y.U. College of Engr. Rpt. (1961).
79. Sonett, C. P., Coupling of the Solar Wind and the Exosphere, *Phys. Rev. Letters,* **5,** 46 (1960).

80. See, for example, C. S. Gardner, H. Goertzerl, H. Grad, C. S. Morawetz, M. H. Rose, and H. Rubin, Hydromagnetic Shock Waves in High Temperature Plasmas, in *Progress in Nuclear Energy*, Ser. XI, Vol. 1, p. 232, Pergamon Press, 1958.

81. Sonett, C. P., Hyperwaves, Shock-like Phenomena in the Outer Exosphere, Proceedings of the International Conference on Cosmic Rays and the Earth Storm (Kyoto, September 1961), *J. Phys. Soc. Japan*, **17**, Supp. II-A, 528 (1962).

82. Van Allen, J. A., and L. A. Frank, Radiation Measurements to 658,300 km with Pioneer IV, *Nature (London)*, **184**, 219 (1960).

83. Axford, W. I., and C. O. Hines, A Unifying Theory of High Latitude Geophysical Phenomena and Geomagnetic Storms, *Can. J. Phys.*, **39**, 1433 (1961).

84. Meyer, P., E. N. Parker, and J. A. Simpson, Solar Cosmic Rays of February 1956 and Their Propagation through Interplanetary Space, *Phys. Rev.*, **104**, 768 (1956).

85. Davis, L., Jr., Interplanetary Magnetic Fields and Cosmic Rays, *Phys. Rev. Letters*, **100**, 1440 (1955).

86. Cocconi, G., T. Gold, K. Greisen, S. Hayakawa, and P. Morrison, IUPAP Cosmic Ray Conf., Verona (1957).

87. Chamberlain, J. W., Interplanetary Gas III, A Hydrodynamic Model of the Corona, *Ap. J.*, **133**, 675 (1960).

88. MacDonald, G. J. F., private communication.

89. Alfvén, H., The Sun's General Magnetic Field, *Tellus*, **8**, 1 (1956).

90. Davis, L., Jr., private communication.

91. Parker, E. N., Sweet's Mechanism for Merging Magnetic Fields in Conducting Fluids, *J. Geophys. Res.*, **62**, 509 (1957).

92. Sonett, C. P., L. Davis, Jr., and P. J. Coleman, Jr., Some Aspects of the Internal Structure of a Solar Flare Plasma Cloud, Proceedings of the International Conference on Cosmic Rays and the Earth Storm (Kyoto, September 1961).

93. Brandt, J. C., Interplanetary Gas. IV: Neutral Hydrogen in a Model Solar Corona, *Ap. J.*, **133**, 688 (1961), *J. Phys. Soc. Japan*, **17**, Supp. II-A, 524 (1962).

94. For example, L. Biermann, R. Lust, and E. Trafftz, Comet Tails and Solar Corpuscular Radiation at Times of Small Solar Activity (unpublished).

95. Johnson, F. S., Solar Radiation, Chapter 4 in *Satellite Environment Handbook*, ed. F. S. Johnson, Stanford University Press, Stanford, 1961.

96. Quoted by L. Biermann, Physical Processes in Comet Tails and Their Relation to Solar Activity, *Soc. Roy. Sci. Liége*, **13**, 291 (1953).

97. Beyer, M., Brightness of Comets and Solar Activity, *Soc. Roy. Sci. Liége*, **13**, 276 (1953).

98. Lüst, Rhea, Activity of Comet Tails in Periods of Geomagnetic Calmness, *Z. Astrophys.* 51No3, 163, 1961.

99. Dolginov, S. Sh., E. G. Eroshenko, L. N. Zhuzgov, N. V. Pushkov, and L. O. Tyurmina, Measuring the Magnetic Fields of the Earth and Moon by Means of Sputnik III and Space Rockets I and II, Academy of Sciences, Moscow, USSR, in *Space Science*, ed. H. K. Kallmann-Bijl, North Holland, Amsterdam, 1960, p. 863.

100. Mustel, E. R., USSR Report to Commission 16 (Magnetohydrodynamics), IAU General Assembly, Berkeley (August 1961).

101. See, for example, C. Y. Fan, P. Meyer, and J. A. Simpson, Trapped and Cosmic Ray Measurements from Explorer VI, *Space Research,* ed. H. K. Kallmann-Bijl, North Holland, Amsterdam, 1960, pp. 951–960.

102. Fan, C. Y., Peter Meyer, and J. A. Simpson, The Rapid Reduction of Cosmic Radiation Intensity Measured in Interplanetary Space, *Phys. Rev. Letters,* **5,** 43 (1960).

103. Arnoldy, R. L., R. A. Hoffman, and J. R. Winckler, Solar Cosmic Rays and Soft Radiation Observed at 5,000,000 km from Earth, *J. Geophys. Res.,* **65,** 3004 (1960).

CHAPTER 11

THE PRODUCTION AND PROPAGATION OF ENERGETIC PARTICLES FROM THE SUN

JOHN R. WINCKLER

University of Minnesota

Despite the fact that the bulk of its radiation is characteristic of the temperature of the photosphere and is in thermal equilibrium with this temperature, the sun at times develops instabilities that result in the production and dissemination into the solar system of protons and heavy nuclei with energies in the relativistic ranges. The study of these energetic particles is of great interest because clues to the mechanism by which the sun burns its magnetic field to produce these outbursts may come from the observation of the time history, the energy spectrum, and the composition of these energetic particles. When the particles are released from the sun, they are affected because of their considerable momentum and their electric charge by magnetic fields in interplanetary space and near the earth in such a way as to provide sensitive probes for studying the magnetic-field configurations in these regions.

Discussed in this chapter are various features of these energetic particles as they are received on the earth and some deductions that have been obtained about the magnetic field of the earth and the interplanetary magnetic configurations.

11-1   DETECTION OF NONRELATIVISTIC SOLAR PROTONS

To introduce the subject, a remarkable nuclear emulsion photograph of the solar particles is shown in Figure 11-1. This photomicrograph, which in actual size is 100 μ in width, was obtained on a high-altitude balloon flight at Minneapolis, Minnesota, on May 12, 1959, following a large flare on May 10 which was the source of the cosmic-ray particles. The picture was obtained by E. P. Ney with an emulsion pellicle flown on the University of Minnesota balloon-monitoring program. This photograph shows at a glance many of the characteristics of the solar particles. One notices near the center of the photograph, and also in the lower left, two particles that come to rest. By measuring the range of these particles, including the air path back to the top of the atmosphere and the ionization density, it is possible to identify these particles unambiguously as protons. The measurements of the range and also of the grain density permit the energy

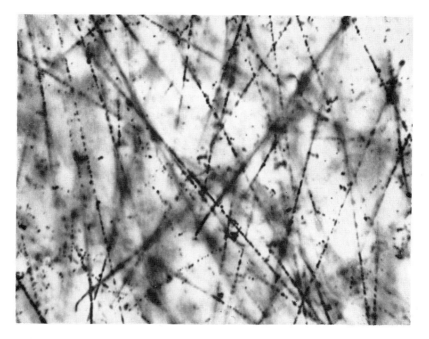

Figure 11-1 Nuclear emulsion tracks of 100-Mev photons in a large solar flare on May 10, 1959. This exposure was obtained on a balloon flying over Minneapolis at 30-km altitude on May 12, 1959. The original size of the above picture is approximately 100 microns. See text for complete description.

spectrum to be evaluated. It is found that the energy spectrum contains a large number of low-energy particles and that the number of particles drops off very rapidly as the higher energies are reached —quite different from the ordinary primary cosmic-ray spectrum. It can also be seen from the photograph that most of the tracks pass through the emulsion from the vertical direction. This effect is produced by the steepness of the spectrum and by the atmosphere above the balloon, so that most of the particles are those that can reach the emulsion through the least thickness of air, that is, from the vertical direction. The high intensity of the particle flux is also shown in this photograph. For normal cosmic rays approximately one tenth of a particle would be seen in this area. From such emulsion exposures, although most of the particles consist of protons, it is known that the sun also is able to accelerate alpha-particles and heavier nuclei with varying intensities. This event represents the first intense case studied with balloon instruments, including ionization chambers, counters, scintillation counter, and nuclear emulsions. It has been analyzed extensively and reported in the literature (1). However, the launching of the balloon and the recovery of the data was not accidental but a result of previous findings which will now be described because they provided insight into some of the features of these energetic solar processes.

The first direct evidence that the sun produces these large fluxes of low-energy protons in the energy range around several hundred Mev was obtained by chance on March 26, 1958, when a balloon was flown at Minneapolis during the main phase of a moderate geomagnetic storm. At that time studies were being made of the auroral X rays at balloon altitudes that had been discovered about a year earlier at the start of the International Geophysical Year (2). The balloon flight on March 26 showed counting-rate increases on the electronic detectors which were not specifically identified but which had a time history unlike that of the precipitation of the auroral particles and the ensuing X rays. Rather, the instrumental rates increased quite smoothly during many hours of balloon flight. Subsequent analysis of the nuclear emulsions on this flight showed an appreciable flux of protons with energy in the 100-Mev region which accounted for the increases in rates seen on the ion chambers and counters. Further correlation indicated that the particles may have originated in a large flare on the eastern edge of the sun on March 23, 1958 (3). It was also determined, coincident with this event, that a strong blackout of radio communications occurred over the polar region. These ionospheric observations were made by Lein-

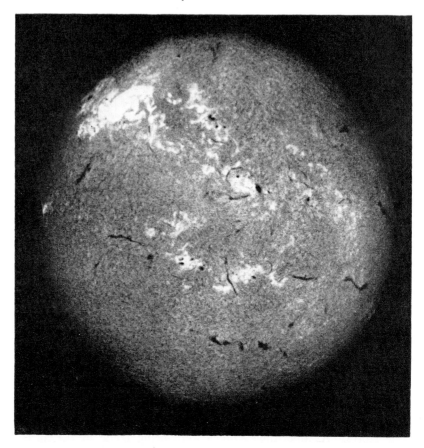

Figure 11-2 The solar disk as recorded in the light of H_α emission by the Sac Peak Observatory, Cloudcroft, New Mexico. (Courtesy of U. S. Air Force on May 10, 1959.) Note the large flare in the upper left portion of the photograph. This great flare was the source of the energetic solar protons shown in Figure 11-1.

bach and Reid at the Geophysical Institute, University of Alaska. There was evidence from earlier work by Reid and Collins (4) and by Bailey (5) that the sun could produce these widespread polar blackouts, which, at least in one case, were known to be associated with flare cosmic rays detected at sea level. A subsequent analysis by Leinbach revealed that indeed events occurred in which the polar ionosphere showed strong absorption of radio waves in the D layer following closely a large solar flare. The characteristics of the process indicated that it was not the usual magnetic storm effect, which occurs a day or two after the flare, but that the effects were quite prompt and uniformly distributed over a large area of the poles of the earth. These findings were reported by Leinbach and Reid early in 1959 in *Physical Review Letters* (6). Meanwhile, in August 1958, Anderson had the good fortune to have a balloon flying at high altitude at Fort Churchill during a large solar flare, and an immediate response was obtained on the balloon counter to show the incidence of these low-energy solar cosmic-ray particles (7). These particle events also were observed with the Explorer IV earth satellite by the University of Iowa team. As a result of these findings, an arrangement was made with Leinbach to notify the various balloon groups immediately if a polar blackout was recorded on the ground-level ionospheric monitoring stations. Accordingly, after the flare on May 10, 1959, warning was received that a strong polar blackout had begun, and the balloon flight was launched at Minneapolis.

Figure 11-2 is a photograph of the May 10 flare obtained in the light of H_α by the Sac Peak Observatory. It was a class 3+ and, as discussed below, it had all the characteristics that are generally associated with the production of high-intensity energetic proton beams. Figure 11-3 shows the polar-cap absorption record obtained by Leinbach. This gives the absorption in decibels of the galactic radio-noise signal which normally is incident on the atmosphere and penetrates through the D layer to the ground, where it is detected by a suitable radio receiver and recorder called a riometer (radio ionospheric opacity meter). The principle of operation of the riometer is shown in

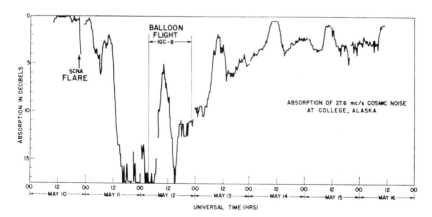

Figure 11-3   The record of the absorption in the ionospheric D-layer of galactic radio noise obtained at College, Alaska, by Harold Leinbach. The absorption, in decibels, is a function of the ionization produced in the D-layer by the solar protons and therefore represents as a function of time, the incidence of the low-energy particles between 1 and 50 Mev at the earth during this event.

Figure 11-4. The instrument usually measures at 27 Mc or at 50 Mc, or at least above the ionospheric cutoff frequency and on a frequency in which man-made radio interference is at a minimum. Normally the intensity of the galactic radio noise varies sinusoidally as the earth's rotation sweeps the beam of the receiving antenna across the galaxy. If ionizing radiation penetrates into the D layer, an enhanced density of free electrons is produced which then increases the absorption of the radio waves by virtue of collisions between the electrons and the atmosphere. The radio energy is absorbed by the common exponential relationship (Figure 11-4). The absorption constant K, however, is a function of distance S because of the variation of collision frequency and electron density with height. Therefore, the exponent is usually expressed as an integral. From magnetoionic theory, the absorption factor can be given in terms of the radio angular frequency w, the electron charge e and mass m, the electron density N, and the collision frequency between electrons and air molecules. For a 27-Mc riometer, the absorption in decibels can then be reduced to the simple expression shown in Figure 11-4.

There is a strong effect of sunlight on the D-layer regions in which the absorption occurs because of the photo-detachment of the absorbing electrons from oxygen molecules. It can be shown as a result that in the daytime the absorption in decibels should be proportional to the flux of particles, considering that the energy spectrum of the

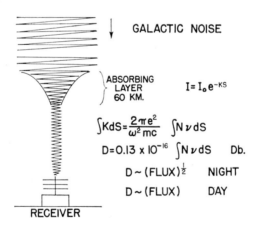

Figure 11-4 Principle of the riometer. The riometer operates by viewing the sky with a wide-angle antenna at a frequency located between 20 and 100 Mc. The absorbing layer is centered around approximately 60-km height, where the primary ionization, the free electron density, and the collision frequency of these electrons produces the maximum effect.

particles remains fixed so that the primary ionization is the same. At night the absorption should be proportional to the square root of the flux of particles of the same energy spectrum. The day-night effect is clearly seen in Figure 11-3; we note that the absorption is less at night and that the length of night to day is just that for the sunlight on the upper atmosphere in the polar regions in May. The absorption of the extragalactic radio waves depends critically on the height in the ionosphere for a number of reasons. The rate of production of ions and electrons depends critically on the energy spectrum of the incident particles and the depth in the atmosphere because of the rapid fall off of density with greater height. The electron lifetime increases with height and the collision frequency decreases with height. A combination of these factors will produce a maximum in the absorption which is located between 60 and 80 km. A typical set of absorption curves plotted against height in kilometers (Figure 11-5) is the result of an analysis by Bailey for a specific solar cosmic-ray event on February 23, 1956 (5). These curves show the absorption during the day (upper) and at night (lower) at different latitudes and reflect the spectrum of the incident solar cosmic-ray particles. In this case the particle spectrum extends well into the relativistic region.

Beginning with the IGY period, an extensive series of high-altitude-balloon sounding flights were carried out by Charakhchian, Tulinov, and Charakhchian. Launchings were conducted at latitudes 64°, 51°, and 41° geomagnetic latitude in the Soviet Union. Single counters and vertical telescopes were sent to the top of the atmosphere twice daily during the IGY-IGC and were continued in 1960–1961. The Russian flight log for the IGY-IGC period is available at the Cosmic Ray Data Center A for the IGY.* A summary of observations is reported in "Cosmic Rays Emitted by the Sun," the article by Charakhchian and co-workers published in *Space Research* edited by Hilde K. Bijl.

Charakhchian and collaborators reported the occurrence of a strong event on July 8, 1958, and have made observations on all of the major events since. These observations are particularly valuable because they are made at high latitude and are not affected by the geomagnetic field or its changes. We have compared Minneapolis observations with those of Charakhchian for the May 1959 event (1). Further observations were reported at the Kyoto Conference, September 1961 (see General References). Charakhchian's observations give spectral and flux information by the technique of Geiger counters

* School of Physics, University of Minnesota, Minneapolis 14, Minnesota.

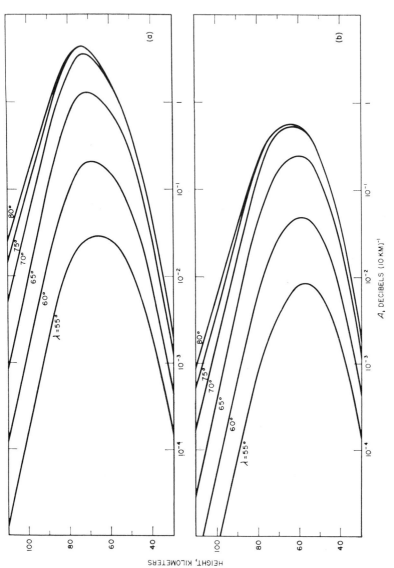

Figure 11-5 Absorption curves calculated by Bailey (5) for a cosmic-ray spectrum resulting from the great energetic flare of February 23, 1956. These curves show the absorption for daytime (*upper*) and nighttime (*lower*) as a function of height in the ionosphere and as a function of geomagnetic latitude. They apply to the particular particle rigidity spectrum assumed for this event, but the absorption as a function of height is similar to other events.

ascending through the atmosphere during solar proton bombardment. The interpretation follows the procedure outlined in Section 11-7.

11-2 DETECTION OF RELATIVISTIC PARTICLES AT SEA LEVEL

The observations with balloons and with the ionospheric effects of the nonrelativistic solar flare protons were not the first evidence that the sun produces high-energy particles. Before the events of the IGY, five cases of solar flare accelerations were known because the particle-energy spectrum extended into the high-energy region so that sea-level monitors responded to the flare particles as well as to the galactic, high-energy cosmic rays (8). Currently the most widely used cosmic-ray detector for sea-level locations is the neutron pile developed by Simpson and collaborators at the University of Chicago (9). The typical geometry is shown in Figure 11-6. The detectors in each section of the pile, as illustrated in Figure 11-6, are two boron-tri-

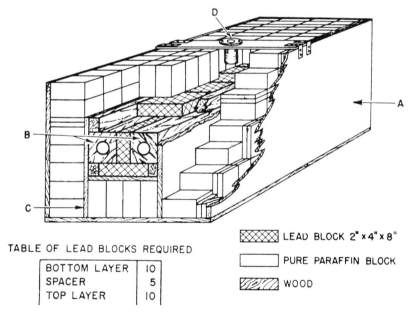

TABLE OF LEAD BLOCKS REQUIRED

BOTTOM LAYER	10
SPACER	5
TOP LAYER	10

▨ LEAD BLOCK 2"x4"x8"

☐ PURE PARAFFIN BLOCK

▨ WOOD

Figure 11-6 Constructional details of a section of a ground-level neutron pile. The two round objects embedded in the center of the pile are boron-triglouride-enriched counters sensitive to thermal neutrons. The threshold of sensitivity is roughly 1 bev of energy per nucleon of the primary particles. (From Solar Modulation of Cosmic Radiation, by J. A. Simpson, in *Science and Space*, p. 262, McGraw-Hill Book Company, 1961.)

fluoride-enriched proportional counters which disclose thermal neutrons. These counters are surrounded by wood and paraffin and are
immersed in a lead structure. The lead structure is further surrounded
by paraffin on the outside, and the entire assembly is sealed into a
wooden box. A given monitor may be built up of many sections of
identical construction. The thermal neutrons are produced by the
incident energetic cosmic-ray nucleons striking the lead and under-
going nuclear interactions which produce neutrons as spallation products. These neutrons are moderated by the hydrogenous material
around the counters to thermal energies and are detected. The paraffin

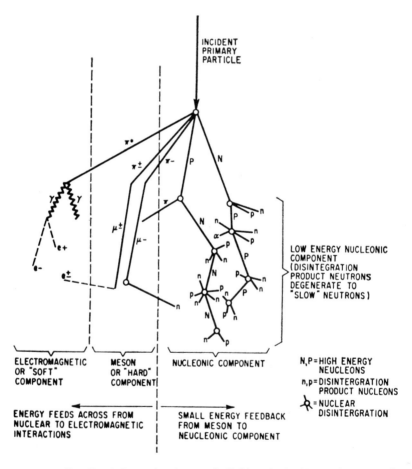

Figure 11-7 Details of the nucleonic cascade linking the incident primary particle
with the sea-level monitor.

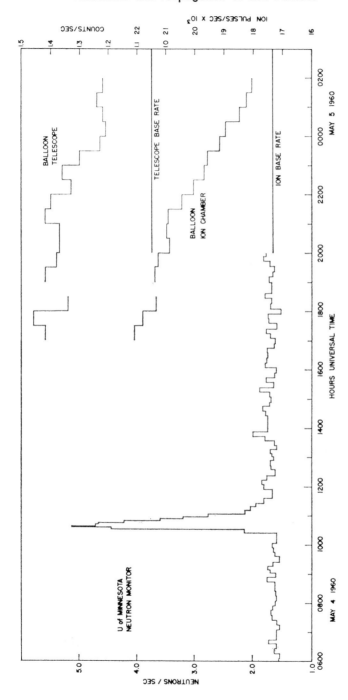

Figure 11-8 Response of a small neutron monitor (*left portion of figure*) to a high-energy solar flare event beginning approximately 1020 UT on May 4, 1960. Curves (*upper right*) are from balloon records.

jacket shields the assembly from thermal neutrons produced locally in the atmosphere or surrounding objects. The monitor is thus insensitive to changes in local conditions; for example, rain, snow, or the rearrangement of objects nearby. The pile responds only to the energetic nucleons which come down through the atmosphere. The atmospheric cascade process is shown schematically in Figure 11-7. The incident primary particle of kinetic energy greater than 1 billion ev produces a nuclear collision high in the atmosphere from which mesons, protons, and neutrons emerge. The protons and neutrons then multiply into a nucleonic cascade in which some of the particles eventually reach the ground and are detected by the monitor. The chance that a primary particle itself will be counted on the ground is negligibly small. The mesons can reach sea level only if the incident particle energy is high, above 10 bev, so that the relativistic time dilatation will increase the lifetime of the mesons sufficiently to enable them to travel through the atmosphere. The nucleonic component is thus the most sensitive method for monitoring the incident cosmic rays at sea level.

The response of a small neutron pile to a solar cosmic-ray outburst occurring on May 4, 1960, is shown in Figure 11-8 (10). The normal counting rate of this monitor is about 1.6 counts/sec, seen as the background line, but at approximately 1020 UT on May 4 a sudden sharp increase of about five times normal occurred in the rate of the monitor. The counting rate rapidly returned and reached background levels again by 1200 UT. It was known that this outburst of relativistic particles detected at sea level was generated by a class 3+ flare on the west limb of the sun and that the rapid transfer of the particles from the sun to the earth was facilitated by the conditions in interplanetary space. This event is discussed in more detail later in this chapter.

11-3   SOLAR FLARES

Since one of the purposes of the study of the energetic solar particles as they reach the earth is the better understanding of solar flare mechanisms, some features of solar flares which seem to be important for these processes will now be discussed. Figure 11-9 is a series of photographs of the great cosmic-ray flare on November 12, 1960, photographed in the red light of atomic hydrogen by M. A. Ellison at the Royal Observatory, Cape of Good Hope. These photographs illustrate certain features of solar flares that are known producers of energetic particles. First of all, flares are located in complex sunspot regions. This is seen in the upper left frame and certain succeeding frames. The flare of November 12 appears to have developed between two large sunspots and may actually have appeared along a region occupied by filaments observed previously. Flares may also develop along magnetically neutral regions located between the dipole fields of the spots. In these photographs note the striations that reach out from the complex spot group into the surrounding photosphere of the sun. Cosmic-ray-producing flares are always on the visible disk, or at least not more than 1 day around the limb. The flares that produce large fluxes of energetic particles are of giant size and are usually classed as 3 or 3+. Frequently the sunspot group in which the flare occurs develops rapidly and the number of spots and the complexity increases from day to day. It can be seen in Figure 11-9 that as the flare develops the luminosity spreads over the umbra of the sunspots. It has been pointed out by Dodson that this may be associated with the production of the relativistic particles (11). Relativistic particles are more frequently associated with flares on the western hemisphere of the sun. This, however, is not a specific property of the flare itself but concerns a general solar feature that regulates the propagation paths or magnetic-field lines in interplanetary space. An idea of the time scale of flare development may also be obtained from Figure 11-9. Between 1323 and 1333 UT the flare obtained most of its development. This is called explosive phase of the flare, and during this time it is generally thought that the energetic particles are produced. The flare, however, continued to be luminous for many hours; for example, at 1424 UT (the last frame in Figure 11-9) the flare was just beginning to fade.

Another characteristic of cosmic-ray-producing flares is that they always yield large bursts of radio noise. This characteristic of flares has been known generally for a number of years—ever since the discovery of solar radio-noise bursts by British radar receivers during World War II (12). Cosmic-ray-producing flares emit radio noise over a wide range of frequencies and in many cases with a time profile lasting for a number of hours. Figure 11-10 shows the time history of the H_α emission from the flare (upper), the very-high-frequency radio emission at 1000 Mc (center), and low-frequency emission at 200 Mc (bottom). The wideband emission occurs during the explosive rise of the flare shown on the H_α curve. It is generally considered that the wideband radio noise is produced by high-energy electrons radiating by the synchrotron process in the magnetic fields associated with the flare. It is well known that synchrotron radiation has a wide frequency spectrum beginning at the cyclotron frequency

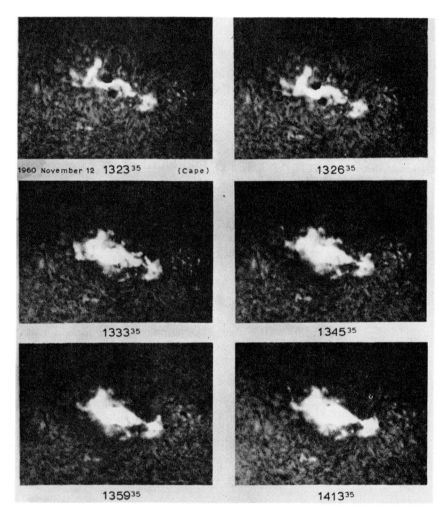

Figure 11-9 Photographs of the large flare on November 12, 1960, which generated intense solar cosmic rays. These photographs were taken at the Royal Observatory, Cape of Good Hope, with the Lyot H_α heliograph. (Courtesy of

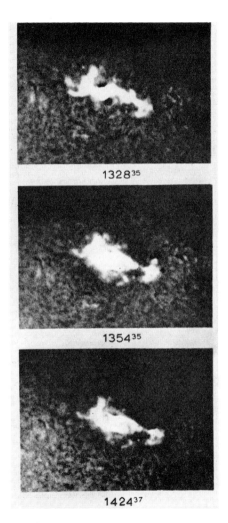

1328³⁵

1354³⁵

1424³⁷

M. A. Ellison, Dunskin Observatory.)   Note the appearance of the flare (*upper left*) between the two large sunspots, its rapid rise in the first 10 minutes, and its long persistence over the next hour.

and an increasing energy up to a harmonic determined by the particle energy. The kind of emission shown in Figure 11-10 could be produced by electrons of a few Mev energy in magnetic fields in the flare region of a few hundred gauss. The very-high-frequency burst associated with the explosive rise is generally considered to be closely associated with the production of the energetic protons. Sometimes during this phase of the flare a vigorous burst of X rays which originates completely on the sun in the flare region may be observed. These X-ray bursts may last for just a few minutes and are localized in time near the maximum phase of the flare. Such X-ray bursts may be produced by the same electrons which radiate the synchrotron radiation and which are able to flow down the magnetic field lines and strike the photosphere where the X-rays are produced by the Bremsstrahlung process. The wideband radio emission, which is known as Type IV by the radio astronomers, has a high correlation with the production of the energetic protons; in fact, the over-all correlation is as high as 85 percent.

A rare phenomenon associated with the explosive phase of cosmic-ray flares is a white-light flash which may be seen against the continuum light of the solar disk. This has been reported, for example, in the great cosmic-ray flare of February 23, 1956 (13), and was seen also in the September 3, 1960, flare (14). The origin of the white light is somewhat a mystery but certainly represents an energetic process, probably associated with the production of energetic particles. The first observation of what may be one of the largest solar flares on record was in such a whitelight flash. It was made on September 1, 1859, by Carrington and it occurred at 1118 UT. Because his report is of unusual clarity and describes in a dramatic way the appearance of a large solar flare, we quote his remarks as follows:

The image of the sun's disc was, as usual with me, projected on to a plate of coated glass . . . a picture of about 11 inches. I had secured diagrams of all the groups . . . when within the area of the great north group . . . two patches of intensely bright and white light broke out. . . . My first impression was that by some chance a ray of light had penetrated a hole in the (shading) screen attached to the object-glass, for the brilliancy was full equal to that of direct sunlight; but . . . by causing the image to move, I was an unprepared witness of a very different affair. I thereupon noted down the time by the chronometer, and, seeing the outburst to be very rapidly on the increase, and being somewhat flurried by the surprise, I hastily ran to call someone to witness the exhibition with me, and on returning within 60 seconds, was mortified to find that it was already much changed and enfeebled. Very shortly afterwards at 11h. 23m., the last trace was gone. . . . I was certainly surprised, on referring to the sketch finished before the occurrence, at finding

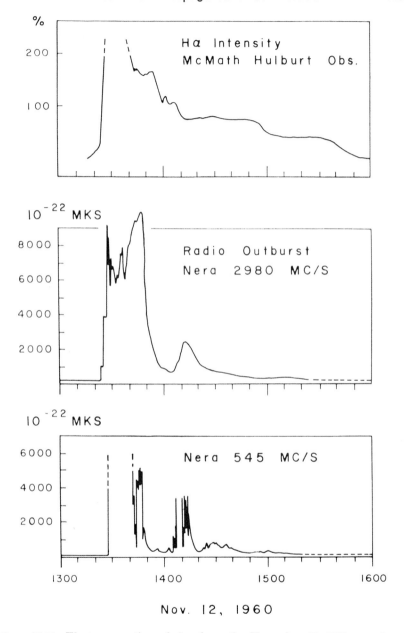

Figure 11-10 Electromagnetic emission from the November 12, 1960, cosmic-ray flare. (Courtesy H. W. Dodson, McMath-Hulbert Observatory and A. D. Fokker, P.T.T., Netherlands.) The vertical scale for the radio emission is expressed in units of 10^{-22} watts/m²·cycle·sec.

myself unable to recognize any change whatsoever as having taken place. The impression left upon me is that the phenomenon took place at an elevation considerably above the general surface of the sun and accordingly, altogether above and over the great group in which it was seen projected . . . (15).

11-4 SOLAR TERRESTRIAL RELATIONSHIPS

The analysis of many of the solar cosmic-ray events produced by large flares involves the general use of solar-terrestrial relationships associated with flares, magnetic storms, and plasma clouds. The typical sequence of events is as follows.

An active region crosses the solar disk as the sun rotates in a 27-day period. Geomagnetic conditions at the beginning of this rotation may be quiet. A large flare occurs on the sun which produces some immediate terrestrial effects, such as ionospheric fade-outs associated with ultraviolet light or X rays from the flare. If energetic particles are produced, they may proceed quickly to the earth and, in a complicated manner, penetrate through the earth's dipole field and reach the surface. Such large flares frequently produce plasma clouds which by direct experiment have been shown to contain magnetic lines of force probably originating in the sunspot region. These plasma clouds proceed out over a large solid angle into interplanetary space with velocities of around 1000 km/sec and reach the position of the earth's orbit in a day or two. The interaction of this plasma cloud with the geomagnetic field of the earth produces the various features associated with a typical geomagnetic storm. Such a geomagnetic storm in its classical form begins with a sudden increase of the horizontal field of the earth measured, for example, at the equator. This is called the sudden commencement and is believed to be produced by the compression of the earth's field due to the momentum of the solar plasma particles. The compression phase of the storm may last for several hours before the field at the equator swings negative into the main phase. The main phase is thought to be due to the setting up of circulating currents around the earth in the trapped radiation which depresses the field at the equator and dilutes the lines of force of the earth's field. After a period of several days the field gradually returns to normal. During the compression phase the magnetic excursions may range from a few gamma to a hundred gamma. In the main phase the field is often depressed to 500 gammas at the equator in a large storm. The main phase is often marked by large fluctuations, the occurrence of major aurorae in both hemispheres of the earth, disturbances in the radiation belt, and considerable alterations in the general form of the earth's dipole field. Typical large storm disturbances are shown in Figures 11-17 and 11-18.

To return now to the passage of the solar cosmic rays, we note that these particles may leave the sun and pass quickly to the earth, arriving well ahead of the plasma cloud, for the plasma particle energies are in the low-kilovolt range and the solar cosmic rays are in the energy range of Mev to bev. Knowledge of the way in which these cosmic-ray particles can reach the surface of the earth through the deflecting field of the dipole lines of force is very useful because it permits the use, in effect, of the earth as a giant magnetic spectrometer to examine the rigidity spectrum of the incident particles.

11-5 STÖRMER THEORY OF COSMIC RAYS

The geomagnetic cutoff may be simply understood as follows. Since the equations of motion do not depend on the algebraic sign of the time, instead of inquiring whether a particle from infinity can reach the location of the detector in the earth's field, it is much more useful to consider the particle as starting from the detector in a given direction and to ask (1) whether it will escape to infinity and (2), if so, what its asymptotic direction will be at great distance from the earth with respect to coordinates fixed to the dipole.

If the particle does not escape to infinity, its orbit may wind around the earth in a complicated manner, finally striking the surface again near the geomagnetic latitude of origin or in the corresponding latitude in the opposite hemisphere of the earth. For low-rigidity particles the orbits closely follow the magnetic lines of force as do the Van Allen trapped particles. However, for higher rigidities the bound regions may not be shaped like the geomagnetic field lines.

It can be shown that a given particle may escape to infinity if the value of a parameter γ lies between -1 and 0, with the critical value at -1. For particles near vertical incidence γ is given by the equation $-2\gamma = \cos^2 \lambda/r$, where λ is the geomagnetic latitude and $r = PcA^2/ZeM$. To compute the critical rigidity at a given latitude, we set $\gamma = -1$ and find $r = \cos^2 \lambda/2$, or $R = Pc/Ze = M/4A^2 \cos^4 \lambda$. The particle rigidity $R = Pc/Ze$ (see definition below) is thus expressed in terms of the constants M (the earth's dipole moment), A (the distance from the dipole center, e.g., earth radius), and the geomagnetic latitude λ. We find that for $\lambda = 0$, $PC/Ze = 15$ bev of rigidity. Therefore,

$$R = 15 \cos^4 \lambda \text{ bv} \tag{11-1}$$

represents the simplest relationship that is valid for solar-flare particles or low-energy cosmic rays incident at higher latitudes. The meaning of particle rigidity and its relation to kinetic energy are explained below. If the particles are directionally isotropic at large distances from the static dipole field, then, as a result of Liouville's theorem, we know that a detector operating inside the field will measure the same directional flux as at infinity down to the appropriate Störmer rigidity cutoff limit.

To determine the orbit and its asymptotic direction in space, numerical computing methods, currently carried out by high-speed electronic computers, must be used because the differential equations of motion for charged particles in the dipole field cannot be solved in closed form.

At low latitudes the cutoff rigidity is a strong function of direction as well as of latitude. Because the geomagnetic field is not strictly of dipole nature, the determination of the equivalent geomagnetic latitude at each point on the earth's surface requires consideration of the detailed surface field. A consistent set of cutoff rigidities and equivalent geomagnetic latitudes is now available, based on empirical methods (16).

Since this discussion is concerned mainly with low-rigidity flare particles measured principally at higher latitudes, no discussion has been made of the "earth shadow" effects important for galactic primaries.

The measurement of the solar cosmic-ray particles may be done before the arrival of the plasma cloud when the geomagnetic field of the earth is in a quiet condition. As will be shown later, the disturbed condition of the field affects the cutoff energies at each latitude and the solar particles may be used to study this effect, its causes, and complications.

To understand the meaning of particle rigidity and its relationship to the momentum and energy of the cosmic rays, a brief discussion of the relativistic relationships essential to the problem is in order.

The basic unit of energy is the electron volt, defined as the energy acquired by one fundamental unit of charge, 1.6×10^{-19} coulomb, in falling through a potential difference of one practical volt. Therefore, 1 ev = 1.6×10^{-19} joule = 1.6×10^{-12} erg. The corresponding kinetic energy will be acquired by the particle mass attached to this charge. This kinetic energy is expressed by the usual relativistic relation

$$T = m_0 c^2 (\gamma - 1); \tag{11-2}$$

m_0c^2 is the rest mass energy of the particle, expressible in electron volts, and $\gamma = 1/\sqrt{1 - \beta^2}$ is the relativistic factor ($\beta = v/c$). In a purely magnetic field the momentum of the particle remains fixed. The momentum, $P = mv = \gamma m_0 \beta c$, is related to the total energy of the particle by the relation

$$W^2 = P^2c^2 + m_0{}^2c^4. \tag{11-3}$$

The momentum P is commonly expressed in units of electron volts/c, or Pc in electron volts. The dimensions of each term of equation (11.3) are (energy)^2, and the equation is valid in any system of units. The total energy W is the sum of the kinetic and rest mass energies: $W = T + m_0c^2 = \gamma m_0c^2$. Thus the total energy and the kinetic energy of a particle moving in a static magnetic field remain fixed. One frequently encounters in cosmical phenomena magnetic fields in motion. In such cases the particle energy is constant only in a frame of reference fixed to the field.

The force acting on a particle of charge q moving in a magnetic field B with velocity v is known as the Lorentz force and follows the relation $F = q/c\ V \times B$. The radius of curvature R for motion across a field B is such that

$$BR = \frac{Pc}{Ze}. \tag{11-4}$$

With Pc expressed in electron volts, for a particle of charge Z times the electronic charge, with B expressed in gauss, the radius of curvature in centimeters is given by

$$R = \frac{Pc(\text{ev})}{300ZB}. \tag{11-5}$$

Thus the magnetic rigidity expressed in volts is given by

$$300B\ (\text{gauss})\ R(\text{cm}) = \frac{Pc(\text{ev})}{Z} = \text{rigidity (volts)}. \tag{11-6}$$

For example, a proton ($Z = 1$) of 1 billion volts rigidity has a radius of curvature in a field of 1 gamma (10^{-5} gauss) of $R = 10^9/(300 \times 10^{-5}) = 3.3 \times 10^{11}$ cm $= 3.3 \times 10^6$ km, that is, about 1/50 AU.

$$[T(\text{ev}) + m_0c^2]^2 = [W(\text{ev})]^2 = [\text{rigidity (volts)}]^2 \times Z^2 + [m_0c^2(\text{ev})]^2. \tag{11-7}$$

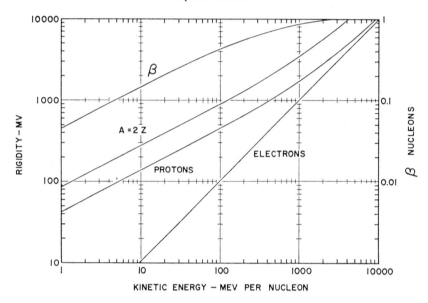

Figure 11-11 Relationship between the rigidity and the kinetic energy for electrons, protons, and heavy nuclei.

For protons, $m_0c^2 = 938$ Mev; for electrons, $m_0c^2 = 0.51$ Mev. For heavy nuclei energies are commonly expressed on a per nucleon basis. Note that for the same energy per nucleon (i.e., the same velocity), rigidity (proton) $= \frac{1}{2}$ rigidity (heavy nuclei). Figure 11-11 gives the kinetic energy T as a function of rigidity for electrons, protons, and heavy nuclei. Also given is the relative velocity β, computed from the kinetic-energy expression.

The strong dependence of the minimum rigidity on latitude means that for the solar-flare protons, which are rich in low-rigidity particles, the areas of incidence will be confined to high latitudes. This is shown in a striking manner in Figure 11-12 compiled by T. Obayashi on the basis of polar-cap blackouts of radio communications (17). This phenomenon represents an absorption in the D layer similar to the riometer effects discussed earlier but was detected by the vertical ionospheric sounding technique which has the advantage that about 60 stations were available during the IGY period, distributed over the polar regions. The map of the blackout region due to the incidence of solar cosmic rays shows that these particles are confined to the magnetic polar zone in accordance with the low rigidity and the Störmer equation.

If the cos⁴ λ law were applied to the incident particles, it would be found that at the latitude of Minnesota particles of approximately 600-Mev energy would be the minimum allowed. However, it has already been pointed out at the beginning of this chapter that protons from solar flares are seen at Minneapolis down to the minimum energy

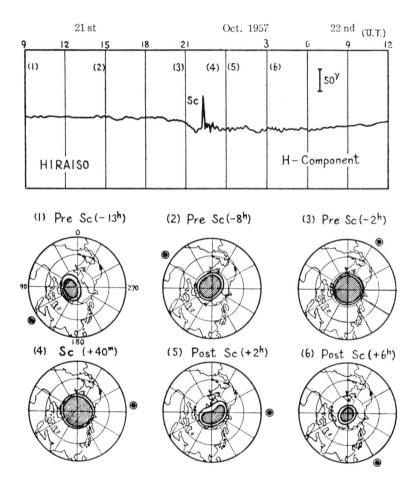

Figure 11-12   Maps of a polar blackout detected by a network of ionosonde stations over the polar region. The cross-hatch region indicates complete blackout in the ionospheric D-layer caused by low-energy solar flare protons. Note that the region of incidence is confined about the geomagnetic pole and the particles are incident before the sudden commencement of the geomagnetic storm. The black dot shows the solar position for each map. There is some solar dependence due to the sunlight effect on the ionosphere. [Courtesy T. Obayashi from IGY data (17).]

allowed by the atmosphere above the balloon (about 80 Mev). Further investigation has shown that this effect occurs because of a change in the Störmer cutoffs with time, produced in a complicated way by the incidence of the solar plasma cloud on the geomagnetic field. In order to investigate this point further, it is necessary to discuss in some detail the measurement of the particle spectrum at intermediate geomagnetic latitudes.

11-6   MEASUREMENT OF ENERGY SPECTRUM

A simple way to determine the spectrum is shown in Figure 11-13. A single Geiger counter preferably of isotropic response is sent up through the atmosphere on a balloon to the highest possible altitude. The counting rate due to the incident solar protons will then increase rapidly as the atmospheric depth decreases. This is because the counter is able to see particles of lower and lower energy as the residual air path decreases; at the same time, particles from larger and larger angles may reach the counter for a given energy. If background effects are negligible and if the beam is isotropic above the atmosphere and assumed to consist entirely of protons, an analysis can be carried out in the form of the spectrum, which then gives the slope of the spectrum and the flux of particles. The analysis shows, according to the equations in Figure 11-13, that the counting rate

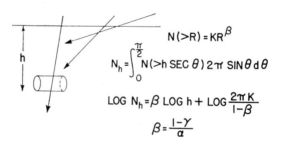

$$N(>R) = KR^{\beta}$$

$$N_h = \int_0^{\frac{\pi}{2}} N(>h \operatorname{SEC} \theta) \, 2\pi \operatorname{SIN} \theta \, d\theta$$

$$\operatorname{LOG} N_h = \beta \operatorname{LOG} h + \operatorname{LOG} \frac{2\pi K}{1-\beta}$$

$$\beta = \frac{1-\gamma}{\alpha}$$

$$\frac{dN}{dE} = CE^{-\gamma} \quad \text{(DIFFERENTIAL ENERGY SPECTRUM)}$$

Figure 11-13   The counting rate of a Geiger counter due to a proton beam incident isotropically on the top of the atmosphere may be used to determine the energy spectrum of the incident particles. The range relationship is shown in the top equation, and the counting rate can then be given by the integral. Finally, the exponent γ of the assumed power-law differential energy spectrum (*below*), as well as the flux constant C, may be determined from the absolute dimensions and counting rate of the counter.

when plotted against the log of the atmospheric depth should give a straight line. This is because the particle differential energy spectrum may be represented by a power law as well as the range relationship for the protons in air. An example of an experiment is shown in Figure 11-14, in which a Geiger counter and also an ionization chamber were flown into an intense solar proton event on July 15, 1959 (18). It may be noted that the counting rate of the Geiger counter below 30 gm/cm² is a good straight line on a log-log plot. At greater depths the interpretation becomes difficult because of nuclear interactions and secondary gamma rays and neutrons. At high altitudes below 50 gm/cm² depth the straight line becomes significant and a spectrum may be evaluated. Considerable improvement results in the measurements if a narrow-angle vertical coincidence counter train is used instead of the single counter.

In order to understand the measurement of energy by this technique or, as a matter of fact, by all techniques that use the stopping power of materials, we shall discuss briefly the range, ionization, and energy relationships for charged particles moving through matter.

The stopping power of various materials for charged particles may be used to evaluate their energy distribution if the type of particle is known and the range is experimentally determined. For protons we use the relation

$$\text{range} = K_1 E^\alpha \text{gm/cm}^2, \tag{11-8}$$

valid between 80 and 500 Mev kinetic energy, with $\alpha = 1.70$ and E in Mev. The unit (gm/cm²) may be converted to thickness in centimeters by the relation $R(\text{gm/cm}^2) = R(\text{cm}) \times \rho(\text{gm/cm}^3)$, where ρ is the density. For the lighter elements, in which the ratio (atomic number)/(mass number) is constant, the range expressed in gm/cm² is not dependent on the material. For the same velocity (i.e., the same energy per nucleon) the ranges of various particles of charge Z units of the electronic charge and rest mass energy $m_0 c^2$ can be shown to be proportional to $m_0 c^2/Z^2$, so that $Z^2 R/m_0 c^2$ is a universal function of the velocity and therefore of the kinetic energy per nucleon. Such a relationship is given in Figure 11-15 for convenient ranges of the variables.

Both the detection and identification of ionizing particles in traversing matter requires the computation of the energy loss which appears as ionization. Theory shows that the ionization produced, or energy loss rate dE/dX, is a function only of the value of Z and β of the particle. Thus

$$I \sim dE/dX \sim Z^2 f(\beta). \tag{11-9}$$

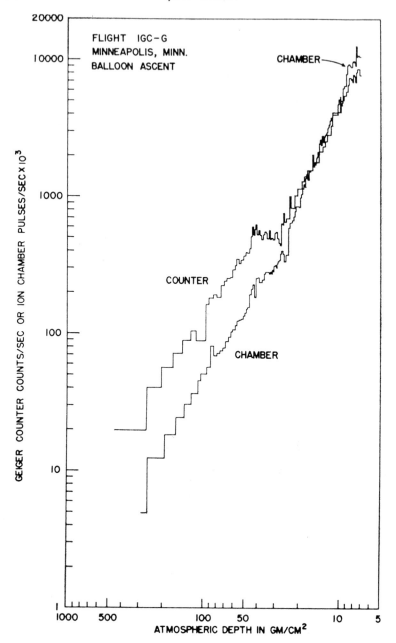

Figure 11-14 Counting rate of a Geiger counter and associated ion chamber during the intense solar cosmic-ray event on July 15, 1959. The low-energy spectrum of the solar cosmic rays may be determined from the straight-line response with pressure below about 30 gm/cm².

This function reaches a minimum value near $\beta = 1$ and, for singly charged particles, $(dE/dX)_{\min}$ has the value 1.83 Mev/gm/cm^2 for air and is similar for other light elements. The ratio $I/I_{\min}$ is a function only of the kinetic energy/nucleon and is included in Figure 11-15. If the element of matter traversed is small compared to the range of the particle or to a mean-free-path for energy loss by processes other than ionization, then the energy-loss rate in the element is independent of its shape or orientation in the particle beam. The mean ionization rate for a given spectrum of particles and the average omnidirectional intensity J_0 may be used to compute, for example, the rate of an ion chamber, the number of grains/cm^3 developed in a nuclear emulsion, or the radiation dosage in various substances. Thus

$$I\alpha\,\frac{\overline{dE}}{dX}\,(\text{average})\ J_0\ \text{Mev/gm/sec.} \qquad (11\text{-}10)$$

The radiation dosage in rad(1 rad = 100 ergs/gm energy loss) is then

$$\text{rad} = 2.93 \times 10^{-8} I/I_{\min} Z^2 J_0 t, \qquad (11\text{-}11)$$

with t in seconds and J_0 in particles/cm^{-2} sec^{-1}.

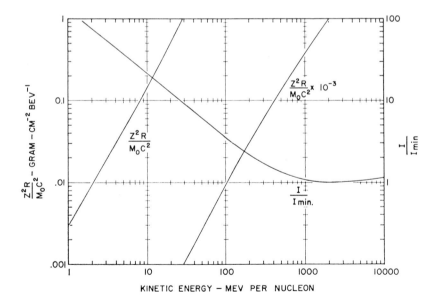

Figure 11-15 Range and relative ionization for charged particles traversing matter.

With the aid of the necessary assumptions and the range-energy theory, we return to the spectral analysis from the Geiger counter on ascent, as shown in Figure 11-14. An energy spectrum has been evaluated and is given by the following relationship:

$$N(E) = 3.0 \times 10^8 E^{-3.9} \text{ particles sec}^{-1} \text{ cm}^{-2} \text{ ster}^{-1} \text{ Mev}^{-1}$$

and was measured on July 15, 1959, at 1046 UT at Minneapolis. We see that the Geiger counter rate in Figure 11-14 increases to the highest altitudes reached, which implies that the spectrum of particles continued to follow the power-law relationship down to the very lowest energies of about 80 Mev. This is a typical lower limit for most balloon measuring equipment.

A much better but less simple method is to use nuclear emulsions in the manner outlined at the beginning of this chapter. Nuclear emulsion measurements, however, have to be averaged over some period of time, such as several hours, and a background correction may be necessary because of accumulated events during balloon ascent and descent. Other types of measuring devices utilizing combinations of energy-loss rate and total range have been applied to these problems but are not discussed here.

11-7   STÖRMER CUTOFF CHANGES DURING GEOMAGNETIC STORMS

A significant fact is that if the solar proton spectrum is measured during the main phase of a geomagnetic disturbance it will be found that the spectrum extends unchanged down to the lowest energies detectable with balloons, namely, about 80 Mev. To illustrate the difference in appearance when the solar particles are measured by an ascending counter without this changed Störmer cutoff, Figure 11-16 shows measurements of a solar proton event that occurred on September 4, 1960, in which balloons were flown almost simultaneously at high latitude at Fort Churchill, Manitoba, Canada, and at an intermediate latitude at Minneapolis. It should be noted that the Fort Churchill balloon showed the continuing increase of the counting rate and spectrum down to the lowest energies detectable, whereas the Minneapolis balloon showed that the counting rate of the Geiger counter tended to level as the balloon rose, showing that the spectrum did not continue to increase. In this case it was known that magnetic conditions were approximately normal and that the magnetic field was exerting its expected Störmer cutoff effect at Minneapolis. At Fort Churchill, however, the normal geomagnetic cutoff is always low, much below that of the air above the balloon. An emulsion

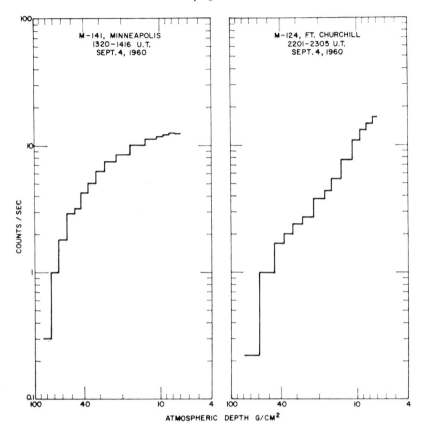

Figure 11-16 Geiger-counter rate curves during balloon ascent at two latitudes, showing the presence at high latitude (Fort Churchill) of particles down to the lowest energy permitted by the atmosphere above the balloon. At Minneapolis the low-energy particles are greatly reduced in the spectrum.

analysis of this same situation carried out by Dr. Phyllis Freier at the University of Minnesota is shown in Figure 11-17, in which the differential spectrum of the particles during the normal conditions was determined. Note that the detailed spectral analysis indeed shows the presence of a geomagnetic cutoff as expected, but it is rather less sharp and occurs at somewhat lower kinetic energies than given by analysis of the magnetic field of the earth. Certain interesting problems remain in the interpretation of these results. However, it is clear that the large magnetic storms during the main phase have the effect of lowering the magnetic cutoffs down to a small

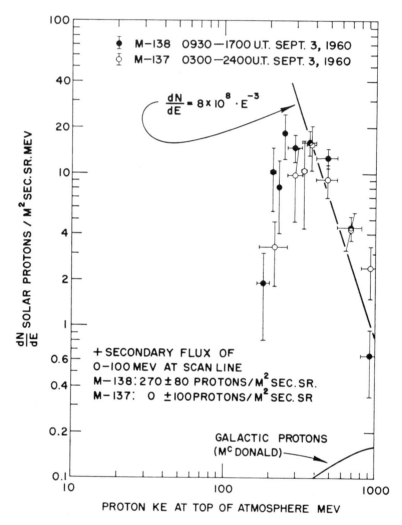

Figure 11-17 Emulsion analysis by P. Freier (21), showing the direct measurement of the differential proton particles spectrum under normal conditions of the geomagnetic field at Minneapolis. Note that the particle flux drops rapidly at energies well above the atmospheric cutoff of about 85 Mev, showing the effect of the geomagnetic field on limiting the energy of the incident particles.

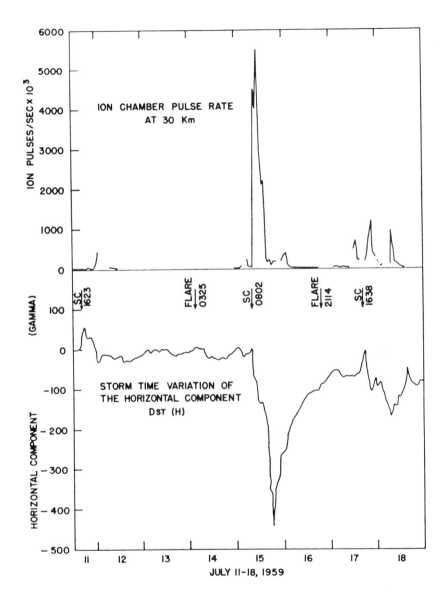

Figure 11-18 Correlation between the main phase of the geomagnetic storm (*lower*) and the incidence of the full spectrum of solar cosmic rays (*upper*) for the three solar cosmic-ray events in July 1959.

value at intermediate latitudes. Furthermore, the direct evidence given above is confirmed by measurements by the ionospheric techniques, sea-level monitors, and satellite observations.

A clue to the mechanism responsible for the cutoff alteration was obtained by studying the detailed time variations of the solar cosmic rays during magnetic storms with counting instruments on high-altitude, constant-level balloons at Minneapolis. Figure 11-18 shows the results obtained during the three large solar cosmic-ray outbursts in July 1959 correlated with the storm time variation of the earth's field averaged for equatorial stations. It can be seen at the top of the figure that the ionization rate (which is a measure of the incident particle flux) grew rapidly when the field switched negative during the main phase of the storms on July 11, July 15, and July 17. A detail of the first storm in July 1959 is shown in Figure 11-19. Here we see the typical profile of the magnetic field of the earth during the storms, showing the sudden commencement, the positive phase, and the swing of the earth's field negative. Note that the

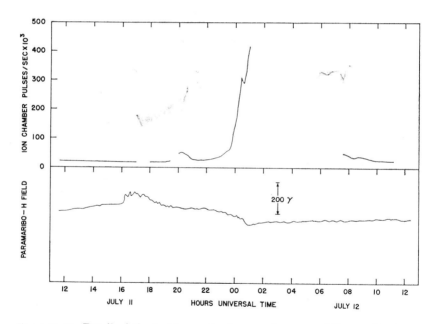

Figure 11-19 Detail of the incidence of solar cosmic rays at Minneapolis during the first July 1959 magnetic storm. Note that no particle increase is seen at the moment of the SC at 1600 UT on July 11, but rather the increase occurs near 2300 UT at the time of the main phase and the negative excursion of the equatorial field.

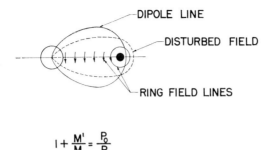

$$I + \frac{M'}{M} = \frac{P_0}{P}$$

Figure 11-20 Alteration of the earth's dipole field by a ring current. The ring-current process acting on the cutoff values of the incident solar protons may produce the observed decrease in the minimum rigidity according to the relationship shown in the lower part of the figure (see text).

cosmic-ray flux remains at galactic background until the main phase of the storm when the field swings negative, although over the polar region where particles can gain normal entry the full intensity of the solar cosmic-ray beam was observed. The change of the Störmer cutoffs at the time of the main phase of the storm may be interpreted in terms of the formation of a ring current of the trapped radiation in the earth's dipole field. This ring current added to the normal dipole field of the earth has the effect of reducing the particle rigidity necessary for entrance at a given latitude. A qualitative description of this process is shown in Figure 11-20. The cross section of the ring is represented by the solid black circle, the normal dipole line of the earth, and the curved arrows show the shape of the field due to the ring which, near the earth's surface at the equator, is horizontal and opposite to the dipole field. The addition of these two fields produces the disturbed line of force which stretches out further from the earth at a given latitude so that the solar cosmic rays that enter from infinity and spiral down these lines of force can eventually be incident at lower latitudes. The mathematical treatment by Kellogg shows that the normal Störmer mathematical statement of the problem is modified so that the cutoff rigidity compared with normal is given by the simple relationship shown in the lower part of the figure, where M' is the magnetic moment of the ring and M is the magnetic moment of the earth (19). This type of analysis then permits the evaluation of both the moment of the ring and its approximate radius. It is found that a moment about equal to that of the earth, perhaps twice that of the earth, located at 7 to 10 R_E can account for the observed change in Störmer cutoffs at the time of the main phase of the magnetic storm.

Finally, there is illustrated another feature of the time variations of the cosmic rays at intermediate latitude which reflects on the behavior of the earth's magnetic field. Figure 11-21 shows the record of two separate balloon flights flown several hundred miles apart near

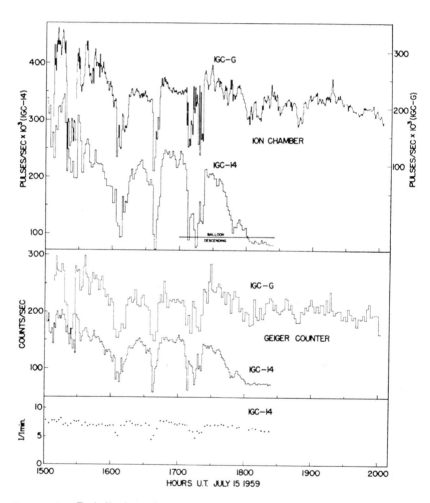

Figure 11-21 Periodic intensity variations observed at Minneapolis during an intense solar proton event by two separate balloons flying about 200 miles apart in longitude. The intensity variations are probably due to periodic cutoff changes and may be associated with large-scale oscillations of the ring current or geomagnetic field of the earth.

Minneapolis in the later stages of the great storm on July 15, when the geomagnetic cutoffs were returning to normal. Note the oscillations in intensity observed on all of the instruments on both balloons which rise and fall with a period of approximately 1.5 hr. This semiperiodic behavior is suggestive of a periodic change in the geomagnetic cutoff operating on the incident cosmic-ray spectrum and producing the change in flux of particles observed. It may be due to oscillations in the intensity or size of the ring and may indicate standing waves in the ring or large-scale oscillations in the dipole field of the earth with its contained particles. Hydromagnetic waves traveling around the earth, across the field lines at the approximate location of the ring, would have the right speed to traverse once around in about half an hour and might account for this phenomenon. Thus it can be seen that detailed measurements of the solar particles are productive of much information about the environment of the earth and its behavior during times when it is disturbed by solar or plasma clouds.

11-8 REPRESENTATIVE SPECTRA OF SOLAR-FLARE COSMIC RAYS

Basic information about the nonrelativistic particles consists of their energy spectra and composition. Both factors are known to change with time following a flare event, on a time scale of many hours or days. This is long compared to the probable acceleration time in the flare of a few tens of minutes and must therefore be a property of the propagating medium.

Figure 11-22 shows a collection of energy spectra available from 14 events studied by the various techniques described earlier for balloons, rockets, and satellites. Balloon spectra seldom extend below 80 Mev. Rocket and satellite data in some cases extend the spectra to as low as a few Mev. Table 11-1 identifies the source of each spectrum, the associated flare, and the time interval between the flare and the spectrum measurement. These spectra are for protons.

For comparison, Figure 11-22 shows the galactic cosmic-ray proton spectrum measured both at solar maximum and solar minimum. Note the steep flare spectrum compared to galactic particles and the large range of flux values.

The spectra shown in Figure 11-22 are measured under conditions in which the geomagnetic rigidity cutoff is lower than the minimum energy on the curves, either because the data were obtained at high latitude or at intermediate latitudes when a strong geomagnetic storm had lowered the cutoff. Thus they are representative of free-space intensities near the earth.

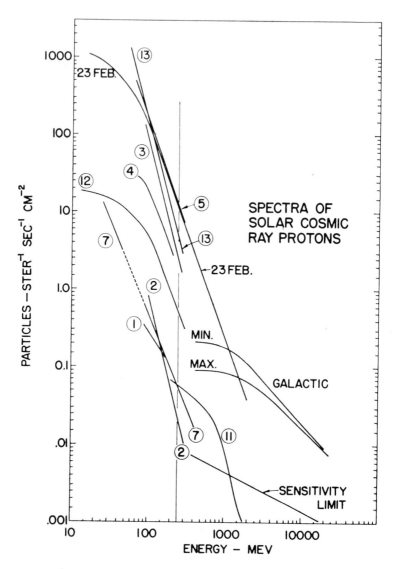

Figure 11-22 Integral energy spectrum of solar cosmic-ray protons as measured for a selected series of events by balloons, rockets, and satellites. For comparison the galactic proton spectrum at solar minimum and solar maximum is shown as measured by MacDonald. See Table 11-1 for identification.

Some of these events, namely No. 6 (July 16, 1959), No. 11 (May 4, 1960), No. 12 (September 3, 1960), No. 13 (November 12, 1960), No. 14 (November 15, 1960), and the event on February 23, 1956, were detected by sea-level monitors. Since the detection of these events by neutron monitors depends sensitively on the solar cosmic-ray flux in the galactic range of energies, a small decrease in slope of the spectra, such as shown in Figure 11-22, may result in a "high-energy" flare event detectable by sea-level monitors. High-energy events do not seem basically unique in any way but represent less frequent cases of spectra dropping off somewhat less rapidly with increasing energy. Because of the uncertain neutron monitor response in the 1-bev and lower region, the sea-level neutron-monitor data cannot be used with certainty at present to extend the high-altitude spectra to intermediate energies, that is, near 400 Mev where balloon data end.

The various spectra in Figure 11-22 show other marked differences:

1. Certain spectra bend over at low energies; for example, February 23, No. 4, No. 11, and No. 12. There are apparent exceptions; for example, No. 7 and No. 13.

2. Frequently the most intense low-energy events contain negligible numbers of relativistic particles; for example, Nos. 2, 3, 4, and 5.

3. Some relativistic events are markedly deficient in low-energy particles; for example, February 23 and No. 11 (May 4, 1960).

These features may be explained by propagation effects and are discussed in Section 11-10.

11-9 COMPOSITION

Protons are the most abundant component of the energetic solar particles; but the application of nuclear emulsion techniques to the solar cosmic-ray problem has now shown the existence of both alpha-particles and heavier nuclei from solar flares. Ney and Stein (20) and Freier and Biswas (21) have measured alpha-particles at Fort Churchill, Manitoba, and Minneapolis, accompanying the protons. As pointed out by Ney, the heavier Z component can be resolved best when "normal" geomagnetic cutoffs are operative, for the proton flux is then greatly reduced compared to the alphas. The spectral cutoff is limited for both components by the minimum Störmer magnetic rigidity and not by atmospheric range. The alpha-particle-to-proton ratio is found to vary between 1:1 and 1:30 in different events, reflecting possible propagation differences.

TABLE 11-1
Solar Cosmic-Ray Energy Spectra

Event No.	Flare Date, Time UT	Spectra Measurement Date, Time UT	T, hr	$N(>E) = CE^{-\gamma}$ (Mev) Equ. of Spectra		Literature Source	Notes
				C	γ		
1	March 23, 1958 0950	March 26—1300–1800	78	7.2×10^5	2.7	(a) (c)	Flare assignment tentative; first PCA on 25 March at time of SC, indicating cosmic rays contained in magnetic solar cloud; spectra from nuclear emulsions at Minneapolis
2	August 22, 1958 1417	August 23—0500	15	8.0×10^7	4	(b)	Spectra from counters on ascent at Fort Churchill
3	May 10, 1959 2055	May 12—0500	32	2.5×10^9	6	(c) (d)	Spectra from counters on ascent; emulsions give $\gamma = 5$ as average
4	July 10, 1959 0210	July 11—1800–1600	30 to 38 av. 34	—	—	(e)	Spectra falls off at low energies; not a simple power law; exponential fit is good; see Figure 11-25
5	July 14, 1959	July 15—1030	31	1.1×10^8	2.9	(f)	Spectra from counters on ascent; approximate agreement with emulsions averaged from 0900–1430 UT, July 15
6	July 16, 1959 2114					(f)	Produced sea-level effect
7	April 1, 1960 0843	April 1—0945	1		2.4	(g) (h) (i)	Spectrum from balloon and satellite counters—measured simultaneously

8	April 5, 1960	April 5–6			(h) (i)	Spectrum probably similar to (7); seen only by satellite and space probe
9	April 28, 1960 0130				(g)	Spectra not measured for these events
10	April 29, 1960 0107				(g)	Spectra not measured for these events
11	May 4, 1960 1020	May 4—1700–2500	7 to 15 av. 11	—	(j)	Not a power law spectrum; has exponential form
12	September 3, 1960 0040	September 3—1400	13	—	(k) (l)	Region 10E, 100 Mev from rocket; 100E, 300 balloons at two latitudes
13	November 12, 1960 1322	November 13—2000	31		(m)	Emulsion spectra; short balloon exposure
14	November 15, 1960					

Literature Source:

(a) Reference 3
(b) Reference 7
(c) Protons from the Sun on May 12, 1959, E. P. Ney, J. R. Winckler, and P. S. Freier, *Phys. Rev. Letters*, **3**, 183–185, 1959
(d) Reference 1
(e) P. S. Freier and E. P. Ney (private communication)
(f) Reference 18
(g) Reference 25
(h) Reference 26
(i) Reference 23
(j) Reference 10
(k) Delayed Propagation of Solar Cosmic Rays on September 3, 1960, J. R. Winckler, P. D. Bhavsar, A. J. Masley, and T. C. May, *Phys. Rev. Lett.*, **6**, 488–491, 1961
(l) Reference 22
(m) Solar Cosmic Rays in November 1960, E. P. Ney and W. Stein, *J. Geophys. Research*, **66**, 8, 2550, 1961

TABLE 11-2

Relative Abundances

	P	Be, B	C	N	O
Galactic cosmic rays (same rigidity interval)	2.6×10^3	5	10	5	6
Sun	20×10^3	10^{-5}	10	2	18
Solar cosmic rays (same rigidity interval)	$(2.6 \text{ to } 50) \times 10^3$	0.5	10	6	19

Because for the same rigidity the range of the particles in the atmosphere decreases rapidly with increasing Z, the detection of $Z > 2$ nuclei was made possible by nuclear emulsions recovered from sounding rockets at Fort Churchill by Davis, Fichtel, Guss, and Ogilvie (22) for the events of September 3, 1960, and November 12 to 15, 1960. Relative values of the higher Z components from these measurements are summarized in Table 11-2 and are compared with galactic cosmic rays and solar photospheric abundances (normalized to carbon). The solar beams tend to be rich in protons but deficient, as expected, in Be or B compared to the galactic spectrum. The relative intensities and spectra of the protons compared to the heavy nuclei may provide clues to the mechanisms of acceleration and propagation in the flare processes because of the differing charge to mass ratio. So far no energetic electrons have been directly observed from solar flares.

11-10 TIME VARIATIONS IN SPACE

A solar cosmic-ray detector located at high geomagnetic latitude and high altitude, or outside the geomagnetic field completely, will exhibit time variations of intensity characteristic of the solar particle streams in space. A detector at intermediate latitudes frequently shows in addition much more complex variations associated with rapid changes in the Störmer rigidity cutoff during magnetic storms. Such variations were discussed earlier in this chapter.

An example of the time changes in the free-space spectrum during a solar-flare, cosmic-ray event originating on the extreme east limb of the sun is shown in Figure 11-23. The spectrum has been determined from Geiger counters on balloons at two latitudes, using the geomagnetic effect, and from rocket observations at high latitude. The slow growth of the low-energy particle flux is typical of many

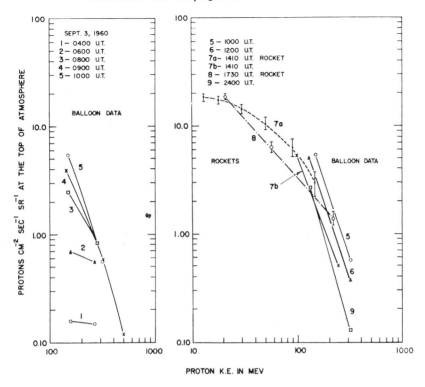

Figure 11-23 Integral energy spectra of solar protons for the event on September 3, 1960. Note that the spectrum begins flat (No. 1), increases in steepness, and then dies away. The low-energy particles are increasing when the high-energy part is decreasing. This event originated in a flare on the solar east limb. For a detector with a definite energy cutoff the rate as a function of time would be the value of the curves along a vertical cut.

events. It was observed that 14 hr after the flare, in the region of 10 to 50 Mev, the intensity was rising at a time when the bev rigidity particles detected at sea level were well into the decay mode. The flare (which was also observed to emit white light) is shown in Figure 11-24, photographed by the red hydrogen emission H_α.

A counter with an energy threshold E_{min} will furnish a certain characteristic time variation given by the integral spectrum N $(>E)$ which, for example, may be derived from Figure 11-23 by taking a vertical cut. A series of such time-variation curves is shown in Figure 11-25 for the 14 selected events. This figure is an estimate of the changes in the integral intensity above 100 Mev as a function of time from the start of the flares. The black points are the times at which

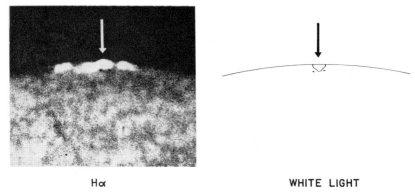

Hα   WHITE LIGHT

0105:00 U.T.

WHITE LIGHT FLARE

Figure 11-24   The east limb flare of September 3, 1960, viewed in the light of H_α (*left*) and as seen in white light (*right*). This flare produced a weak response even at sea level, which is unusual for a flare in the eastern solar hemisphere. It was probably a large event. (Photograph courtesy of Dr. Gail Moreton, Lockheed Solar Observatory.)

the various spectra shown earlier in Figure 11-22 are measured. The curves of Figure 11-25 have been normalized at 100 Mev, using these spectra. In some cases the integral intensity at 100 Mev is not known within a few hours of the flare; but decays in a regular fashion at later times, for example, February 23, 1956. Observations back to within 1 hr of the time of the flare for cases 7 and 11 show a continual decay, following approximately the power law $I = I_0 T^{-2}$, where I_0 is the intensity at 1 hr from the flare and T is the time in hours.

A number of cases show striking delays in which the intensity rises to a maximum 10 to 15 hr after the flare and then drops away. On the other hand, the most rapidly rising event of the 14 studied in the 100-Mev range was detected by a balloon flown by K. A. Anderson (7) at Fort Churchill in 1958. Protons of 100-Mev energy arrived at the earth with the direct transit time of about 20 min from a central meridian flare, but no effect was detected above 1.2 bev rigidity whether by a simultaneous balloon at Minneapolis or by sea-level monitors.

In late March and early April 1960 an active region developed on the visible solar disk and produced a series of flares, solar cosmic-ray events, and a large geomagnetic storm. Although the solar cosmic rays had only moderate intensity, the events were documented by many techniques which provided an excellent study of the energies and time histories of the flare particles. The observations were as follows:

1. The ion chamber and Geiger counter on the deep space probe Pioneer V showed the presence of solar cosmic rays from many flares from March 27 to April 9. The largest events occurred on April 1 and April 5 (23). The April 1 event was also detected by the coincidence counter telescope on Pioneer V (24). The ionization and counting rates are shown in Figure 11-26. Before and after this period only galactic cosmic rays were detected. Pioneer V was about 5×10^6 km from earth at the time of the events. Note that the two major events showed a slow decay requiring many days, but only the April 1 event

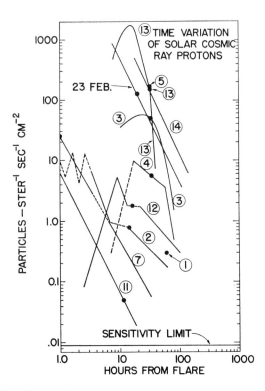

Figure 11-25 The time variations of a series of events for particles above 100-Mev energy. The black dots represent the time at which spectra given in Figure 11-22 were measured. In many cases the values at early times after the flare by direct measurement are not available.

showed a fast rise (see Figure 11-25, curve No. 7, for the April 1 event).

2. Balloon flights at Minneapolis (geomagnetic latitude 55°N) over the period detected the solar cosmic-ray event on April 1 and gave spectral information to about 300-Mev energy (25).

3. The earth satellite Explorer VII detected the solar cosmic rays on April 1 and April 5 at high latitude over North America (26). The Pioneer V, Explorer VII, and balloon results together have given the composite spectrum shown as No. 7, Figure 11-22.

4. Sea-level neutron monitors did not detect the solar cosmic rays in these cases but showed that a large decrease (Forbush type) occurred in the galactic background. This change in background at the beginning of the magnetic storm was also detected by the Pioneer V instruments and the balloon flight series (see Figure 11-26).

5. The magnetometer on Pioneer V showed surprisingly large magnetic clouds in interplanetary space, with field strengths of 50-γ peak (27). The appearance of the magnetic fields corresponded exactly in time with the Forbush decrease and showed that the galactic cosmic rays were partly swept away by the solar plasma stream and its "frozen in" magnetic field (see Figure 11-27).

6. Polar ionosondes showed decreases in F-Min, or complete blackouts that correspond in great detail to the ion chamber increases on Pioneer V, and that both techniques were detecting the separate beams of solar protons from each flare event [see Figure 11-27 (28)]. Since the ionosonde observations were made at Thule near the geomagnetic pole, one would expect the geomagnetic cutoff energy to be small and the ionosonde observations to be a measure of the low-energy, solar cosmic-ray flux in interplanetary space.

The combination of polar ionosonde and Pioneer V data may be interpreted to show the effect of successive magnetic plasma clouds on the flare particles. The arrival of the clouds is identified by the sudden magnetic storm commencements on earth. Visualize a cloud produced on March 28 or 29 that carried out magnetic lines of force rooted in the flare region. The solar cosmic rays produced on March 30 in the same region (see Figures 11-26 and 11-27) were trapped temporarily in this cloud. To reach the vicinity of earth and to produce the slow rise seen on Pioneer V instruments on that date, the particles had to "leak out" of this cloud. The March 30 flare produced its own magnetic cloud, a further large magnetic storm, and the Forbush event mentioned earlier on April 1 at 0307 UT. The largest solar cosmic-ray event of the series occurred on April 1 at 1935 UT.

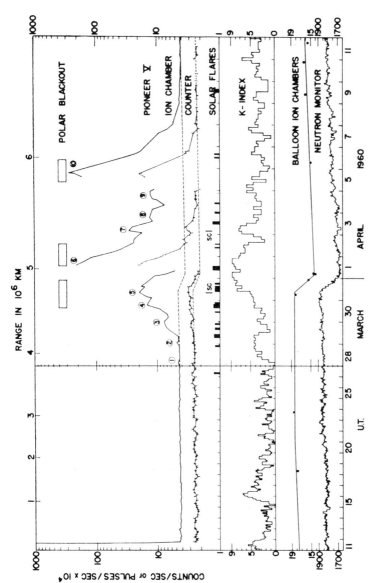

Figure 11-26 *Upper section:* the ionization rate and counting rate in the Pioneer V deep space probe as it proceeded out from the earth during March and April 1960. Major solar flares are shown by short vertical bars. Also shown in lower sections are the K index of magnetic activity, galactic cosmic rays as measured by balloon-borne ionization chambers at Minneapolis, and (*bottom*) the Deep River, Ontario, Canada, neutron monitor. (Courtesy of Hugh Carmichael.)

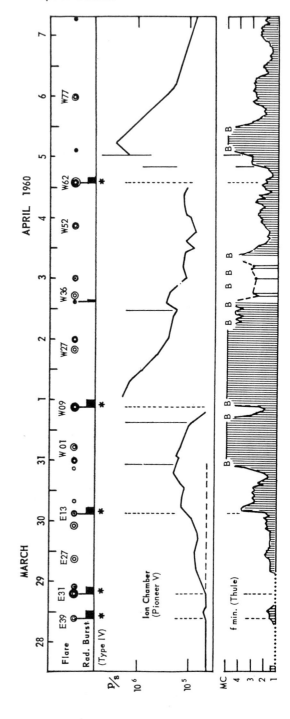

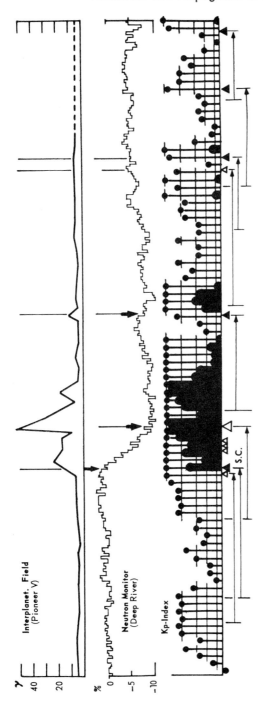

Figure 11-27 Correlation of solar, terrestrial, and interplanetary observations during the March-April period of solar activity in 1960. (*Top to bottom*) Flare and radio burst data, particularly Type IV (asterisks), the ionization rate on the deep space probe Pioneer V attributed to solar cosmic rays, the ionospheric response over the polar region at Thule, the interplanetary magnetic field measured by Pioneer V, the Deep River neutron monitor, and (*bottom*) the magnetic K indices and indications of the sudden commencements of magnetic storms. Note the close correlations between the increases in ionization seen in Pioneer V and the increase in F minimum for the ionosondes at Thule, suggesting that the particle streams detected by Pioneer V are the same ones incident on the polar ionosphere. Also note the good correlation between the appearance of the interplanetary field up to 50 gammas in Pioneer V and the incidence of the Forbush decrease of galactic cosmic rays. (Courtesy of T. Obayashi.)

These cosmic rays arrived rapidly, and with greater intensity than in the preceding events, in the channel produced by the March 30 cloud which had previously enveloped the earth. On April 5 there was a considerable delay in solar cosmic-ray arrival, presumably because of intermediate plasma clouds resembling the situation on March 30. These processes are shown schematically in Figure 11-28.

Solar cosmic-ray outbursts on November 12, 1960, and again on November 15, 1960, have attracted wide interest (1) because the relativistic particle content was detected throughout the world by ground-level, cosmic-ray monitors, (2) because of balloon, rocket, and satellite measurements, and (3) because of clear evidence of a dominant role played by solar-ejected magnetic fields in guiding the solar cosmic rays in interplanetary space.

The typical time variation for the first event seen at ground level at fairly high latitude is shown in Figure 11-29a. This plot shows a neutron monitor, sensitive to particles of 1-bev rigidity and a meson counter not sensitive below 10 bev (29, 33). The cosmic-ray flare occurred at 1322 UT and was followed within 10 min by the solar cosmic-ray increase. The peak intensity was reached in about 3 hr, and then the decline began. A further increase occurred at 1900 UT and reached a peak at 2000 UT, when the final decay phase began.

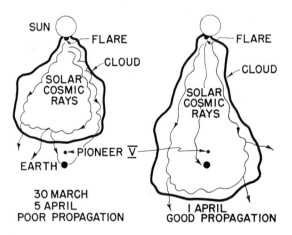

Figure 11-28 Artist's conception of a magnetic cloud arising from a solar flare and influencing the propagation of solar cosmic rays from a further flare. On March 30 and April 5, 1960, the cloud would impede the propagation of particles from the sun to earth. However, on April 1, with Pioneer V and the earth located inside the cloud, good propagation and rapid passage of the particles from the sun to the earth would be expected.

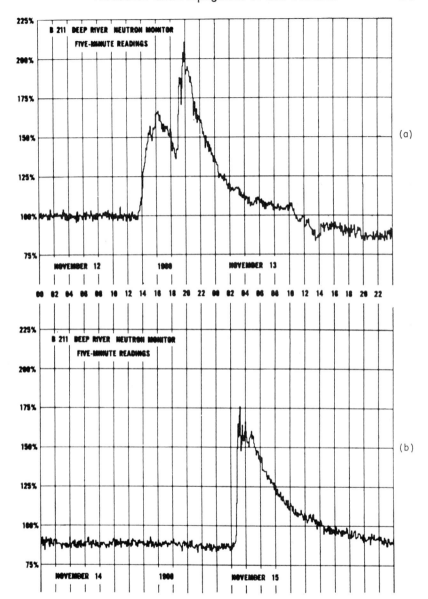

Figure 11-29 Neutron monitor record of the cosmic-ray increase on November 12, 1960(a) and on November 15, 1960(b). [Deep River Neutron Monitor, courtesy of Hugh Carmichael (34).] The double peak in (a) is evidence for the containment of the solar cosmic rays in a magnetic cloud produced by a previous flare. Note in (b) the rapid rise to maximum intensity and the smooth decay.

It is known that the second increase at 1900 UT was not associated with another flare on the sun. Furthermore, the meson detector, sensitive only to galactic particles, showed a decrease at the time the neutron monitor showed a second increase. We must conclude that a magnetic shock front or "bottle" spread out from the sun and enveloped the earth at 1900 UT on November 12. It probably originated in an earlier large flare in the same sunspot group at 0300 UT on November 11 and required 40 hr for transit. The big cosmic-ray-producing flare on November 12 then injected its particles into this already formed bottle. A large flux of particles was contained in the bottle and reached the earth only when the bottle arrived. The arrival was signaled by a drop in galactic cosmic rays and the sudden commencement of a magnetic storm at 1900 UT on November 12. The initial cosmic-ray increase directly following the flare is probably caused by particles leaking through or channeled around the bottle to the earth, inasmuch as the long rise time of several hours to maximum intensity is many times the direct transit time, which is about 10 min for the particles detected at sea level. Figure 11-30, left diagram, is a concept of the interplanetary fields at 1322 UT on November 12, which shows the earth just outside the bottle (29).

The second cosmic-ray flare on November 15, 1960, at 0207 UT, produced a fast rise in the counting rate of neutron monitors (29). At this time the earth was presumed to be already inside a bottle caused by the cosmic-ray flare on November 12 and was therefore well connected to the new source in the flare. The neutron monitor record for November 15 is shown in Figure 11-29b and the interplanetary conditions, in Figure 11-30, right diagram.

These events in November 1960 had the highest particle fluxes measured during the present solar cycle, and considerable data were obtained during the period with balloons, rockets, and satellites. At high latitude measurements by several methods showed that the bottle on November 12 contained a spectrum rich in low-energy particles compared with the initial increase. Furthermore, the low-energy portion of the particle spectrum from 10 to 100 Mev continued to increase until at least 1600 UT on November 13, when the relativistic particles detected at ground level had returned almost to normal (30). The time history of the spectrum of particles below 500-Mev energy follows a behavior very similar to the September 3, 1960, event shown in Figure 4-23. Thus it is impossible to give a unique spectrum for the event.

A portion of the time history of the integral flux above 100 Mev is given in Figure 11-25, curve 13. The spectrum determined from

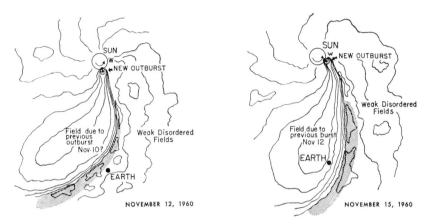

Figure 11-30   Artist's conception of the general shape of the ejected solar cloud and its magnetic lines of force on November 12 and November 15, 1960, which possibly accounts for the propagation features of cosmic rays on those two occasions (34).

nuclear emulsions on a balloon at 2000 UT on November 13 is given in Figure 11-22, curve 13. These results were obtained at Minneapolis but are nevertheless valid to the air cutoff energy of 80 Mev, since a strong magnetic storm was in progress and the Störmer cutoffs were below this value.

Rocket measurements at Fort Churchill near a time of peak intensity showed a flux of particles above 10 Mev of about 10^5/cm²/sec (31). This value and a somewhat more intense case on November 16, following the second November flare, represent the highest directly measured fluxes of energetic solar particles on record. The time integral over the period November 12 to 16, 1960, obtained from the satellite Explorer VII (32), is about 2×10^9 particles/cm² greater than 40-Mev energy. Using equation (11-11), we find that the total dosage represented by a spatially isotropic flux of this value is about 700 rad.

The combination of solar events which led to the efficient trapping of particles from the November 12 flare is uncommon. Only a few such cases exist in the 45 known solar cosmic-ray accelerations.

11-11   THE GUIDING OF RELATIVISTIC SOLAR PARTICLES

Fourteen cases are now on record in the last two solar cycles in which solar flares have produced effects at ground level (33). The

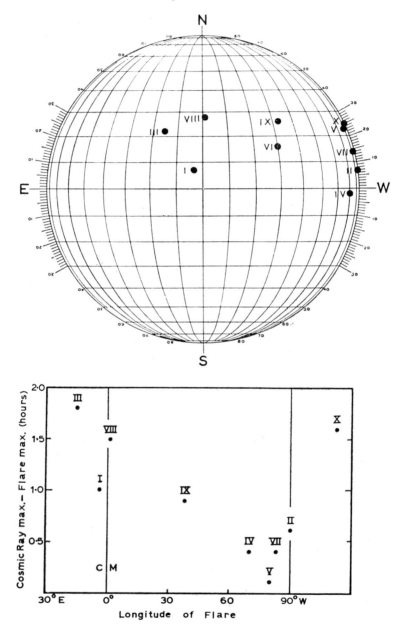

Figure 11-31   (*Top*). Heliographic coordinates of a series of energetic cosmic-ray flares. (*Below*). Estimates of delay time of the arrival of cosmic ray particles. (From M. A. Ellison, Dunsink Observatory Publications, Vol. I, No. 3 preprint, "Cosmic Ray Flares." This information was also presented at I.A.U. Conference, Berkeley, California, August 1961.)

particles therefore have energies greater than 1 bev and perhaps reach 20 bev on rare occasions.

The largest of these events was the great west-quadrant flare of February 23, 1956, which has been widely studied, particularly by J. A. Simpson and collaborators. In these studies it was shown how the flare particles could be used to infer the state of the interplanetary medium. Since much has been published concerning this event (34), it will not be discussed here.

If the heliograph coordinates of the flares (Figure 11-31) are plotted, the striking fact that they are predominately in the western hemisphere will emerge. Since the distribution of all large flares visually observed is uniform over the solar disk, it must be concluded that the relativistic particles tend to be guided along a magnetic field which sweeps backward and outward from the sun's rotational sense in the manner of a pinwheel or rotating garden hose. Such a curve in space was pictured long ago to account for the properties of solar beams resulting in magnetic storms (35). The delay times for west-limb particles also tend to be shorter, suggesting a more direct propagation as shown in the lower section of Figure 11-31.

Confirmation of the above concept has been obtained by K. G. McCracken by examining the counting rates of neutron monitors arranged according to the directions of the asymptotic trajectories leading into free space from the various locations (36). In Figure 11-32 the percentage enhancement early in a cosmic-ray flare on May 4, 1960, is indicated inside the circles that locate the asymptotic directions of the respective neutron monitors on a celestial map. An axis of symmetry may be found so that the intensities drop off uniformly as the angle to this axis is increased (in any direction about the axis). The axis of symmetry is found to be about 50 degrees west of the sun-earth line (see Figure 11-33). The particles appear to be spiraling about this direction with a certain pitch-angle distribution, probably determined by inhomogeneities in the field.

The relativistic particles are sensitive to fields with a scale size larger than the radii of curvature, or about 1/50 AU [from equation (11-5)]. The nonrelativistic particles, however, may follow the lines of force on a much smaller scale, travel across regions like Figure 11-33, and proceed more or less radially out from the sun like the low-energy plasma, thus reaching the earth preferentially from the center of the visible disk. This behavior provides a natural energy selector which would have the result that, even if every flare basically had the same production spectrum, the energy spectrum would be a function of solar longitude; that is, west-limb flares would be enriched

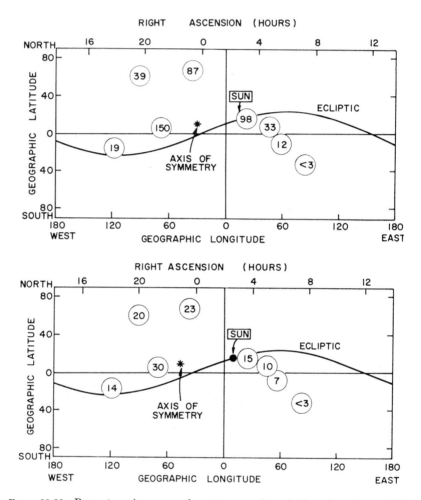

Figure 11-32 Percentage increases of neutron monitors indicated at the position of the asymptotic direction in space on a celestial map. (Courtesy of K. McCracken, Proceedings of the Kyoto Conference, September 1961, University of Tokyo, Bunkyo-ku, Tokyo, Japan.)

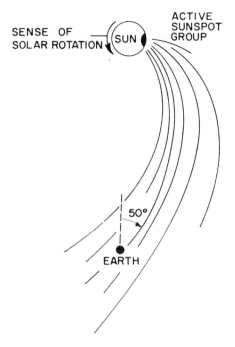

Figure 11-33 Conception of the average guiding field effective for bev and higher rigidity particles traveling from the sun to the earth. (Courtesy of K. Mc-Cracken, Proceedings of Kyoto Conference, September 1961, University of Tokyo, Bunkyo-ku, Tokyo, Japan.)

in relativistic particles compared to central flares. There is some evidence in the spectra shown in Figure 11-22 that such is indeed the case.

11-12 SUMMARY

In this chapter we have discussed the characteristics of solar flares associated with the production of energetic particles and the various methods of measuring these particles near the earth: balloons, earth satellites, the ionosphere, and ground-level monitors. The time variations both in free space and inside the magnetic field of the earth have been described, and the spectra of the particles and their time variations, discussed. It has been shown how information may be deduced, from the detailed measurements of the particles, about the energetic processes of the flares themselves, about the magnetic condition of interplanetary space, and about the earth's magnetic field and its changes during magnetic storms. Since the approach has been empirical, we have not discussed theories that are available concerning the interplanetary medium and the magnetic environment of the earth. In time, when more measurements of this type become available and the theories are developed further, it may be possible to delineate the theoretical ideas on the basis of the energetic solar-particle measurements.

REFERENCES

1. Winckler, J. R., and P. D. Bhavsar, Low Energy Solar Cosmic Rays and the Geomagnetic Storm of May 12, 1959, *J. Geophys. Res.*, **65**, 2637–2655 (1960).
2. Winckler, J. R., Balloon Study of High Altitude Radiations during the International Geophysical Year, *J. Geophys. Res.*, **65**, 1331–1359 (1960).
3. Freier, P. S., E. P. Ney, and J. R. Winckler, Balloon Observation of Solar Cosmic Rays on March 26, 1958, *J. Geophys. Res.*, **64**, 685–688 (1959).
4. Reid, G. C., and C. Collins, Observations of Abnormal VHF Radio Wave Absorption at Medium and High Latitudes, *J. Atm. Terr. Phys.*, **14**, 1 and 2, 63–81 (1959).
5. Bailey, D. K., Abnormal Ionization in the Lower Ionosphere Associated with Cosmic-Ray Flux Enhancements, *Proc. IRE*, **47**, 2, 255–267 (1959).
6. Leinbach, H., and G. C. Reid, Ionization of the Upper Atmosphere by Cosmic Rays of Solar Origin, *Phys. Rev. Letters*, **2**, 2, 61–63 (January 15, 1959). See also, G. C. Reid and H. Leinbach, Low Energy Cosmic Ray Events Associated with Solar Flares, *J. Geophys. Res.*, **64**, 1801–1805 (1959).
7. Anderson, K. A., R. Arnoldy, R. Hoffman, L. Peterson, and J. R. Winckler, Observations of Low-energy Solar Cosmic Rays from the Flare of 22 August 1958, *J. Geophys. Res.*, **64**, 9, 1133–1147 (1959).
8. McCracken, K. G., and R. A. R. Palmeira, Comparison of Solar Cosmic Ray Injection including July 17, 1959 and May 4, 1960, *J. Geophys. Res.*, **65**, 2673–2683 (1960).
9. Simpson, J. A., Cosmic-Radiation Neutron Intensity Monitor, *Ann. Intern. Geophys. Yr.*, IV, IV–VII, 351–373, 1957.
10. Winckler, J. R., A. J. Masley, and T. C. May, The High-Energy Cosmic Ray Flare of May 4, 1960. Part 1. High Altitude Ionization and Counter Measurements. Part 2. The Emulsion Measurements, P. S. Freier and S. Biswas, *J. Geophys. Res.*, **66**, 1023–1033 (1961).
11. Dodson, Helen W., reported to the International Astronomical Union, Berkeley, California, August 1961.
12. Haddock, F. T., Introduction to Radio Astronomy, *Proc. IRE*, **46**, 1, 3–12 (1958).
13. Notuki, Hatanka, and Unno, *Publ. Astron. Soc., Japan*, **8**, 52 (1956).
14. Morton, Dr. Gale, Lockheed Solar Observatory, Burbank, California, private communication.
15. Carrington, *Geomagnetism*, p. 334, quoted by Carl Störmer in *The Polar Aurora*, Oxford at the Clarendon Press, 1955, pp. 205–206.

16. Quenby, J. J., and G. J. Wenk, Tables of Cosmic Ray Threshold Rigidities, preprint, Imperial College of Science and Technology, London (1962).

17. Obayashi, Tatsuzo, and Yukio Hakura, Enhanced Ionization in the Polar Ionosphere Caused by Solar Corpuscular Emissions, *J. Radio Res. Lab.*, **7**, 29, 27–66 (1960).

18. Winckler, J. R., P. D. Bhavsar, and L. E. Peterson, The Time Variations of Solar Cosmic Rays during July 1959 at Minneapolis, *J. Geophys. Res.*, **66**, 995–1022 (1961).

19. Kellogg, P. J., and J. R. Winckler, Cosmic Ray Evidence for a Ring Current, *J. Geophys. Res.*, **66**, 12, 3991–4001 (1961).

20. Ney, E. P., and W. Stein, Solar Protons in November 1960, Proceedings of the International Conference on Cosmic Rays and the Earth Storm, Kyoto, September 1961, **17**, 345–353 (1962).

21. Freier, P. S., S. Biswas, and W. Stein, Solar Protons and α-Particles from the September 3, 1960, Flare, *J. Geophys. Res.*, **67**, 13–24 (1962).

22. Davis, L. R., C. E. Fichtel, D. E. Guss, and K. W. Ogilvie, Rocket Observations of Solar Protons on September 3, 1960, *Phys. Rev. Letters*, **6**, 492–495 (1961). Also available in NASA publication entitled Goddard Space Flight Center Contributions to 1961 Kyoto Conference on Cosmic Rays and the Earth Storm. See also C. E. Fichtel and D. E. Guss, Heavy Nuclei in Solar Cosmic Rays, in the same NASA publication.

23. Arnoldy, R. L., R. A. Hoffman, and J. R. Winckler, Solar Cosmic Rays and Soft Radiation Observed at 5,000,000 Kilometers from Earth, *J. Geophys. Res.*, **65**, 3004–3007 (1960).

24. Fan, C. Y., P. Meyer, and J. A. Simpson, Preliminary Results from the Space Probe Pioneer V, *J. Geophys. Res.*, **65**, 1862–1863 (1960).

25. Masley, Andrew J., Analysis of Balloon Observations during the April 1960 Solar Cosmic Ray Events, Tech. Rept. No. 35, Cosmic Ray Group, University of Minnesota, Minneapolis 14, Minnesota, March 1961.

26. Van Allen, James A., and Wei Ching Lin, Outer Radiation Belt and Solar Proton Observations with Explorer VII during March–April 1960, *J. Geophys. Res.*, **65**, 2998–3004 (1960).

27. Coleman, P. J., Jr., C. P. Sonett, D. L. Judge, and E. J. Smith, Some Preliminary Results of the Pioneer V Magnetometer Experiment, *J. Geophys. Res.*, **65**, 1856–1858 (1960).

28. Obayashi, T., Kyoto University, Kyoto, Japan, private communication.

29. Steljes, J. F., H. Carmichael, and K. G. McCracken, *J. Geophys. Res.*, **66**, 1363 (1961).

30. Obayashi, T., Résumé of the Conference on the Solar-Terrestrial Events of November 1960, Research Paper No. 14, Arctic Institute of North America, Washington 5, D. C., June 1, 1961.

31. Ogilvie, K. W., D. A. Bryant, and L. R. Davis, Rocket Observations of Solar Protons during the November 1, 1960 Event, NASA, Goddard Space Flight Center Contributions to 1961 Kyoto Conference on Cosmic Rays and the Earth Storm.

32. Lin, Wei Ching, Observation of Galactic and Solar Cosmic Rays from October 31, 1959, to February 17, 1961, with Explorer VII, Tech. Rept., Dept. of Physics and Astronomy, State University of Iowa, August 1961.

33. Carmichael, H., and J. F. Steljes, Review of Recent High Energy Solar Particle Events including November 1960, CRGP-1056, Deep River Labo-

ratory, Deep River, Ontario, October 1961. See also Proceedings of the International Conference on Cosmic Rays and the Earth Storm, Kyoto, September 1961, **17**, 337–344 (1962).
34. Meyer, P., E. N. Parker, and J. A. Simpson, Solar Cosmic Rays of February 1956 and their Propagation through Interplanetary Space, *Phys. Rev.*, **104**, 768–783 (November 1956). See also in *Science in Space*, ed. Lloyd V. Berkner and Hugh Odishaw, The Acceleration and Propagation of Particles within the Solar System, J. A. Simpson, 239 ff., McGraw-Hill, New York, 1961.
35. Chapman, Sydney, and Julius Bartel, *Geomagnetism*, Vol. II, Oxford University Press, London, 1951, p. 806.
36. McCracken, K. G., The Cosmic Ray Flare Effect, Part I: Some New Methods of Analysis, *J. Geophys. Res.*, **67**, 423–434 (1962). Also available in Proceedings of the International Conference on Cosmic Rays and the Earth Storm, Kyoto, September 1961, **17**, 310–314, with A. Fréon, 455–456 (1962).

GENERAL REFERENCES

ARTICLES, TECHNICAL REPORTS and CONFERENCE PROCEEDINGS

Rich, M., and R. Madey, Range-Energy Tables, UCRL-2301, Radiation Laboratory, University of California, Berkeley, California (March 1954).
Dodson, Helen W., Studies at the McMath-Hulbert Observatory of Radio Frequency Radiation at the Time of Solar Flares, *Proc. IRE,* **46**, 1, 149–159 (January 1958).
International Union of Geodesy and Geophysics, Symposium on the July 1959 Events and Associated Phenomena, Helsinki, July 1960, printed by L'Institut Geographique National, Paris.
Webber, W. R., Time Variations of Low Rigidity Cosmic Rays during the Recent Sunspot Cycle, preprint, Imperial College of Science and Technology, London (November 1960).
Obayashi, T., Resume of the Conference on the Solar Terrestrial Events of November 1960, Research Paper No. 14, Arctic Institute of North America, June 1961. Conference held at Air Force Cambridge Research Laboratories, Hanscom Field, Bedford, Massachusetts.
Proceedings of the International Conference on Cosmic Rays and the Earth Storm, Kyoto, Japan, September 4–15, 1961, published by Physical Society of Japan, **17** (1962).
Winckler, J. R., Primary Cosmic Rays, *Radiation Res.,* **14**, 521–539 (1961).
Winckler, J. R., T. C. May, and A. J. Masley, Observation of Solar Bremsstralung Burst of 1926 UT, August 11, 1960, *J. Geophys. Res.,* **66**, 316–320 (1961).

BOOKS

Chapman, S., and J. Bartels, *Geomagnetism*, Vols. I and II, Oxford University Press, London, 1951.
Rossi, B., *High Energy Particles,* Prentice-Hall, New York, 1952.
Dorman, L. I., *Cosmic Ray Variations* (Variatsii Kosmicheskikh Luckey), State Publishing House for Technical and Theoretical Literature, Moscow 1957,

prepared by Technical Documents Liaison Office, Wright-Patterson Air Force Base, Ohio.

Bijl, Hilde, *Space Research,* North Holland, Amsterdam, 1960.

Berkner, Lloyd V., and Hugh Odishaw, eds., *Science in Space,* McGraw-Hill, New York, 1961.

Proceedings of I. R. E., **46**, 1, Radio Astronomy Issue (January 1958).

Proceedings of I. R. E., **47**, 2, Ionosphere-IGY Issue (February 1959).

Kuiper, G., *The Sun,* The Solar System, 1, University of Chicago Press, Chicago, 1958.

CHAPTER 12

THEORETICAL AND
EXPERIMENTAL ASPECTS
OF COSMIC RAYS

LEVERETT DAVIS, JR.

California Institute of Technology

Space science did not begin with Sputnik I or even with the V-2.
The astronomers feel that they have been studying this subject for
hundreds, if not thousands, of years. Some aspects of it have also
been studied by physicists and geophysicists. But in the last decade
new and very different techniques have become available, and new
and very different aspects of the subject will, in the next decades, be
extensively and fruitfully investigated. This will require the collaboration of workers in the different disciplines and a synthesis of
information obtained by many methods. Cosmic-ray physics provides an interesting and somewhat older example of the way in which
an unconventional technique from an apparently extraneous discipline
will allow us to study the properties of the space about us. The investigation of the conductivity of gas in closed chambers seems an
unlikely way to get information on the magnetic structure of our
Galaxy, but such investigations are where the subject of this chapter
began about 50 years ago and one of the outcomes has been this information. Since a historical review (1, 2) of the subject would be
too lengthy, let us jump at once to the present status of cosmic-ray
physics as applied to astronomy and space science. As with all other
active areas in science, there is a great deal that is definitely known

but many of the most interesting topics concern questions that are still to be answered.

Cosmic rays are high-energy particles and photons that come from outside the atmosphere. They are mainly atomic nuclei, indeed, mostly protons, moving with velocities close to that of light. Their kinetic energies range from the order of their rest mass energy, 10^9 ev for a proton, up to an occasional particle with 10^{19} ev, a fantastic energy for a single proton. Although concentrated in a single nucleon, these energies are really macroscopic, 10^9 ev being the energy acquired by a milligram in falling 1.6 μ in the earth's gravity and 10^{19} ev $= 1.6$ joule being the energy acquired by a kilogram in falling 16 cm. Cosmic rays may be classified into several categories. In a discussion such as this the unqualified term usually means the particles found in interstellar space, unmodified by passage through our atmosphere. More specifically, these particles are usually called primary or galactic (or interstellar) cosmic rays. In passing through the atmosphere, each primary cosmic ray produces many more secondary cosmic rays. In addition to ordinary nuclei, they include electrons, photons, mesons, and other exotic and unstable particles. At one time the main emphasis in cosmic-ray physics was the discovery and study of these fundamental particles, but more recently these studies have been carried on principally with the big accelerators. Such work is important in fundamental particle physics, but it will not concern us further. Occasionally, associated with a flare on the sun, a transient —but sometimes intense—burst of energetic particles is observed that clearly originates from the sun; these are often called solar cosmic rays. Since they were the subject of Chapter 11, they will get little emphasis here.

12-1 OBSERVED CHARACTERISTICS OF COSMIC RAYS

Any discussion of the nature, origin, and astronomical importance of cosmic rays must start from a number of characteristics that are derived from observation. Without considering the details of the experimental procedures, it is convenient to survey the basic observational results. Some conclusions on the origin and astronomical role of cosmic rays are best included in this summary, but the most recent ideas and opinions will be reviewed in subsequent sections.

Energy density

The flux and energy density of cosmic rays can be determined from observations of the flux that reaches the ground and the ionization losses coming down through the atmosphere. If the effect of the geo-magnetic field is allowed for, the flux and energy density just outside this field, that is, in the solar system, may be found. The kinetic-energy density there in particles with kinetic energies greater than 1 bev/nucleon is very nearly 1 ev/cm³ $= 1.6 \times 10^{-12}$ erg/cm³. This is approximately the energy density of starlight outside the solar system. The kinetic energy flux of cosmic rays is of the order of 10^{-2} erg/cm²/sec or 10 watts/km². The energy flux in starlight is about the same; that due to sunlight is 10^8 times as great at the earth. Thus, if the cosmic rays were to originate at the sun and were to decrease in intensity with the square of the distance from the sun, only a negligible fraction of the solar power would be needed to produce the cosmic rays we observe, and they could be a trivial by-product of some minor process. On the other hand, if they fill up the space between the stars uniformly to the density we observe, it would appear that cosmic rays are about as important as starlight and that the galaxy must somehow produce as much cosmic-ray energy as starlight. But stars can keep on producing starlight for billions of years only by using nuclear energy. They must convert a substantial fraction of their hydrogen into heavier elements. Thus if the galaxy is full of cosmic rays, it appears at first that they must come from some process that involves as much energy as stellar evolution and the production of starlight. This is about as preposterous as the assertion that half of the energy of a bonfire should come off as heat and half as X rays.

Isotropy

If we look at the sky on a clear night, we observe that much more starlight comes from the plane of the Milky Way than from other directions. Cosmic rays, on the other hand, show no such anisotropy. This can be studied by observing as a function of time the flux of cosmic rays arriving at detectors at various places on earth. The earth shields out all cosmic rays that might come from directions below the horizon, and atmospheric absorption discriminates rather strongly against cosmic rays that do not come in from fairly near the zenith. Thus any particular cosmic-ray detector at the surface of the earth looks out mainly along the vertical, and as the earth rotates the direction from which it receives the cosmic-ray flux sweeps across the sky. Since, ordinarily, there is no difference not due to atmospheric effects between day and night, it has long been realized that most cosmic rays do not come from the sun. Since there is no detectable difference between times when the Milky Way passes directly overhead and times when few stars lie on the vertical, it is clear that cosmic rays do not come to us in straight lines from the visible stars.

In actual practice such studies are greatly complicated by atmospheric and magnetic effects. The mass and absorption of the air over a detector are proportional to the barometric pressure at the detector and the vertical distribution of the air depends on the temperature distribution. The response of a detector to a given flux at the top of the atmosphere always depends on the barometric pressure and, for most detectors, to some extent on the temperature distribution. From studies of the correlation between detector response and meteorological data, and by averaging over long periods of time, it is possible to do quite a good job of correcting for these effects and to get measures of the anisotropy in which there is only a very small uncertainty. When observations made at various locations on the earth are compared, differences in cosmic-ray intensity are found. These depend not on the direction in space in which the detector looks but on its location in the geomagnetic field. This demonstrates that the cosmic rays are charged particles that are deflected in the earth's magnetic field. Near the geomagnetic poles particles of all energies can come in along the lines of force, but at the geomagnetic equator only protons whose energy is greater than 15 bev can cross the earth's field and reach the top of the atmosphere moving vertically. Thus the earth's field can be used as a magnetic spectrograph to investigate the energy dependence of cosmic rays in the low-energy range. High energies can be investigated by means of the extensive air showers discussed below.

A great deal of work has been done looking for variations of the cosmic-ray flux with time that are due to anisotropies in the primary flux and not just to variations in the atmosphere or in the interplanetary fields. Any anisotropy in the galactic cosmic rays will produce variations that have the period of a sidereal day, that is, in phase with the rotation with respect to the stars. Several authors have claimed to have found significant anisotropies or local sources, but further investigation has always made their claims appear dubious. Reviews by Elliot (3) and Greissen (4) give as the ratio of the amplitudes of such variations to the total flux in various energy ranges: 2×10^{-4} for the total cosmic radiation, 3×10^{-4} at energies of 10^{13} ev, about 3×10^{-3} at 10^{15} ev, and less than 0.1 at 10^{17} ev. In all cases the errors are large enough so that the true amplitude could be zero.

This isotropy and the high-energy density of cosmic rays can be explained by the assumption that cosmic rays are stored in some large region, which is often thought to be the galaxy. Until it was discovered that cosmic rays were deflected in the geomagnetic field, hence were charged particles, there were no known forces that would result in this storage. The interstellar medium is such a good conductor that there can be no electrostatic fields that would result in the storage of charged particles; but just because it is a good conductor it is easy for currents that produce magnetic fields to flow. These fields make the charged particles move in curved trajectories. Thus they do not escape in straight lines like starlight. If they wander back and forth for, say, 10^3 or 10^4 times as long as starlight before they escape, they will become isotropic, and the power supplied by the source need be only 10^{-3} or 10^{-4} that going into starlight.

Other variations have been observed in the cosmic-ray flux with periods or characteristic times that run from the order of a solar day to 11 years and with amplitudes that run from a few hundredths of a percent to a few percent. They are all the result of the sporadic production of cosmic rays by the sun, of atmospheric or geomagnetic effects that are not properly compensated for, or of the effects of magnetic fields embedded in moving gas in the solar system. Since these have no large-scale or "cosmic" significance, they can be ignored for our present purposes; but we shall return to them when considering the interplanetary magnetic fields where they are important. The fact that there are strong indications that the cosmic-ray flux has not varied much in its average value over long periods is of considerable significance in understanding the origin of cosmic rays. That the flux averaged over a thousand years or so has not changed much during the last 50,000 years is shown by the success of the C^{14} dating technique. C^{14} ages are obtained by comparing the ratio of radioactive C^{14} to ordinary C^{12} in the specimen with the ratio in the atmosphere. Any decrease of the ratio in the specimen is ascribed to decay of the C^{14} with its half-life of 5600 years during the time that elapsed since the specimen removed the C^{14} from the atmosphere. C^{14} is produced in the atmosphere by cosmic rays, and its level there will remain constant only if the cosmic-ray flux remains constant on the average. Investigations of the validity of the C^{14} dates indicate that there cannot have been much change in the cosmic-ray flux in the last 50,000 years. Similar investigations of the abundances of various isotopes in meteorites give some confidence that the average flux has not changed drastically over the last 10^9 years, although there can be no assurance that there have not been substantial short-period fluctuations.

Nuclear composition of cosmic rays

Nuclei of moderate cosmic-ray energies leave tracks in photographic emulsion from which the nuclei can be identified. If the emulsion is flown to high altitudes by balloons, or, better, with rockets, the nuclear composition of the primary cosmic rays can be determined. Cloud chambers and a variety of counters have also been used. Work along these lines has been in progress for more than a decade, and although at first there was considerable uncertainty in the identifications and the corrections to be made for the effect of the air above the point of observation the situation has recently been greatly improved. Table 12-1 summarizes the information (5) that is known with reasonable assurance. The first three columns identify the groups into which it is convenient to classify the nuclei. The fourth column gives the abundances in cosmic rays, counting all particles having more than about 3 bev total energy/nucleon. The last two columns give two different estimates of the astronomical, or cosmic, abundances, essentially the abundance in stars like the sun. The last column gives the estimates of Cameron (6), and the fifth column, those of Suess and Urey (7). The discrepancy between the two is not important for our purposes, but it does serve as a warning of the lack of precision in our knowledge of these things. Our knowledge of the cosmic-ray abundances is probably equally imprecise.

The most important information in this table is the fact that helium and heavier nuclei are present in cosmic rays. If there were only protons, which are rugged elementary particles, one could imagine that cosmic rays were produced by some kind of exotic nuclear explosion or the disintegration product of some unknown kind of par-

TABLE 12-1

Nuclear Abundances in Cosmic Rays and Astronomy

| | | | Relative Abundances | | |
Group	Z	Elements	CR	S + U	Cam
p	1	H	1000	1000	1000
α	2	He	60	80	150
L	3 to 5	Li, Be, B	1.1	$10^{-5.5}$	$10^{-5.2}$
M	6 to 9	C, N, O, F	3.8	0.79	1.5
H	10 to 19	Ne, Si, ...	1.3	0.28	0.14
VH	≥ 20	Ca, Fe, ...	0.5	0.017	0.007

ticle. But the heavier particles will break up if they are given a few Mev of internal energy. It seems inconceivable that any violent process that gave 10^{13} ev to a carbon nucleus would not give an energy spread among the nucleons of one part in 10^6. But in this case the carbon nucleus would break up. The difference between accelerating protons and heavier nuclei with nuclear processes is very much like the difference between accelerating golf balls and raw eggs with a baseball bat. Hence from the presence of the heavy nuclei it must be concluded that cosmic rays are accelerated gently by reasonably large scale fields.

Note that lithium, beryllium, and boron, the light (L) group, are about one fifth as abundant in cosmic rays as all the heavier nuclei together. In stars and most other places in the universe the light group is less than 10^{-5} as abundant as the heavier elements. This enormous discrepancy can be explained if the heavier nuclei in cosmic rays are broken up by nuclear encounters. If the heavier nuclei have passed through 2 to 5 gm/cm² of gas in their wanderings around the galaxy since their acceleration to cosmic-ray energies, there will be enough nuclear collisions to produce the light group in the cosmic rays. In the part of the galaxy near us, the gas has an average density of about 1 atom/cm³, and this means that the heavier nuclei must have been traveling in gas of this density for about 2 million years. Since starlight has to travel only about 1000 light years to get out of the disk of the galaxy, where this gas is concentrated, it does so in 5×10^{-4} as long as the cosmic rays take. Thus we see that the energy supply to cosmic rays need be only 5×10^{-4} times that of starlight. Since the geometrical factors are hard to estimate precisely, it is safer to estimate this ratio to lie between 10^{-3} and 10^{-4}. This reduces the problem of getting an adequate energy supply for the acceleration of cosmic rays from one whose solution is inconceivable to one which is merely almost impossible.

Table 12-1 shows that the heavier nuclei are relatively more abundant in cosmic rays than in stars and that this overabundance increases with increasing atomic weight. To explain this it must be argued either that cosmic rays are accelerated by some process that favors the heavy elements or that they originate in places in which the heavier elements are unusually abundant. In the discussion of the origin of cosmic rays we shall see that the selective acceleration of heavy nuclei seems needed in the Fermi theory, but if cosmic rays originate in supernovae it is natural to assume the heavy nuclei are unusually abundant there. Some experts still toy with the possibility that all cosmic rays originated as heavy nuclei such as iron, but it is usually believed that the observed abundances are inconsistent with this extreme possibility. Observations of the abundances of individual isotopes, particularly of He^3 and He^4, promise in the near future to shed much light on this question and may go a long way toward providing a much more convincing theory of the origin of cosmic rays.

Some electrons have been observed in the primary cosmic radiation perhaps 0.1 to 1 percent as many as protons of the same energy. However, the energy distribution and number of electrons are still uncertain. These observations are important because they eliminate some kinds of acceleration mechanisms and because, if relativistic electrons are not present, it will be hard to explain some components of the radio noise that originated in the galaxy. If the acceleration process were to give the same energy to electrons as to nuclei, as it would if acceleration were due to electrostatic potentials through which the particles fell, then at least as many electrons as protons in cosmic rays would be expected. But with an acceleration process that gives all particles the same velocity, the electrons, with their small mass, will get only 1/1840 times as much energy in the primary acceleration. More electrons, perhaps as many as 1 percent of the protons, will be produced as secondaries in the nuclear collisions in the interstellar gas. The observed low flux of energetic electrons is consistent with an electromagnetic but not an electrostatic acceleration. Both the overabundance of heavy nuclei and the underabundance of electrons suggest that the heavier a particle is, the easier it is to make it into a cosmic ray.

Observed sources of relativistic particles

It has just been argued that acceleration by changing electromagnetic fields is the most plausible origin of cosmic rays. It is natural to ask if there are any observations to show that such fields actually produce relativistic particles somewhere in the universe. As discussed in Chapter 11, big solar flares often produce solar cosmic rays and are often accompanied by the Type IV radio noise bursts that are ascribed to synchrotron emission from relativistic electrons moving in magnetic fields in the solar atmosphere. Thus electromagnetic processes appear to be involved in the production of solar cosmic rays. The sun is quite an ordinary star, and it is reasonable to expect that most other stars produce as many cosmic rays. However, even if all stars in the galaxy were as productive as the sun, the total cosmic-ray output would be many powers of ten too low to explain the observed level of cosmic rays. Hence other sources must be looked for. One object that we feel sure contains relativistic particles is the Crab nebula, which produces polarized visible light and radio noise throughout a large volume. When charged particles are accelerated, they radiate; hence electrons spiraling in a magnetic field convert kinetic energy into electromagnetic radiation. If the particles are nonrelativistic, the radiation is mainly at the cyclotron frequency and is trivial under most circumstances. If the particles are highly relativistic, the radiation will be strongly polarized and will be at much higher frequencies, extending into the radio noise and even the visible range for appropriate particle energies and field strengths. This radiation is named synchrotron radiation after the machines in which it was first observed. The characteristics of the light and radio noise coming from the Crab nebula can best be explained as due to electrons of 10^{12} to 10^{14} ev in a magnetic field of 10^{-3} to 10^{-4} gauss (8). Now the Crab nebula was formed by a supernova seen in A.D. 1054. A number of other sources of radio noise have been identified as relativistic electrons in supernova remnants. Any mechanism that accounts for the electrons is almost certain to explain the acceleration of nuclei to relativistic energies; hence it is highly probable that some cosmic rays originate in supernovae. It seems difficult to explain the behavior of the electrons stored in the outer Van Allen belt without invoking an electromagnetic acceleration mechanism. Jupiter emits polarized radio noise in the decimeter range which is explained as due to relativistic electrons. The least unreasonable source for these electrons seems to be some kind of electromagnetic acceleration. The recently discovered radio galaxies, discussed in Chapter 2, are extraordinarily powerful radio noise sources. Again, no origin other than relativistic electrons has been suggested. Apparently, whenever hot gas is vigorously stirred on a very large scale, energy is converted to magnetic fields and relativistic particles.

The contrast with the laboratory situation is striking. If man wishes to make a magnetic field, he needs a carefully arranged combination of conductors and insulators fed by a generator, which is a complicated precision device using a commutator, magnetic materials, etc. A cyclotron, synchrotron, or other accelerator is still more intricate and requires precise symmetry, good insulation, and a long period of careful adjustment. The ratio of the power output in relativistic particles to the power coming into the laboratory is infinitesimal. The natural accelerators have none of these properties. They do have the advantage of large dimensions and long time scales. They work in gases that are simultaneously good vacuums and good conductors by laboratory standards, but they have no particular symmetry and no insulators. The "apparatus" is just thrown together at random, stirred vigorously, and it works. The efficiency with which the mechanical energy available in gas motion is converted into observed relativistic particles is astonishingly high. In the case of the galactic cosmic rays the total thermal power available to run the acceleration mechanism, whether they come from supernovae, from stars, or from processes in the interstellar plasma, seems unlikely to be greater than 10^2 to 10^4 times the power appearing in the cosmic rays.

Energy spectrum

An important characteristic of cosmic rays is the number as a function of energy. It is usually expressed in terms of the flux as a function of energy per nucleon, but flux is easily converted to particle density since the velocity is a known function of the energy. The differential energy spectrum, $N(E)$, is the function defined by the statement that $N(E)\, dE$ is the number of particles of the specified kind in the energy range from E to $E + dE$ crossing unit area per unit time in unit solid angle. The integral energy spectrum

$$N(>E) = \int_E^\infty N(E)\, dE \qquad (12\text{-}1)$$

is the corresponding number of particles with energies greater than E. The energy spectrum is now known from energies of about 10^8 ev up to about 10^{17} ev, and some particles have been observed up to 10^{19} ev. A severe test of any theory of cosmic rays is the requirement that it apply to this enormous range of energies.

The energy spectrum has been determined by several kinds of observations. The geomagnetic field serves as a magnetic spectrograph over the energy range from a few bev to a few tens of bev because the energy required to reach the surface of the earth without being deflected away by the geomagnetic field increases with decreasing magnetic latitude. Observations at different latitudes give the integral flux above the corresponding cutoff energy. Photographic emulsions flown near the top of the atmosphere enable one to identify the various nuclei and to determine the flux as a function of both energy and kind of particle. The energy spectrum below a few bev can be determined from observations of the flux as a function of depth in the atmosphere at high geomagnetic latitudes, where all cosmic-ray particles can reach the top of the atmosphere by coming in along a line of force. Similarly, from the range below the surface of the earth, the energy spectrum up to about 10^{15} ev can be investigated. The upper end of the energy spectrum is determined

from studies of the extensive air showers. When a very high energy
primary enters the top of the atmosphere, it soon makes a nuclear encounter out of which emerge a number of secondary particles, mainly
mesons, which decay into highly relativistic electrons. A rapid multiplication then ensues, the electrons producing photons by Bremsstrahlung (9) and the photons making electron pairs as they interact with
nuclei. The shower first grows and then decays as the lower energy
secondaries are absorbed in the atmosphere. By setting up suitable
arrays of detectors on the ground to sample a shower at a number of
places, the total number of electrons reaching the ground can be determined. From this, the energy of the primary is deduced, and, from the
area of the shower, the area of the detector system, and the frequency
with which each size is observed, the energy spectrum is obtained. Although primaries in the 10^{18} to 10^{19} energy range are rare, the large size
of the showers they produce, 10^9 particles spread out over the order of a
square kilometer, makes them relatively easier to detect than the low
flux density of the primaries would lead one to suspect. The MIT group,
under the supervision of Rossi, has set up several detecting arrays, the
one at Volcano Ranch, New Mexico, covering 2 km², and it is with this
that one or two particles in the 10^{19} ev range are detected per year.
Below 10^{10} ev the cosmic-ray flux varies considerably over the 11-year
solar cycle, and it is impossible to tell how much the observed energy
spectrum represents the true spectrum in interstellar space and how
much it reflects local disturbances due to electromagnetic fields in the
solar system. Thus the behavior of the low energy end of the spectrum
is relevant to the discussion below of the interplanetary magnetic field,
but for discussions of the origin and general properties of cosmic rays
attention should be given mainly to energies above 10^{11} or 10^{12} ev. Figure 12-1 shows the flux observed at a number of different energies as
compiled by Waddington (5). It is striking how all determinations to
within the observational errors fit a smooth curve of nearly constant
slope over the energy range from 10^9 to 10^{17} ev. This is the well-known
power law, described mathematically in integral and differential form,
respectively, by

$$N(>E_t) = kE_t^{-n}, \qquad (12\text{-}2)$$

$$N(E_t)\,dE_t = nkE_t^{-n-1}\,dE_t, \qquad (12\text{-}3)$$

where n is called the exponent of the power law, E_t is the total energy,
kinetic plus rest mass energy, and the curve in Figure 12-1 would be a
straight line if n were constant. Actually n is very nearly 1.5 from 2 $\times$
10^{10} to 10^{14} ev and then increases slowly to about 1.9 at 10^{17} ev.

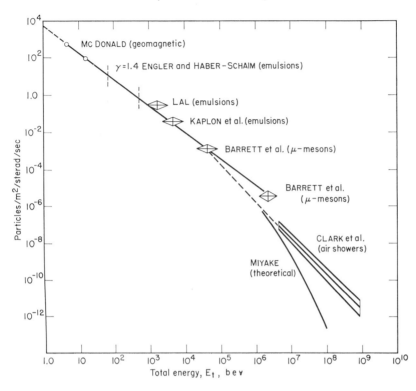

Figure 12-1 The flux of galactic cosmic ray protons with energies greater than E_t, taken from Waddington (5).

The energy spectrum for the various nuclear species can be investigated only at low energies. Typical results, taken from Peters (11) are shown in Figure 12-2, the abscissa being kinetic energy per nucleon E and the ordinate being flux. It is striking how similar the curves for the various species are. It is also of interest to note, in comparing Figures 12-1 and 12-2, that near the rest mass energy the curve is much straighter if the total energy rather than the kinetic energy is used as the independent variable. These remarkable results may be a combination of pure accident and experimental uncertainty, as many experts urge; but it is very attractive to say that nothing so regular should come about by chance. This was Fermi's point of view. He felt that this was a major clue to the origin of cosmic rays, and his famous acceleration mechanism, to be discussed below, gets its main support from its explanation of the energy spectrum.

Summary of observations and implications

From the brief review of the observed characteristics of galactic cosmic rays the following major points emerge. The essential isotropy of the cosmic rays and the fact that the flux of particles above 1 bev is about the same as that of starlight in this part of the galaxy imply that the primary cosmic rays are stored in the galaxy, or some part of it, by magnetic fields. The observation that the primary cosmic rays consist of nuclei of all the common elements, in proportions much like those in the sun but with relatively few electrons and some tendency to favor heavier nuclei, argues for an electromagnetic rather than a nuclear or an electrostatic acceleration. The occasional pro-

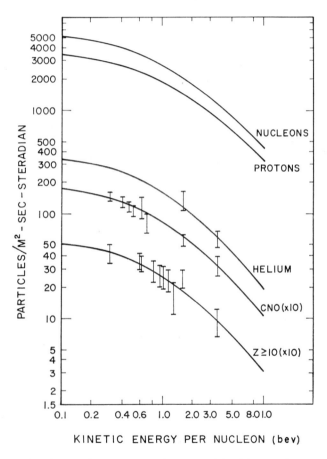

Figure 12-2 The fluxes of various cosmic-ray nuclei with energies greater than E, based on a figure by Peters (11).

duction of cosmic rays by the sun shows that this acceleration does not require an extraordinary environment. The presence of relativistic electrons, and presumably nuclei, in the remains of supernovae and in certain extraordinary galaxies leads to the conclusion that whenever a low-density plasma is vigorously stirred on a large scale magnetic fields and relativistic particles are generated. The occurrence of the so-called light nuclei, Li, Be, and B, in cosmic rays with an abundance of about one fifth that of all heavier nuclei, instead of 10^{-5} as on the sun, shows that the cosmic rays have traveled through about 5 gm/cm^2 of gas since being accelerated. The simplest explanation of this is that they have been stored in this part of our Galaxy by magnetic fields for the order of 2×10^6 years and that the energy supply to cosmic rays is 10^{-3} to 10^{-4} the thermal supply to starlight. The power-law energy spectrum may be an accident, but it does lend support to the Fermi mechanism.

12-2 MAGNETIC STRUCTURE OF THE GALAXY

Attention must now be turned from cosmic rays to the magnetic fields which are invoked to explain their storage and isotropy. In order to discuss the magnetic fields in the galaxy and the various arguments for their existence, it is necessary to review briefly some of the basic information on the distributions of stars, gas, and dust that define the galactic structure.

The observed structure of stars and gas

It is difficult to observe the structure of our Galaxy, with its distant, and presumably irregular, boundaries, its irregular detailed nearby structure, and its dust clouds that obscure the more distant regions in many directions. Extensive work along many lines has led to the following reasonably well-accepted model (12). The basic structure is a set of concentric oblate ellipsoids with the sun near the common equatorial plane and about 30,000 light years from the center. (One light year is 0.95×10^{18} cm, or 0.324 parsec.) Most of the gas and dust is confined to a thin disk whose thickness is of the order of 700 light years and whose radius is of the order of 50,000 light years. The disk in which the bright, recent stars are confined has, presumably, about the same radius but a somewhat greater thickness, say 1000 light years, to the point at which the density is half that in the plane of symmetry. The spiral arm structure shows up in both components of the galactic disk. The older types of stars are distributed more uniformly over oblate ellipsoids of progressively smaller eccentricity, to form a halo outside the disk. The halo must also be occupied by relativistic electrons and magnetic field, since it produces radio noise whose only plausible explanation is that it is synchrotron radiation. This radio halo may be spherical or somewhat flattened and may well have a maximum radius that is somewhere between 50,000 and 75,000 light years. The uncertainty in the presently accepted values of all of these numbers is emphasized by the fact that it was only a year ago that the distance from the center of the Galaxy to the sun was changed from 25,000 to 30,000 light years, and this should be one of the more certain values.

Magnetic fields

For our purposes, the most important aspect of galactic structure is the magnetic field. Classically, it was always ignored, although actually both it and the cosmic rays seem to produce forces that are much larger than gas pressure. However, before a statement such as this can pass unchallenged, convincing arguments must be given for the presence of a galactic magnetic field and its probable strength and configuration must be considered. As we shall now see, there are many independent lines of evidence for a galactic magnetic field. The isotropy and storage of cosmic rays is one of the prime bits of evidence, since magnetic fields provide the only reasonable forces that can bend a cosmic-ray trajectory inside the Galaxy. A charged particle of charge Ze, rest mass m_0, velocity v, total energy $E_t = mc^2 = m_0c^2/(1 - v^2/c^2)^{1/2}$, kinetic energy $E = E_t - m_0c^2$, whose velocity has a component $v_\perp = v \cos \theta$ normal to a uniform magnetic field of strength B gauss, moves in a helix wound on a cylinder of radius

$$a = \frac{\cos \theta}{300ZB} \left[2Em_0c^2 \left(1 + \frac{E}{2m_0c^2} \right) \right]^{1/2} \text{cm}$$

$$= \frac{\cos \theta}{300ZB} (E_t^2 - m_0^2c^4)^{1/2} \text{cm}, \qquad (12\text{-}4)$$

where E and m_0c^2 are given in ev ($m_0c^2 = 0.938 \times 10^9$ ev for a proton). For a 10-bev proton moving normal to a field of 10^{-5} gauss, this gives a radius of curvature of 3×10^{12} cm $= 1/5$ AU $= 3 \times 10^{-6}$ light years. For a 10^{19}-ev proton moving normal to the same field, the radius of curvature is 3000 light years. The field strength of 10^{-5} gauss $= 1\gamma$ is not chosen at random; the galactic field is usually thought to have this strength. These examples show that even a much weaker magnetic field is able to deflect ordinary cosmic rays within distances of the order of those in the solar system, hence would have no difficulty in making low-energy cosmic rays isotropic and storing them in a small fraction of the galaxy. But to produce the observed isotropy in the range from 10^{15} to 10^{17} ev requires fields of the order of 1γ reasonably uniform over distances of hundreds of light years at the very minimum, and the discovery of such particles seemed a strong argument for such a galactic structure. The discovery of 10^{19}-ev particles is embarrassing because the storage of these particles requires fields of the order of 1γ with a simple, fairly uniform structure over distances long compared to 3000 light years. Even the halo does not seem big enough. Since this line of argument is plausible at small energies but breaks down at large and we have no idea why or at what energy this happens, we can get little idea of the strength of the galactic field from the dynamics of the individual particles.

If the cosmic rays are considered as a gas that is confined by the magnetic field, then either the field must be strong enough that its Maxwell stresses can balance the cosmic-ray pressure or, if the field is weaker, it must be anchored in some stronger supporting structure. If it is supposed that such a weak field confines the cosmic rays, it must be supposed that it is imbedded in a thermal plasma held down by gravity. The gas density and gravitational acceleration in the disk of the Galaxy are large enough to provide a gravitational force that will balance the cosmic-ray pressure, but this model does not seem at all stable. If the density is increased somewhere by a random fluctuation, the field lines in this region will be pulled down to lower gravitational potentials. Then the neighboring thermal gas will drain down to the low point, still further increasing the density there. Meanwhile the neighboring depleted regions will be blown upward by the cosmic-ray pressure, and the instability will grow. If cosmic rays are not stored at all but fill all space uniformly, then there are no pressure gradients to be balanced. This requires a total cosmic-ray energy in the universe that seems completely impossible. The remaining possibility is that the field is anchored in the disk by gravity but extends out in long loops in the halo, the Maxwell stresses of the field balancing the cosmic-ray pressure. Whether this model is stable is not clear, but it may well provide an adequately slow escape for cosmic rays. An estimate of the field strength can be obtained by requiring that $B^2/8\pi$ be greater than the cosmic-ray pressure. Assuming that at least the cosmic rays in the 1 to 100 bev range are stored, their pressure is of the order of 1 ev/cm^3 = 1.6×10^{-12} dyne/cm^2 and $B \geq 5 \times 10^{-6}$ gauss. More precisely, their kinetic-energy density is about 1 ev/cm^2 and the pressure is two thirds the kinetic-energy density for a gas of nonrelativistic particles and one third the total energy density for a gas of highly relativistic particles. If higher energy particles were included, they would increase the pressure by about 10 percent at most. Presumably the cosmic-ray gas escapes rapidly to the halo and the pressure and field are those found there. The magnetic field in the disk of the galaxy might be somewhat larger. Thus, even though the trajectories of the individual cosmic-ray particles signify only that there is a galactic field of unknown strength, the requirement that the cosmic-ray gas be confined gives a significant lower limit to the field strength.

A very different kind of evidence for a galactic magnetic field is provided by the polarization of starlight. It is a familiar fact that the setting sun is often reddened and made less bright by dust in the air. Some stars are observed to be redder than their detailed spectra indicate they should be, and this can be explained only as the result of clouds of dust scattered through the galactic disk. The light from these stars is often observed to be partly plane polarized, which seems to indicate that the dust grains are nonspherical and tend to be partly aligned in some preferred direction. Each grain would preferentially weaken that component of the light whose electric vector is parallel to the long axes of the grain. When an observation is made normal to one of the spiral arms of the galaxy, there is a strong tendency for the planes of vibration of the light from all polarized stars, even when they are separated by hundreds of light years, to be parallel to the plane of the disk; when made along a spiral arm, the planes of vibration are nearly random. There are not many fields that could be expected to be reasonably uniform over large distances along a spiral arm, and the only one that might align dust grains seems to be a magnetic field. Apparently the most plausible alignment mechanism is that of Davis and Greenstein (13). It depends on dissipative magnetic effects in slightly paramagnetic dust grains to set the grains spinning gradually about their shortest axis and to set this axis parallel to the magnetic field. Thus more grains tend to have their long axes perpendicular to the magnetic field than in a random distribution. In order to explain the observed polarization of starlight, it must be supposed that the galactic magnetic field runs at least roughly parallel to the spiral arms but with superposed transverse magnetic waves or irregularities. Then, when an observation is made in a direction normal to a spiral arm, the result is the required regular alignment of the planes of polarization, the dispersion about the average field direction being due to the waves. If the observation were made precisely parallel to a uniform field, there would be no anisotropy to define a plane of polarization. But if it were made along a spiral arm, the transverse waves, as seen end on, would give local regions of alignment whose planes are uncorrelated from region to region. Thus the observed polarization of starlight strongly suggests that a galactic magnetic field exists and that it runs along the spiral arms in the plane of the disk. A quantitative discussion of the alignment mechanism provides an uncertain estimate that the field strength is in the general region of 10^{-4} to 10^{-5} gauss. A much better estimate is provided by the dispersion in the planes of polarization. If this is ascribed to Alfvén waves, it is easy to deduce from the elementary hydromagnetic theory of these waves the connection between the gas density, mean transverse gas velocity, mean slope of the waves, and magnetic field strength. Astronomy will furnish the values of the first two quantities and observation of the dispersion in the planes of polarization determines the third; hence a value $B \approx 10^{-5}$ gauss is obtained for the field strength.

This result is supported by another argument, attributed to Fermi and Chandrasekhar. In describing the galaxy, it was pointed out that the gas is confined to a thin disk. Gravity, due to the observed stars, and centrifugal force, due to the observed rotation of the galaxy, combine to give a net known force driving the gas toward the plane of symmetry of the galaxy. In fact, the problem is not to explain the thinness of the gas disk but instead to explain why it is not much thinner. Neither thermal gas pressure nor random motion of gas clouds explain why gravity does not compress it drastically. But a magnetic field parallel to the plane of the disk could provide the necessary supporting forces, and the strength required was estimated by Chandrasekhar and Fermi (14) to be about 6×10^{-6} gauss, which differs from 10^{-5} gauss by less than the uncertainty in the data. This argument is sometimes criticized; but it is encouraging that to whatever extent it is valid it supports the most plausible model. Even if other ways of balancing the gravitational forces turn out to be possible, it is clear that the magnetic fields of the order of 10^{-5} gauss required by other evidence and the $B^2/8\pi = 4 \times 10^{-12}$ dyne/cm^2 stresses associated with them must be important in discussions of galactic structure. Also the cosmic-ray pressure, which is of the order of 1 ev/cm$^3 = 1.6 \times 10^{-2}$ dyne/cm^2, is by no means to be neglected.

Further information on the galactic magnetic field is provided by radio astronomy. Part of the observed radio noise seems best explained as synchrotron radiation emitted in the disk and halo, the source intensity per unit volume in the halo being about one tenth that in a spiral arm. The presence of synchrotron radiation implies magnetic fields and stored, relativistic electrons in the disk and halo. Any field that keeps electrons from wandering off into the vast empty spaces between the galaxies will also trap cosmic-ray nuclei, so we must expect them to be stored in the halo. Since there seems to be no barrier that keeps cosmic rays or electrons from escaping from the disk, the density of relativistic electrons is expected to be the same in the spiral arms and in the halo, and the variation in source density is accounted for by a variation in magnetic-field strength. From the density of relativistic electrons observed in cosmic rays, the field strength required to produce the observed radio noise can be computed, and it turns out to be about 2×10^{-5} gauss in the spiral arms and about 5×10^{-6} gauss in the halo. At least two objections may be raised to this argument. It is just possible, although not widely accepted, that the radio noise in the disk and halo is due to a large number of point sources formed from supernova remnants rather than to synchrotron radiation in a general magnetic field. Also, it is by no means certain that such strong magnetic fields will not overbalance the gravitational forces holding the galaxy together. However, analysis by Biermann and Davis (15) does come to the tentative conclusion that such a structure is consistent with present inaccurate knowledge of the properties of the galaxy.

In principle, it should be possible for radio astronomy to detect the galactic magnetic field directly by observing the Zeeman effect in the 21-cm hydrogen absorption line or the Faraday rotation of the plane of polarization. Several such attempts have been made, and although some have been inconclusive some indicate that the component of the field along the line of sight, averaged over a considerable volume, is much less than 10^{-5} gauss. It is not clear whether this disagreement with the several lines of less direct evidence merely indicates some special structure of the field or some flaw in the more direct observations or whether it indicates that the galactic field is really small. For the present it seems preferable to take the field to be of the order of 10^{-5} gauss but to realize that future observations and analysis may require a revision of this value.

A consideration of the possible origin of the galactic magnetic field makes some contribution to this discussion. Observation indicates that all large-scale, irregularly moving natural plasmas somehow generate magnetic fields. Some modification of the following mechanism may be a possible explanation. Inertial effects will produce a small charge separation in such a plasma, and, as these charges move, an exceedingly weak magnetic field will be generated. Because of the high conductivity, the field lines may be regarded as embedded in, or "frozen in," the gas. The field lines must move with the gas, and thus they will be stretched out and amplified by any irregular or turbulent motions. The field strength will increase until the magnetic forces become great enough to affect the motion. This happens as equipartition, the state in which the magnetic-energy density $B^2/8\pi$ equals the kinetic-energy density of mass motion, is approached. The irregularities of the field produced in this way will correspond to the irregularities in the motion. In the case of the galaxy two additional steps seem plausible. At some stage in the evolution of the galaxy, as the random gas motions were damped out, the gas and the field embedded in it, which originally filled the halo region, were compressed by gravity into the flat disk. They were not compressed into a small sphere because of the angular momentum of the system. The disk rotates about its axis, the inner parts having a higher angular velocity than the outer. The magnetic field moved with the gas in both processes. In forming the disk, a three-dimensional field would come to lie predominantly in the plane of the disk and its strength would be increased by the compression. The differential rotation of the disk would then tend to produce a more regular spiral pattern of field lines, the shear further increasing the field strength. This should result in a field so strong that the random motion of the gas clouds would make waves in a regular field rather than snarling the lines of force to produce a random field. This model makes it plausible that in the disk the field runs along the spiral arms and has a strength of at least 10^{-5} gauss. At the ends of the spiral arms and at various irregularities the field will leak out into the halo which should then be filled with a weaker field. Whether this field is regular or turbulent will depend in part on the nature of the gas motions in the halo and perhaps in part on the effect of the cosmic-ray pressure in stretching out the field.

The diffusion of cosmic rays in the galactic magnetic field

It is now time to consider how cosmic rays are stored in the galaxy by the fields that have just been discussed. It will be recalled from the discussion of the nuclear abundances that the fragmentation of the heavier nuclei is such that they must have passed through 2 to 5 gm/cm^2 of material since being accelerated. From this it was argued that they must have spent a few million years in the disk of the galaxy. We must not devise a trapping field that keeps them longer, on the average, or there will be too many disintegrations and too much Li, Be, and B. Thus we require a leaky storage mechanism. This is obtained if the cosmic rays wander around in the magnetic field until they locate an exit. The most obvious model is ordinary diffusion, with a particle starting off in an arbitrary direction and continuing until it is scattered from a magnetic singularity. This gives a random walk in three dimensions. Actually, each charged particle spirals around a line of force, and when it is scattered at a singularity, such as a hydromagnetic shock wave, it moves only over a distance of the order of the radius of its helix to a neighboring line and continues to follow it, usually with a different pitch angle, hence a different velocity component parallel to the field. Thus all the particles that start at one place remain close to the line of force they start on, perhaps wandering back and forth along it. They will never get to a region near which their original line of force does not run, and they escape from the trapping region only if the lines of force lead them out. It is true that if the magnetic field is curved or non-uniform there will also be a slow transverse drift of the particles from one field line to another (16), but the drift velocity is only of the order of c times the ratio of the radius of curvature of the trajectory, as given by equation (12-4), to the scale of the inhomogeneity, which is likely to range from a few to thousands of light years. Thus cosmic rays in the 10^9-to-10^{14}-ev range cannot drift far compared to the thickness of the disk. On the other hand, in very high energies, say 10^{17} ev, the 30-light-year radii of curvature in fields of 10^{-5} gauss become large enough compared to the thickness of the disk that confinement in the disk for 10^6 years appears difficult. However, it seems quite reasonable that such particles should be stored and made isotropic in the halo field, which is of much greater extent. But if high-energy cosmic rays are stored in the halo, low-energy particles must also be stored. Since the density in the halo is low, long storage times are possible. Thus one is led to the following model. The lower energy cosmic rays wander back and forth along a single line of force, perhaps going from disk to halo and return several times. This continues long enough so that a particle passes through, on the average, about 3 gm/cm^2, mostly in the disk. Eventually the cosmic rays escape from the halo either by finding a line of force that leads to infinity or by being caught in a loop of field lines blown out of the galaxy by cosmic-ray pressure. The fact that the magnetic fields in the disk and halo are not static but distort continuously because of the fluid motions as well as occasionally reconnecting to form new patterns will complicate this model but should require no essential modifications. The higher energy particles up to 10^{17} or 10^{18} ev behave very much like the lower energy particles, although they drift from one line to another much more rapidly and probably enter and leave the disk more frequently. Somewhere in the range of 10^{18} to 10^{20} ev it becomes difficult to see how trapping is possible, even in the halo. Then it must be argued either that intergalactic space is filled with the observed low density of extremely high energy particles or that there are no such particles, some mistake having been made in the interpretation of the extensive air-shower data, or that somehow the halo can trap higher energy particles than it would at first have been supposed. Many experts seem to prefer the first alternative, but it seems to the writer that all are about equally unpalatable.

12-3 THEORIES OF THE ORIGIN OF COSMIC RAYS

From the original discovery of an ionizing radiation coming from outer space through the atmosphere to the modern realization that an appreciable fraction of the kinetic energy of all matter outside stars (not counting any kinetic energy of expansion of the universe) is found in relativistic particles rather than in bulk motion or in the thermal range, the problem of the origin of cosmic rays has been a fascinating challenge to the imagination. Many solutions have been proposed with confidence and defended with enthusiasm, even heat. The general area in which to look for a solution now seems reasonably clear, and many previously plausible theories can be definitely excluded, but it is still not possible to get general agreement on just where the bulk of the cosmic rays get most of their energy.

Unacceptable theories

It is well to begin by clearing away some of the suggested origins of cosmic rays that have become completely unacceptable.

It might be supposed that cosmic rays fill the entire universe and were somehow produced during the mysterious earlier stages of its creation or evolution. But to fill the intergalactic space takes thousands of times as much energy as just to fill the galaxies with cosmic rays. Even worse, since the red shift shows that the universe is expanding and that the galaxies are moving apart, any gas, including a cosmic-ray gas, that fills the universe must be expanding and cooling adiabatically. This means that cosmic-ray particles steadily lose kinetic energy as they interact with receding galaxies and their magnetic fields. Thus at the beginning of the expansion, when all the cosmic rays were much more energetic than at present, they would have demanded an impossibly large fraction of the total energy in the universe. Moreover, since some cosmic rays are observed to come from the sun and from supernovae, it seems rather timid to push the origin of the rest of the cosmic rays back into the undiscussible past.

Another of the early suggestions was that cosmic rays originate from exotic nuclear processes. This was perhaps conceivable when cosmic rays were thought to be fundamental particles and before their great energy was known, but now the objections are manifold. One would have to use all the rest mass energy of 10^9 protons, presumably in a single explosion, to produce one 10^{18}-ev cosmic ray. Such processes would only break up heavy nuclei, not accelerate them; and there is no reason why they should give cosmic rays in conjunction with solar flares. Occasionally, acceleration by electrostatic fields is considered; but on any large scale the universe is everywhere too good a conductor to support large electric potential differences. This is true whether stars or interstellar gas are considered. Also this theory should give of the order of 1 bev electron for each bev proton, and the flux of electrons in cosmic rays is less by two orders of magnitude.

Many difficulties would be eliminated if cosmic rays were accelerated in the solar system and stored in a small volume by a suitable magnetic field. Then only a completely trivial fraction of the sun's output of energy would need to be converted into cosmic rays. However, the discovery of high-energy cosmic rays, above 10^{15} ev, made this completely impossible, since there is no way to store such particles in a small volume by any reasonable magnetic field.

Acceleration by induced electromotive forces

In the discussion of the observed characteristics of cosmic rays it was concluded that an acceleration by induced electromotive forces was strongly indicated. Such mechanisms may be classified as betatron processes of the type proposed by Swann or statistical processes of the type proposed by Fermi.

In 1933 W. F. G. Swann suggested that the induced emf around a sunspot or other region where magnetic fields changed rapidly could accelerate particles in one fairly rapid continuous process to relativistic energies just as particles are accelerated in a betatron. When a sunspot appears on the sun, its magnetic field grows at a rate between 10^{-1} and 10^{-2} gauss/sec from a value near zero often to more than 1000 gauss over areas 10^9 cm across. If the emf around the perimeter is computed, it will be seen that a few turns will raise a particle to cosmic-ray energies. However, as Swann pointed out, in a simple case such as this a particle will not move around the perimeter but, because of the field, will move in a small circle in which the induced emf is correspondingly small. More complicated magnetic fields can be suggested in which the induced emf has a component along the magnetic field and then acceleration appears possible. A variety of possible configurations involving pairs of sunspots, double magnetic variable stars, and interacting galaxies has been suggested. If one is not distracted by the complexities of the analysis, all such proposals are invalidated by an objection that can be put in several forms. One way to put the difficulty is to point out that all particles present are accelerated, the available energy being shared essentially equally, and it is very difficult to devise circumstances in which each particle can get a significant amount of energy.

In other words, the accelerator is shorted out by the highly conducting plasma always present. Another, more fundamental, way to put the difficulty is to point out that in all these situations the magnetic field is frozen into the highly conducting plasma and that when the field is changed the plasma is convected to produce the change. A sunspot develops a magnetic field not because currents are started up but because plasma containing magnetic field inside the sun is convected up to the surface, bringing the field with it. In most such cases the electric field, as seen in a frame of reference moving with the fluid, is zero by a basic principle of plasma physics. Now, the particles to be accelerated are initially thermal particles, moving with the fluid, and they do not experience electromagnetic acceleration. There are special situations along neutral lines in a magnetic field in which some acceleration may occasionally occur. This may be important in connection with solar flares. Any exceptional process seems more likely to accelerate electrons than protons; it does not appear that it can possibly produce particles with energies up to 10^{18} ev or that it would yield a power-law energy spectrum. Thus we must look elsewhere for the origin of cosmic rays.

In 1949 and 1954 Enrico Fermi published papers that developed a very different mechanism in which acceleration is a statistical effect whereby the individual interactions may increase or decrease the energy of the particle. This mechanism will operate, to a greater or lesser extent, in any irregularly moving conducting gas that contains a magnetic field. It acts not on thermal particles but only on particles that already have a considerable amount of energy and whose motion is affected by the magnetic field but not significantly by the gas. At each point, in the frame of reference moving with the gas, there is a magnetic field but no electric field because the gas is a good conductor. If a Lorentz transformation is made from the gas frame to the common inertial frame used to discuss the entire motion of the particle to be accelerated, the result is an assortment of changing electric fields. The high-energy particle goes through such fields nearly at random, gaining or losing energy along various segments of its trajectory. The thermal particles always remain in the same element of fluid, and the electric fields seen in the inertial frame of reference merely produce the fluid mass motion of these particles. If it is preferred, the acceleration of the higher energy particles can be treated in terms of magnetic effects. As a particle spirals around a field line in a region in which the magnetic-field strength is increasing or decreasing, it gains or loses energy as in a betatron because of the induced emf. If in its spiraling it follows a line of force embedded in a gas cloud around a bend, it essentially makes an elastic collision with the cloud and gains or loses energy, depending on whether it is a head-on or an overtaking collision. Since head-on collisions are slightly more likely, an energy gain is more probable than an energy loss in such a collision. For further analyses of the many varieties of collisions and of the resulting energy distributions, the original papers (17) or any of various review articles (e.g., 18, 19, 22) should be consulted.

The result is that under very general circumstances, the power-law energy distribution of equation (12-2) is obtained. This comes about as follows. As the particles randomly gain and lose energy, some make more gains and some more losses. Those with more gains spread out over the cosmic-ray spectrum; those with too many losses drop down to velocities in which ionization losses are large and are then brought down to thermal energies. If the region in which each of the random energy changes takes place is large compared to the particle cyclotron radius in the magnetic field, then the energy change for relativistic particles is of the order of the energy times $\pm\beta_g = \pm V_g/c$, where V_g is the gas velocity. Let t_1 be the mean time between the energy changes. If we are to have a steady state, particles must be injected into the system by some mechanism which we have yet to discuss and must be removed at a steady rate. The foregoing discussion suggests that removal should be due mainly to wandering out of the trapping region but partly to making a nuclear interaction. This is characterized by saying that τ is the mean life time in the system or that dt/τ is the probability of removal in the time dt. Then if t_1 and τ are independent of energy and if the energy changes are $\pm\beta_g$ times the energy, the exponent in the energy spectrum is given by

$$n = F\left(\frac{t_1}{\beta_g^2 \tau},\right) \qquad (12\text{-}5)$$

where F is some function that depends on the details of the interactions. For a wide range of models $n \approx 1 - 2$ for $t_1/\beta_g^2\tau$ somewhere in the range of 1 to 30.

This model has both good and bad features. For cosmic-ray energies up to about 10^{16} ev the scale of the irregularities in the galactic field should be such that the various conditions needed to make n independent of energy are met. This is the major triumph of the Fermi theory; and it, together with the fact that here is a mechanism that can clearly work, are the main reasons why any attention is paid to the theory. At first it was believed that the parameters V_g, t_1, and τ were such that in the disk of the galaxy $t_1/\beta_g^2\tau \approx 1$, as required to give $n \approx 1.5$ on Fermi's original model. But then the astronomers' estimates of V_g were lowered considerably, and it was discovered that cosmic rays included heavy nuclei as well as protons, thus requiring that the storage time τ be smaller to allow escape before too much Li, Be, and B were produced. This gave a large value of $t_1/\beta_g{}^2\tau$, and, on Fermi's original theory, gave $n \approx 100$. Under the circumstances the mechanism worked in principle, but in practice it was so feeble it could be disregarded. This has led to an extensive (19) and not very fruitful search for more efficient variants of the Fermi mechanism that would give $n \approx 1.5$ even for conditions in a spiral arm. It may be that a solution along these lines will emerge, but it seems more likely that the acceleration will be found to take place in other regions as discussed below.

It has been argued that it is unlikely that the Fermi mechanism is important anywhere, for even if conditions could be found in which $t_1/\beta_g{}^2\tau$ were small enough it would require a very unlikely coincidence for three unrelated parameters to combine to give n a value near unity. Values of $1/10$ or 10 should be as likely. This argument fails if the acceleration of cosmic rays is an important damping mechanism for the gas motions, as suggested by the large fraction of the energy of the gas motions that must be converted into cosmic rays in any case. Then only values of n near unity give the right amount of damping. With larger values of n, there are few high-energy cosmic rays, hence not much damping, and V_g increases. As n approaches unity, the energy in cosmic rays approaches infinity, and V_g is damped down.

There seems to be enough energy available in the gas motions of the galaxy to produce the observed cosmic-ray flux. These motions are driven by hot new stars, hence derive ultimately from the nuclear energy that heats the stars. However, the details of the processes are not clear and do not seem to fit well the needs of the Fermi mechanism. The high-energy particles, those in the 10^{18}- and 10^{19}-ev range, to say nothing of the 10^{20}-ev particles whose imminent discovery is confidently expected by the extensive air-shower specialists, pose great difficulties. The conditions for getting constant n seem almost surely to be violated for particles with such large radii of curvature; in fact it seems difficult to confine them in the galaxy at all. Of course, all other theories of the origin of cosmic rays have even more difficulty with these energies, and at present it is usual to retreat to the unknown and to say that somehow they are of extragalactic origin.

One final problem is that all variations of the Fermi mechanism tend to make the flux anisotropic, it being stronger parallel to the direction of the magnetic field. There are two ways out of this dilemma. One is to suppose that there are many small scale irregularities, perhaps hydromagnetic shocks, in the galactic magnetic field. Some such mechanism as this is necessary in the region in which the Fermi process is effective. The other, and probably the most likely for our neighborhood, is to assume that the spiral-arm magnetic field in our vicinity is relatively quiet and that no acceleration is now taking place. We then turn to look for regions in which acceleration might occur.

The injection problem

The preceding discussion of the origin of cosmic rays suggests that the Fermi process may be the best way to accelerate particles from medium to high energies, provided we can find a region in which conditions are such that it will work and provided the injection problem can be solved; that is, provided we can find a way to get thermal particles started. This suggests that we consider separately the way in which thermal particles are first accelerated. This injection, or primary acceleration, must take place near the surface of stars, since there seems to be no way to accelerate thermal particles in interstellar space and escape from stellar interiors is impossible. We know that somehow acceleration from thermal energies can take place on stars, for the sun is observed to produce some low-energy cosmic rays and Type IV radio noise bursts on the sun are ascribed to relativistic electrons. The sun, and the large number of similar ordinary stars, may well produce many more particles in the Mev than in the cosmic-ray range. Since such particles lose energy to the electrons in interstellar space fairly rapidly, it does not seem likely that they can be accelerated efficiently enough by a galactic Fermi mechanism to become cosmic rays. But at least 10 percent of the starlight comes from the relatively few hot bright stars. Such stars are much more active than the sun in every way. They usually rotate faster, they seem to have much larger and more rapidly variable magnetic fields, and they are believed to eject much more hot gas. All this activity is expected to lead to a production of nonthermal particles much more copiously than on the sun. Thus these stars should inject into interstellar space many more, and much more energetic, particles than stars like the sun. It does not seem at all unreasonable that it is from the hot, active stars that injection takes place. Probably the most widely accepted possibility of all is that the still more violent processes associated with novae and supernovae may provide the injection mechanism. The frequencies of novae and supernovae in the galaxy, the energies released, and the masses ejected are all great enough to suggest this possibility. Finally, the synchrotron radiation from supernovae shows that they do produce relativistic particles. The details of the injection process are not clear. We do not know how the sun produces the occasional solar cosmic-ray outbursts; but the fact that it is observed to do so proves that such acceleration is possible. The same mechanisms should operate more efficiently in more active stars and in novae and supernovae. It may well be that some varient of the Fermi statistical mechanism operates in turbulent stellar magnetic fields. Conceivably, either the high-energy tail of the Boltzmann distribution or flare phenomena, perhaps at magnetic neutral points, or shocks may provide a number of particles with energies somewhat above thermal. A small fraction may then succeed in being accelerated by the Fermi process, while the great majority return to thermal energies. Thus the available energy may ultimately be drained off by a few high-energy particles rather than distributed in small quantities to all the particles present. It must be emphasized that this proposal is only a speculation that may be completely wrong. There are a number of other possibilities, each appearing to have serious objections. One spectacular suggestion, due to Colgate and Johnson (20), is that a supernova produces a strong shock that propagates outward with steadily increasing velocity as the density decreases until at last the flow velocity is relativistic and the particles finally left in the wave become cosmic rays.

It has been suggested that the greater abundance of heavy nuclei in cosmic rays should provide an important clue to their origin. It is often urged that the origin in supernovae is supported in this way, since theories of the formation of supernovae (18) are often based on models in which most of the star's hydrogen has been burned into heavy nuclei, particularly iron. Some caution is needed here because observation of supernovae does not seem to demonstrate an excessive abundance of heavy elements in the atmosphere and because the theory of stellar evolution through a supernova stage is not well established. If one turns from the novae and supernovae to the active stars, including the magnetic stars of Babcock, it will be found that these stars are relatively new and have condensed from the interstellar gas more recently than the sun. Since the interstellar gas is believed to be growing continuously richer in heavy elements produced in and ejected from the stars in the course of their evolution, it is to be expected that if cosmic rays were injected from the active stars heavy nuclei would be more abundant in cosmic rays than in the sun. Finally, it may be that wherever injection occurs heavy nuclei are systematically favored, perhaps because if they are only partly ionized during the critical starting process they find it easier to acquire energy than protons with their higher ratio of charge to mass. Thus the excess abundance of heavy nuclei may be possible even for injection from ordinary stars like the sun. Although this argument favors either the supernovae or the active stars compared to the sun as the injection site, it is by no means decisive.

The secondary acceleration

If nuclei are accelerated from thermal energies to moderate energies near stars, where do they get energies in the 10^9-to-10^{18}-ev range? They may get all of their energy in the first process, in which case only the primary acceleration need be considered. But it is difficult to see how a mechanism scaled to accelerate nonrelativistic particles with their small radii of curvature can continue to accelerate particles with the radii of curvature that correspond to the highest energies. In fact, it seems impossible to confine 10^{18}-ev particles for acceleration within a region of stellar dimensions, or within a supernova remnant, by any reasonable magnetic field. Finally, it is unlikely that near a star t_1 and τ would be independent of energy as required to get the integral energy spectrum. One possibility, urged by Cocconi (21) and Morrison (22), is that there is a vast number of different kinds of sources, ordinary stars, active stars, supernovae, and perhaps extraordinarily active galaxies. Each source produces particles spread over several powers of ten in energy, and when the whole output is stored in the galaxy and mixed together one gets by chance a reasonably smooth approximation to the power-law spectrum. It is impossible to argue that this cannot be so, but it is difficult to see how the high-energy particles can be accelerated in any of these sources except the extraordinary galaxies, and then it is hard to see why the number predicted by the power law should arrive at our Galaxy. Also, it is unesthetic that the power law should be an accident instead of a basic property of cosmic rays.

There are two alternatives to this view. One is that the supernovae do all of the accelerating, presumably in a Fermi process inside a young supernova envelope in which conditions are more favorable than in intersellar space. This is the model proposed and developed by Ginzburg (10) and Shklovsky, numerous references to which are given in Shapiro's review (18). The other alternative is that injection merely involves acceleration to a relatively modest energy, perhaps 10^8 or 10^9 ev/nucleon, and that there is a secondary Fermi acceleration that produces the higher energies, smooths out the spectrum, and explains the fact that it follows a power law. If a region can be found in which such a secondary acceleration is possible, that is, where $t_1/\beta_g^2\tau$ has a value near unity and independent of energy, and if adequate power is available, a very satisfactory theory of the acceleration of cosmic rays will result. The whole difficulty is in finding a suitable region for the secondary acceleration. There seems to be enough power available in the gas motions in the spiral arms, but no mechanism has yet been found that assures confidence that the correct value of n will be obtained. On the other hand, there are many ways in which particles can interact with hydromagnetic waves, and perhaps the most efficient process has not yet been discovered. It is also possible that the relatively unknown conditions in the galactic halo, or those in the nucleus (the region within 10,000 light years of the center) or in some other special region, may be more appropriate than those in our neighborhood. It is barely possible that the main acceleration took place long ago when the Galaxy was younger, had more gas, more hot young stars, and more activity of all kinds than at present, and that the cosmic rays have been stored in the halo ever since. For the present, the only safe conclusion is that a Fermi secondary acceleration will be very attractive if it can be worked out. The pure supernova explanation is a good possibility. Its proponents feel sure that enough power is available, but there may be some question on this score. The other stellar sources are not to be completely ignored. As the consequences of these various assumptions regarding the source or sources are worked out and as more astronomical and cosmic-ray data are required, it should become clear where cosmic rays originate. It is just possible that a great surprise awaits us.

12-4 COSMIC RAYS IN THE SOLAR SYSTEM AND INTERPLANETARY MAGNETIC FIELDS

Throughout the preceding discussion the intimate connection between galactic cosmic rays and galactic magnetic fields has been apparent. Let us now see what can be learned if we confine our attention to the solar system. Cosmic rays in the range above 10^{12} ev have such large radii of curvature that they are but little affected by conditions in the solar system. The solar and galactic cosmic rays in the 10^9- and 10^{10}-ev range drift very slowly across the field lines, and a study of the variations in flux at these energies enables us to trace out the field lines and deduce a number of important characteristics of the interplanetary magnetic field. To do justice to this subject would require at least a full chapter; but, since many aspects have already been covered in Chapter 11, only a brief survey of a few points is attempted here.

Basic observations

During an 11-year sunspot cycle the galactic cosmic-ray flux at the earth has been observed to vary by more than a factor of two at the lowest energies that can be studied by balloon flights near the geomagnetic pole. At higher energies the variation is less, but it is still present above 10^{10} ev. During the part of the cycle when there are many spots on the sun, when flares are most frequent, and when geomagnetic activity shows that the sun is emitting the most clouds of gas, the galactic cosmic-ray flux is reduced. It is by no means certain, although it is often assumed, that the maximum in the cosmic-ray flux observed some months after the sun becomes least active is the true interstellar value. The region of the earth may still be partially screened and the true interstellar level somewhat higher. From the run of the energy spectrum at higher energies, where such a reduction is unimportant, we are led to believe that the depression in intensity at the quietest sunspot minima may not be large. This variation in intensity over the solar cycles shows that, except possibly at sunspot minimum, the galactic magnetic field lines do not lead smoothly into the solar system as far as the earth. If they did, the galactic cosmic rays would follow them in. A number of models have been proposed to explain the screening out of the low-energy cosmic rays. Most models require a flow of gas out from the sun; this seems required for a number of other reasons as well. One possibility is that this gas flow convects outward a tangled or very irregular magnetic field through which the low-energy galactic cosmic rays diffuse slowly. When the sun is active, the field is more irregular and the gas flow is faster; thus the sweeping out process is more complete. It can also be supposed that the galactic field lines detour around the region occupied by solar plasma and that the low-energy galactic cosmic rays in their motion through the galaxy follow these field lines, only a few leaking into and becoming trapped inside the cavity in the galactic field occupied by solar plasma. In any case, this effect gives clear evidence that much of the time the magnetic connection between the region of the earth and the galactic magnetic field is not smooth and continuous.

A second important observed effect is the decrease in galactic cosmic-ray intensity on the occasion of magnetic storms which was discovered by Forbush. In a Forbush decrease the galactic cosmic-ray intensity at the earth drops suddenly at the time of arrival of the disturbance from the sun, the drop being greater for low energies than for high. Recovery follows slowly over a period of days or weeks. Essentially the same effects were observed at the earth and at Pioneer V when it was 5,000,000 km away, proving that this is not a geomagnetic effect. Galactic cosmic rays are partly screened out of a large volume in the solar system during a Forbush decrease. On the other hand, the entire solar system out to the earth's orbit is not affected, since Forbush decreases are believed to be associated with disturbances on the visible side of the sun. Unseen disturbances on the other side do not produce such a decrease. To explain a Forbush decrease, it is not enough to introduce a magnetic cloud somewhere outside the earth's orbit to screen away the cosmic rays, for then cosmic rays could come past the sun through the undisturbed region on the other side and reach us from that direction. The earth must be surrounded by some kind of temporary screen that prevents galactic cosmic rays from reaching us from any direction, and this screen must be predominantly on one side of the sun.

The third set of observations to be considered concerns the solar cosmic rays. Only a few of the main features can be reviewed here. Following a flare or similar major disturbance on the visible face of the sun, there is often an increase in the cosmic-ray flux at energies ranging up to various upper limits between 10^8 and 10^{10} ev. This must be ascribed to particles emitted from the sun. Sometimes the increase is slow, as though the particles had to diffuse through a screening field to reach the earth. Sometimes it is prompt, implying that then the particles come by a quite direct path, perhaps nearly as short as a straight line, perhaps twice as long. There is a tendency for solar cosmic rays that are associated with events on the west half of the sun to arrive with less difficulty than for those associated with events on the east limb. Solar cosmic rays from events that cannot be seen from the earth never seem to reach the earth. The solar cosmic rays seen at the earth decay away in several hours or days, whereas the event that appears to produce them lasts only in the order of an hour or less. Thus they seem to be stored in a rather leaky region that extends only over a limited range in longitude around the sun. Sometimes solar cosmic rays originate from a flare on the sun in a region in which there had been an earlier flare that produced a Forbush decrease. In events of this kind solar cosmic rays reach the earth quickly. This is just what would be expected if on these occasions the earth were poorly connected to the galactic magnetic field but were well connected with the sun, for then solar particles could reach us easily but could not leak away to interstellar regions nor could low-energy galactic cosmic rays easily leak in. The galactic cosmic-ray intensity recovers more slowly than the solar cosmic-ray intensity decreases, indicating either a barrier that is more easily penetrated in one direction than the other, which seems highly improbable, or a screened region that is expanding in volume. Finally, McCracken (23) has observed that at least on some occasions solar cosmic rays that arrive promptly come from a direction in the plane of the ecliptic but lying some 60 degrees west of the sun. Presumably, this is the direction of the field line about which they are spiraling.

Models of the interplanetary magnetic field

There are two models of the interplanetary field that are currently widely used in attempts to explain these observations. One, developed by Gold (24) and McCracken (23), may be called the tongue or bottle model. It assumes that when a burst of gas is emitted from the sun it pulls the solar field out in a tongue or bottle as indicated

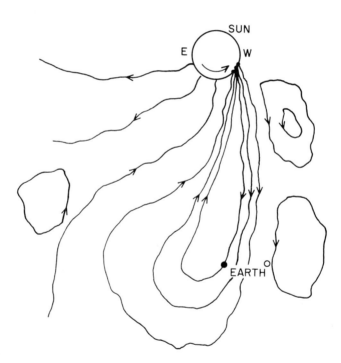

Figure 12-3 A schematic representation of a tongue of magnetic lines of force drawn out from the sun. The solid circle represents a possible position of the earth within the storage region; the open circle represents a possible position outside the storage region.

in Figure 12-3. The rest of interplanetary space is filled with irregular blobs of gas and field left over from previous events. Galactic cosmic rays cannot easily diffuse into this storage region, whereas solar cosmic rays reach the earth quickly and are stored. As the blob of gas and field come straight out from the sun, the roots of the field remain attached to the sun and are pulled around to the west by the solar rotation. Thus the east-west asymmetries are explained. If the earth happens to be outside the storage region, solar cosmic rays diffuse to it only very slowly and by the time they arrive are essentially isotropic. However, it is not really clear why, in a structure of the kind shown in Figure 12-3, the cosmic rays cannot come out along both sides of the bottle, hence sometimes arrive first coming from the east. This model is quite successful in explaining most of the observed effects in a natural way, but it does not solve all problems. Incidentally, it should be remarked that when adjacent field lines run essentially parallel but have opposite senses there is a tendency after a time for the lines to reconnect and form loops. Thus the tongues are expected to become detached from the sun after a few days and float away as self-contained magnetic clouds, so that one is not left with too many lines of force trailing off from the sun.

Another attractive model, due to Parker (25), is shown in Figure 12-4; the arrows indicating possible field directions have been added to his figure. In this it is assumed that gas streams radially out from the sun at all times in a way vividly described as a solar wind. Mostly, this is a smooth steady flow, and it stretches any field lines that emerge from the sun out far beyond the earth. The rotation of the sun drags the inner end of the lines of force around in a spiral, smoother than in the other case. A flare on the sun produces a blast wave that goes out much more rapidly than the ordinary wind and produces the narrow compressed zone in which the spiral becomes flatter. All of this spiral structure comes from pure kinematics, and the various deflections in the field lines are sharp because shock waves are involved. With this structure the Forbush decreases are explained as the result of the scattering of incoming galactic cosmic rays when they come to the abrupt deflections in the field lines at the shock fronts. Similarly, the solar cosmic rays tend to be trapped between the shocks, where they are scattered back as they go outward from the sun, and to mirror as they go in. The radial structure explains why effects are confined to the side of the sun where the disturbance occurred. This model also is quite successful in explaining many of the observations.

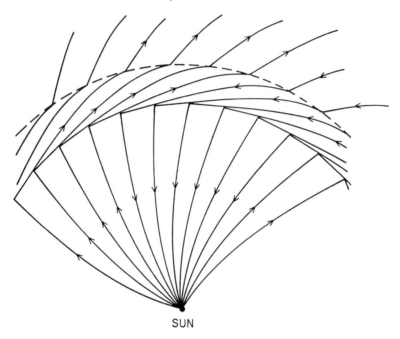

SUN

Figure 12-4   Magnetic lines of force drawn out from the sun by a blast wave overtaking a steady solar wind.

Actually, the two models are probably not so different as they might appear at first sight.   If Parker's model is made somewhat irregular and some reconnection of the field lines is introduced where they run parallel but in opposite senses, the resemblance of Figure 12-4 to Figure 12-3 will be considerably increased.   Numerous complications must be introduced into both models to explain the details of complicated cosmic-ray events.

Further progress in understanding the structure of the interplanetary magnetic field and the way it changes during the solar cycle and during the various disturbances should come with the exploration of interplanetary space by suitable vehicles.   It is clear that measurements of the magnetic field are important, but those of the gas velocity are equally important, since this largely determines the field patterns. Observations of solar and galactic cosmic rays both at the earth and on space probes will give information on the large-scale structure and connectivity of the field lines that cannot easily be obtained in any other way.

REFERENCES

1. Millikan, R. A., *Electrons* (+ *and* −), *Protons, Photons, Neutrons, Mesotrons, and Cosmic Rays*, University of Chicago Press, Chicago, 1947.
2. Janossy, L., *Cosmic Rays*, Oxford at the Clarendon Press, 1948.
3. Elliot, H., *Progr. Cosmic Ray Phys.*, **1**, 455–514 (1952).
4. Greisen, K., *Progr. Cosmic Ray Phys.*, **3**, 1–141 (1956).
5. Waddington, C. J., *Progr. Nucl. Phys.*, **8**, 1–45 (1960).
6. Cameron, A. G. W., *Astrophys. J.*, **129**, 676 (1959).
7. Suess, H. E., and H. C. Urey, *Rev. Mod. Phys.*, **28**, 53–74 (1956).
8. Oort, J. H., and T. Walraven, *Bull. Astron. Inst. Neth.*, **12**, 285–308 (1956).
9. Leighton, R. B., *Principles of Modern Physics*, McGraw-Hill, New York, 1959, p. 690.
10. Ginzburg, L., *Progr. Cosmic Ray Phys.*, **4**, 339–421 (1958).
11. Peters, B., *Progr. Cosmic Ray Phys.*, **1**, 193–242 (1952).
12. Oort, J. H., *Stellar Populations*, ed. D. J. K. O'Connell, Interscience Publishers, New York, 1958, pp. 415–425.
13. Davis, L., Jr., and J. L. Greenstein, *Astrophys. J.*, **114**, 206–240 (1951).
14. Chandrasekhar, S., and E. Fermi, *Astrophys. J.*, **118**, 113–115 (1953).
15. Biermann, L., and L. Davis, Jr., *Z. Astrophys.*, **51**, 19–31 (1960).
16. Spitzer, L., *Physics of Fully Ionized Gases*, Interscience Publishers, New York, 1956, pp. 1–7.
17. Fermi, E., *Phys. Rev.*, **75**, 1169–1174 (1949); *Astrophys. J.*, **119**, 1–6 (1954).
18. Shapiro, M. M., *Science*, 175–193 (1962).
19. Davis, L., Jr., *Suppl. Nuovo Cimento*, **8**, 444–459 (1958).
20. Colgate, S. A., and M. H. Johnson, *Phys. Rev. Letters*, **5**, 235–238 (1960).
21. Cocconi, G., *Astrophys. J. Suppl.*, **4**, No. 44, 417–422 (1960).
22. Morrison, P., *Handbuch der Physik*, Vol. 46, ed. S. Flügge, Springer, Berlin, 1961, pp. 1–87.
23. McCracken, K. G., *J. Geophys. Res.*, **67**, 447–459 (1962).
24. Gold, T., *J. Geophys. Res.*, **64**, 1665–1674 (1959).
25. Parker, E. N., *Astrophys. J.*, **133**, 1014–1033 (1961).

CHAPTER 13

THE EARTH'S EXOSPHERE

S. FRED SINGER *

National Weather Satellite Center
United States Weather Bureau

The exosphere is the uppermost region of the atmosphere from which molecules may escape out into space. At lower altitudes molecules are prevented from escaping by collisions with other molecules in the overlying atmosphere. Thus the exosphere is the "fringe" of the atmosphere that extends into space.

Actually the "fringe" occupies a large altitude region, from about 530 km out to many earth-radii, perhaps 60,000 to 1,000,000 km. No precise limit can yet be placed where the exosphere blends into the interplanetary gas.

It is of great interest in many problems to know the density of particles in the exosphere. For example, in order to calculate the drag on a satellite or other space vehicle or to calculate the lifetime of trapped radiation belt particles, we need to know both the neutral- and ionized-particle density. Although the ionized-particle density is partly controlled by the earth's magnetic field and other factors, the concentration of neutral particles is controlled entirely by the gravitational field of the earth and by the temperature at the base. Starting with these two ingredients, we can calculate the exospheric densities, provided we have a theory that gives the density distribution.

* On leave at the University of Maryland.

Preliminary relations and definitions

Before discussing the properties of the exosphere, we shall first derive some useful relations concerning the barosphere (by which we mean the whole of the atmosphere below the exosphere). We will then show why these relations can no longer be applied to the exosphere, a region so rarefied that atoms hardly ever collide with one another.

The distribution of pressure and density with altitude in an isothermal atmosphere is easily derived. Consider an infinitesimal volume of atmosphere of height δh. In going from the bottom to the top surface the drop in pressure is given by the hydrostatic equation

$$-\delta p = g\rho \cdot \delta h, \tag{13-1}$$

where g is the local acceleration of gravity and ρ, the density (in gm/cm^3). But p and ρ are also related by the equation of state of a perfect gas

$$p = \frac{\rho}{\bar{m}} kT, \tag{13-2}$$

where $\bar{m}$ is the mean molecular weight,* T is the temperature in °K, and k is Boltzmann's constant (8.31×10^7 erg/°K/mole).

Dividing equation (13-2) into (13-1), we obtain

$$-\frac{\delta p}{p} = \frac{\bar{m}g}{kT} \delta h = \frac{\delta h}{H} \tag{13-3}$$

where we define the so-called "scale height" *

$$H = \frac{kT}{\bar{m}g}. \tag{13-4}$$

If m and T are constant, then we can also write

$$-\frac{1}{\rho}\frac{d\rho}{dh} = -\frac{1}{p}\frac{dp}{dh} = \frac{1}{H}. \tag{13-5}$$

Therefore, for an *isothermal* atmosphere, we have

$$\frac{\rho}{\rho_0} = \frac{p}{p_0} = \exp -\frac{h}{H}. \tag{13-6}$$

---

* Applicable when perfect mixing occurs; in diffusive equilibrium each species follows a scale height given by its own molecular weight m.

In equation (13-4) g is considered nearly constant in the lower atmosphere. Actually, the following relations hold true:

$$g = \frac{GM_E}{r^2} \tag{13-7}$$

where G is the gravitational constant (6.67×10^{-8} dyne/cm^2/gm^2), M_E the mass of the earth (5.98×10^{27} gm), and where r is measured from the center of the earth. Noting that $dh = dr$, we can rewrite equation (13-5):

$$-\frac{1}{\rho}\frac{d\rho}{dr} = \frac{m}{kT} \cdot \frac{GM_E}{r^2}. \tag{13-8}$$

Integration then yields the well-known barometric equation which gives the density distribution in an isothermal atmosphere:

$$\frac{\rho(r)}{\rho_0} = \exp\left[\frac{GM_E m}{kT}\left(\frac{1}{r} - \frac{1}{r_0}\right)\right]. \tag{13-9}$$

It is useful at times to introduce the concept of "reduced height" r'. We can write equation (13-9) as

$$\log \rho(r) - \log \rho_0 = \frac{GM_E m}{kT}\frac{r_0 - r}{r_0 r}$$

$$= -\frac{GM_E m}{kT}\frac{1}{r'}. \tag{13-9a}$$

Hence

$$r' = \frac{r r_0}{h}.$$

Also

$$h' = \frac{h r_0}{r} \tag{13-9b}$$

and

$$h'r' = r_0{}^2.$$

We can also write the right-hand side of equation (13-9) as

$$\exp\left[\frac{GM_E m/r_0}{kT}\left(\frac{r_0}{r} - 1\right)\right] ;$$

with the use of the nondimensional notation

$$y = \frac{r_0}{r} \tag{13-10}$$

as the inverse distance in terms of r_0 and

$$E = \frac{GMm/r_0}{kT}, \tag{13-11}$$

we can write the barometric equation as

$$\frac{\rho}{\rho_0} = \exp E(y - 1). \tag{13-12}$$

It should be noted that at an infinite distance (i.e., $r = \infty$, $y = 0$) the density approaches a finite value that is physically unrealistic; that is,

$$\rho_\infty = \rho_0 \exp(-E). \tag{13-13}$$

The neutral components

The equations in the preceding section were derived without regard to the actual density. However, in any planetary atmosphere a level of altitude is reached at which the density of the atmosphere is so low that the mean free path becomes of the order of the scale height H. To a good approximation, we may assume that above this level the mean free path in fact becomes infinite so that molecules that travel in this region, named the exosphere, would experience no collisions with other molecules. It can be easily seen, then, that molecules that issue from the base of the exosphere will describe ballistic orbits, that is, portions of ellipses that will take them out to high altitudes before they again re-enter the atmosphere at a different point. Some of the molecules will travel beyond the gravitational field of the planet.

It is useful to point out the analogy between the orbits of space vehicles on the one hand and those of neutral atoms or molecules. In both cases only the gravitational field of the earth exerts any appreciable forces on them, and it is well known that the acceleration, hence the trajectory, is independent of the mass. We shall distinguish three main components of the neutral exosphere for each atomic species separately. (It is clear that in the absence of collisions atoms of oxygen, hydrogen, etc., will describe their orbits independently without interfering with one another; hence each species can be treated separately.)

1. The ballistic re-entry component, consisting of molecules ejected upward from the base of the exosphere with less than escape velocity and again returning to the base (elliptic ballistic orbits).

2. The ballistic escape component, consisting of molecules ejected upward from the base of the exosphere with more than escape velocity and ultimately leaving the exosphere (hyperbolic ballistic orbits).

3. The bound orbiting (satellite) component, consisting of molecules circling the planet in elliptic orbits *not* intersecting the base of the exosphere (bound elliptic orbits).

The time spent inside the exosphere is short for components (1) and (2) and long for component (3). Therefore, the density distribution of (1) and (2) are little affected by other factors. We shall treat them separately in a later section and then return to the satellite component.

The base of the neutral exosphere

The "base of the exosphere," that is, the level above which collisions between neutral atoms may be neglected, cannot be defined without a certain amount of ambiguity (1). In practice, however, the arbitrariness of the definition does not affect the calculated distribution above the base. We take this level at a distance R where the number density of neutral atoms $N(R) = N_0$ is such that one half of the escaping atoms will undergo a collision. It follows therefore that (1)

$$N_0 \sim \tfrac{1}{2}(H\sigma)^{-1}, \qquad (13\text{-}14)$$

where σ is the gas-kinetic cross section and equal to 3×10^{-15} cm^2 (2), and H is given by equation (13-4).

The actual position of the critical level for the earth can be found by a detailed analysis of available data on the upper atmosphere (3). King-Hele's analysis (4) of satellite-orbit data furnishes the best starting point for both densities and scale heights versus altitude. Near 500 km, H $\sim$ 8×10^6 cm and is varying slowly. We use now the additional fact that the atmosphere near this level is almost completely composed of neutral dissociated oxygen. (Only below about 350 km does N_2 become an important constituent.)

Therefore, the mass densities near 500 km can be directly translated into number densities of O by using $N = \rho/m$, where $m = 16\, m_\mathrm{H}$. From equation (13-14) the value of N_0 turns out to be 7.5×10^7/cm^3, and this number density occurs at an altitude of 530 km. The level of the base $R = R_E + 530$ is 6900 km.

13-1 ESCAPE OF GASES FROM A PLANETARY ATMOSPHERE

As we shall see, the problems of exospheric-density distribution and escape of molecules are intrinsically related. The escape of molecules was first discussed by Stoney (5); the classical theory has been developed by Jeans (6) and Lennard-Jones (7), and a concise discussion has been given by Spitzer (8). It has been critically re-examined by Öpik and Singer (1), whose treatment we follow here.

At the critical level R we may assume that the molecules are distributed isotropically with a Maxwellian velocity distribution function

$$P(v) = 4\pi v^2 \left(\frac{m}{2\pi kT}\right) e^{-mv^2/2kT}. \qquad (13\text{-}15)$$

The effective injection rate from level R into the exosphere is given by

$$dF = \tfrac{1}{2}P(v)\cdot v\cos\theta\cdot\sin\theta\,d\theta \qquad (13\text{-}16)$$

in molecules per second in velocity interval v to $v + dv$ and zenithal angle cone comprised between θ and $\theta + d\theta$. (The angle θ is between the velocity vector and the radius.) Equation (13-16) was obtained by multiplying the upward moving molecules, that is, $\tfrac{1}{2}P(v)$, by the radial velocity and solid angle interval. Integration of equation (13-16) over the limits $\theta = 0$ to $\pi/2$ and $v = v_\infty$ to ∞ leads directly to the rate of escape

$$F(R) = 4\pi R^2 \times N_0 \times \left(\frac{kT}{2\pi m}\right)^{1/2} (1 + E)e^{-E}. \qquad (13\text{-}17)$$

The escape velocity v_∞ from the level R is defined in the usual way as

$$\tfrac{1}{2}v_\infty{}^2 = 2gR = \frac{GM_E}{R}. \qquad (13\text{-}18)$$

Examination of equation (13-17) reveals that for small values of E the escape flux approaches simply N (rms thermal velocity).

13-2 DISTRIBUTION OF DENSITY IN A NEUTRAL EXOSPHERE

After showing the inadequacy of the barometric formula [equation (13.9)], we shall derive the correct theory for the ballistic components (1) and (2). The contribution of the satellite component (3) can be roughly estimated and is probably not important.

Inadequacy of barometric formula

In the published literature it is conventionally assumed (and sometimes stated explicitly) that the gas in the exosphere is "isothermal," and in fact has the same temperature as the base of the exosphere. This assumption implies that the (isotropic) Maxivellian velocity distribution which exists at the base also *exists at all levels above it.* But this statement means that the density distribution *must follow* the barometric formula [equation (13-9)]. (A formal proof of their equivalence has been given in Reference (1), Appendix.)

Further reflection shows that this approach cannot be correct. In the first place, if we consider for a moment the situation at large distances from the earth, then we should find there only particles that at the base of the exosphere have had escape velocity or greater. These particles, of course, are destined to escape and will form the escape flux at any level. At large distances from the earth these particles will be streaming outward with nearly radial velocity. It is clear that the velocity distribution of these particles is not isotropic, and we may, therefore, raise the question concerning the significance of the concept of a temperature. Second, and this is the main point, in the absence of collisions between particles, which is, of course, assumed in the exosphere, the assumption of local thermodynamic equilibrium underlying the hydrostatic equation is unfounded. Local thermodynamic equilibrium means complete statistical exchange of the kinetic energy and momentum of the molecules, within a volume, small as compared with the volume to which the problem is applied; in the absence of collisions this cannot take place, and the concept of gas pressure balancing gravitation has no meaning. Also, the concept of temperature cannot be strictly defined. At best we can talk only about a mean kinetic energy of the molecules.

Furthermore, as can be seen from equation (13-13), the barometric formula leads to a finite and not to a zero density at infinity.

Derivation of density distribution

The density distribution may be calculated by considering the statistical distribution of particle orbits issuing from the base of the exosphere and integrating their contribution to the density of each level r. It is instructive to carry out this derivation *ab initio*, following the treatment in (9).

The contribution to the density within a spherical shell r to $r + \Delta r$ by a particle leaving the earth with velocity v_0 at zenith angle θ is proportional to the time spent traversing Δr, that is, inversely to the radial velocity v_r,

$$\Delta t = \frac{\Delta r}{v_r}. \tag{13-19}$$

To find v_r, we note that

$$v_r{}^2 = v^2 - v_t{}^2, \tag{13-20}$$

where v_t is the transversal velocity. Because of conservation of angular momentum

$$Rv_{t0} = rv_t, \tag{13-21}$$

where R is the radius of the base of the exosphere and v_{t0}, the transversal velocity at the base. Because of conservation of energy,

$$\tfrac{1}{2}(v_0{}^2 - v^2) = g_0R\left(1 - \frac{R}{r}\right). \tag{13-22}$$

Therefore, on substituting (13-21) and (13-22) into (13-20), we find, remembering that $v_{t0} = v_0 \sin \theta$ and the definition of equation (13-10),

$$v_r{}^2 = v_0{}^2(1 - y^2 \sin^2 \theta) - 2g_0R(1 - y). \tag{13-23}$$

By using an isotropic emission from a horizontal surface element at the base of the exosphere of particles with Maxwellian velocity distribution $P(v)$, the relative density $\rho(y)$ in a unit volume of the shell at r is given by integrating over v_0 and θ, using weight factors $\sin \theta \, d\theta$ and $\cos \theta$ (to allow for the decrease in the projected area element).

$$\rho(y) = y^2 \int_0^{\pi/2} \sin \theta \cos \theta \, d\theta \int_{v_0 \min}^{v_\infty} P(v_0) \left(\frac{v_0}{v_r}\right) dv_0$$

$$+ \tfrac{1}{2}y^2 \int_0^{\pi/2} \sin \theta \cos \theta \, d\theta \int_{v_\infty} P(v_0) \left(\frac{v_0}{v_r}\right) dv_0. \tag{13-24}$$

The first term of equation (13-24) is doubled, since the ballistic-elliptic component contributes twice, both going up and going down. The second term of (13-24) gives the contribution of the escaping particles.

We must now consider the limits on the integral in (13-24). If we fix our attention on, say $\rho(y_1)$, then the minimum value of v_0 can be found from (13-23) by setting $v_r = 0$, which gives

$$v_0{}^2 {}_{\min} = v_\infty{}^2 \frac{1 - y_1}{1 - y_1{}^2 \sin^2 \theta}. \tag{13-25}$$

The maximum value of v_0 for re-entry is the escape velocity v (independent of y).

Equation (13-24) can be simplified as follows. We introduce

$$a^2 = \frac{1 - y}{1 - y^2 \sin^2 \theta} \tag{13-26}$$

and express all velocities in terms of v_∞, so that

$$v_{0\,min} = a.$$

Also we recall from equations (13-11) and (13-18) that

$$E = \tfrac{1}{2}\frac{mv_0^2}{kT}. \tag{13-27}$$

Finally we can write equation (13-24), giving the relative density as a function of inverse distance (dropping all subscripts):

$$\frac{\rho(y)}{y^2} = \int_0^{\pi/2}\int_a^1 \frac{\sin\theta\cos\theta\,d\theta}{(1-y^2\sin^2\theta)^{1/2}}\frac{v^3e^{-Ev^2}\,dv}{(v^2-a^2)^{1/2}}$$

$$+ \tfrac{1}{2}\int_0^{\pi/2}\int_1^\infty \frac{\sin\theta\cos\theta\,d\theta}{(1-y^2\sin^2\theta)^{1/2}}\frac{v^3e^{-E^2}\,dv}{(v^2-a^2)^{1/2}}. \tag{13-28}$$

The integration over velocity can be carried out most conveniently by defining

$$b^2 \equiv E(1-a^2) \tag{13-29}$$

and by using the error integral

$$\phi = \phi(b) = \frac{2}{\sqrt{\pi}}\int_0^b e^{-x^2}\,dx \tag{13-30}$$

and its derivative

$$\phi' = \phi'(b) = \frac{2}{\sqrt{\pi}}e^{-b^2}. \tag{13-31}$$

Then the integral in equation (13-28) can be expressed as

$$\frac{\rho(y)}{y^2} = \int_0^{\pi/2}\frac{\sin\theta\cos\theta\,d\theta\exp(-Ea^2)}{(1-y^2\sin^2\theta)^{1/2}}[(1+2Ea^2)\phi - b\phi']$$

$$+ \tfrac{1}{2}\int_0^{\pi/2}\frac{\sin\theta\cos\theta\,d\theta\exp(-Ea^2)}{(1-y^2\sin^2\theta)^{1/2}}[(1+2Ea^2)(1-\phi) + b\phi']. \tag{13-32}$$

The first integral represents the contribution of the elliptic (re-entry) component, the second, the contribution of the hyperbolic (escape) component. The integrals must be evaluated numerically for various values of E, representing different cases of interest. We give the results of such evaluations for hydrogen atoms at 1500°K (Table 13-1), at 1250°, 1800°, and 3000°K (Table 13-2), and for oxygen atoms at 1500°K (Table 13-3).

TABLE 13-1

Barometric (ρ_h) and Exospheric Re-entry (ρ_r), Escape (ρ_e), Ballistic (ρ_B), Bound (ρ_0) and Total (ρ_t) Density Distributions for $E = 4.65$

$(T = 1500°$ for neutral hydrogen in earth's exosphere)

y	r/R	ρ_h	ρ_r	ρ_e	ρ_B	ρ_0	ρ_t	$\bar{w}^2$
1.0	1.000	100.000	98.715	1.285	100.000	0.000	100.000	0.5000
0.9	1.111	62.813	58.17	0.776	58.95	2.976	61.93	0.4263
0.8	1.250	39.455	34.16	0.592	34.75	3.455	38.20	0.3556
0.7	1.429	24.783	19.49	0.452	19.94	3.378	23.32	0.2882
0.6	1.667	15.567	10.65	0.337	10.99	3.003	13.99	0.2250
0.5	2.000	9.778	5.467	0.2408	5.708	2.465	8.173	0.1667
0.4	2.500	6.142	2.545	0.1615	2.707	1.852	4.559	0.1143
0.3	3.333	3.858	1.011	0.0973	1.108	1.236	2.344	0.06000
0.2	5.000	2.423	0.299	0.0478	0.347	0.679	1.026	0.03333
0.1	10.000	1.522	0.0429	0.0141	0.0570	0.238	0.295	0.00909

Note.

$$\rho_B = \rho_r + \rho_e$$

$$\rho_t = \rho_B + \rho_0$$

The last column gives $\bar{w}^2$, which is proportional to the mean kinetic energy of particles existing at a particular level.

The complete integration of equation (13-32) has been performed by Herring and Kyle (10) with the following result:

$$\frac{\rho(y)}{\rho_0} = (1 - \tfrac{1}{2} \operatorname{erf} \sqrt{Ey}\,) \exp\left[-E(1 - y)\right] - (1 - y^2)^{1/2}$$

$$(1 - \tfrac{1}{2} \operatorname{erf} \sqrt{Ey/(1 + y)}\,) \exp\left(\frac{-E}{1 + y}\right)$$

$$- \left(\frac{Ey}{\pi}\right)^{1/2} (1 - \sqrt{1 - y}\,) \exp{-E}, \qquad (13\text{-}32a)$$

where

$$\operatorname{erf}(x) = 1 - \phi(x) = \frac{2}{\sqrt{\pi}} \int_x^\infty e^{-y^2}\, dy.$$

In Figure 13-1 we plot the three components as a function of distance and show the large discrepancy between our results and the barometric formula.

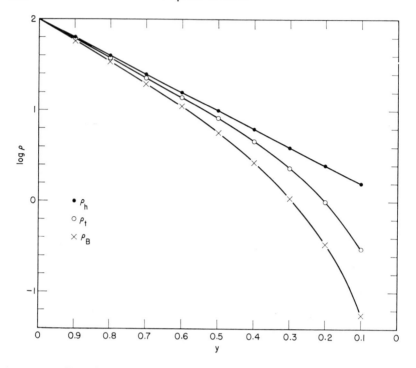

Figure 13-1 Logarithm of exospheric density as function of reciprocal distance. $y = Rr$, for $E = 4.65$ (neutral hydrogen at $T = 1500°\,$K in terrestrial exosphere). Dots and straight line = barometric formula; centered circles = ballistic + bound orbiting components; crosses = ballistic (re-entry + escape) components only.

TABLE 13-2

Partial Density Distributions for Small Values of E (approximate calculation)

(Temperatures are for hydrogen in earth's exosphere; cf. Table 13-1 for notation)

$y = R/r$	ρ_h	ρ_B	ρ_e	ρ_h	ρ_B	ρ_e	ρ_h	ρ_B	ρ_e
	$E = 5.580$ ($T = 1250°$)			$E = 3.870$ ($T = 1801°$)			$E = 2.325$ ($T = 3000°$)		
1.0	100.0	100.0	0.51	100.0	100.0	2.36	100.0	100.0	9.4
0.9	57.2	54.9	0.35	67.9	62.2	1.69	79.2	67.3	6.9
0.8	32.7	30.3	0.25	46.1	38.7	1.24	62.8	45.9	5.0
0.5	6.1	4.1	0.10	14.4	7.5	0.49	31.3	12.4	1.93
0.333	2.4	0.95	0.050	7.6	2.2	0.24	21.5	4.4	0.94
0.2	1.15	0.19	0.021	4.5	0.54	0.10	15.6	1.25	0.38
0.1	0.66	0.030	0.0064	3.1	0.096	0.029	12.3	0.252	0.112
0.08	0.59	0.017	0.0043	2.8	0.055	0.019	11.8	0.152	0.070

TABLE 13-3

Density Distribution for Large Value of E = 74.4

($T = 1500°$K for neutral atomic oxygen in earth's exosphere;
cf. Table 13-1 for notations)

$y =$	1.00	0.99	0.98	0.96	0.94	0.92	0.90	0.88
$\rho_h =$	100.00	47.52	22.58	5.099	1.152	0.2600	0.05872	0.01326
$\rho_B =$	100.000	47.49	22.56	5.086	1.147	0.2587	0.05833	0.01316

Two special cases can be easily calculated.

1. At the base of the exosphere $y = 1$, $a = 0$,

$$\rho \rightarrow \rho_0 = \tfrac{1}{2}[1 + \phi(E^{1/2}) - E^{1/2}\phi'(E^{1/2})]. \qquad (13\text{-}33) *$$

2. At $r = \infty$, $y = 0$, $a^2 = 1$, $b = 0$, and only the escape term contributes

$$\frac{\rho_\infty}{y^2} = \tfrac{1}{4}(1 + 2E) \exp(-E). \qquad (13\text{-}34)$$

Another derivation of this formula has been given recently starting from the collisionless Boltzmann equation.

The bound ("satellite") component

The existence of a bound component can be made plausible by the following argument. A particle can be placed into a satellite orbit only by means of a collision *above* the base of the exosphere. Hence, if we adopt our strict mathematical definition of *no* collisions above the base, then it would seem that there should be no bound orbits. Actually, there would be no particles *injected* into bound orbits, but neither could they be removed. In the physically more realistic case collisions above the base do produce bound particles, and since they may survive for long times even a small number can contribute appreciably to the total density in the exosphere. (In fact, the situation is somewhat analogous to the high-energy charged particles trapped in the earth's magnetic field; their concentration is controlled by the rate of injection and their lifetime in trapped orbits.)

* It will be noted that ρ does not quite normalize to unity at $r = R$. This matter is discussed in detail in Reference (1).

The problem is best divided into two parts. In Part 1 we consider a physically unrealistic model in which there are no external factors (such as solar ultraviolet and corpuscular radiation and ionized component of the exosphere) and allow as the only injection and removal mechanism for bound orbits collisions among molecules in ballistic orbits. In Part 2 the influence of these external factors is then considered.

Part 1. This problem has been solved by means of the so-called principle of detailed balancing (1). It allows the derivation of the *equilibrium* intensity in the bound orbits. The *rate* of collision tells only how rapidly this equilibrium state is reached if, for example, some external "demon" suddenly swept out all particles in bound orbits.

The main result of the study (1) was to establish at each level the velocity range in which bound orbits *could* exist. The minimum velocity is that which just intersects the base of the exosphere; the maximum velocity is always the escape velocity appropriate to the level *r*. According to the principle of detailed balancing, within this velocity interval the cone of direction not occupied by the ballistic component will be completely filled to saturation density if sufficient time is allowed.

The results of this study are given in Table 13-1 and Figure 3-1; for further details Reference (1) should be consulted.

Part 2. It should be remembered that the contribution from the bound component calculated above represents generally a maximum estimate. The real degree of occupancy depends on the actual physical situation considered and no general statements can be made. An important problem for the case of the earth is the density of neutral hydrogen at large distances. This case has been discussed, but the conclusions differ by large factors (11, 12). It seems likely however that the flux of solar ultraviolet radiation by itself is strong enough to photoionize and thereby limit the lifetime of bound hydrogen atoms, with a resultant decrease in their contribution to the density. A final resolution of this important problem is not yet possible.

13-3 DISTRIBUTION OF THE NEUTRAL COMPONENTS

Having derived a theory which gives the relative density distribution of neutral atoms, equation (13-32), we must find a method of normalization based on certain experimental data or observations. Different techniques must be applied for atomic oxygen and atomic hydrogen.

The temperature at the base is a matter of considerable importance, since it determines the complete distribution with altitude of all neutral constituents of the exosphere.

Neutral oxygen

Since oxygen is by far the most important constituent at and just above the base, there is no ambiguity. All of the number density $N_0 = 7.5 \times 10^7/\text{cm}^3$ can be assigned to atomic oxygen. The temperature near 500 km can be derived from satellite orbit data as about 1600°K, but not very accurately (4). Quite a different approach is to deduce the rate of escape of helium from the earth's atmosphere over geological times and thereby an "effective" temperature of about 1500°K (8). However, the rate of escape is so sensitive to temperature that a lower average temperature, plus brief temperature peaks, could give the same rate of escape.

A much more satisfactory method consists in comparing the density values from satellite orbit data above the base of the exosphere with the variation predicted by equation (13-32) and adjusting the value of E, and therefore T, for best fit (3). When this is done, we find that a temperature of the base of 1500°K gives the most satisfactory agreement. Additional supporting evidence comes from radiation-belt data on trapped protons. The intensity of the trapped protons measured in satellite experiments is proportional to their lifetime, which in turn depends on the atmospheric density near this level. A detailed analysis has been performed (3) on the radiation belt flux versus altitude data taken at the magnetic equator. This analysis gives consistent density values up to an altitude of $\sim$1000 km, where the satellite orbit drag data are quite uncertain.

In addition, the radiation-belt data also serve to assure us that atomic oxygen remains the most important constituent up to *at least* 1000 km. The significance of the deviation of the curve above 1000 km is discussed in Section 13-4.

With the normalization established, the complete variation of atomic oxygen with altitude can now be given from equation (13-32). The "best" values are given in Table 13-4.

Neutral hydrogen

The relative distribution of neutral hydrogen is given by equation (13-32), with $E = 4.65$ corresponding to a base temperature of 1500°K. The contribution from the bound orbits will be neglected for the time being, so that our result constitutes a minimum value of $\rho(\text{H})$ at each level.

TABLE 13-4

Distribution of Major Exospheric Components with Altitude

(Mean values have been chosen, corresponding to an exospheric base
at 530 km and temperature 1500°K)

r/R	Altitude (km)	n(O) (cm^{-3})	n(H)	n(O$^+$)	n(H$^+$)
		(a)	(b)	(c)	(d)
1.000	530	4×10^7	10^4	9×10^5	
1.010	600	1.9×10^7		6.2×10^5	
1.025	700	6.4×10^6		3.6×10^5	
1.050	870	1.2×10^6		1.6×10^5	
1.075	1040	2.3×10^5		6.7×10^4	
1.100	1220	4×10^4	6.3×10^3	3.1×10^4	
1.125	1390	1×10^4		1.4×10^4	
1.150	1560	2.5×10^3		6.9×10^3	
1.175	1730	6.4×10^2		3.5×10^3	
1.200	1910	1.6×10^2	4.2×10^3	1.8×10^3	
1.250			3.5×10^3		
1.667			1.1×10^3		
2.000			5.7×10^2		10^3
2.500			2.7×10^2		5×10^2
3.333			1.1×10^2		2×10^2
5.000			3.5×10		70
10.000			6		10

(a) Calculated from exosphere theory for $T = 1500°K$ and normalized to
satellite-drag data at the point $r = R$.

(b) Calculated from exosphere theory for $T = 1500°K$ and normalized to
Lyman-alpha data.

(c) Calculated from exosphere theory for $T = 1500°K$ and normalized to
Alpert's electron density at the point $r = R$.

(d) Deduced from radio whistler data (Helliwell).

Note. He, He$^+$, and O^{2+}, O^{3+}, and He^{2+} are not shown; they may become
important between 1000 and 2000 km.

Unfortunately, no precise normalization is possible for H as in the
case of O. At one time it was believed that radiation-belt data could
be used to derive $\rho(H)$ above 1000 km, but this expectation was not
borne out.

However, an integral normalization method, propounded by F. S. Johnson, can be used to good advantage. The method makes use of the fact that atomic hydrogen in the exosphere will resonance scatter solar Lyman-alpha radiation * on the *night* side of the earth. One way of explaining its existence there is by scattering from exospheric hydrogen on the daylight side into the earth's shadow. In the meantime, a more direct method of measuring the total thickness of neutral hydrogen in the exosphere has become available. Tousey and colleagues have obtained a high-dispersion picture of the solar Lyman-alpha line which shows a narrow central absorption core superimposed on the emission line. Presumably, the core is produced by the "scattering out" of Lyman-alpha protons by exospheric hydrogen. On this assumption, Tousey (13) obtained a total vertical thickness of 2×10^{12} H atoms/cm²-column.

In order to normalize, we must integrate equation (13-32). To a fairly close order of magnitude, we find

$$\int_R^\infty N(\mathrm{H}) \, dr = 0.32 \, N_0 R. \tag{13-35}$$

Using $R = 6900$ km, we obtain

$$N_0(\mathrm{H}) = 2 \times 10^{12}/0.32 \times 6.9 \times 10^8 = 10^4 \text{ atoms/cm}^3. \tag{13-36}$$

With this normalization, we can obtain the complete distribution of neutral hydrogen atoms. It is tabulated in Table 13-4.

"Temperature"

It is clear from the foregoing discussion that in the absence of collisions there will be no thermodynamic equilibrium and, in general, no Maxwellian distribution of velocities. Therefore, the concept of "temperature" cannot be used and becomes progressively inappropriate at higher altitudes. As a result, any statement that the exosphere is isothermal is incorrect, and any attempt to extrapolate a temperature *gradient* from the lower barosphere into the exosphere is even worse.

We can, in fact, find the mean kinetic energy of molecules at each level. It can be seen from Table 13-1 that this mean energy *decreases* with distance.

---

* This line lies in the far-ultraviolet, with a wavelength of 1216 Å. It is produced by the transition of the bound electron in the H atom from quantum level $n = 2$ to $n = 1$. The Lyman-alpha radiation is strongly absorbed in the lower ionosphere.

13-4 THE IONIZED COMPONENT OF THE EXOSPHERE

Evidence for the existence of ionized gas around the earth, at levels well above the usual ionosphere, came first from the observations of the propagation of "radio whistlers." It yielded a mean electron density of about $600/cm^3$ at a few earth radii (14), which was coincidentally similar to the electron density of the interplanetary gas derived from optical observations to the zodiacal light (15).*

This coincidence was chiefly responsible for the incorrect identification of the origin of the whistler medium. The case for its terrestrial origin was first stated by F. S. Johnson, but as we shall see, it is possible to deduce its terrestrial origin as a natural extension of the ionosphere from a priori arguments.

It is not possible, however, to deduce the ionized component in relation to the neutral components.

Origin of the magnetosphere

We shall refer to the ionized portion of the exosphere as the "magnetosphere," although the names "whistler medium," "protonosphere," and "outer ionosphere" are often used. It forms, however, a plasma in every sense of the word, a plasma that is pervaded by a magnetic field, the earth's dipole field, and is under the influence of a gravitational field as well.

The zeroth-order effect of the magnetic field is to cause ions and electrons to spiral around the lines of force, thus "tying" them to the lines of force. This prevents the escape of ions, even if their velocity exceeds the escape value. Only near the poles is escape possible, where lines of force may go far out into interplanetary space.

By the same token, the magnetic field prevents the entry and accretion of interplanetary ions (except again near the poles). By this argument, the telluric origin of the plasmosphere is assured, at least out to several earth-radii.

We may distinguish two components of the magnetosphere, somewhat analogous to the classification of the components of the neutral exosphere. We must keep in mind however that the escape component is now missing.

1. Re-entry component. An ion starting upward at the base of the plasmosphere will spiral about a given line of force. Depending on

---

* Quite recent observations, based on an examination of Fraunhofer lines rather than on photometry, give an interplanetary electron density near the earth of not more than 50 to $100/cm^3$ (19).

initial conditions, it may (a) reach its summit before it crosses the
plane of the magnetic equator and return close to where it started
or (b) cross the equatorial plane and re-enter in the opposite hemisphere.

2. Trapped component. An ion may move so that the magnetic
field reflects it before it reaches the base. It is then "trapped" and
moves back and forth between mirror points until, for example, a
collision puts it into component (1) (re-entry orbit). There are two
sources of trapped ions—(a) collisions among ions of component (1)
and (b) injection of ions created by photoionization of the neutral
component.

A detailed discussion of these components is given in Reference (16)
and is summarized here.

Re-entry Component. One starts by considering the motion of a
single ion under the influence of two fields of force, a magnetic dipole
field and a gravitational inverse-square central field. Fortunately,
the rather complicated motion of the ion can be expressed in a simple
form, since its radius of gyration in the magnetic field is much smaller
than the scale of either force field. The contribution to the density
at each level is then found (by an extension of Liouville's theorem
from statistical mechanics). Finally, we replace the single ion by
a group with a Maxwellian velocity distribution at the base and perform the necessary integrations. (The procedure is quite analogous
but more involved than that used in Section 13-2.) As a final result,
we obtain the distributions of ions (and therefore also of electrons)
as a function of altitude *along a line of force.* It should be noted that
different solutions are obtained along different lines of force (defined
by the distance r_e at which it crosses the equator). Hence the density
distribution of the ionized re-entry component depends not only on r
but also on latitude λ; it is symmetric about the earth's magnetic axis
and not spherically symmetric as the neutral component.

Trapped Component. (a) The importance of the trapped component can again be estimated from the principle of detailed balancing, since collisions among ions of component (1) both generate and
remove trapped ions. It is shown in Reference (16) that for some
distance above the base of the ion-exosphere the trapped orbits are
populated at about equilibrium intensity. (b) Injection from the
neutral component cannot be finally assessed at the present time but
appears to be unimportant numerically compared to process (a).

As a final result, with the trapped orbits filled to full intensity and

with the escape component absent, it appears justified to use a barometric formula, similar to equation (13-9) not only below but also
for some considerable distance above the base of the ion-exosphere.

Base of the ion-exosphere

In an ionized gas the collision cross section σ for low-energy electrons
with ions is $\sim 2.4 \times 10^5 T_e^{-2}/\text{cm}^2$ and depends only weakly on the electron density (17). T_e is the electron temperature that may on occasion
exceed the ion temperature, since electrons are created by photoionization with initially high energies.

At $T_e = 1500°K$, $\sigma \sim 10^{-11}/\text{cm}^2$, or about 10^4 times larger than the
collision cross section involving neutral atoms only. The base of the
ion-exosphere may be defined as the level at which the electron density
N_e is such that the mfp λ equals 1 R_E; that is,

$$\lambda = \frac{1}{N_e \sigma} = R_E. \tag{13-37}$$

Substituting into equation (13-37), we derive

$$N_e \sim 1.5 \times 10^2/\text{cm}^3 \tag{13-38}$$

as a minimum value for the critical electron density, corresponding to a
minimum T_e of 1500°K.

The exact position of the base is not too important, since, as mentioned before, no sudden transition occurs for the distribution of the
ionized component; a barometric formula holds below and for some
distance above the base. Furthermore, the electron distribution is
almost certainly not Maxwellian but peaked at higher velocities.
Therefore, in any case, the barometric formula can hold only approximately.

Distribution of density with altitude

If ions and electrons did not interact with each other, then each
species would be distributed according to its own scale-height, which,
for the electrons would be at least 1840 times as large as for protons.
Also, the electrons, because of their higher thermal velocities, would
rapidly escape. Such a situation is clearly impossible, since it leads
to a large charge separation which sets up an electric field. This
field supplies additional electrostatic forces which equalize the scale
heights so that no net space charge is created and so that the escape
rates of electrons and ions become equal.

The distribution of ions with altitude is given by

$$\frac{N(r)}{N_0} = \exp - \left[\frac{1}{2}\frac{GM_E}{kT}\left(\frac{1}{R} - \frac{1}{r}\right)\right] = \exp\left[\tfrac{1}{2}E(y - 1)\right]. \quad (13\text{-}39)$$

The factor $\frac{1}{2}$ enters because of the presence of the electrostatic field produced by electron diffusion. If the electron temperature is higher, then the factor will be $T_{\text{ion}}/(T_{\text{ion}} + T_e)$ instead of $\frac{1}{2}$.

The distribution given by equation (13-39) holds for the dominant ionic species. The difficult case of the distribution of a minor ionic species in the presence of a dominant one has been treated by a number of authors (Mange, Öpik and Singer, and Hanson).

Consider the case of a mixed (oxygen + hydrogen) plasma. The electrostatic field created by diffusion of the electrons may lead to negative apparent gravity for the lighter component (e.g., $-7g$ for a trace of protons among oxygen ions and $-1.25g$ for 50 percent protons with 50 percent oxygen ions) and to a positive density gradient outward. The separation of ionized hydrogen from the heavier ions with altitude must therefore proceed much faster than according to the usual formulas of diffusive equilibrium of neutral gas. This follows from the condition of negligible or zero-space charge in macroscopic environment, as shown below.

Let x be the altitude, N the number density of a gaseous component, or mixture of components, and H the local scale height defined in the most general way by

$$H = \frac{-N}{\partial N/\partial x}. \quad (13\text{-}40)$$

Let N_1 and N_2 be the number densities and m_1 and m_2, the ionic masses of the two singly ionized constituents of a plasma, so that the electron density at zero space charge is

$$N_e = N_1 + N_2. \quad (13\text{-}41)$$

In diffusive equilibrium equation (13-40) holds separately for each constituent, with

$$H = \frac{kT}{mg}, \quad (13\text{-}42)$$

where g is the total acceleration from gravity and electrostatic field. If U denotes the electrostatic force acting on unit charge, g_0 the acceleration of gravity, the accelerations of the two ionic and the electronic components are

$$g_1 = g_0 - \frac{U}{m_1}, \qquad g_2 = g_0 - \frac{U}{m_2}, \qquad g_e = g_0 + \frac{U}{m_e}. \qquad (13\text{-}43)$$

These accelerations define the scale heights separately for each component, according to equation (13-42). From equation (13-40) the gradient of positive charge is

$$\frac{\partial N_i}{\partial x} = -\frac{N_1}{H_1} - \frac{N_2}{H_2}, \qquad (13\text{-}44)$$

and this must equal the gradient of negative charge

$$\frac{\partial N_e}{\partial x} = -\frac{N_e}{H_e}. \qquad (13\text{-}45)$$

Substituting the scale heights from equation (13-42) with g_1, g_2, and g_e, according to equation (13-43), into equations (13-44) and (13-45) and equating them, we obtain

$$N_1(g_0 m_1 - U) + N_2(g_0 m_2 - U) = N_e(g_0 m_e + U). \qquad (13\text{-}46)$$

With equation (13-41) this gives

$$U = \frac{g_0(N_1 m_1 + N_2 m_2 - N_e m_e)}{2N_e}. \qquad (13\text{-}47)$$

When $m_e \ll m_1$ or m_2, the third term in equation (13-47) can be neglected. Setting

$$\frac{N_1}{N_e} = X, \qquad \frac{N_2}{N_e} = 1 - X,$$

and substituting equation (13-47) into (13-43), the effective accelerations in static equilibrium become

$$g_1 = \tfrac{1}{2} g_0 \left[2 - X - \frac{(1 - X)m_2}{m_1} \right], \qquad (13\text{-}48a)$$

$$g_2 = \tfrac{1}{2} g_0 \left(1 + X - \frac{X m_1}{m_2} \right), \qquad (13\text{-}48b)$$

$$g_e = \tfrac{1}{2} g_0 \left[1 + \frac{X m_1}{m_e} + \frac{(1 - X)m_2}{m_e} \right]. \qquad (13\text{-}48c)$$

When $X \to 0$ for hydrogen, with oxygen ions as the major constituent, $m_2/m_1 = 16$, the acceleration of protons becomes strongly negative:

$$g_1 = -7g_0,$$

their scale height is also negative, and their increment is positive with altitude:

$$\frac{dN_1}{N_1} = -\frac{dx}{H_1} = +\frac{7m_1 g_0\, dx}{kT}.$$

It is easy to extend similar considerations to an arbitrary mixture of ionic components in diffusive equilibrium.

We thus note that for a nonhomogeneous plasma in diffusive equilibrium equation (13-39) does not represent the distribution of density of the components. The solution, although clearly defined, is more complicated than the simple exponential law. Equations (13-40), (13-45), (13-41a), and (13-48c) can be partially integrated to yield a general solution:

$$X(1 - X)^{-\mu} = N_e^{-2(1-\mu)} \times \text{constant}; \qquad (13\text{-}49)$$

where $\mu = m_1/m_2$.

Equation (13-49) gives the variation of X, the concentration of m_1, as a function of the electron density. The electron density as a function of altitude x is to be found from numerical integration of the differential equation

$$\frac{dN_e}{N_e\, dx} = -\frac{m_2 g_0[1 - (1 - \mu)X]}{2kT}. \qquad (13\text{-}50)$$

The solution represented by equations (13-49) and (13-50) is valid insofar as the diffusion of the plasma along the magnetic lines of force is intense enough to override local exchange with the neutral component by way of photoionization, collisional ionization, and recombination; exchange of charge is only of secondary importance in this respect, since it does not change the ionic population and affects only the kinetic energy (if the temperatures of plasma and neutral component are different). In that case the equations are valid upward from a certain denser base of the plasma where ionization equilibrium is established by local processes rather than by diffusional exchange.

Quite recently Hanson (18) applied this theory to deduce the distribution of He^+, which he finds to be dominant around 1200 km. On the other hand, Nakada and Singer (19) have shown that O^{2+}, O^{3+}, and even O^{4+} ions, which may be dominant around 1200 km, should exist.

13-5 DISTRIBUTION OF IONIZED OXYGEN

O^+ ions are created by solar UV, mainly within the ionospheric layers by the photoionization of O atoms. Since they make frequent elastic collisions with neutral atoms, we may assume that the O^+ temperature near 530 km is also 1500°K.

The relative distribution with altitude of O^+ is then given by equation (13-39). Again, in order to make a normalization, it will be necessary to go to experimental observations. We shall use direct measurements of electron density by Berning as well as an analysis of radiation-belt data.

Berning's measurements

A technique for the measurement of electron densities has been perfected by Berning. His early attempts in V-2 rockets gave electron densities up into the F layer. Quite recently he has been successful in making a measurement up to 1500 km (20). The method makes use of Doppler shift measurements at two or more frequencies that are harmonically related. The lowest frequency is affected most by the plasma surrounding the rocket and measures in effect a "local refractive index" from which the ambient electron density can be derived. At $r = R$ he obtains an electron density of $9 \times 10^4/\text{cm}^3$. If we identify the corresponding (but unobserved) ions as O^+, the mass concentration N_0, in equation (13-39), becomes 1.4×10^6 cm^{-3}.

There are two arguments to support this identification: (1) no other ionic species could be more predominant than O^+ at this level; (2) the subsequent slope agrees well with the theoretical curve for O^+ at 1500°K up to an altitude of about 1000 km above sea level.

Radiation-belt analysis

Counting rates of a Geiger counter in satellite Explorer IV, in particular the dependence of counting rate with altitude up to 1200 km above the magnetic equator, have been reported.

These data can be analyzed with the point of view of deducing the properties of the exosphere (3). We shall reproduce here the basic ideas behind this analysis. It is presumed that the data, as they stand, refer primarily to trapped protons. Their intensity depends on their lifetime, which in turn is inversely proportional to atmospheric density. The dependence with altitude is not quite so simple, since such factors as trapping efficiency and injection coefficient also vary with altitude, but not very rapidly. The analysis is further complicated by the fact that the earth's magnetic field is eccentric, the dipole being displaced by $\Delta = 436$ km from the center of the earth. Hence the trapped protons do not remain at a constant geocentric distance as they move around the earth but follow instead a magnetic surface equidistant from the dipole.

It is shown, however, that when the atmosphere is homologous (i.e., of constant scale height over an altitude interval of 2Δ) then the variation of density derived from the radiation-belt data corresponds to the actual density variation. This view is well supported by the good agreement between radiation-belt density results on neutral oxygen and those from satellite-orbit data and from theory.

The deviation in the radiation-belt data at around 1000 km indicates that another atmospheric constituent with a scale height larger than O appears in the altitude interval between 1000 km and $1000 + 2\Delta$. However, since the highest altitudes are only slightly weighted, because of their lower densities, we may say that this new constituent becomes more important than O at an altitude of 1300 to 1600 km. This result may be compared with an analysis of Berning's data. If we assign his electron densities to O^+, then O^+ takes over from O as the most important constituent at a distance of $\sim 1.14\ R$ (or ~ 1500 km above sea level).

However, as discussed earlier, He^+ may play an important role there. No definitive experimental data are yet available.

13-6 DISTRIBUTION OF IONIZED HYDROGEN

Theoretical conclusions

The variation of H^+ concentration with altitude has proved to be the most difficult to derive on the basis of presently available data. Near the earth it is a minor ionic constituent; hence its distribution is affected by that of O^+, the major constituent. Eventually the O^+ concentration must fall to a low enough level so that H^+ will predominate, possibly above 1000 to 1500 km, as far as number concentration is concerned, or above 2000 to 2500 km, as far as mass concentration is concerned.

Beyond this level the H^+ distribution should follow the barometric law [equation (13-39)], with $E = 4.65$ corresponding to a temperature of 1500°K. This theoretical variation is shown in Table 13-4. Again, as in the case of O^+, the temperature may actually be higher because of the influence of high-velocity electrons.

At higher altitudes the simple barometric formula may be modified by the inclusion of a centrifugal potential term, as suggested by F. S. Johnson (21). This term will appear only if the ions actually rotate with the angular velocity of the earth or a good fraction thereof. This difficult point has not been completely settled.

At a height of several earth radii the base of the iono-exosphere is reached. Eventually the distribution will not follow a barometric formula, for the trapped orbits become less filled up, but at that point the H^+ exosphere may already be merging into the interplanetary gas.

Analysis of whistler data

Lightning strokes that produce the usual kind of atmospheric static also give rise to "whistling atmospherics." Equipped with a long antenna and only an audio amplifier, one can pick up a signal that starts at a frequency of several kilocycles and within a couple of seconds drops to 100 cycles or less. The explanation of this effect runs as follows: The pulse of radio energy created by the lightning stroke penetrates to some extent through the ionosphere. The low-frequency components then propagate through the plasmosphere roughly along a magnetic line of force and arrive in the opposite hemisphere, where they are detected. The propagation velocity is a function of frequency, that is, dispersion exists; the higher frequencies have a higher propagation velocity (14). The dispersion D (in units of sec$^{1/2}$) is defined by

$$D = t_f f^{1/2} \tag{13-51}$$

where t_f is the time of transit of a whistler component of frequency f.

It should be noted that the frequencies f we are dealing with propagate with velocities very much less than c, the velocity of light, typically $0.01c$. Also f is very much less than either the gyrofrequency $f_B = eB/(2\pi m)$ or the critical (plasma) frequency $f_0 = (N_e c^2/\pi m)^{1/2}$ everywhere along the whistler path. Under these conditions Storey has shown that

$$D = \tfrac{1}{2}c \int (f_0 f_B)^{-1/2}\, ds = \left(\frac{c}{2}\right)^{1/2} \int \left(\frac{N_e}{B}\right)^{1/2} ds. \tag{13-52}$$

Therefore, from experimental data that give the dispersion as a function of latitude the electron density may be deduced as a function of altitude, subject to certain assumptions about the magnetic field.

Such analyses have been carried out by a number of authors (22, 23, 24). The wide divergence shows the uncertainties involved in this method. The most recent analysis has been carried out by Allcock (25), who gives for electron density per cm^3 in the height range 1000 to 13,000 km the empirical relation

$$N_e = 5.75 \times 10^4 \exp \left(\frac{-h}{2640} \right), \qquad (13\text{-}53)$$

where h is measured in kilometers. We can rewrite equation (13-42) in our notation as

$$N_e = 6.45 \times 10^5 \exp \left(\frac{-2.6r}{R} \right). \qquad (13\text{-}54)$$

The slope of the distribution turns out to be in fair agreement with the theoretical curve for H^+ at 1500°K.

It is evident, however, that more precise experimental data are required before the distribution of ionized hydrogen can be definitely established.

13-7 SUMMARY

The purpose of this chapter has been to review recent work, partly theoretical and partly experimental, on the earth's exosphere. The exosphere is defined as the region from which neutral atoms with the necessary energy may escape unhindered by collisions. It is this absence of collisions that makes necessary a new theoretical treatment which is not based on the idea of thermodynamic equilibrium.

From an analysis of satellite-orbit data the "base" of the exosphere is found to be at 530 km. A temperature of 1500°K is appropriate to that level. The distribution of O and H with altitude can be given with considerable certainty. It is supported and normalized by densities derived from satellite-orbit data, radiation-belt data, and observations of the solar Lyman-alpha emission line. The content of He is less certain.

The distribution of ionized O^+, He^+, and H^+ is less certain, although O^+ can be reasonably fixed from direct electron-density measurements and from an analysis of radiation-belt data. The H^+ distribution is imperfectly known on the basis of analyses from the dispersion of radio whistlers.

From the viewpoint of mass density, O is the most important constituent up to ∼1000 km, when O^+, which falls off somewhat less rapidly, takes over. Between 2000 and 2500 km H^+ becomes dominant. The neutral hydrogen component is nowhere dominant. Around 1500 km.

REFERENCES

1. Öpik, E. J., and S. F. Singer, Distribution of Density in a Planetary Exosphere, Part II; *Phys. Fluids,* **4,** 221–233 (1961).
2. Critical tables.
3. Singer, S. F., Exospheric Structure (deduced from Satellite Radiation Belt and Drag Data), *J. Geophys. Res.,* **65,** 2577 (1960).
4. King-Hele, D. G., Properties of the Atmosphere Revealed by Satellite Orbits, in *Progress in the Astronautical Sciences,* Vol. I, ed. S. F. Singer, North Holland, Amsterdam, 1962.
5. Stoney, G. Johnston, *Astrophys. J.,* **7,** 25 (1898).
6. Jeans, J. H., *The Dynamical Theory of Gases,* Cambridge University Press, 1916, Fourth Edition, 1925.
7. Lennard-Jones, J. E., *Trans. Cambridge Phil. Soc.,* **22,** 535 (1923). See also E. K. Bytner, *Astron. Zh.,* **35,** 572 (1958) and **36,** 92 (1959).
8. Spitzer, L., Jr., The Terrestrial Atmosphere above 300 km, in *The Atmosphere of the Earth and Planets,* ed. G. P. Kuiper, Second Edition, University of Chicago Press, Chicago, 1952, pp. 211–247.
9. Öpik, E. J., and S. F. Singer, Density Distribution in an Exosphere, *Phys. Fluids,* **2,** 653–655 (1959).
10. Herring, J., and L. Kyle, *J. Geophys. Res.,* **66,** 1980 (1961).
11. Brandt, J. C., and J. W. Chamberlain, Density of Neutral Gas in a Planetary Exosphere, *Phys. Fluids,* **6,** 485–486 (1960).
12. Öpik, E. J., and S. F. Singer, Distribution of Density in a Planetary Exosphere, *Phys. Fluids,* **3,** 486–488 (1960).
13. Purcell, J. D., and R. Tousey, The Profile of Solar Hydrogen Lyman-α, *J. Geophys. Res.,* **65,** 370 (1960).
14. Storey, L. R. O., *Phil. Trans.,* **A246,** 113 (1953).
15. Behr, A., and H. Siedentopf, *Z. Astroph.,* **32,** 19 (1953).
16. Öpik, E. J., and S. F. Singer, Distribution of Density in a Planetary Exosphere. Part III, Ionized Component, *Phys. Fluids* (to be published).
17. Öpik, E. J., in *Interaction of Space Vehicles with an Ionized Atmosphere,* ed. S. F. Singer, Plenum Press, New York, 1962.
18. Hanson, W. B., Upper Atmosphere Helium Ions, *J. Geophys. Res.,* **67,** 183–188 (1962).
19. Nakada, M. P., and S. F. Singer, Multiply Ionized Ions in the Magnetosphere, *J. Geophys. Res.* (To be published.)
20. Berning, W. W., A Sounding Rocket Measurement of Electron Densities to 1500 km, *J. Geophys. Res.,* **65,** 2589 (1960).
21. Johnson, F. S., *J. Geophys. Res.,* **64** (1959).
22. Helliwell, R. A., Low Frequency Radio Propagation Studies, Part I, Radio Prop. Lab., Stanford, California, 1956.
23. Storey, L. R. O., *Can. J. Phys.,* **35,** 1107 (1957).
24. Maeda, K., and I. Kimura, *Rept. Ionosph. Space Res.,* Japan, **10,** 105 (1956).
25. Allcock, G. McK., The Electron Density Distribution in the Outer Ionosphere Derived from Whistler Data, *J. Atmospheric Terrest. Phys.,* **14,** 185–199 (1959).

CHAPTER 14

ROCKET SPECTROSCOPY

HERBERT FRIEDMAN

U. S. Naval Research Laboratory

Before the advent of rocket astronomy, man's knowledge of the spectra of the sun and the stars was restricted to two narrow windows in the visible and radio regions of the spectrum. The nature of the solar ultraviolet spectrum and the possibility of X-ray emission were inferred largely from the behavior of the ionosphere as observed from the ground. The first direct observations above the atmosphere were accomplished in 1946 with the aid of a spectrograph carried aloft in a V-2 rocket, launched from the White Sands Proving Ground in New Mexico.

Solar radiation reaching ground level cuts off rather abruptly near 3000 Å, yet it has been known for more than 100 years that the spectra of laboratory discharge sources extend far into the vacuum ultraviolet. Hartley (1) discovered in 1889 the absorption band of ozone that now bears his name and suggested that the onset of atmospheric absorption at 3000 Å was caused by ozone. The correctness of this hypothesis was established by Fabry and Buisson (2) in 1913. If the terrestrial atmosphere, whose density decreases exponentially with height, were compressed to sea-level pressure, it would be 8-km thick and ozone would constitute only about 2 mm of the total; yet ozone absorbs so strongly at 2500 Å that only 10^{-40} of the incident solar flux can penetrate.

At shorter wavelengths ordinary molecular oxygen becomes opaque. Victor Schumann (3) constructed the first vacuum spectrograph in 1893 and discovered the broad region from about 1200 to 2000 Å, now known as the Schumann region. Throughout this range O_2 is the principal atmospheric absorber and is dissociated in the process. At 1450 Å, near the peak of the oxygen dissociation continuum, a few thousandths of an inch of gas is almost totally absorbing.

Schumann's work was limited by the transmission of his fluorite prism, but Theodore Lyman (4), using a concave grating, was able in 1914 to photograph the hydrogen series; its principal resonance line at 1216 Å is now known as Lyman-alpha. Lyman's work extended to wavelengths as short as 500 Å. Subsequently, Millikan (5) studied the spectra of spark sources to 140 Å, and the French physicists Dauvillier (6) and Thibaud (7) used crystals and grazing incidence ruled gratings to reach the soft X-ray region. These early laboratory studies prepared the background for rocket spectroscopy by establishing the variation in opacity of air as a function of wavelength and revealing the intense ultraviolet emission spectra of the common gases known to exist in the solar atmosphere.

The V-2 rocket was capable of transporting as much as 2000 lb of equipment to about 90 miles. The first spectrograph was prepared by scientists of the Naval Research Laboratory (8) and launched on June 28, 1946. The rocket returned to earth intact but buried itself deep in the ground, and nothing of the instrumentation was recovered. This lesson led to techniques for separation of the instrument section to induce a more gentle tumbling, and on October 10, 1946, the next experiment succeeded. Spectra were obtained to about 2200 Å. It was clear, however, that the solar intensity fell so rapidly with decreasing wavelength that some means of pointing a spectrograph constantly at the sun during flight was necessary if exposures adequate to photograph the extreme ultraviolet were to be achieved. The need for a stabilized rocket-borne platform from which to point a spectrograph at the sun led to the development of the biaxial pointing control at the University of Colorado, under the direction of W. B. Pietenpol. Before this was achieved, however, nondispersive photometry was applied with success to the detection of solar Lyman-alpha and X rays (9). Photoionization Geiger counters combined with filters were used to isolate wavelength bands in the ultraviolet and X-ray regions. These early photometric experiments defined the dependence of atmospheric absorption on altitude and the qualitative distribution of solar energy versus wavelength from 10 to 2000 Å.

The biaxial pointing control was first flown successfully in 1952 when W. A. Rense and W. B. Pietenpol (10) photographed Lyman-alpha for the first time, using a grazing incidence spectrograph. It is typical of Aerobee flights that a spin of about 0.5 rps is imparted on launching and that a slow precession develops as flight progresses, opening up into a yaw cone of perhaps 30 degrees half-angle. The pointed spar, which carries the spectrograph, fits inside the Aerobee rocket nose cone and is mounted on two orthogonal sets of gimbals. One set of gimbals with axis parallel to the length of the rocket counterspins the entire nose section to counteract the spin of the rocket; the second set of gimbals permits the spar to swing out of the nose cone about an axis perpendicular to the long axis of the rocket. The sun is sensed by photoelectric eyes to an accuracy of about 1 min of arc.

In 1958 and 1959 Rense (11) and his associates photographed the first spectra revealing the He I (584 Å) and He II (304 Å) resonance lines and detected emission lines to wavelengths as short as 83.9 Å. The biaxial pointing control was also adopted by Tousey and his associates at the Naval Research Laboratory and by Hinteregger's group at the U. S. Air Force Cambridge Research Laboratories. The NRL group has striven for high resolution and quantitative intensities by using normal incidence grating spectrographs. The AFCRL program has applied photoelectric scanning to its spectrographs. By subordinating resolution to the requirement of rapid scanning, they have been able to study effectively the variation of optical depth of the terrestrial atmosphere versus wavelength. Before going further into details of the design of spectrographs and spectral analysis, let us consider the problems of sensors for ultraviolet and X-ray detection.

14-1 ULTRAVIOLET AND X-RAY SENSORS

The measurement of X-ray and ultraviolet emissions may be accomplished by photographic registration or by photoelectric detection. When detailed spectral information is sought, photography offers distinct advantages. The entire spectrum image is exposed simultaneously to reveal detailed variations in individual line profiles as related to detailed features in the source, that is, center-to-limb brightness variations when the sun is the object. Photoelectric image scanning may provide the same information, but the image elements must be scanned sequentially. Unless the photoelectric system has much greater optical speed, it can compete with photography for image detail only if recording time is not a limiting factor. However, it is often advantageous to sacrifice detail for speed in recording only major features, and then the photoelectric scanner shows to great advantage. Spectroscopy may also be done nondispersively with photometers sensitive to narrow spectral intervals, and, in fact, much of the knowledge gained so far of ultraviolet and X-ray radiation outside the atmosphere has been acquired in this way.

Gelatin absorbs strongly in the ultraviolet, making it necessary to use emulsions with virtually no gelatin binder, as was first done by Schumann. Schumann-type emulsions are available from Eastman Kodak in the United States, Kodak-Pathé in France, and Ilford in England. An emulsion prepared by the Audran centrifuging and transferring process, labeled SC-5, and available from Kodak-Pathé, combines especially high speed and good detail.

Middle ultraviolet detectors

Early efforts to develop photodetectors with narrow ranges of spectral sensitivity were concerned with the wavelength region immediately below 3000 Å. So-called "solar blind" photon counters utilized the photoelectric thresholds of gold, silver, nickel, or copper in combination with the transmission characteristics of quartz or high silica glasses. The spectral response was limited to the approximate range 2000 to 3000 Å, often called "the middle ultraviolet" as distinct from the vacuum ultraviolet below 2000 Å. Although photoelectric yields from alkaline metal surfaces such as Cs-Sb may exceed 0.1, most nonalkali metals are characterized by yields of less than 10^{-4} in the middle ultraviolet. The location of the photoelectric threshold is usually not sharply defined because of a tail of weak sensitivity extending to longer wavelengths. An exception, however, is a surface of copper iodide (12, 13) which exhibits a yield in excess of 0.1 near 1500 Å, 10^{-2} near 2000 Å, and then drops precipitously to 10^{-9} at 2500 Å. It is interesting to compare copper iodide with nickel, a typical metallic surface, which has a yield of 10^{-2} at 1500 Å, 10^{-3} at 2000 Å, 10^{-4} at 2500 Å, and about 10^{-7} at 2800 Å.

Extreme ultraviolet detectors

Composite surfaces of the alkali tellurides were first reported as having high yields in the middle and vacuum ultraviolet by Taft and Apker (14) in 1953. Rubidium telluride (Figure 14-1) exhibits a threshold in the range 3000 to 3500 Å and reaches yields of better than 0.1 at 2500 Å. When the films are thick enough to be opaque rather than transparent, the yields are somewhat lower but the threshold characteristics are sharper.

Higher work functions are obtained with alkali halide surfaces such as CsI, RbI, KBr, and LiF. For use in an end-window photomultiplier sensitive to the vacuum ultraviolet, CsI may be de-

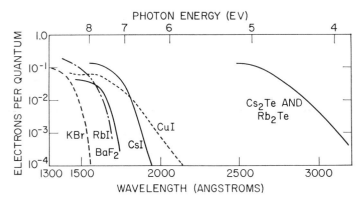

Figure 14-1 Photoelectric yield curves for various tellurides and halides.

posited over a thin conducting substrate of tungsten on a LiF window, giving a yield in excess of 0.1 from 1600 Å to the transmission limit of LiF at 1050 Å. Its threshold lies near 2200 Å. Still shorter wavelength thresholds are given by RbI ($\sim$1750 Å) and KBr ($\sim$1550 Å). Chubb (15) has studied the behavior of an evaporated LiF photosurface in the extreme ultraviolet and obtained yields as high as 60 percent near 500 Å, falling rapidly above 1000 Å to less than 1 percent at Lyman-alpha.

Inner photoelectric effect

It was observed as early as 1933 by Kenty (16) that below 1400 Å almost all metals exhibit yields several orders of magnitude greater than are obtained in the middle ultraviolet. It appears that two distinct photoelectric thresholds are involved: that of the longer wavelength is related to a surface photoeffect and that of the shorter wavelength, to a volume, or inner, photoeffect. Whereas the surface effect is extremely sensitive to absorbed gas, oxidation, and any variation of surface treatment, the volume effect is almost independent of these factors. For most semiconductors, and even glass as well as metals, the threshold of the inner photoeffect occurs near 1400 Å and the yield rises rapidly to a relatively broad plateau below 1000 Å. Most volume effect emitters actually decrease in yield when degassed by prolonged heat treatment in vacuum, but the change is roughly a factor of 2. The relative insensitivity to composition and absorbed gas makes it possible to expose repeatedly the photoemitters to air and then to pump to vacuum for operation without markedly affect-

TABLE 14-1

Values of Photoelectric Yields of Various Cathodes (%)

Wavelength of Characteristic Line (Å)

Photocathode Material	$OK_\alpha(23.6)$	$CK_\alpha(44)$	$BK_\alpha(67)$	$BeK_\alpha(113)$
Be	0.7	1.1	2.35	2.0
Ni	2.1	2.3	3.7	4.9
W	3.6	4.0	2.2	0.94
LiF	—	6.0	17.0	61.0
NaF	3.2	12.5	26.0	85.0
CaF_2	15.9	7.1	14.2	25.0
SrF_2	22.0	31.0	27.0	24.0
NaCl	13.5	19.5	13.5	27.0

ing the sensitivity. A detailed description of the inner photoeffect and its adaptation to photomultiplier measurements in the extreme ultraviolet is contained in a paper by Hinteregger and Watanabe (17).

Photoelectric yields at X-ray wavelengths

Tables 14-1 and 14-2 list photoelectric yields in the X-ray region from about 1.5 to 113 Å for a variety of surfaces. The remarkably

TABLE 14-2

Values of Photoelectric Yields of Various Cathodes (%)

Radiation (Å)

Photo-cathode Material	CuK_α 1.537	CrK_α 2.278	TiK_α 2.74	CaK_α 3.35	ClK_α 4.72	AlK_α 8.32	NaK_α 11.9	CuL_α 13.3
Ti	0.26	0.41	0.09	0.10	0.27	0.66	1.60	—
W	0.36	0.82	0.60	0.80	1.50	0.94	1.70	2.3
Pt	0.44	0.90	1.1	1.6	2.0	1.18	2.5	3.3
NaBr	1.3	4.6	3.5	3.6	6.1	3.3	5.6	17.8
CsI	5.7	10.8	4.9	31.5	14.1	35.8	76.0	94.5
SrF_2	1.4	5.8	3.6	6.6	11.6	21.6	12.3	15.5

high yields of the alkali halides and the alkaline earth halides was a surprising discovery (18).

Ultraviolet filters

In the region above 1050 Å it is possible to control the short wavelength limit of the spectral sensitivity band (Figure 14-2a) by the use of filters such as LiF (1050 Å), CaF₂ (1225 Å), strontium fluoride (1280 Å), barium fluoride (1350 Å), sapphire (1425 Å), pure silica (1600 Å), and crystalline quartz (1700 Å). Below 1000 Å transmission bands appear in thin metal films. An aluminum film about 1000 Å thick, for example, has been used to isolate the band 170 to 850 Å.

The short wavelength discrimination obtainable with a CaF₂ filter can be adjusted over a wide range by temperature control. Figure 14-2b shows the dependence of transmission on temperature from liquid air to room temperature. Although the transmission limit falls on the long wavelength side of Lyman-alpha at the higher temperatures, it moves to well below 1200 Å at lower temperatures and becomes much sharper. Temperature control of the transmission characteristic has been employed by Byram, Chubb, and Friedman (19) with the aid of Peltier refrigeration units to cool calcium fluoride

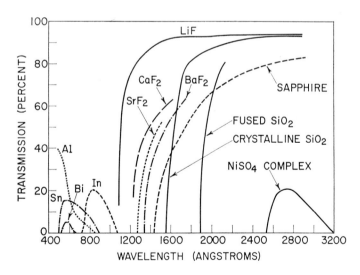

Figure 14-2a Transmission characteristics of various ultraviolet filters. The LiF, CaF₂, SrF₂, BaF₂ crystalline and fused quartz data are for plates 1 mm thick. The metal films are 1000 Å in thickness.

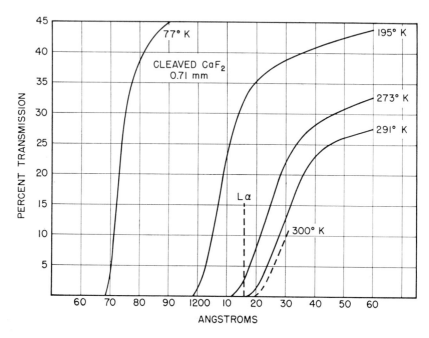

Figure 14-2b   Temperature dependence of the transmission of CaF_2. [A. R. Knudsen and J. E. Kupperian, Jr., O.S.A. 47, 440 (1957).]

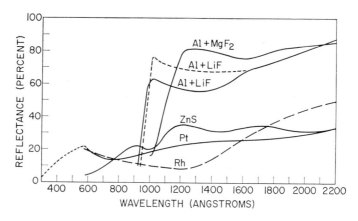

Figure 14-3   Spectral reflectivities of various evaporated coatings. The solid line curve for Al + LiF corresponds to a LiF film thickness of 170 Å. The dashed curve corresponds to a LiF film thickness of 220 Å.

filters used in conjunction with ion chamber stellar photometers in Aerobee rocket experiments.

Ultraviolet reflectivity

When the photodetector is combined with a collecting mirror, it is possible to use the decrease in reflectivity with decreasing wavelength to control the short wavelength response (Figure 14-3). For example, an aluminized mirror may reflect 90 percent at 2000 Å but falls steadily in reflectivity to less than 5 percent at 1000 Å (20). Aluminum coated with magnesium fluoride, however, reflects about 80 percent at 1200 Å and drops abruptly to about 15 percent at 1000 Å. Aluminum overcoated with evaporated lithium fluoride reflects as much as 70 percent at Lyman-beta (1025.7 Å) but very poorly immediately to shorter wavelengths. Rhodium exhibits a minimum of 8 percent at 1200 Å and then increases to about 25 percent at 500 Å. Further adjustment of the limit of far-ultraviolet reflectivity can be obtained by controlling the angle of incidence on the reflecting surface, since the reflectivity in the extreme ultraviolet increases markedly with increasing angle of incidence.

Gaseous photoionization

Relatively precise control of long wavelength thresholds below 1600 Å can be obtained by using ionization chambers or photon counters (21). Gases may be selected with ionization potentials as low as 7 ev (xylene) to 22 ev (helium). By operating an ionization chamber with negative potential on the wire, the surface photoelectric emission is suppressed and the measured current is almost purely a gas ionization current. A photon counter, however, must be operated with positive potential on the wire. To suppress long wavelength surface photoemission, an electronegative gas such as a halogen or nitric oxide must be added to the primary gas content. The electronegative gas captures the photoelectrons as soon as they are released in the weak field region near the cathode surface. The resulting negative ions reach the anode wire where they are neutralized without triggering discharges. Figure 14-4 illustrates the effects of surface photoemission in the middle ultraviolet, the onset of inner photoemission in the extreme ultraviolet, and the gas ionization threshold at the shortest wavelengths, which combine to produce the spectral response of a photon counter filled with ethyl formate and neon. Surface photoemission accounts for the response from 3000 to 1500 Å. The surface response would continue to rise slowly below 1800 Å, but strong molecular absorption by ethyl formate between 1800 and 1500

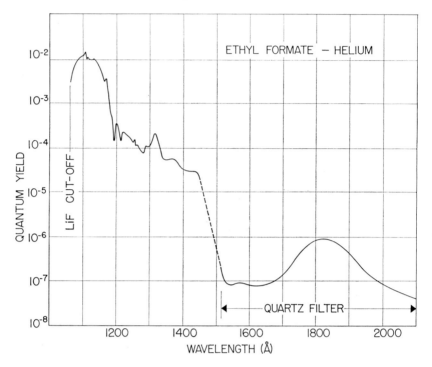

Figure 14-4 Spectral response of a photon counter in the form of a stainless steel cathode, equipped with a lithium fluoride window and filled with helium and ethyl formate.

Å introduces a minimum in the response. At about 1500 Å the threshold for the inner photoeffect increases the yield abruptly by two to three orders of magnitude. At about 1180 Å the ionization potential of ethyl formate is reached and the yield jumps again by another factor of 50. Finally, the limit of transmission of the lithium fluoride window is reached at 1050 Å.

Figure 14-5 shows the response curve of an ionization chamber filled with nitric oxide and operated with negative potential on the wire. Virtually no detectable yield is obtained above 1350 Å, the ionization threshold of nitric oxide. The fluctuation in spectral response represents the variation in efficiency of photoionization of the gas as a function of wavelength. If the tube were filled with a counting gas mixture of nitric oxide and neon and operated as a photon counter with positive wire, the nitric oxide would scavenge photoelectrons released at the cathode surface, leaving a gaseous photoionization characteristic essentially identical to that obtained with the ion chamber.

The use of gas-filled detectors need not be limited to the short wavelength cutoff of window materials, such as lithium fluoride, which provide gas-tight seals. Below 1050 Å only the thinnest films of metals and plastics provide appreciable ultraviolet transmission. Even though these thin windows cannot be depended on for vacuum tightness, they may be used with continuous-flow gas systems. In fact, it is possible to dispense with the window entirely and flow the gas freely into the tube via a tubulation in the envelope and out again through the window aperture. In monitoring solar radiation, the flux is so high that windows as small as 0.005 in. have been adequate for photon counters. The amount of gas required can be stored conveniently in a small high-pressure flask and dispensed over the lifetime of a rocket or satellite experiment. By choosing from the rare gases, it is possible to control the threshold wavelengths at the photoionization thresholds: 1027, 890, 791, 577, and 507 Å, corresponding to xenon, krypton, argon, neon, and helium. A helium free-flow ion chamber, for example, would be a strongly selective detector for the He II 304 Å resonance line.

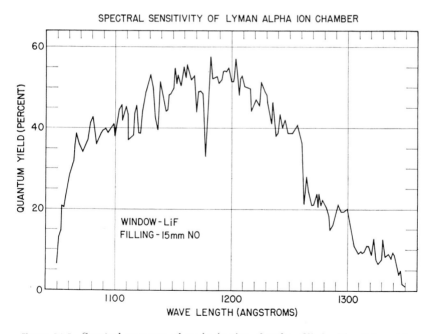

Figure 14-5 Spectral response of an ionization chamber filled with nitric oxide.

Phototransducers

Ordinary visible light sensitive photomultipliers may be combined with fluorescent surfaces that act as transducers to convert ultraviolet to visible light. In the conversion process, however, inefficiency is introduced because of the imperfect yield of fluorescence and the fact that only a fraction of the fluorescent light reaches the photocathode. The effective quantum efficiency of a fluorescence-sensitized photodetector can therefore rarely exceed 5 to 10 percent. Furthermore, it is difficult to eliminate response to long wavelength light because suitable external filters are not available. Sodium salicylate has been widely used as an ultraviolet-to-visible light transducer because its quantum efficiency is high and almost constant between about 2000 and 584 Å, the shortest wavelength at which it has been measured.

X-ray photometers

In the X-ray region from 1 to 100 Å discrimination can be achieved with filters (22). The K-series absorption edges of aluminum and carbon fall at 8 and 44 Å, respectively. Absorption coefficients increase abruptly by about an order of magnitude in going from the long to the short wavelength side of an absorption edge. On either side of the edge the absorption coefficient varies with the wavelength cubed. When combined with a gaseous detector whose photoelectric absorption coefficient is increasing rapidly with wavelength, the combined effect of filter and gas absorption is to produce a narrow-band spectral response, as shown in Figures 14-6, 14-7, and 14-8.

Below 10 Å in wavelength it is possible to use pulse-amplitude discriminators such as proportional counters and scintillation counters to provide crude spectral resolution. Rocket experiments have been performed (23) with detectors in which the individual pulse amplitudes were transmitted in real time via FM/FM telemetry. Alternatively, the data may be sorted by multichannel analyzers and stored in memory devices before command readout. Figure 14-9 illustrates the spectral response of an X-ray scintillation spectrometer when exposed to an almost monochromatic source of 123 kev radiation from Co^{57}. This spectrometer was used in rocket experiments to map the X-ray spectra of solar flares from 20 to 200 kev.

Resonance cells

An interesting technique for detecting resonance radiation involves the use of a gas absorption cell. If the resonance radiation of a particular element shines on a gas of the same element, fluorescence at

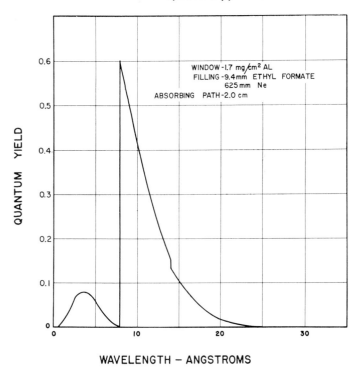

WAVELENGTH – ANGSTROMS

Figure 14-6 Spectral response of X-ray photon counter equipped with aluminum window.

the resonant wavelength is stimulated. If the source is viewed through the length of a gas column, the resonance line will appear strongly absorbed. When the column is viewed sidewise, the resonance radiation re-emitted in fluorescence can be observed. If the gas is cold relative to the source, only the central core of the resonance line is absorbed and scattered. To observe stellar Lyman-alpha sources through the bright background of fluorescence from the hydrogen geocorona, Morton and Purcell (24) employed a hydrogen absorption cell. Although the geocoronal fluorescence is bright, the scattered Lyman-alpha profile is rather narrow, corresponding to a temperature not exceeding a few thousand degrees. Accordingly, an atomic hydrogen column containing about 10^{14} atoms/cm^2 should be an effective absorber for the narrow profile Lyman-alpha (<0.1 Å) resonantly scattered by the upper atmosphere but should pass most of the flux of the relatively broad Lyman-alpha profiles (>1 Å) from stellar sources.

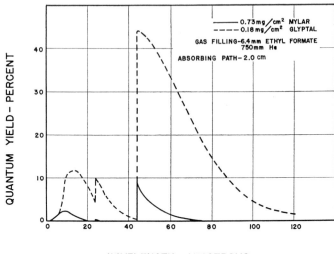

WAVELENGTH –ANGSTROMS

Figure 14-7 Spectral responses of X-ray photon counters equipped with windows of Mylar and Glyptal films.

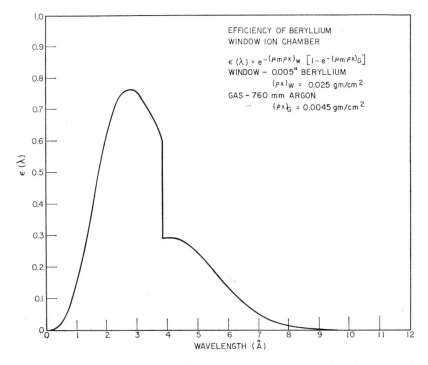

Figure 14-8 Spectral response of X-ray ionization chamber equipped with beryllium window and filled with argon.

562

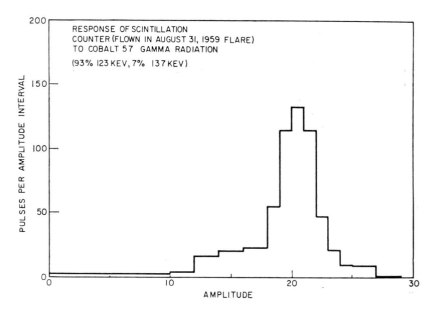

Figure 14-9 Pulse amplitude distribution from scintillation counter exposed to Co⁵⁷ radiation source.

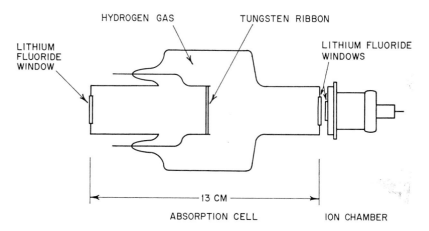

Figure 14-10 Hydrogen absorption cell. Molecular hydrogen is dissociated at incandescent tungsten ribbon. Lyman-α radiation, entering through LiF window at left, is absorbed by gas column before emerging through window at right. Ionization chamber detects the transmitted radiation.

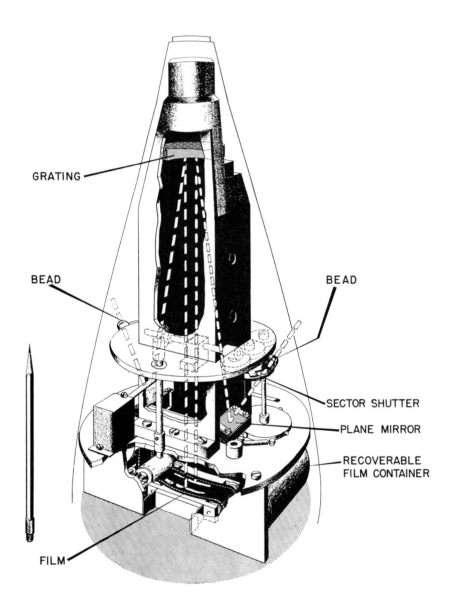

GRATING

BEAD

BEAD

SECTOR SHUTTER

PLANE MIRROR

RECOVERABLE
FILM CONTAINER

FILM

SPECTROGRAPH

Figure 14-11 1946 version of NRL spectrograph flown in V-2 rocket.

The hydrogen absorption cell used in the NRL experiments is illustrated in Figure 14-10. The cell was equipped with lithium fluoride windows and a tungsten ribbon filament and filled with molecular hydrogen. Laboratory measurements with the filament turned on indicated an absorption profile with a width at half-intensity of about 0.08 Å. Sufficient atomic hydrogen was produced to saturate the absorption profile in the center of the line. The results obtained with this absorption cell in a rocket experiment are described below with other observations of the night-sky Lyman-alpha glow.

In principle, resonant scattering cells may be used to detect the concentrations of any of the atomic constituents of the upper atmosphere at altitudes at which the appropriate solar resonance lines are absorbed. Blamont (25) has used a sodium cell to observe the sodium airglow and has suggested the application of the Zeeman effect, using a variable magnetic field to map out the resonance line profile.

14-2 SPECTROGRAPHIC EXPERIMENTS

The spectral region, 2000 to 3000 Å

The first spectrum of the sun below 2000 Å (8) was obtained with the spectrograph shown in Figure 14-11. A 600-line/mm reflection grating with 40-cm radius of curvature was used at normal incidence. Because the spectrograph was mounted in the nose of a spinning V-2 rocket, with no provision for stabilization, a wide-angle light collector was required. For this purpose a lithium fluoride bead 2 mm in diameter focused sunlight internally to a point source. To double the exposure, two beads were placed symmetrically in relation to the grating, 180 degrees apart. An automatic film transport device permitted a sequence of exposures to be made during flight. In 1949 the instrument was improved by replacing the lithium fluoride beads with slit jaws made of mirrors to expand the field of view (26). The results of that experiment are shown in Figure 14-12. From the progressive extension of the spectrum into the ultraviolet with increasing height, it was possible to determine the ozone distribution with altitude.

The cumulative progress from these early beginnings can best be appreciated by considering the most recent spectrum of the sun in the same wavelength range, obtained by Garrett, Michels, Purcell, and Tousey (27). The spectrogram of Figure 14-13 was obtained

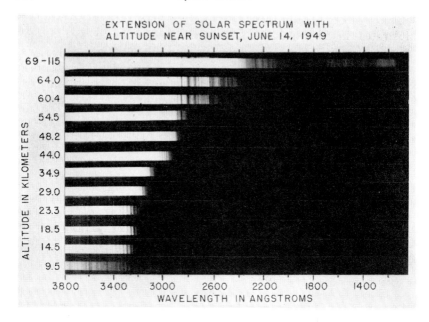

Figure 14-12 Solar spectrum observed from various altitudes, showing effect of ozone absorption.

with the echelle grating spectrograph diagramed in Figure 14-14. The instrument was mounted on a biaxial pointing control flown in an Aerobee-Hi rocket. Whereas the resolution of the first instruments flown in 1946 was only 3 Å, the new spectra are 100 times better resolved. The echelle grating was ruled at the Massachusetts Institute of Technology with 73 steps/mm, each step of this optical staircase being accurate to 10^{-7} in. A total length of 5 in. of ruled grating was utilized. The echelle derives its high resolution from the high order of interference in the diffraction pattern, from 81st order at 3000 Å to 122nd order at 2000 Å. To separate the orders, the echelle is crossed with a fluorite prism that provides the vertical dispersion in Figure 14-13. Light enters the instrument through a slit, is collimated by a quartz-lithium fluoride triplet lens, and dispersed by the prism. The echelle disperses the light at right angles to the prism dispersion and reflects it back through the prism once again. Next the light is focused by the lens, passes through a field flattener, and is imaged on the film, which is bent to the required curvature.

The spectrum of Figure 14-13 was one of 12 exposures varying from as short as 2 sec to as long as 84 sec, registered during the 5 min of flight. The dispersion of the fluorite prism is indicated by the vertical wavelength scale. On the original 35-mm film each exposure covered about 1 in.[2] Essentially, the pattern recorded on the film can be thought of as one long spectrum which has been segmented and rearranged in horizontal strips. Each successive strip of spectrum picks up at approximately the same wavelength as the end of the strip immediately above. Laid end to end, the strips would make a spectrum 3 ft long.

In the laboratory the echelle spectrograph produced a resolution of between 20 and 30 mÅ. This compares very favorably with the best results published in the "Göttingen Solar Atlas" between 3000

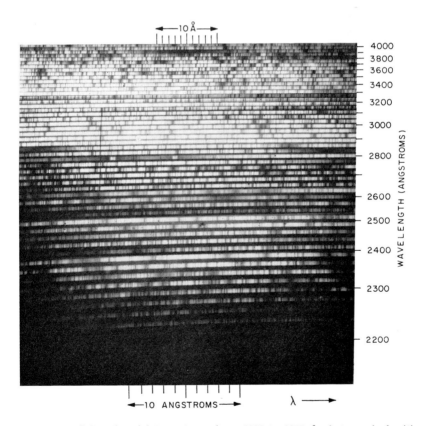

Figure 14-13 Solar ultraviolet spectrum from 4000 to 2200 Å photographed with rocket-borne echelle spectrograph. (U. S. Naval Research Laboratory, August 29, 1961.)

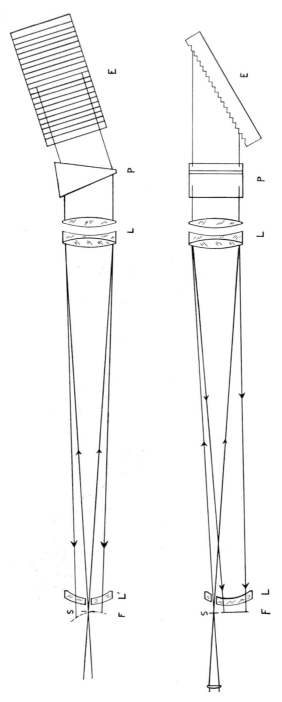

Figure 14-14 High resolution echelle spectrograph designed for flight in solar-pointed section of an Aerobee rocket. Line L is a quartz-lithium fluoride triplet achromatized from 3500 to 2000 Å of 40-cm focal length. P is a 30° fluorite prism to separate orders. E is a 73-groove/mm echelle. The remaining elements are a quartz field corrector and a cylindrical guide for the 35 mm film.

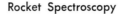

GÖTTINGEN ATLAS
NRL ROCKET

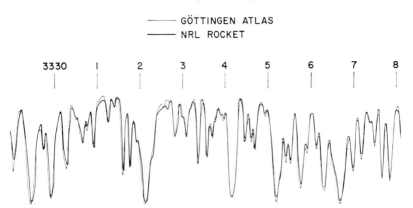

Figure 14-15 Comparison of NRL rocket-borne echelle spectrograph results with Gottingen Atlas in region accessible to ground based instrumentation.

and 4000 Å, based on spectra obtained from the ground with a 21-ft grating spectrograph. Figure 14-15 compares the NRL spectrum with the Göttingen spectrum near 3340 Å, and it is clear that both instruments achieved comparable resolution.

One of the more interesting features of this range of the ultraviolet solar spectrum is the Mg II doublet (Figure 14-16), which resembles the Ca H and K lines of the visible spectrum. The two lines of the magnesium doublet are only 7 Å apart, which indicates the dispersion. The great absorption feature is the first component of each line of the doublet, and the double black emission lines can be seen forming the second component and the central depression in each one forming the third component. A number of Fraunhofer lines from other elements appear against the broad absorption wings of the magnesium lines.

The vacuum ultraviolet

The 15-year interval between the first rocket solar spectrograms and the echelle spectrograph experiment was marked by several milestones of progress. Rense and his colleagues at the University of Colorado succeeded in reaching the shortest ultraviolet wavelengths by the use of grazing incidence grating spectrographs. Violett and Rense (11) photographed the ultraviolet spectrum below 500 Å for the first time in 1958. The spectrum was fairly dense with lines to wavelengths as short as 83.9 Å. He II (304 Å) was by far the most intense. The true intensity of He I (584 Å) was masked by the large

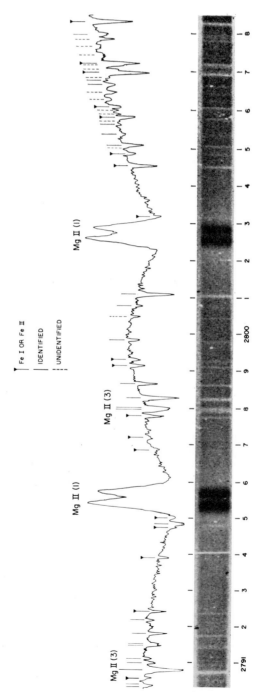

Figure 14-16 Mg II doublet photographed with rocket-borne echelle spectrograph.

optical depth remaining at 200 km, the peak of the rocket flight. The spectrograms were badly fogged by scattered light, however, and precise spectrum analysis was very difficult.

Following the development of the biaxial pointing control, it was adopted both by the U. S. Naval Research Laboratory group, under R. Tousey's direction, and the U. S. Air Force Cambridge Research Laboratories group, under H. E. Hinteregger. The NRL work was based on photographic techniques and normal incidence grating spectrographs in an effort to achieve maximum resolution and quantitative intensity measurements; the AFCRL used photoelectric scanning and grazing incidence gratings to achieve high speed and continuous telemetry of spectral distribution versus altitude. Beginning in 1954, the Naval Research Laboratory flew spectrographs of the type illustrated in Figure 14-17. The outside collecting mirror was bent slightly to toroidal shape to remove astigmatism. In 1955 the first spectrograms that showed emission lines other than Lyman-alpha were obtained. The continuum seemed to disappear rapidly below 1800 Å, but the limit of detectability was set by stray light. It was clear that observations of continua and weaker emission-line features to shorter wavelengths would require effective means to suppress stray light. Just how difficult the problem is may be appreciated when it is recognized that only a few parts per million of the solar constant are radiated below 1000 Å.

In the next few years efforts were made to increase the spectrographic speed at short wavelengths by improving grating reflectivity. Most gratings used in that period were replicas. Aluminum was removed because the plastic replica surface was almost equal to aluminum as a reflector near Lyman-alpha and the aluminum only added to the stray light, which it reflected much more efficiently than a plastic surface at longer wavelengths. The first major improvement came from G. Hass in 1959, when he produced a coating of germanium overlaid with aluminum oxide. This combination was highly efficient for the ultraviolet but very poor in the blue. Purcell and Tousey (28) used a grating coated in this way to obtain a spectrum showing continuum to 1500 Å before stray light overwhelmed it and the first quantitative intensity data for the Lyman continuum from 912 to 850 Å. Eight lines of the Lyman series were distinguishable, and more than 100 emission lines were identified between 500 and 1800 Å.

The next step in the NRL program was the development of a doubly dispersing instrument, illustrated in Figure 14-18. Added to the simple, normal incidence grating was a predisperser external to the slit and replacing the collecting mirror previously used. Both

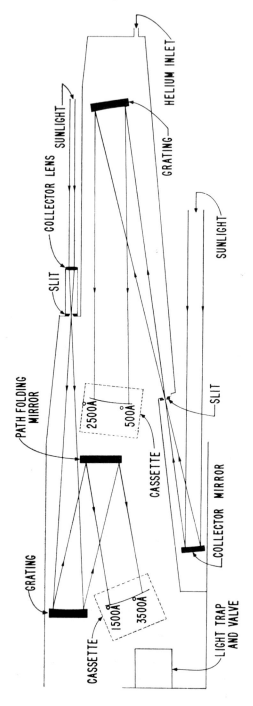

Figure 14-17a Diagram of double spectrograph used by NRL in 1955.

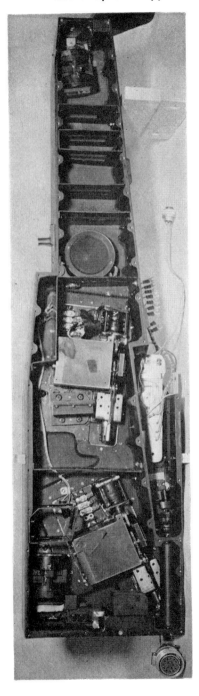

Figure 14-17b Photograph of double spectrograph used by NRL in 1955.

gratings were ruled with 600 lines/mm on a 40-cm radius of curvature and were arranged to diffract in the first order. The rulings of the two gratings were oriented at right angles to each other so that the dispersion of the first grating was normal to the length of the slit. To reduce stray light, the dispersion along the slit was arranged so that all of the visible and near ultraviolet was predispersed beyond the end of the slit and could not reach the principal grating. A reduction of stray-light intensity by several orders of magnitude was accomplished in this way. Stigmatic lines were again produced by distorting the predisperser grating mechanically. Because of the crossed dispersion, the resulting spectral lines (Figure 14-19) are skewed relative to the direction of dispersion. The first successful flight of the doubly dispersing spectrograph took place on

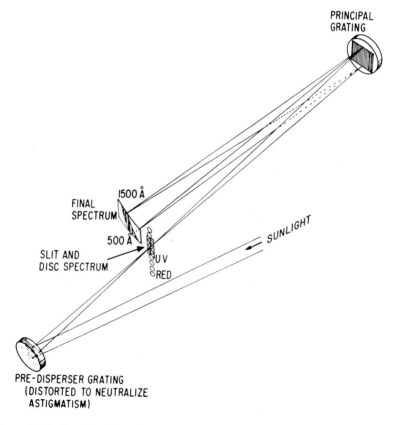

Figure 14-18 Double dispersion spectrograph designed to minimize stray light background.

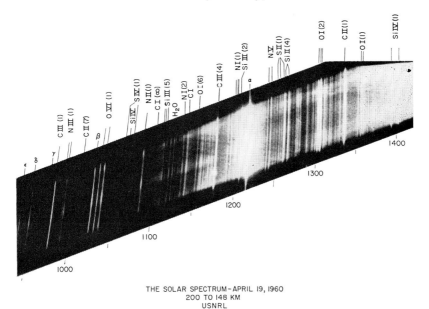

THE SOLAR SPECTRUM-APRIL 19, 1960
200 TO 148 KM
USNRL

Figure 14-19 Portion of solar spectrum photographed with double dispersion spectrograph of Figure 12-18.

April 19, 1960. The spectrogram covered the range 500 to 2000 Å and revealed more than 200 emission lines. The continuum was measurable down to 1000 Å.

The solar spectrum, 500 to 3000 Å

Before proceeding with descriptions of spectroscopy at wavelengths shorter than 500 Å, let us review the major features of the solar spectrum revealed by the experiments described so far. In the visible region of the spectrum the sun approximates a black body at a temperature of 6000 degrees K. In the infrared and in the ultraviolet the opacity of the solar atmosphere increases and the equivalent black body temperature is lowered. Although rocket observations gave us the first measurements of solar flux at short wavelengths, it was recognized much earlier that the continuous spectrum of a 6000-degree sun could not produce the ultraviolet flux necessary to explain the formation of the ionosphere. The spectrum of the chromosphere, which flashes into view at the instant of total eclipse, contains lines of ionized helium which require excitation temperatures of 20,000 degrees K. Spectroscopy of the visible corona reveals lines whose origins were identified by Edlén (29) in 1940 with highly ionized elements such as Fe XIV, which has been stripped of half of its normal complement of 26 electrons. A plasma containing such highly stripped atoms requires electron temperatures of the order of 1 million degrees K.

The evidence derived from rocket measurements shows that the solar constant of 2.00 cal/cm²/min is produced almost entirely in the visible and near infrared regions. In the far-ultraviolet the black-body flux of the photosphere falls rapidly and is exceeded by emission originating in the high atmosphere of the sun under conditions that depart completely from thermodynamic equilibrium. The radiation of the chromosphere consists almost entirely of emission lines, predominantly the resonance lines of hydrogen and helium. At the million-degree electron temperature of the corona X rays are generated. If the corona radiated as a black body at this high temperature, the flux would be great enough to vaporize the earth in a matter of minutes; instead, the corona radiates X rays at about 10^{-14} the power of a black-body radiator. This flux, however, is adequate to create a major portion of the E-region ionosphere (30).

The spectrum of the solar photosphere, as observed from the ground, is a white-light continuum channeled by Fraunhofer absorption lines. As the wavelength decreases, the Fraunhofer lines crowd closer together. The most prominent features of the spectrum immediately below 3000 Å are the lines of singly ionized magnesium at 2795.52 and 2802.70 Å (Figure 14-16). Near 2100 Å (Figure 14-20) the spectrum becomes much weaker; the brightness of the continuum drops to 5500 degrees K and the Fraunhofer lines to about 5000 degrees K. At 2085 Å there appears to be a new source of continuous absorption; the Fraunhofer lines almost vanish and the continuum temperature drops to 5000 degrees K. The onset of strong absorption coincides with the ionization continuum of aluminum.

In the region from 1850 to 1550 Å the normal Fraunhofer spectrum gradually fades out and is replaced by an emission-line spectrum. Below 1530 Å no Fraunhofer lines are detectable against the continuum, and down to 1280 Å the solar radiation must emerge from the top of the photosphere at a level at which the temperature of the solar atmosphere reaches its lowest value, about 4700 degrees K. The first strong emission lines in the solar ultraviolet spectrum are those of Si II at 1808.0 and 1816.9 Å. Lyman-alpha of hydrogen at 1216 Å is the strongest emission line in the entire spectrum; its great intensity relative to other chromospheric lines is apparent in Figure 14-19, and what seems to be a broad profile is simply the result of great overexposure.

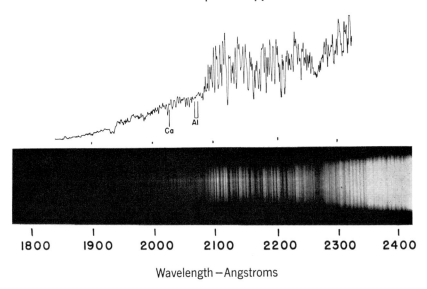

Figure 14-20 Solar spectrum, 1800 to 2400 Å.

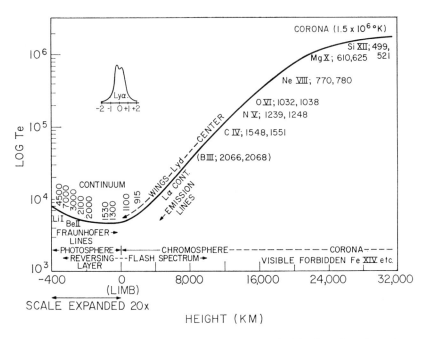

Figure 14-21 Model of electron temperature versus height in solar atmosphere, showing levels of origin of various ultraviolet emission lines.

Approximately 200 lines appear in the rocket spectrograms between 2000 and 500 Å, most of which are identified as the resonance lines or lines of low excitation potential of various stages of ionization. The lines belonging to the lithiumlike isoelectronic sequence, beginning with C IV at 1548.2, 1550.8 Å and continuing through N V, O VI to Ne VIII at 770.4, 780.3 Å are all present except for F VII, which is too rare to be detected. In Figure 14-21 these lines are plotted on a curve of emission levels in the solar chromosphere or corona versus electron temperatures corresponding to their excitation (31). The Ne VIII lines are the first spectrum lines of that element observed in the sun. Since the excitation temperature is 5×10^5 degrees K, their origin must be coronal. Na VIII, with a cosmic abundance only $\frac{1}{40}$th of that of neon is not evident in the spectra. The Mg X lines, however, are clearly present at 609.7, 624.9 Å. The lines of highest excitation are those Si XII at 499.3 and 521.1 Å. Table 14-3 lists the intensities of the solar emission lines and continuum in 50 Å intervals between 2600 and 1750 Å, from the work of Tousey and his colleagues at NRL. Table 14-4 lists the intensities

TABLE 14-3

The Intensity of the Solar Spectrum at a Distance of
1 Astronomical Unit (continuum and lines), in 50-Å Intervals

$\lambda \pm 25$ Å	Erg/cm²/sec	$\lambda \pm 25$ Å	Erg/cm²/sec
2600	700	1700	8.2
2550	560	1650	5.0
2500	380	1600	3.2
2450	390	1550	1.7
2400	340	1500	0.96
2350	320	1450	0.50
2300	360	1400	0.26
2250	350	1350	0.26
2200	310	1300	0.18
2150	340	1250	0.15
2100	145	1200	5.7
2050	90	1150	0.08
2000	70	1100	0.06
1950	55	1050	0.10
1900	41	1000	0.18
1850	28	950	0.15
1800	19	900	0.25
1750	12	850	0.11

TABLE 14-4

Intensity at 1 Astronomical Unit Produced by the
Strongest Solar Emission Lines

λ(Å)	Identification	Erg/cm²/sec
1892.03	Si III (1)	0.10
1817.42 *	Si II (1)	0.45
1808.01		0.15
1670.81	Al II (2)	0.08
1657.00 *	C I (2)	0.16
1640.47	He II (12)	0.07
1561.40 *	C I (3)	0.09
1550.77	C IV (1)	0.06
1548.19	C IV (1)	0.11
1533.44	Si II (2)	0.041
1526.70	Si II (2)	0.038
1402.73	Si IV (1)	0.013
1393.73	Si IV (1)	0.030
1335.68	C II (1)	0.050
1334.51	C II (1)	0.050
1306.02	O I (2)	0.025
1304.86	O I (2)	0.020
1302.17	O I (2)	0.013
1265.04	Si II (4)	0.020
1260.66 *	Si II (4)	0.010
1242.78 *	N V	0.003
1238.80	N V	0.004
1215.67	H Ly-α	5.1
1206.52	Si III (2)	0.030
1175.70 *	C III (4)	0.010
1139.89 *	C I (20–23)	0.003
1085.70 *	N II (1)	0.006
1037.61 *	O VI (1)	0.025
1031.91	O VI (1)	0.020
1025.72	H Ly-β	0.060
991.58 *	N III (1)	0.010
989.79 *	N III (1)	0.006
977.03	C III (1)	0.050
949.74	H Ly	0.010
937.80	H Ly	0.005
835 *	O II, III	0.010

The value for Lyman-α applies to the intensity within the 1-Å wide central part of the line (based on an ion-chamber reading of 6.0 erg/cm²/sec).

* Indicated that the line is a blend of lines of other elements or is an unresolved multiplet.

at zero optical depth produced by the strongest solar emission lines in the range of 1892 to 835 Å.

The telemetering monochromator

Although the preceding photographic experiments provided high resolution and much detail with regard to source distribution on the sun, they failed to reach the shortest ultraviolet wavelengths. The telemetering monochromator developed by Hinteregger, Damon, Heroux, and Hall (32) utilizes grazing incidence to reach the shortest wavelengths and with some sacrifice in resolution can scan the solar spectrum fast enough to reveal the changes that occur within 5-to-10-km altitude increments during the course of an Aerobee flight. Although Hinteregger's instrument employs grazing incidence, the stray-light problem is greatly minimized by the characteristic long wavelength insensitivity of his photoelectric detector. The first successful flights with this instrument clearly recorded the helium resonance lines and many emission lines to much shorter wavelengths.

Figure 14-22 illustrates the design of the telemetering monochromator. The over-all length is about 1 meter. To scan in wavelength, four equally distant slits are carried on a thin, continuous steel belt along the Rowland circle. The grating is ruled on a 2-meter radius of curvature with either 7500, 15,000, or 30,000 lines/in. for scanning 1300 to 250, 650 to 125, or 325 to 62 Å, respectively. The angle of incidence is 86 degrees for the first range and is increased for the shorter wavelength ranges.

The detector for this telemetering monochromator was originally developed by Wiley and Goodrich of the Bendix Corporation for ion counting in mass spectrometry and was later adapted in collaboration with Hinteregger to the ultraviolet detection problem (33). Referring to Figure 14-23, the detector consists of a cathode section and a secondary emission multiplier section. Radiation emerging from the exit slit of the monochromator strikes the photocathode after passing through the apertures in a fine mesh grid of high transmission. Secondary multiplication takes place along the length of the dynode strip. Both the dynode strip D and the field strip F are semiconducting films of tin oxide coated on glass. With the voltages applied as in Figure 14-23 and with a crossed magnetic field, photoelectrons are constrained to move along trochoidal paths toward the bend leading into the dynode section. Inside the dynode section secondary emission multiplication proceeds at the rate of about a factor of 10 per 300 volts of potential difference as the electrons execute their trochoidal loops and repeatedly strike the dynode strip. In practice, a gain of

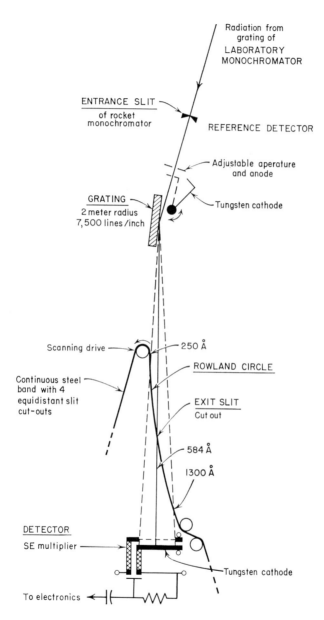

Figure 14-22 AFCRC telemetering monochromator.

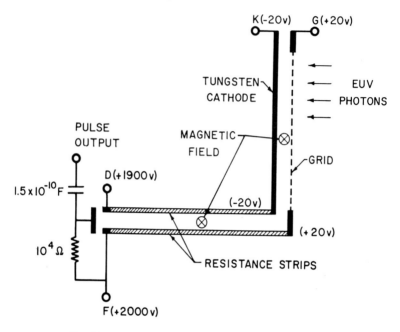

Figure 14-23 Bendix secondary emission photomultiplier used with monochromator of Figure 12-22.

10^8 is readily achieved. Compared to conventional focused dynode structures, however, the dispersion in gain is much greater. A great practical advantage of the tin-oxide dynode surface is its insensitivity to exposure to air. Typical of the results obtained with this instrument is the spectrum shown in the upper portion of Figure 14-24. Among the more striking features of this spectrogram are the strong emission near 975 Å, produced largely by the C III line, the helium resonance lines at 584 and 304 Å, and an increase in continuum intensity near 200 Å, possibly associated with the He II Lyman limit at 228 Å. It is likely that the 584 Å line is still seriously attenuated by the atmosphere at 210 km. The abrupt fall of intensity near 165 Å has not been explained and may be instrumental.

Photographic spectroscopy below 800 Å

In an Aerobee rocket experiment flown on June 21, 1961, Austin, Purcell, and Tousey (34) succeeded in eliminating the scattered-light problem which plagued previous photographic work with grazing incidence spectrographs by employing a thin aluminum filter. The

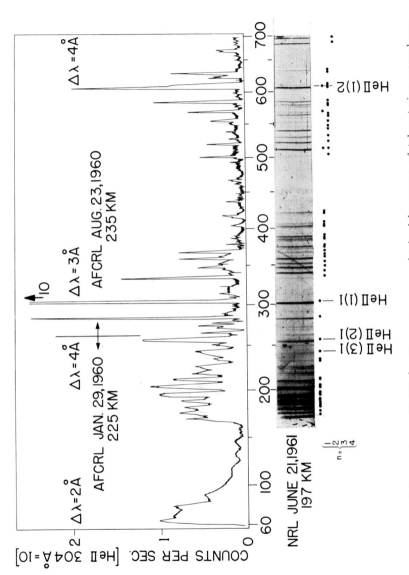

Figure 14-24 Solar spectrum, 60–700 Å. Upper trace was obtained by means of telemetering monochromator. Lower photographic spectrum exhibits low stray light background as a result of the use of an Al filter over the entrance slit.

aluminum was 1000 Å thick and strong enough to be self-supporting. Opaque to longer wavelengths, it began to transmit effectively at the plasma frequency near 830 Å, reached 20 percent transparency at 500 Å, and became opaque again at the L III edge (170 Å). The filter almost completely eliminated stray-light background, clearly revealing weak emission lines which would most certainly have been lost in background fog without the filter effect.

The spectrogram obtained with the NRL instrument, at a height of about 190 km, is shown in Figure 14-24, with the photoelectric scan obtained by Hinteregger at 235 km. Allowing for the absorption of the residual atmosphere above 190 km, which passes little radiation of wavelength longer than 310 Å, the agreement in detail is satisfactory. What appear to be longer wavelength lines in the photographic spectrum are mostly second-, third-, and fourth-order lines of the 170-to-310-Å range. In the photoelectric spectrum, however, the lines from 310 to 700 Å are almost all diffracted in the first order, the absorption of N_2 being comparatively weak at 235 km.

The wavelength accuracy of the photographic spectrum is about 0.1 Å, limited largely by the 1 Å-line width that resulted from the use of a wide slit and partly by the absence of a sufficient number of standard lines for comparison. The broad slit was used in the hope of detecting continuum emission. If a narrower slit were employed, the resolution could readily be reduced to a few hundredths of an angstrom. What is most interesting about the photographed spectrum is that few of the 50 lines measured have been identified. Lyman-alpha of He II (303.8 Å) is present in first and second orders. Multiplets (2) and (3) of He II are present but (4) is not detectable. Tousey identified the line at 182.3 Å with the first line of the Balmer series of C VI and the lines at 173.08 and 172.93 Å with multiplet (4) of O VI. The lines at 335 and 362 Å may be the resonance lines of Fe XVI, computed by Edlén to lie at 336.17 and 361.66 Å. With the exception of these identifications, the origins of the lines remain undetermined.

Future flights to higher altitudes and higher resolution should reveal many more lines. The filter techniques may be extended by the use of films other than aluminum. For example, indium transmits from 735 to 1100 Å, tin, from 510 to 900 Å, and bismuth, from 500 to 700 Å in thicknesses of about 1000 Å (see Figure 14-2).

X-ray spectroscopy

The extension of ruled grating spectroscopy to the 1-to-60-Å region of the spectrum appears to offer great difficulties. Although the focusing properties of a mirror in principle are independent of the wavelength and should apply to X rays as well as to ultraviolet light, the efficiency of reflection falls so rapidly in the X-ray portion of the spectrum that focusing in the ordinary sense is not practical. Since the refractive index of materials for X rays is less than 1, it is possible to utilize total reflection at small angles. X rays are totally reflected back into air at an air-solid interface at a critical glancing angle given by the formula

$$\theta_c = 2.4 \times 10^5 k\lambda, \tag{14-1}$$

where k may vary from 1 to 3, depending on the nature of the reflecting surface. For X rays of wavelength 10 Å, the critical angle is of the order of 1 degree for aluminum and 5 degrees for a gold or platinum surface. The reflection is never truly total, and the cutoff with the angle of incidence is not critically sharp but depends on the material of the surface and the wavelength of the X rays. Appreciable efficiency of reflection is achieved only at and below the critical angle, so that any practical mirror system must employ grazing incidence. Focusing can be achieved only in the plane of incidence, and a point image of a point object can be obtained only by placing a second mirror normal to the first in order to correct its astigmatism.

Plane-grating spectrometers have been used for accurate wavelength determination in the X-ray region near 1 Å, but since there are no lenses for X rays focused slit images cannot be obtained with plane gratings. Consequently, narrow beams are required, and only a small part of the ruled surface can be utilized, with the result that the resolving power must be comparatively small. The resolving power, therefore, cannot be increased by simply increasing the total number of lines on the reflecting surface. Instead, it is necessary to rule a large number of lines per unit length. X-ray gratings used by Siegbahn have been ruled with as many as 1800 lines/mm.

In the soft X-ray region concave grating spectrographs have been used quite extensively. Small glancing angles must be used, and the grating cannot therefore be doubly focusing, the beam being divergent perpendicular to the plane of the Rowland circle. The small glancing angle also makes it necessary to use gratings with a comparatively long radius of curvature. If the length of the ruled surface is too long, the lines are usually badly distorted by the appearance of glancing incidence ghosts. It is necessary to give the grooves such fine rules that they cannot cut off part of the incident radiation. Examination of the grooves of optical gratings often shows that they

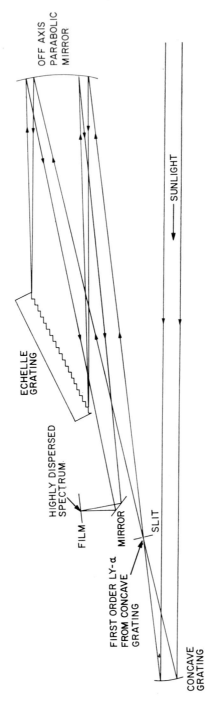

Figure 14-25 Echelle spectrograph designed by J. D. Purcell for the extreme ultraviolet. An off-axis paraboloid of 65-cm focal length collimates the light received from the slit and also focuses the returned spectrum from the echelle onto the film. The grating predisperser before the slit serves to separate orders and to reduce stray light.

are surrounded by piles of debris from the original surface, accumulated to a height that would screen the remaining surface from radiation if these gratings were used at X-ray glancing angles. To be effective in the X-ray spectrum, the lines must be ruled so cleanly that glancing angles of minutes of arc are possible.

A promising possibility for X-ray spectroscopy is the use of organic crystal gratings with spacings in the range 20 to 90 Å. Suitable crystals are now available, and it appears possible to achieve reflectivities of the order of a few tenths of a percent at the shorter wavelengths and a resolution of about ½ Å in spectrographs of a size appropriate for use in an Aerobee rocket. At the short wavelength end of the scale from 1 to 20 Å, the region primarily associated with solar activity and flares, inorganic crystal spectrometers of the classical Bragg type are capable of resolving the solar spectrum to about 1/10 Å in the short time available during a rocket flight.

High resolution spectroscopy

The echelle spectrograph described earlier is inherently capable of achieving resolving powers as high as 10^6. It appears possible to extend this Littrow-type of echelle spectrograph with improved optics to wavelengths as short as 1500 Å. Beyond that wavelength it is necessary to replace the fluorite prism and lenses by reflection optics, as shown in Figure 14-25. This instrument in the laboratory has achieved a resolution of 0.01 Å at Lyman-alpha, but further research in the ruling of echelle gratings is required before we can succeed in measuring the profiles of fainter emission lines such as Lyman-beta, the O VI lines at 1031 Å, and the neutral oxygen resonance lines near 1300 Å. Another promising development for improved spectroscopy is the solar-pointed Aerobee. If, instead of the relatively short spar that can now be pointed with a biaxial control, it were possible to point the entire Aerobee to the sun, gratings with focal lengths as long as 2 meters could be housed in the nose cone with proportionate improvement in spectral resolution.

An interim step toward improving high resolution was taken by R. T. Meltzer and by J. D. Purcell and R. Tousey (35), with the instrument of Figure 14-26. This spectrograph was designed specifically for the purpose of photographing the hydrogen Lyman-alpha line. High resolution was achieved by using the thirteenth order of diffraction from a 1200-line/mm Bausch & Lomb replica grating of 50-cm radius of curvature. The dispersion was 0.4 Å/mm. A grating G1, similar to G2, was used in the first order to project its Lyman-alpha image on the slit, thus preventing stray light and overlapping

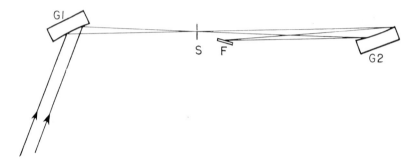

Figure 14-26 High dispersion spectrograph designed to photograph the profile of Lyman-α in the thirteenth order.

orders from reaching G2. By selecting the angles appropriately, the astigmatisms of the two gratings were made to neutralize each other and to yield a spectral line stigmatic with respect to the sun. In the photographed spectral line (Figure 14-27) strips across the line reproduce the profile of emission sources in a slice across the sun.

A most important development contributing to the success of the profile spectrograph was the high reflectivity aluminum-magnesium fluoride coating (80 percent reflectivity at Lyman-alpha). Second in importance was an extremely fast film, SC 4, produced by Kodak-Pathé. This Schumann-type emulsion, developed by R. Audran, is prepared by centrifuging a tightly packed layer of grains against a support, without gelatin binder. Its rear side is then attached to a backing, and the film is stripped from the centrifuge surface, leaving the grains completely exposed to irradiation. Silver bromo-iodide grains were used, giving an emulsion 10 times more sensitive than SWR at 1216 Å.

High resolution spectrograms of the profiles of lines, such as Lyman-alpha, the Mg-K doublet, and the Ca H and K lines, contain important clues to the temperature structure and density of the chromosphere at various elevations. As is evident in Figure 14-27, the Lyman-alpha profile is a broad emission feature with wings extending to 1 Å or more on either side of center. It strongly resembles the profiles of Ca H and K and of Mg II (Figure 14-16). At half-maximum the width of Lyman-alpha is about 1 Å. Instead of the simple Doppler profile that would be expected if thermodynamic equilibrium prevailed in the source, the line is truncated and depressed into a broad, shallow minimum across its center. The resulting effect is that of a doubly peaked emission. In the center of the broad re-

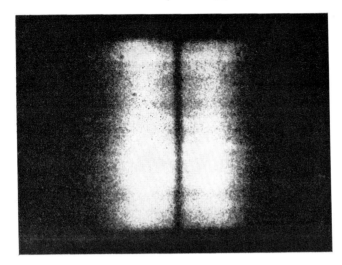

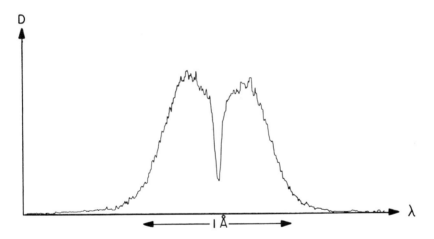

Figure 14-27   Lyman-α profile as photographed from a height of 145 km.

versal is a deep and narrow absorption core. This feature can be attributed to absorption by telluric neutral hydrogen and is discussed later.

According to an analysis by Morton and Widing (36), following the theory developed by Jefferies and Thomas, the broader features of the Lyman-alpha profile are formed by noncoherent scattering in chromospheric regions of high electron temperature relative to the observed radiation temperature. As indicated in Figure 14-21, the various portions of the line are produced over a temperature range of 55,000 to 115,000°K. Differences in profile were detectable between plage regions and the quiet solar atmosphere. The central broad reversal was wider and deeper in quiet portions of the chromosphere than over the plages. It turns out surprisingly that the theoretical analysis indicates a kinetic temperature about 20,000 degrees lower in the plage regions than in the quiet areas.

14-3 CHROMOSPHERIC MODELS AND ULTRAVIOLET SPECTRA

The ultraviolet spectra contribute information which describes only a gross average structure of the chromosphere. The simplest theoretical models treat a spherically symmetrical chromosphere, and it is possible to predict emission spectra for various temperature versus height profiles. In essence, the rocket spectra show that the average temperature rises with height as plotted in Figure 14-21. Chromospheric models in which the temperature remains fairly constant up to a given height and then rises abruptly to a high level characteristic of the corona would predict emissions from neutral atoms and high states of ionization; intermediate states of ionization would be almost absent. The rocket observations show the entire range of intermediate excitations and therefore conform to a model of relatively low temperature gradient versus height from lower chromosphere to corona.

The true picture of the chromosphere departs radically from spherical symmetry. Coronagraphs cannot photograph the chromosphere close to its boundary with the photosphere, but at heights above 3000 km they show a characteristic spicule structure. These small jet prominences surge up from the lower chromosphere and fall back again or vanish into the corona in a matter of 5 to 10 min. On the average they rise at speeds of about 20 km/sec to heights of 10,000 km. Each spicule is about 800 km in diameter at the base. At any given time as many as 100,000 spicules may be evolving over the face of the sun, and any given spot on the disk undergoes spicule activity about once a day. Athay (37) believes that the chromosphere is divided into hot and cold regions, beginning at a height of about 1300 km, in which the spicules are hot, high-density columns but the intervening atmosphere is hotter and of lower density. Coates (38) fitted his radio observations at 4 and 8 mm to a model in which spicules reached the temperature of 6400 degrees K and the interspicular material was much hotter. The reverse arrangement of hot and cold regions was deduced by Shklovsky and Kononovitch (39), who used both radio and optical data. They concluded that the hot regions achieved a temperature of 12,000 degrees K at a height of 8000 km and covered less than 10 percent of the surface; the cool regions, at temperatures as low as 4000 degrees K, did not exceed 6000 km in height. To resolve further the structure of the chromosphere will require high resolution spectroscopy of a great many lines besides Lyman-alpha, in particular Lyman-beta and higher lines of the series, the O VI lines at 1031 Å, He I (584 Å), He II (304 Å), and the more intense lines of the corona-chromosphere transition region such as Mg X and Si XII. Spectroheliographic mapping in all these wavelengths would be very useful.

14-4 X-RAY PHOTOMETRY

The quiet sun

At the time of a solar eclipse the corona appears as a faintly luminescent gas with a slightly greenish cast, reaching millions of miles into space. The source of solar X-ray emission lies within the corona near its base where the temperature is of the order of 1 million degrees K. How the corona reaches this remarkably high temperature when the visible surface of the sun is only 6000 degrees K is explainable in terms of the dissipation of shock-wave energy. Immediately below the surface of the sun energy is transported outward by the violent convection of hydrogen gas. Sound waves generated by turbulence start within the hydrogen convection zone and propagate outward, increasing in amplitude as the density decreases until shock waves develop. Energy is thus transferred from the interior of the sun to the corona. Because the corona is so thin, it radiates poorly, and only a small fraction of the sun's energy needs to be dissipated in the corona to achieve high temperatures.

X-ray photometry from rockets has been carried on by the author and his colleagues at the U. S. Naval Research Laboratory (30) for more than a full sunspot cycle, beginning in 1949. More recently, similar experiments have been reported by Russian (40, 41, 42) and by British (43) scientists. In a typical rocket experiment the detector is mounted against an aperture in the skin of the rocket looking outward. Its view of space during the course of a flight depends entirely on the spin and yaw motion of the rocket. As the rocket traverses the upper atmosphere, signals are telemetered continuously via radio transmitter in the rocket to a receiver on the ground. When the spinning rocket reaches altitudes to which solar X-rays can penetrate, modulated signals appear in the record with the roll frequency, maximizing whenever the detector looks closest to the direction to the sun. Essential to such an experiment is a visible photocell measurement which permits the calculation of the aspect of the rocket at all times during the flight and therefrom the appropriate correction for the dependence of X-ray signals on the angle of incidence of the radiation.

Near sunspot minimum, in 1953 and 1954, the rocket measurements indicated a marked reduction in X-ray emission below 20 Å. In some experiments no emission at all was detected below 10 Å. With the approach to solar maximum, the over-all X-ray flux increased, especially at the shorter wavelengths. In the 2-to-8-Å band the minimum-to-maximum variation was a factor of several hundred; from 8 to 20 Å, at least a factor of 45; in the 44-to-60-Å band the variation was approximately sevenfold. Assuming that the X-ray spectrum had a gray-body distribution, it was not possible to fit the measurements in these three wavelength intervals by a single temperature. The longer wavelength emission could be adequately described by a temperature between 0.5 and 1×10^6 degrees K, but the shorter wavelength range, below 20 Å, required a temperature closer to 2×10^6 degrees K. At the higher temperature the gray-body emission needed to supply the observed counting rate at 8 to 20 Å contained only 1 percent of the flux deduced for the 20-to-100-Å range from the longer wavelength measurements. It was concluded, therefore, that the shortest wavelength X-ray emission was associated with hotter local regions occupying perhaps no more than 1 percent of the volume of the corona, in which the temperature was of the order of 2 million degrees K. These hotter regions were presumably distributed within a corona whose general temperature did not exceed 1 million degrees K. Figure 14-28 is a plot of the solar spectral energy distribution which illustrates the results of these measurements. The curve marked "A-16" is for 1953 and "A-43" for 1956. They represent the minimum and maximum fluxes observed during the last sunspot cycle. The shaded region added to the A-16 curve is the increment of flux measured below 20 Å and attributed to localized hot spots at 2 million degrees K.

Nearly all of our knowledge of the ionosphere before direct rocket measurements were available was based on radio soundings. A pulse of radio waves entering a cloud of electrons is reflected when the density of the electrons reaches a critical value proportional to the square of the frequency. The time required for the pulse to travel to the ionosphere and back to ground is a measure of the height of the reflecting region. At certain critical frequencies abrupt discon-

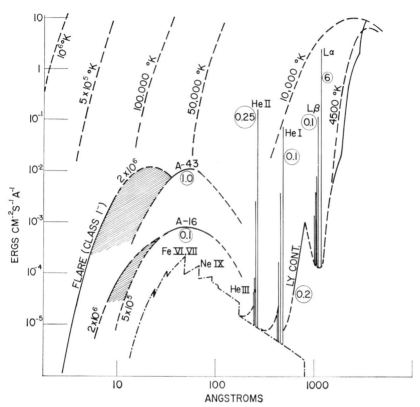

Figure 14-28 Solar spectral energy distribution from 2000 Å to X-rays. Solid lined portions of curves represent rocket measurements. Elwert's theoretically computed continuum is represented by the dot-dash curve. Black body curves are indicated for various temperatures up to 10^6 degrees K.

tinuities in reflection heights appear, as though the electron density were distributed in several well-defined layers. These layers are named E, F_1, and F_2. In the lowest region of the ionosphere, named "D," the electron density is too small to reflect megacycle-per-second frequencies. The lower ionosphere normally acts as an absorbing region for these short waves and a good reflector for long waves, such as the static generated by thunderstorms.

The variation of intensity with altitude showed that solar X rays were absorbed in the E region of the ionosphere between 100 and 140 km (22). Furthermore, the X-ray energy absorbed there appeared adequate to account for a major portion of the ionization. A direct check on the relationship between X rays absorbed in the E region and the resulting electron density there can be obtained by comparing X-ray fluxes with the observed variation in critical frequency of the E region. According to the theory of the formation of an ionospheric layer, the critical frequency is proportional to the fourth root of the intensity of ionizing radiation. The observed sevenfold variation in total flux from minimum to maximum would therefore produce a factor of $7\frac{1}{4}$, or 1.6 in the critical frequency for E region if X rays were the sole source. When values of the critical frequency corresponding to the times of rocket flights were used, the variations were about 0.27 to 4.1 Mc/sec, a factor of 1.5, in good agreement with the variation expected from the X-ray observations. Actually, an important contribution to the ionization of E region is made by solar ultraviolet radiation, and it is theoretically difficult to evaluate the relative importance of X-ray and ultraviolet contributions. However, an analysis based on the best information available at the present time indicates that the X-ray influence is predominant.

Activity centers

Observations over more than two sunspot cycles have clearly established correlations between the fluxes of ionizing radiation and active centers on the sun. If the ionizing radiation were uniformly distributed over the face of the sun, an eclipse would lead to a smooth decline in the ionospheric electron density to a minimum value at totality, followed by a smooth recovery to normal in much the same fashion, followed by the visible light curve. Instead, an irregular course of ionospheric electron-density changes has been noted in almost all observations conducted during eclipses. Monthly averages of critical frequencies show detailed agreement with the pattern followed by monthly values of sunspot numbers, indicating that at least part of the ionizing flux emanates from the vicinity of sunspots. Before 1958, however, no direct identification of localized sources of X-ray emission in the corona had been made.

The eclipse of October 12, 1958, offered an opportunity to launch rockets bearing ultraviolet and X-ray detectors to observe the distribution of emission sources over the disk and to determine whether any residual emission of X rays or ultraviolet radiation was detectable at totality (44). During the totality phase of an eclipse the E region of the ionosphere does not disappear completely, as would be expected if the source of the ionizing radiation were totally obscured and recombination were very fast. The residual ionization could be attributed to a sluggishness of the recombination process or to a portion of the ionizing radiation originating at sufficient height in the corona to by-pass the edge of the moon.

The rocket experiment was carried out from shipboard near the Danger Islands of the South Pacific. Solid propellant rockets were mounted on the helicopter deck of the U.S.S. *Point Defiance* and were launched at the appropriate times and in a direction to carry them through the eclipse shadow at E-region altitudes. Each rocket was equipped with X-ray detectors sensitive to two wavelength bands, 8–18 and 44–60 Å, and a Lyman-alpha ionization chamber. Signals from these detectors and from aspect indicators were telemetered to the ground station aboard ship throughout the flight. Two rockets launched during totality indicated about 0.05 percent residual Lyman-alpha flux and from 10 to 13 percent residual X-ray flux. The eclipse of February 1961, which passed over the Crimea, was observed in similar fashion by Russian rocket astronomers (45) with essentially the same results.

A second objective of the 1958 eclipse experiment was to identify localized sources of emission over the disk. Figure 14-29 shows the optical distribution of active regions on the day of the rocket eclipse experiment. The area of the disk near the east limb contained a number of active regions identified by plages, whereas an equivalent area bordering the west limb was almost free of activity. Rockets were fired to observe exposed crescents on the east and west limbs before second contact and after third contact, as marked by the curves NN8.59F and NN8.62F in the figure. The east-limb crescent, containing the plage areas, was observed to be six times as bright in X-ray emission as the west-limb crescent, which was almost clear of plage activity (making allowance for the relative disk areas exposed).

In principle, X-ray image-forming devices of high light-gathering power can be achieved in the form of a grazing incidence reflection telescope or a zone plate, but no such devices have yet been perfected for use in rockets. Calculations, based on the intensity measured with X-ray photometers and the evidence of concentrated sources derived from the rocket eclipse experiment, indicated that a simple pinhole camera could produce an X-ray image with a resolution of about a tenth of a solar diameter during the flight time of an Aerobee-Hi rocket if the camera were mounted on a pointing control to aim it continuously at the sun. The first photograph of the sun in its X-ray emission (44) was obtained in this manner on April 19, 1960. The camera was 6 in. long and had a pinhole of 0.005 in. diameter. To exclude visible and ultraviolet light, the pinhole was covered by a

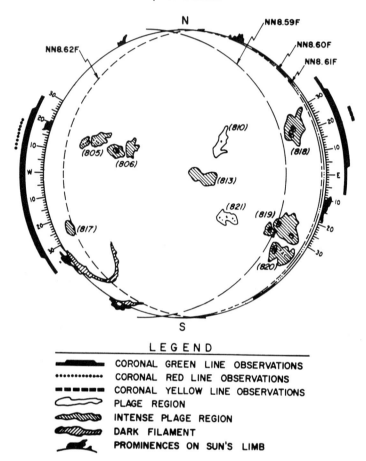

Figure 14-29 Distribution of sunspots and plages over solar disk at time of solar eclipse, October 12, 1958.

plastic film of Parlodion, which was overcoated with an evaporated film of aluminum. This combination transmitted much of the X-ray spectrum below 50 Å.

The X-ray photograph is reproduced in the upper left-hand portion of Figure 14-30. The biaxial pointing control which carried the camera did not compensate for rotation about the sun-camera axis, with the result that the precession of the rocket caused the image to rotate and discrete features to be drawn into extended arcs. Furthermore, the sense of rotation varied during the course of the flight so that the image was first turned about 20 degrees clockwise and then returned counterclockwise to complete the full arc of 160 degrees extent. In spite of the smearing produced, a clear correlation could be observed between the X-ray emission regions and the visible plage regions on the sun.

By direct measurement of the image, the mean diameter of the X-ray outline of the sun was found to be 5 percent greater than the diameter of the optical disk. The maximum diameter was 6 percent greater. Thus, within the limited definition of the camera, the X-ray emission was observed to extend to about 0.06 solar radii (43,000 km) above the visible limb. All of the measured X-ray regions in the photograph were about the size of the resolution circle when allowance was made for the smearing effect of the camera rotation. It appears that the regions of strong X-ray emission are smaller than the corresponding visible plage regions. From the fact that the sizes of the X-ray regions on the limb were nearly the same as those near the center of the disk, it would seem that the X-ray sources have a radial extension comparable to the surface projection.

A strong correlation is known to exist between visible plage regions and the regions of origin of the slowly varying component of radio microwave emission. Solar radio emissions in the decimeter wavelength range also correlate closely with variations in E-region electron density. The lower right-hand portion of Figure 14-30 contains a radioheliograph of the sun at a wavelength of 9.1 cm, obtained at Stanford University with a microsteradian, pencil-beam interferometer, with a resolution of 3.5 min of arc (46). It is interesting to compare the radioheliograph with the X-ray disk photograph because both types of radiation require million-degree sources and vary in intensity with the square of the electron density. To compare the radio map with the X-ray picture, it was photographed while rotated about its center to match the motion of the X-ray camera during the rocket flight. The resulting smeared radio image is shown in the lower left-hand corner of Figure 14-30. Its major features closely resemble the smeared features of the X-ray photograph. In order to enhance the similarity, the contrast of the radioheliograph was heightened by eliminating the two lowest isophote intervals of the original map. In fact, one of the more important differences is the much greater contrast between active regions and background in the X-ray picture than in the radio picture. The bright, nearly central region of the X-ray image is about 80 times as intense as the quiet background, when allowance is made for the effect of smearing, and at least four fifths of the emission is concentrated in the active areas. In comparison, the integrated radio emission from active areas is

SOLAR X-RAY PHOTOGRAPH
NRL, APRIL 19, 1960

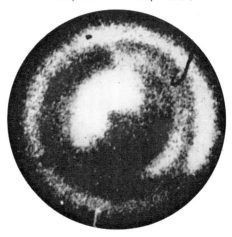

ROTATED RADIOHELIOGRAPH

Figure 14-30 *Upper left:* X-ray pinhole camera photograph of sun. *Upper right:* densitometer map of X-ray photograph. *Lower right:* 9.1-cm radioheliograph. *Lower left:* photograph of rotated radioheliograph.

DENSITY CONTOUR MAP OF
SOLAR X-RAY PHOTOGRAPH

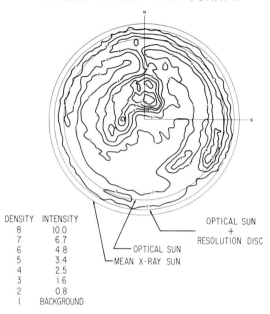

DENSITY	INTENSITY
8	10.0
7	6.7
6	4.8
5	3.4
4	2.5
3	1.6
2	0.8
1	BACKGROUND

OPTICAL SUN
+
RESOLUTION DISC

OPTICAL SUN
MEAN X-RAY SUN

RADIOHELIOGRAPH
9.1 CM
(STANFORD UNIV)

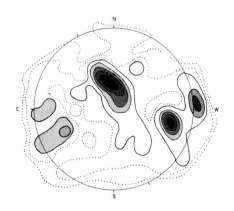

roughly equal to the background emission. The X-ray photograph also matches a 21-cm radioheliograph fairly well, but the detailed correspondence is not so clear as the 9.1-cm map. Studies of the relationship between E-layer ionization and the solar decimeter wave flux show that a good correlation exists between 3 and 30 cm. On a short time scale, the best correlation seems to occur in the range 10 to 15 cm (47).

The X-ray emission and the microwave emission are both associated with regions of greater than normal density in the corona above sunspot groups. These coronal condensations are optically brighter in proportion to the electron density. They appear to have semi-spherical or elliptical forms without any resolvable internal structure. So-called permanent condensations measure 1 to 2 min in arc, range in density from 10^9 to 10^{10} particles/cm^3, and persist for several days. Sporadic condensations may form out of the permanent condensations. The diameter of a sporadic condensation is typically about 0.5 min of arc; its lifetime may be minutes to hours, and it is accompanied by the formation of loop prominences and the emission of bursts of centimeter wave emission and solar flares.

Originally, the condensations were thought to be at elevated temperatures, as high as 6 or 7×10^6 degrees K, but they are now believed to be at near normal coronal temperatures in the range 1.6×10^6 to 0.06×10^6 degrees K. The association of X-ray emission with the coronal condensations implies an upper limit of the order of 2×10^6 degrees K for the temperature of a condensation. It has been argued (48) that thermal conductivity in a condensation is so high that it cannot maintain a high temperature in relation to its surroundings. If a condensation were at a temperature of 6×10^6 degrees, as originally proposed, it would lose all its energy to the neighboring corona in less than 20 min. On the other hand, if a permanent condensation were actually slightly cooler than the normal corona, the excess energy radiated because of its higher density could readily be replaced by heat conduction from the surrounding corona. To help us understand the details of the structure of the corona, we may look forward to the achievement of X-ray photographs of much higher resolution. Satellites will offer the possibility of mapping finer details because of the longer observing times available.

Solar flares

Superposed on the slowly varying X-ray emission associated with plages are short-lived, transient outbursts synchronized with flare activity. Flares have only rarely been observed in white light. When viewed in the red light of hydrogen Hα, a flare appears to develop with great speed. In a matter of minutes an area of the order of one thousandth of the solar disk may increase tenfold in brightness. Intense radio noise is generated and short-wave radio communications are instantaneously blacked out until the flare disappears. Flares cover a broad spectrum in size from those just barely detectable, so-called microflares, to the most catastrophic explosions, which are accompanied by streams of particles of cosmic-ray energies. These particles arrive within a matter of minutes at the earth; streams of slower moving plasma that may require a day or two to reach the earth are manifested by magnetic storms and auroral displays.

The earliest attempts to detect flare X rays (49) were made in the summer of 1956 with the Rockoon, a small, solid-propellant rocket carried aloft on a Skyhook balloon. The procedure was to launch a Rockoon in the morning from a ship at sea and permit it to float at 80,000 ft. When a flare was detected optically or indirectly indicated by a short-wave fadeout, the rocket was fired by radio command. It was unfortunately necessary to fire the rocket at the end of the day even if a flare did not occur. Although this approach to the problem was not efficient, it succeeded in measuring the emission of one small flare during the course of the expedition and clearly revealed the importance of the accompanying X-ray flux. The result of that particular measurement is included in Figure 14-28 and identified as the portion of the X-ray spectrum associated with a Class 1⁻ flare.

In 1957 two-stage, rail-launched, solid-propellant rockets capable of transporting substantial payloads to ionospheric altitudes became available. Experiments were conducted with the Nike-Deacon and the Nike-Asp during the IGY. The Nike-Asp had the capability of carrying a 50-lb payload about 150 miles. Instrumented rockets could be kept in constant readiness, requiring only the pressing of a button to launch them when a flare was observed. With this approach, a number of measurements of X-ray and ultraviolet emission were obtained during solar flares (23).

At the peak of a moderately large flare the entire X-ray spectrum was observed to increase in brightness up to several times the normal intensity. The increases were orders of magnitude greater at the shortest wavelengths, although the energy content was only a small portion of the total X-ray output. Table 14-5 is a summary by Nicolet (50) of the dependence of X-ray emission in the 1-to-7-Å range on the state of solar activity.

In flares of Class 2 or higher intensity, X-ray quanta with energies in excess of 10^5 ev have been observed in contrast to the normal solar

TABLE 14-5

X-ray Intensities (erg/cm²/sec) for Various States of Solar Activity for
Wavelength Intervals of ± 1 Å Centered at the Indicated Wavelengths

	2 Å	4 Å	6 Å
Completely quiet	10^{-8}	10^{-7}	10^{-6}
Quiet	10^{-7}	10^{-6}	10^{-5}
Slightly disturbed	10^{-6}	10^{-5}	10^{-4}
Disturbed	10^{-5}	10^{-4}	10^{-3}
Flares, Class 2	10^{-4}	10^{-3}	10^{-2}
Flares, Class 3	10^{-3}	10^{-2}	10^{-1}

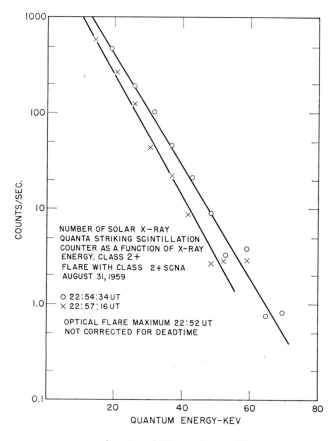

Figure 14-31 Spectra of X-rays from a Class 2+ flare.

X-ray limit of the order of a few thousand electron volts. Figure 14-31 illustrates the observed variation of the number of quanta per second detected by a rocket-borne scintillation spectrometer (Figure 14-9) versus quantum energy, during a Class 2^+ flare. The lifetime of the rocket flight was only 5 min, but the two curves of Figure 14-31 clearly show a softening of the spectrum which occurred during the brief 3-min interval that separated the spectral measurements.

It is interesting to speculate about mechanisms in the production of X-rays with the spectral distributions of Figure 14-31. If it is assumed that the enhanced X-ray emission resulted from a heating of the coronal gas, a temperature as high as 10^8 degrees K would be required. The softening of the later spectrum in Figure 14-31 would correspond approximately to a 15 per cent decrease in temperature. Alternatively, the spectrum could have been produced by streams of suprathermal electrons injected into cooler gas at a temperature not exceeding a few million degrees. To choose between such widely divergent models will require much more detailed spectral information than has been obtained so far.

Satellite photometry

In June 1960 a major step forward in the study of X-ray emission from solar flares was accomplished by the launching of the first satellite observatory by the United States Naval Research Laboratory (51). The satellite, called Solar Radiation I (1960 Eta 2), carried two ionization chambers to measure solar Lyman-alpha (1216 Å) and X rays (2 to 8 Å). These detectors were mounted on the equator of the spherical satellite, which was imparted a high spin rate on separation from the launching vehicle. Each detector viewed the sun once per revolution, giving a spin modulated signal that was transmitted continuously.

Figure 14-32 illustrates a sample record obtained during the passage of the satellite over Blossom Point, Maryland, on August 6, 1960, almost simultaneously with the start of a Class 1 flare, which lasted 18 min. Lyman-alpha signals are indicated by upward deflections from the mid-scale zero level. X-ray signals deflect downward. On the pass illustrated by the first strip of telemetered signals the sun was quiet. A steady Lyman-alpha signal was indicated, with only the barest trace of X-ray intensity. As the satellite returned one orbit later, telemetry reception began almost in coincidence with the eruption of the flare at 1506 UT. At 1509 UT the X-ray emission began to increase. Ionospheric observations and cosmic-noise measurements showed simultaneous starts of various ionospheric disturb-

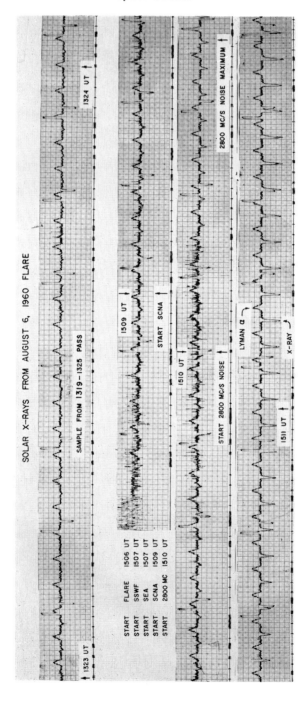

SOLAR X-RAYS FROM AUGUST 6, 1960 FLARE

1323 UT

1324 UT

SAMPLE FROM 1319 – 1325 PASS

START FLARE   1506 UT
START SSWF   1507 UT
START SEA   1507 UT
START SCNA   1509 UT
START 2800 MC 1510 UT

1509 UT

START SCNA

1510 UT

START 2800 MC/S NOISE

1511 UT

2800 MC/S NOISE MAXIMUM

LYMAN α

X-RAY

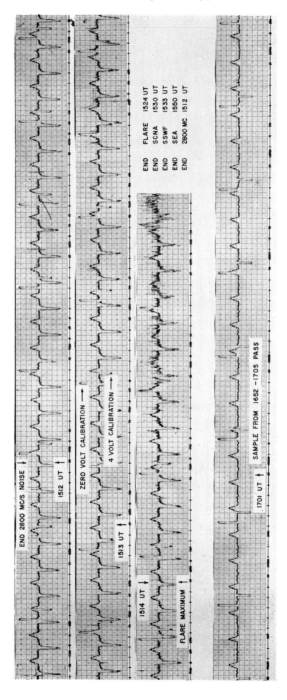

Figure 14-32 Portion of telemetry record from satellite 1960 Eta 2.

ances. Between 1510 and 1511 UT, during a microwave outburst, the X-ray flux increased rapidly to full scale and remained at that level until flare maximum in Hα was reached at 1514 UT. Shortly afterward the satellite passed out of range of the ground station. On the next pass the sun was again quiet. At 1701 UT the record showed only the faintest trace of X-ray emission. Throughout the entire sequence of events the Lyman-alpha flux remained unchanged.

X rays and sudden ionospheric disturbances

The energy radiated as X rays represents a major portion of the total energy output of a solar flare and is entirely adequate to explain the accompanying ionospheric disturbances such as short-wave fade-out, enhancement of atmospherics, and sudden phase anomaly. Nicolet (50) has estimated the contributions of cosmic rays, Lyman-alpha, and flare X rays to the formation of the D-region ionosphere. As indicated in Figure 14-33, flare X rays produce increased ioniza-

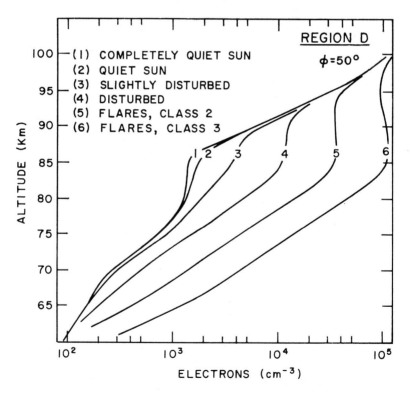

Figure 14-33 The influence of solar activity on the formation of the D-region.

tion at the lowest levels, where the resulting absorption of radio waves is most effective.

Solar flare X rays observed at balloon altitudes

To complete the story of solar-flare X-ray observations, there have been several important measurements at balloon altitudes. Winckler and his associates (52, 53) at the University of Minnesota have used combinations of high-pressure ionization chambers and Geiger counters to distinguish between energetic protons and X rays. The first observation of solar-flare X rays at balloon altitudes occurred in conjunction with a Class 2+ flare in March 1958. The X rays appeared in a short burst of less than 18-sec duration, which was the resolution time of the ionization chamber. It was concluded that the X rays were in the energy region of about 500 kev. Simultaneously with the X-ray flash an intense burst of 800 Mc/sec radio emission appeared. A second X-ray event was observed on August 11, 1960. Although the spectral quality was more like that of the rocket observation of Figure 14-31, it was at least 20 times as intense and therefore still observable at balloon altitude. In this case the X-ray burst coincided with Type III radio-noise bursts, which are known to be associated with charged particles moving through the corona at near relativistic speeds.

Solar X-ray bursts with quantum energies exceeding 80 kev were detected by Vette and Casal (54) during Class 2 and Class 1 flares on October 12, 1960, with balloon-borne scintillation spectrometers. In both events the X-ray bursts were characterized by fast rise times and decayed in a matter of 2 or 3 min. A remarkably close correlation has been noted between the shape of the X-ray burst (20 to 80 kev) and a coincident burst on 2800 Mc/sec during the Class 2 flare (55). As is evident in Figure 14-34, the shapes of the X-ray and radio events agree in minute detail. In contrast, there is no apparent correlation between microwave emission coincident with the flare recorded by the Solar Radiation I satellite (Figure 14-32) and the development of X-ray emission in the 1-to-5-kev range. We can only conclude that flares are complex processes in which a variety of mechanisms may be operative simultaneously in different regimes of the active solar region.

X-ray emission and prominence activity

Many observations are available from the records of Solar Radiation I covering the beginning and ending phases of flares (56). The enhanced X-ray emission started with the visible flare in every case and terminated

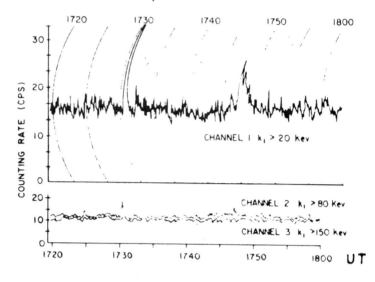

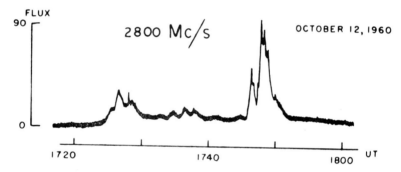

Figure 14-34 Coincident microwave noise burst and X-ray emission ($E > 20$ kev) during flare of October 12, 1960.

with the decay of the flare. In every case in which the X-ray flux exceeded 5×10^{-3} erg/cm²/sec in the 2-to-8-Å bandwidth of the X-ray ion chamber, a short-wave fadeout was observed. On July 24, 1960, there was a sudden disappearance of a large prominence seen above the limb between 0900 and 1200 UT. As this event progressed, enhanced X-ray emission was observed on six successive telemetered records (Figure 14-35), the mean flux reaching 5×10^{-3} erg/cm²/sec at 1020 UT. There were no flares visible on the disk at that time. A search of ionospheric records revealed that radio fadeout occurred simultaneously with the increase of X-ray emission and persisted until the X-ray intensity dropped below the critical level.

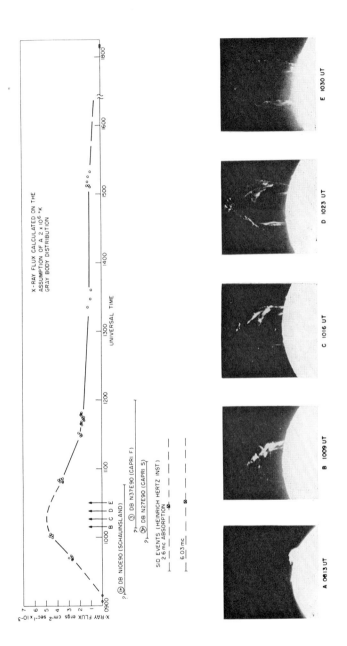

X-RAY EMISSION (2-8Å) FROM ERUPTIVE PROMINENCE OF 24 JULY 1960
Hα (6563 Å) LIMB PHOTOGRAPHS (FRAUNHOFER INSTITUTE)

Figure 14-35 X-ray emission observed by Satellite 1960 Eta 2 during eruptive prominence.

Theoretical dependence of the solar X-ray emission spectrum on temperature

The corona is composed primarily of hydrogen and helium, the light elements C, N, O, Ne, Si, and S, and the relatively heavy element Fe. From 1 to 8 Å the spectrum of the coronal plasma depends strongly on the electron temperature. For temperatures below 3×10^7 degrees K the X-ray emission would be produced primarily by free-bound transitions (photorecombination) to the K shells of C, N, O, and Ne. At higher temperatures the major portion of the X-ray energy, radiated in the 1-to-8-Å region, would arise from free-free transitions (Bremsstrahlung). X rays of energy in excess of 20 kev would be produced mainly by free-bound transitions to the K shell of iron. When an integration is made over the entire frequency range, it is found that the major portion of the emission is due to free-free transitions. Free-bound transitions to excited states are always followed by line emission, and the resulting spectrum is extremely sensitive to temperature. The expected line intensity should be readily detectable and adequately resolved by a simple Bragg crystal spectrometer.

According to theoretical calculations for the normal corona at a temperature of about 10^6 degrees K, the most abundant states of ionization of iron are X to XIV. As the temperature increases, the center of gravity of the ionization equilibrium shifts towards higher states of ionization. According to Elwert (57) and Kawabata (58), the relative abundance of ions of iron varies with temperature as shown in Table 14-6.

As an atom is progressively stripped of electrons, the screening factor for the K shell changes slowly through the early stages of ionization. When the atom is stripped nearly to the K shell, however, the series-

TABLE 14-6

Relative Abundance of Fe Ions as a Function of Coronal Temperature

	$10^7°$K	$5 \times 10^7°$K	$10^8°$K
Fe XX	7×10^{-7}		
XXI	3×10^{-6}		
XXII	1.0×10^{-5}		
XXIII	1.7×10^{-5}		
XXIV	1.5×10^{-5}	3×10^{-6}	6×10^{-7}
XXV	5×10^{-5}	4×10^{-5}	2.1×10^{-5}
XXVI		7×10^{-6}	2.1×10^{-5}
XXVII		4×10^{-7}	8×10^{-6}

TABLE 14-7

X-ray Series-Limit Wavelengths of Coronal Ions

Ne IX	10.4 Å	Fe XXIV	6.1
Ne X	9.1	Si XIII	5.0
Fe XX	7.6	Si XIV	4.7
Fe XXI	7.1	S XV	3.9
Mg XI	7	S XVI	3.2
Fe XXII	6.8	Fe SSV	1.4
Fe XXIII	6.5	Fe XXVI	1.3
Mg XII	6.4		

limit wavelength becomes markedly shorter. For example, the series limit of neutral iron is 1.74 Å; that of Fe XXV is 1.4 Å, and of Fe XXVI it is 1.3 Å. The L-series limit changes from 15.6 Å for Fe I to 6.1 Å for Fe XXIV. Observation of the wavelengths of the series limits is therefore a good temperature index. Table 14-7 lists the series limits of the most abundant ions in the 1-to-10-Å range.

The emission lines that follow recombination into excited states, or which are excited by electron impact, are temperature sensitive. At 10^8 degrees the spectrum would contain essentially nothing other than the K lines of Fe XXV and XXVI and perhaps a barely detectable trace of S XVI. The predicted ratios of the line intensities of Fe XXV and Fe XXVI are $\sim$2:1 at 10^8 degrees K, $\sim$13:1 at 5×10^7 degrees K, and at 2×10^7 degrees K, the Fe XXVI line would be almost unobservable. The K lines of S XV would be strong at 10^7 degrees, increased in strength at 2×10^7 degrees, but undetectable at 5×10^7 degrees. S XVI would not appear strongly below 2×10^7 degrees, but would maximize between 2×10^7 and 5×10^7 degrees K, and would still be detectable at 10^8 degrees K. N VI, O VIII, Fe XX, XXI, and XXII, would be negligibly intense at 5×10^7 degrees K and higher temperatures.

In a typical Class 2 flare the flux observed from 1 to 10 Å is of the order of 10^{-2} erg/cm^2/sec. Let us assume that this energy is distributed in approximately 10 strong lines at roughly 10^{-3} erg/cm^2/sec/line. Using a Bragg single crystal X-ray spectrometer, the efficiency of crystal reflection should exceed 5 percent, and the efficiency of a Geiger-counter detector can be as high as 50 percent near the series limit of iron. The widths of coronal emission lines would be of the order of 0.02 Å, which is comparable to the resolution of the spectrometer. The expected counting rate would then be about 2500/sec/line, if the crystal and detector apertures were about 1 cm^2. Scanning at a rate of 0.02 Å/sec over about

8 Å would require less than 7 min/spectrum scan. It is clear, therefore, that a simple crystal spectrometer carried on a satellite can monitor the temperature variation of a flare region over the range from 10^6 to 10^8 degrees K by virtue of the accompanying spectral changes.

14-5 ULTRAVIOLET PHOTOMETRY OF THE NIGHT SKY

Although the major efforts in rocket and satellite astronomy to date have been directed at the sun, some success has already been achieved in mapping the ultraviolet emissions of the night airglow and of stellar sources. The intensities involved in these measurements are several orders of magnitude weaker than solar fluxes in corresponding spectral bands of the vacuum ultraviolet. As a result, it is difficult to achieve any but the simplest photometric measurements during the short lifetime of a rocket flight and without the benefit of stellar pointing devices. The current development of a stabilized Aerobee with a stellar pointed platform should lead to great refinements in rocket ultraviolet astronomy. These will be succeeded by orbiting atsronomical observatories which eventually will permit the same degree of sophication in ultraviolet astronomy as is now achieved in ground-based visible astronomy.

The Lyman-alpha glow of the night sky

The first exploratory measurements of the ultraviolet emissions of the night sky were made by the U. S. Naval Research Laboratory in 1955 (59). An Aerobee rocket was equipped with photon counters sensitive to the wavelength bands 1050 to 1350 and 1230 to 1350 Å. Several of these detectors were mounted to view a 20-degree field through the skin of the rocket. The rocket was unstabilized, and the scan of the sky was obtained from the roll and precession in free flight. As the rocket rose above 90 km, all counters sensitive to Lyman-alpha (1216 Å) rapidly reached maximum counting rate and remained saturated for the duration of flight regardless of whether they pointed upward to the sky or downward to the earth. In the 1230-to-1350-Å band, which excluded Lyman-alpha, discrete and unsaturated signals were received from the direction of the Milky Way. Bright emission regions were observed in the directions of Gamma Velorum, Zeta Puppis, Alpha Leonis, and Ursa Majoris. The wide angle of reception, however, precluded positive identification of the emission with point sources.

Since the flux of Lyman-alpha was apparently much greater than had been expected, the next experiment (1957) utilized a Lyman-alpha ionization chamber rather than the sensitive photon counter. On-scale signals were obtained which indicated a diffuse luminosity suffusing the entire sky with only small variation from horizon to horizon (60). To define the discrete sources previously observed in the 1225-to-1350-Å band more clearly, the detectors were restricted to a 3-degree field of view by means of collimators consisting of bundles of nickel tubings 0.03 in. in diameter by 0.6 in. in length. With this improved geometrical definition, the areas of celestial emission were much more clearly defined. Before discussing the discrete sources of emission, however, let us consider in detail the diffuse Lyman-alpha glow.

Figure 14-36 is a plot of the isophotes of Lyman-alpha brightness across the night sky as measured on March 28, 1957. The glow was almost uniform across the hemisphere with a shallow minimum in the antisolar direction. As the rocket rose, the glow from above first became detectable near 80 km and increased rapidly with altitude to 120 km, where the attenuation due to molecular oxygen was no longer significant. From 120 to 146 km the brightness did not

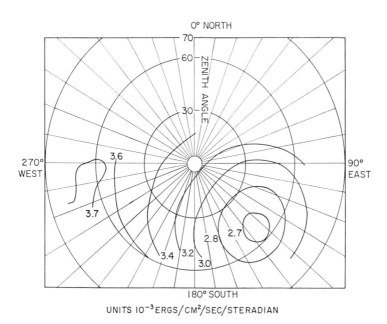

UNITS 10^{-3}ERGS/CM²/SEC/STERADIAN

Figure 14-36 Isophotes of night sky Lyman-α glow observed from an Aerobee rocket at 2200 hours on March 28, 1957. Antisolar point lay within smallest intensity contour circle in southeast direction.

increase measurably. It was also discovered that when the detector looked back toward the earth from above 120 km the atmosphere below glowed with an intensity about 42 percent of that from above. The overhead glow is believed to originate from solar Lyman-alpha resonantly back-scattered to the dark side of the earth by neutral atomic hydrogen well above the rocket. When this scattered radiation encounters the denser hydrogen concentration in the 90-km region, a strong albedo results.

The Lyman-alpha glow was first attributed to scattering by hydrogen in interplanetary space. The observed flux could result if there existed about 0.2 hydrogen atom/cm³ averaged over a distance of about 1 AU near the orbit of the earth. Alternatively, it has been proposed that the scattering takes place in a geocorona (61, 62), extending to about 10 R_E, or in a geocoma (63), extending to an appreciable fraction of an astronomical unit.

The Lyman-alpha glow profile

The Lyman-alpha profile spectrogram of Figure 14-36 provides important clues to the nature of the hydrogen in the night sky, even though it was photographed on the daylight side of the earth. As was explained earlier, the broad emission features are attributable to conditions at the source of the line in the solar chromosphere. The deep, narrow absorption core in the center of the line, however, is produced by relatively cold hydrogen 1000 to 2000 degrees K, somewhere between the rocket and the sun. About 2×10^{12} atoms/cm² column between the rocket at 145 km and the sun were needed to produce the observed absorption. Since a temperature of the order of 2000 degrees is consistent with our present concepts of the temperature of the high atmosphere, this evidence strongly favors a geocoronal distribution rather than an interplanetary source.

The geocorona

F. S. Johnson (64) has argued that the hydrogen must be telluric and can be fitted to a model containing the observed 2×10^{12} neutral atoms/cm² column between 200 km and about 10 R_E. He pointed out that the earth's velocity in relation to a stationary interplanetary gas would introduce a large Doppler shift. The shift, corresponding to 30 km/sec orbital velocity, would reduce the scattering by hydrogen at the 100-km level where the mean thermal velocity is about 2 km/sec to a small percentage in contrast to the observed 42 percent albedo. Brandt and Chamberlain (65) have suggested that the backscattered radiation need not be entirely resonance scattering but may include an airglow excited in some other manner, for example, by particle bombardment. Another possibility is that interplanetary hydrogen at 1 AU may have an orbital motion comparable to the planets, thereby minimizing Johnson's Doppler shift argument.

Two more recent measurements have brought new evidence to bear on this problem. An obvious method of determining the hydrogen distribution is to measure the variation of the brightness of the overhead Lyman-alpha glow with increasing altitude. Since the scale height is of the order of 1000 km, however, it is necessary to employ a rocket with an altitude capability several times that distance. Unfortunately, it has been possible to perform the experiment so far only to an altitude of about 1200 km. The second experiment was one in which evidence was sought for the width of the line profile of the night-sky Lyman-alpha by use of an atomic hydrogen-absorption cell.

The variation of overhead brightness was observed from a Javelin rocket launched in January 1960 from Wallops Island to an altitude of about 1200 km (66). Figure 14-37 illustrates the difference between ionization chamber signals looking upward and looking downward as a function of height. The hydrogen content is related to such observations by the formula

$$[n(\mathrm{H})] \simeq \frac{d(J - E)/dz}{[J - E + 2(E - I)]\sigma}, \qquad (14\text{-}2)$$

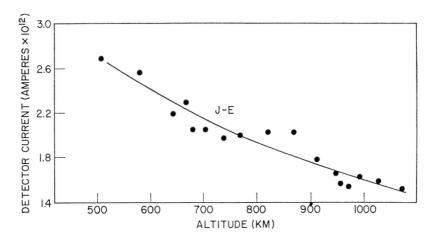

Figure 14-37 Variation of difference between zenith and nadir Lyman-α glow intensities as a function of altitude.

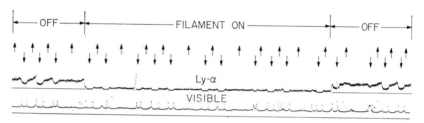

Figure 14-38 Portion of telemetry record of night sky Lyman-α signals transmitted by hydrogen cell. With the filament cold, the cell was transparent and characteristic zenith and nadir signals were observed. (Arrows indicate up and down views.) When the filament was hot, atomic hydrogen was formed, which absorbed the albedo flux almost completely but still passed about 15 percent of the glow intensity from overhead. Visible light telemetry shows strong horizon signals.

where J is the intensity from the zenith and E, from the nadir. I is the intensity averaged over one sweep of sky and earth through the vertical. The computed hydrogen concentrations are $2 \times 10^4/\text{cm}^3$ at 550 km and $1.4 \times 10^4/\text{cm}^3$ at 1000 km. These values are consistent with Johnson's model.

The hydrogen-absorption-cell technique was applied by Morton and Purcell (67) to the study of the night-sky Lyman-alpha profile on April 17, 1961. As described above, neutral atomic hydrogen is produced by dissociation of molecular hydrogen on an incandescent tungsten filament. Figure 14-38 is a portion of the telemetry record from an altitude of about 150 km. As the rocket rolled, Lyman-alpha intensities were observed alternately looking out into space and back toward the earth. When the tungsten filament was cold and no atomic hydrogen was present in the cell, the albedo flux from below was 42 percent of that incident from above. When the filament was incandescent and hydrogen was dissociated, the neutral atomic hydrogen absorbed incident Lyman-alpha strongly. The albedo flux was attenuated to less than 2 percent, proving that its profile had a half-width of less than 0.1 Å consistent with a 300 degrees K temperature for mesospheric hydrogen. Lyman-alpha received from above, however, was attenuated to only 15 percent of its unfiltered intensity. The absorbed radiation must have been Lyman-alpha within a profile of 0.08 Å half-width, based on laboratory measurements of the absorption profile of the hydrogen cell. To explain the 15 percent transmission, it is possible to assign a temperature of about 8500 degrees K, which would produce the required line broadening in excess of the filter width of 0.08 Å. Another possible explanation is that the transmitted 15 percent is due to interplanetary hydrogen, Doppler shifted about 0.12 Å by the earth's velocity in its orbit; however, the measurements showed little change with direction of view, whether in the orbital or antisolar direction. It is clear that more measurements of this type need to be made with improved versions of the absorption cell to refine the profile data.

Stellar ultraviolet fluxes

Let us return now to the observations of stellar emission. The 1957 NRL experiment produced a rough map of the sky in the wavelength band 1225 to 1350 Å, with about 3 degrees resolution. Although the earlier measurements could indicate emission only from the general directions of the hot stars, Regulus, Gamma Velorum, and Zeta Puppis, the improved resolution showed that the sources were broad nebulous regions in which the hot stars were embedded. Very bright areas in Orion and around Spica were mapped in detail (68). In the case of Spica the nebulosity appeared to be almost circularly symmetrical about the position of the star center with a bright core about 11 degrees in diameter and a weaker envelope about 20 degrees wide. The star itself was not detectable against the nebulosity.

The mean surface brightness of the Spica nebulosity was about 3×10^{-4} erg/cm^2/sec/2π ster, and the flux at the earth was about 10^{-5} erg/cm^2/sec. Disregarding interstellar absorption, the total luminosity was found to be 10^{37} ergs/sec. This figure is roughly the expected flux below the Lyman limit (912 Å) if Spica radiates like a black body at 32,000 degrees K. If most of the energy radiated below the Lyman limit is converted to Lyman-alpha before escaping the nebula, the observed ultraviolet flux may possibly be accounted for in this way, provided a mechanism is active to broaden the emission into the 1225-to-1350-Å region. Attempts to explain the observed nebulosity in terms of continuum emission between 1225 and 1350 Å have considered the ordinary optical processes of excitation by stellar radiation, the two-photon emission of hydrogen, and recombination processes involving S, Si, and C. None of these atomic emission processes can provide the observed flux without an observable visible space density of material, yet there is no detectable visible nebulosity about Spica. It is therefore interesting to consider the possibility that the emission is related to molecular hydrogen that is not observable in the visible spectrum. The Lyman bands of H$_2$ fall in the observed region. M. Krook and T. Gold (69) have suggested that Raman scattering of Lyman-alpha by H$_2$ may be effective. The first Raman line falls near 1280 Å. To identify these mechanisms, more spectral detail in the observations is necessary.

Another possible explanation for the observed flux may be corpuscular emission from the star. According to Fesenkov (70) and Massevitch (71), early stars may evolve along the main sequence by continuous ejection of protons. Su-Shu Huang (72) and Struve (73) have proposed high-energy particle emission from stars to explain the extra luminosity of secondary components of some double-lined spectroscopic binaries. The process has been compared to the excitation of the terrestrial atmosphere in auroral displays by the impact of solar protons. Shklovsky (74) has attempted to explain the rocket observations of ultraviolet nebulosity by assuming that a star such as Spica is a strong emitter of protons at velocities exceeding 1000 km/sec. As a result of charge transfer processes in the ground and in excited states, plus excitation and ionization due to collisions, the fast particles lose energy mainly in the form of Lyman-alpha quanta with strong Doppler shifts. Still another source of Doppler-shifted Lyman-alpha results from the scattering of Lyman-alpha in the nebula by fast particles that have been neutralized. Shklovsky's mechanism can theoretically explain the presence of Lyman-alpha Doppler shifted as much as 75 Å. For the case of Spica he proposes that the rate of stellar energy loss due to particle emission may be about five times the observed ultraviolet luminosity. This would correspond to a loss of 5×10^{-6} solar mass per year.

In view of the interesting speculation concerning the origin of the nebulosity observed in this early experiment, much effort has been expended in attempts to verify the original observations and to improve the spectral definition. The experiments, however, have been plagued by a variety of misfortunes and little progress has been made thus far. Boggess (75) has reported a repetition of the observation of nebulosity about Spica in May 1960. The data were marginal, however, because the Aerobee rocket was spinning at a rate of more than 2 rps. With a 2-degree field of view, the photodetector could not achieve reliable signal-to-noise ratios in the few thousandths of a second per scan. Boggess based his conclusions about the nebulosity on the fact that it was detectable on 58 consecutive scans while the rocket precessed through 9 min of arc/scan, or a total of about 9 degrees.

Following the 1957 experiments, subsequent measurements of emission at wavelengths longer than 1285 Å and below 1200 Å have revealed only point sources within the limits of the optical resolution (76). A typical NRL Aerobee instrumentation section employing eight mirror telescopes is shown in Figure 14-39. Each telescope was equipped at the prime focus with a gas-gain ionization chamber behind an aperture exposing a 1.5-degree field of view. The 6-in.-diameter F 1.5 mirrors were coated with aluminum and magnesium fluoride to provide about 70 percent reflectivity, and the ion chambers were chosen to cover various wavelength bands, including 1050 to 1200, 1290 to 1350, and 1350 to 1550 Å. The shortest wavelength band was detected by an ion chamber equipped with a lithium-fluoride window and filled with methyl bromide; the intermediate range detector used a strontium fluoride window and was filled with nitric oxide; and the longest wavelength detector had a barium fluoride window and used a mixture of unsymmetrical dimethyl hydrazine and methane, the window to provide the photoionization threshold at 1550 Å and the mixture to improve the gas-gain behavior of the ion chamber. With a gain of about 1000, it was capable of measuring fluxes as low as 3×10^{-5} erg/cm^2/sec. The shorter wavelength detectors were somewhat more sensitive. Since these

Figure 14-39 Instrumentation section of Aerobee rocket equipped with eight parabolic mirror telescopes. Each telescope focuses light on a detector mounted at its focus. As the rocket traverses the denser atmosphere, the optics are protected by doors which are sprung open above 40 km.

sensitivities are an order of magnitude greater than necessary to detect the nebular glow observed in the 1957 experiment, the fact that no nebulosities have been observed in these wavelength bands displaced from Lyman-alpha indicates that any nebulosity of the magnitude observed in the 1957 experiment would need to be confined to wavelengths fairly close to Lyman-alpha.

More than 40 stars have been measured in the NRL experiments (77) and a partial list is included in Table 14-8. All of the observed stars are in the O, B, and A classes, early types that emit most of

TABLE 14-8

Stars Seen by a 1290-to-1350-Å Photometer in NB3.103,
for Which No Other "Davis Stars" Lie Within 3 Degrees

HD	Star	Spectral Type	F_{1314} erg/ cm^2/sec^1/Å	F_{1314}/F_{5560}
3360	ζ Cas	B 2.5 IV	2.0×10^{-9}	16
5394	γ Cas	B 0 e IV	>3.3	>3.8
11415	ε Cas	B 5 III	1.1	6.6
19356	β Per	B 8 V	1.3	2.7
24760	ε Per	B 0.5 III	>3.3	>13
30836	π₄ Ori	B 2 III	1.1	9.7
31237	π₅ Ori	B 2 III	2.0	14
32630	η Aur	B 4 V	2.1	11
35497	β Tau	B 7 III	2.1	2.9
38771	κ Ori	c B 0 II	>3.3	>6.6
40312	θ Aur	A 0 sp	1.2	2.6
40494	γ Col	B 3	0.8	12
44743	β C Ma	c B 1 II	>3.3	>5.5
44402	ζ C Ma	B 5	2.0	9.1
47839	s Mon	O 7	1.9	37
48915	α C Ma	A 1 V	>3.3	>0.25
50013	κ C Ma	B 2 e	1.9	16
50707	15 C Ma	B 0	2.0	38
58715	β C Mi	B 8 e V	1.4	4.2
74575	α Pyx	B 1	1.9	15
87901	α Leo	B 7 V	2.1	1.9
106625	γ C rv	B 8 III	1.3	6.0
116658	α Vir	B 1 V	>3.3	>2.7
120315	η U Ma	B 5 V	>3.3	>5.1
160762	ι Her	c B 3 s IV	1.3	12
205021	β Cep	B 1 IV	>3.3	>19

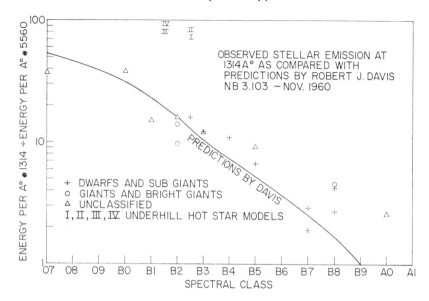

Figure 14-40 Rocket measurements of stellar fluxes in a wavelength band centered at about 1314 Å plotted versus spectral class. Solid curve is from R. J. Davis, *Scientific Uses of Earth Satellites*, J. A. Van Allen, Ed., University Michigan Press, Ann Arbor, 1956, p. 157.

their radiation in the ultraviolet. As plotted in Figure 14-40, the ratio of the observed fluxes in the ultraviolet to the visible fluxes fall about a factor of 5 below the predictions of A. Underhill's (78) theoretical models.

Further observations in the vacuum ultraviolet with greater accuracy and with more detailed spectral resolution will permit significant comparisons with stellar models. The first successful spectrographic observations were recorded in 1961 by Milligan and Stecher (79). An objective grating spectrograph was used with a photomultiplier detector for the range 1700 to 3000 Å. Because the instrument depended on the spin and precession of the Aerobee rocket for scanning, its resolution was limited to about 50 Å in order to provide sufficient signal-to-noise ratio. Preliminary analysis of the results showed varying degrees of deficiency in the ultraviolet flux in relation to predictions of stellar models, the largest discrepancies being associated with the earliest types. Continuation of experiments from unguided rockets will undoubtedly prove useful, but much more refined measurements will become possible as soon as stabilized rockets and stellar pointing devices are perfected. Within a few years the orbiting astronomical observatory satellites may become operational and provide ideal platforms for ultraviolet astronomy.

14-6 ORBITING OBSERVATORIES

March 7, 1962, marked the launching of the first of the orbiting astronomical observatories programmed by the United States National Aeronautics and Space Administration. Designated S-16, it was designed specifically for solar research. A brief description of this satellite and of the kinds of experiments that it can accommodate will serve to indicate the manner in which astronomy from space vehicles is developing.

The first of the orbiting astronomical observatories is illustrated in Figure 14-41. The wheel-like structure is made of nine triangular sections, each capable of housing an experiment. Projecting from the wheel are three booms which carry bottles of compressed nitrogen gas at their tips. The gas may be released through tangentially oriented jets to provide torque and to keep the wheel spinning at about 30 rpm for at least 6 months. The booms also serve as radio antennae. When finally stabilized, the plane of the wheel includes the direction to the sun with an accuracy of ±5 degrees.

Mounted on the hub of the wheel and counterrotating to the wheel is a semicircular "sail" that always presents one face to the sun. This frame carries solar batteries sufficient to produce 25 watts of power. Projecting through the sail and mounted perpendicular to

Figure 14-41 Orbiting solar observatory S-16 of the U. S. National Aeronautics and Space Administration.

its face are two boxes intended to carry telescopes, spectrographs, or spectroheliographs. These boxes are accurately aimed at the sun (± 1 min of arc) by means of thrust applied with gas jets at the top of the sail to precess the spin axis of the wheel.

Among the experiments available for the stabilized spar are (1) various scanning spectrometers to cover the entire spectrum from 3000 Å to soft X rays; (2) photometers to record the shapes of transient X-ray and ultraviolet emission bursts associated with solar flares and other forms of solar activity; (3) a coronagraph to photo-electrically scan the region from 0.5 to 10 solar radii above the limb; (4) spectroheliographs to map the sun in several ultraviolet wavelengths; and (5) X-ray pinhole telescopes to map the distribution of X-ray sources. Means are provided to move the entire pointed section in a scanning motion or to lock it accurately, aimed at a specific portion of the sun. The compartments of the wheel carry experiments not requiring continuous pointing at the sun. These may include photometers to monitor various wavelength bands of ultraviolet and X rays and a wide range of gamma-ray energies.

The synoptic mapping of the sun in various extreme ultraviolet and X-ray wavelengths is one of the primary goals of solar physicists. Each wavelength characterizes a particular density and temperature regime of the solar atmosphere, so that by choosing appropriate spectral lines it is possible to construct a picture of the solar atmosphere in depth. So far, the only extreme ultraviolet wavelength in which the sun has been imaged is Lyman-alpha (80). The Lyman-alpha camera which was flown on an Aerobee rocket consisted of a pair of concave diffraction gratings. The first mirror grating produced dispersed images of the sun on a screen placed in its focal plane. An aperture in the screen passed only the Lyman-alpha image to the second mirror gratings which produced a further monochromatized image on the film. The resulting photograph (Figure 14-42) revealed bright plage-like Lyman-alpha regions corresponding to the H_α and calcium plages but coarser in structure and of greater contrast in relation to the quiet sun background.

Although it is possible to adapt the twin-grating camera technique to other wavelengths than Lyman-alpha, photographic imaging is not suitable for satellite use. Instead, spectroheliographic experiments planned for the orbiting solar observatories make use of the newly developed channel photomultiplier. This device has such novel characteristics that it merits a brief description here.

Figure 14-43 is a photograph of a channel multiplier developed by G. W. Goodrich and W. C. Wiley of the Bendix Research Corporation (81). It consists of a glass capillary with a semiconducting

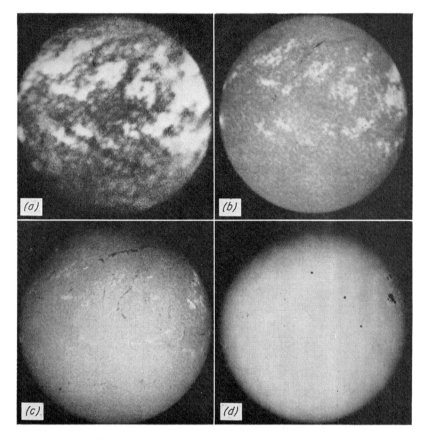

Figure 14-42 (a) Lyman-α photograph of the sun obtained from Aerobee rocket (NRL). (b) CaK photograph, McMath-Hulburt Observatory. (c) H_α photograph, Sacramento Peak Observtory. (d) White light photograph, U. S. Naval Observatory.

internal surface and a secondary emission factor of about 2. If ultraviolet radiation strikes the edge of the capillary surface at one end of the tube, the ejected photoelectrons may be accelerated down the tube by high voltage applied across the ends, as shown in Figure 14-44. With each collision of electrons with the walls, secondary electrons are released so that multiplications as high as 10^8 may be achieved across the length of the tube. The emerging electrons are collected on a plate maintained at about 67 volts positive with respect to the end of the channel. Typical bore diameters are 0.2 to 0.4 mm, and length-to-bore ratios are about 50. The variation of gain with applied voltage is shown in Figure 14-45.

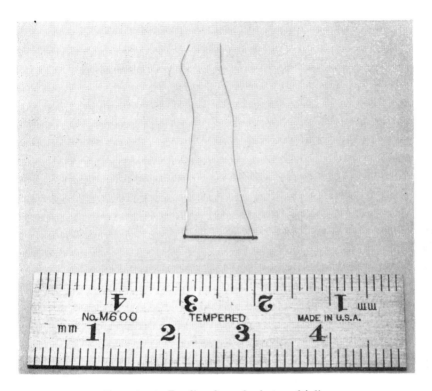

Figure 14-43 Bendix channel photomultiplier.

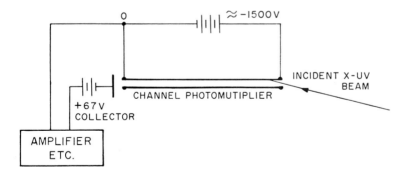

Figure 14-44 Electrical circuit for channel photomultiplier.

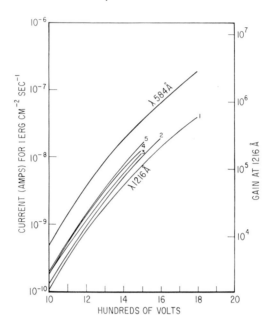

Figure 14-45 Gain curves for the channel photomultiplier. Curves 1, 2, 3, 4 and 5 all refer to Lyman-α and corresponded to a sequence of exposures to air followed by evacuation and desiccation over a period of several days. The sensitivity increased initially with use but approached an asymptotic value.

In the satellite spectroheliograph a concave grating forms nearly stigmatic solar images in the various wavelengths that compose the solar spectrum. A 1-meter grating produces an image 4.6 mm in diameter, so that a channel of 0.15 mm bore will intercept an area of the image only 1 min of arc in diameter. By scanning the grating telescope across the face of the sun, a raster-type image can be constructed. As is typical of photoemitters based on the ultraviolet volume photoelectric effect, the sensitivity to long wavelength stray light is negligible in the channel multiplier.

Because of its small size, several channel multipliers can be placed in proximity to scan in different wavelengths. One instrument (82), for example, has been designed to image the sun in Lyman-alpha, He II (304 Å) and He I (584 Å). Physically, the apparatus consists of a concave-mirror reflection grating which produces dispersed images of the sun in its various ultraviolet wavelengths. The grating is ruled with two sets of differently spaced lines occupying one quarter and three quarters of the grating area, respectively. The three-quarters ruling is used to reflect He II (304 Å) in the third order and He I (584 Å) in the second order onto a pair of channel multipliers spaced only a few millimeters apart in the focal plane. The one-quarter ruling has a larger spacing, so that Lyman-alpha falls between the 584- and 304-Å reflections of the three-quarters ruling. As a result, the three wavelengths (Lyman-alpha, 584 Å, and 304 Å) are picked up by three channel multipliers mounted within a spread of only 8 mm in the focal plane. To eliminate any possible influence of stray Lyman-alpha light on the signals in the 584- and 304-Å channels, they will be protected by thin aluminum filters. As the pointed spar of the Orbiting Solar Observatory scans across the sun, the three channel multipliers can map the ultraviolet images sequentially by switching the inputs to the telemetry system.

The spectroheliographic experiment described above is representative of instrumentation that takes advantage of the latest developments in detection techniques and spacecraft technology. Within the capabilities of the current developments in technology of space research it is possible to accomplish almost complete spectral and image surveillance of the sun on a continuous basis. Spectral resolution can be adequate to map line profiles. Image detail in ultraviolet and X-ray wavelengths can be defined to 10^{-5} rad. Plans for the orbiting astronomical observatories already include requirements for telescopes of 36-in. aperture and pointing accuracies of 0.1 sec of arc. The coming years of exploration with these tools promise to be the most exciting in the annals of astronomy.

REFERENCES

1. Hartley, W. N., *Nature (London)*, **39**, 474 (1889).
2. Fabry, C., and H. Buisson, *J. Phys.*, **2**, 197 (1921).
3. Schumann, V., *Wien. Ber.*, **202**, IIa, 625 (1893).
4. Lyman, T., *The Spectroscopy of the Extreme Ultraviolet*, Longman's Green, New York, 1928.
5. Millikan, A., *Astrophys. J.*, **52**, 47 (1920).
6. Dauvillier, A., *J. Phys.*, **8**, 1 (1927).
7. Thibaud, J., *J. Phys.*, **8**, 13 (1927); **8**, 447 (1927).
8. Baum, W. A., F. S. Johnson, J. J. Oberly, C. C. Rockwood, C. V. Strain, and R. Tousey, *Phys. Rev.*, **70**, 781 (1946).
9. Friedman, H., S. W. Lichtman, and E. T. Byram, *Phys. Rev.*, **83**, 1025 (1952).
10. Rense, W. A., *Phys. Rev.*, **91**, 299 (1953).
11. Violett, T., and W. A. Rense, *Astrophys. J.*, **130**, 954 (1959).
12. Turner, D. W., *Nature (London)*, **179**, 1022 (1957).
13. Shuba, Yu A., and I. V. Smirnova, *Fiz. Tverd. Tela*, **2**, No. 6, 1321 (1960).
14. Taft, E., and L. Apker, *J. Opt. Soc. Am.*, **43**, 81 (1953).

15. Brram, E. T., T. A. Chubb, and H. Friedman, *J. Geophys. Res.*, **66**, 2095 (1961).

16. Kenty, C., *Phys. Rev.*, **44**, 896 (1933).

17. Hinteregger, H. E., and K. Watanabe, *J. Opt. Soc. Am.*, **43**, 604 (1953).

18. Lukirskii, A. P., M. A. Rumsh, and L. A. Smirnov, *Opt. Spectr.* (USSR), **9**, 265 (1960); A. P. Lukirskii, M. A. Rumsh, and I. A. Karpovich, *ibid.*, 343.

19. Friedman, H., *Astron. J.*, **65**, 264 (1960).

20. Hass, G., W. R. Hunter, and R. Tousey, *J. Opt. Soc. Am.*, **46**, 1009 (1956); **47**, 1070 (1957).

21. Chubb, T. A., and H. Friedman, *Rev. Sci. Instr.*, **26**, 493 (1955).

22. Byram, E. T., T. A. Chubb, and H. Friedman, *J. Geophys. Res.*, **61**, 251 (1956).

23. Chubb, T. A., H. Friedman, and R. W. Kreplin, *Space Research*, ed. H. K. Kallmann-Bijl, North Holland, Amsterdam, 1960, p. 695.

24. Morton, D. C., and J. D. Purcell, Planetary and Space Science (to be published).

25. Blamont, J. E., and T. M. Donahue, *J. Geophys. Res.*, **66**, 1407 (1961).

26. Johnson, F. S., J. D. Purcell, R. Tousey, and K. Watanabe, *J. Geophys. Res.*, **57**, 157 (1952).

27. Garrett, D. L., D. J. Michels, J. D. Purcell, and R. Tousey, 1962 Spring Meeting American Optical Society, Washington, D. C.

28. Purcell, J. D., and R. Tousey, *Space Research*, ed. H. K. Kallmann-Bijl, North Holland, Amsterdam, 1960, p. 590.

29. Edlén, D., *Z. Astrophys.*, **22**, 30 (1942).

30. Friedman, H., *Physics of the Upper Atmosphere*, ed. J. Ratcliffe, Academic Press, New York, 1960, p. 190.

31. Tousey, R., *Science*, **134**, 441 (1961).

32. Hinteregger, H. E., K. R. Damon, L. Heroux, and L. A. Hall, *Space Research*, ed. H. K. Kallmann-Bijl, North Holland, Amsterdam, 1960, p. 615.

33. Hinteregger, H. E., *Space Astrophysics*, ed. W. Liller, McGraw-Hill, New York, 1961, p. 34.

34. Austin, W. E., J. D. Purcell, and R. Tousey, 1962 Spring Meeting American Optical Society, Washington, D. C.

35. Purcell, J. D., and R. Tousey, *Mem. Soc. Roy. Sci. Liége*, **4**, 277 (1961).

36. Morton, D. C., and K. Widing, *Astrophys. J.*, **65**, 58 (1961).

37. Athay, R. G., *J. Geophys. Res.*, **66**, 385 (1961).

38. Coates, R. J., *Astrophys. J.*, **128**, 83 (1958).

39. Shklovsky, I. S., and W. E. Kononovitch, *Soviet Astron.—AJ*, **35**, 37 (1958).

40. Vasilyev, B. N., Yu. K. Voronko, S. L. Mandelshtam, I. P. Tindo, and A. I. Shurygin, *Dokl. Akad. Nauk SSSR*, **140**, No. 5, 1058 (1961).

41. Yefremov, A. I., A. L. Podmoshenskiy, M. A. Ivanov, V. N. Nikiforov, O. N. Yefimov, *Artificial Earth Satellites*, **10**, 48 (1961).

42. Yefremov, A. I., A. L. Podmoshenskiy, O. N. Yefimov, A. A. Lebedev, *Artificial Earth Satellites*, **10**, 3 (1961).

43. Willmore, A. P., *Mem. Soc. Roy. Sci. Liége*, **4**, 103 (1961).

44. Chubb, T. A., H. Friedman, R. W. Kreplin, R. L. Blake, and A. E. Unzicker, *Mem. Soc. Roy. Sci. Liége*, **4**, 228 (1961).

45. Mandelshtam, S. L., I. P. Tindo, Yu. K. Voronko, A. I. Shurygin, and B. N. Vasilyev, private communication.

46. Bracewell, R. N., and G. Swarup, *IRE Trans. Antennas Propagation*, **9**, No. 1, 75 (1961).

47. Kundu, M. R., *J. Geophys. Res.*, **65**, 3903 (1960).
48. Tambourini, T., and G. Thiessen, *Mem. Soc. Astro. Ital.*, **30**, 265 (1960).
49. Chubb, T. A., H. Friedman, R. W. Kreplin, and J. E. Kupperian, Jr., *J. Geophys. Res.*, **62**, 389 (1957).
50. Nicolet, M., and A. C. Aikin, *J. Geophys. Res.*, **65**, 1469 (1960).
51. Chubb, T. A., H. Friedman, R. W. Kreplin, W. A. Nichols, A. E. Unzicker, and M. J. Votaw, *Space Research II*, ed. H. C. van de Hulst, C. de Jager, and A. F. Moore, North Holland, Amsterdam, 1961, p. 617.
52. Peterson, L. E., and J. R. Winckler, *J. Geophys. Res.*, **64**, 694 (1959).
53. Winckler, J. R., T. C. May, and A. J. Masley, *J. Geophys. Res.*, **66**, 316 (1961).
54. Vette, J. I., and F. G. Casal, *Phys. Rev. Letters*, **6**, 334 (1961).
55. Kundu, M. R., *J. Geophys. Res.*, **66**, 4308 (1961).
56. Kreplin, R. W., T. A. Chubb, and H. Friedman, *J. Geophys. Res.* (in press).
57. Elwert, G., *Z. Astrophys.*, **41**, 67 (1956); *Z. Naturforsch.*, **9a**, 637 (1954); **7a**, 432 (1952).
58. Kawabata, K., *Rept. Ionosph. Space Res.*, Japan, **14**, 405 (1960).
59. Byram, E. T., T. A. Chubb, H. Friedman, and J. E. Kupperian, Jr., *The Threshold of Space*, ed. M. Zellikoff, Pergamon Press, London, 1957, p. 203.
60. Kupperian, J. E., Jr., E. T. Byram, T. A. Chubb, and H. Friedman, *Planetary Space Sci.*, **1**, 3 (1959).
61. Johnson, F. S., *J. Geophys. Res.*, **65**, 577 (1960).
62. Shklovsky, I. S., *Planetary Space Sci.*, **1**, 63 (1959).
63. Brandt, J. C., *Astrophys. J.*, **134**, 394 (1961).
64. Johnson, F. S., and R. A. Fish, *Astrophys. J.*, **131**, 502 (1960).
65. Brandt, J. C., and J. W. Chamberlain, *Astrophys. J.*, **130**, 670 (1959).
66. Chubb, T. A., H. Friedman, R. W. Kreplin, and P. Mange, *Mem. Soc. Roy. Sci. Liége*, **IV**, 437 (1961); *Planetary Space Sci.*, **9**, 68 (1962).
67. Morton, D. C., and J. D. Purcell, *Planetary Space Sci.* (in press).
68. Kupperian, J. E., Jr., A. Boggess III, and J. E. Milligan, *Astrophys. J.*, **128**, 453 (1958).
69. Krook, M., and T. Gold, private communication.
70. Fesenkov, V. G., *Soviet Astron.—AJ*, **26**, 67 (1949).
71. Massevitch, A., *Soviet Astron.—AJ*, **26**, 207 (1949).
72. Huang, Su-Shu, *Publ. Astron. Soc. Pacific*, **70**, 473 (1958).
73. Struve, O., *Publ. Astron. Soc. Pacific*, **70**, 5 (1958).
74. Shklovsky, I. S., *Soviet Astron.—AJ*, **36**, 579 (1959).
75. Boggess, A., III, *Mem. Soc. Roy. Sci. Liége*, **IV**, 459 (1961).
76. Byram, E. T., T. A. Chubb, and H. Friedman, *Mem. Soc. Roy. Sci. Liége*, **IV**, 469 (1961).
77. Chubb, T. A., private communication.
78. Underhill, A., *Publ. Dominion Astrophys. Obs. (Victoria)*, **10**, 357 (1957).
79. Milligan, J. E., and T. P. Stecher, presented at 108th Meeting of *Am. Astron. Soc.*, June 1961, Cambridge, Massachusetts.
80. Purcell, J. D., D. M. Packer, and R. Tousey, *Nature (London)*, **184**, 8 (1959).
81. Goodrich, G. W., and W. C. Wiley, presented at Image Intensifier Symposium, Fort Belvoir, Virginia, October 1961.
82. J. D. Purcell, private communication.

CHAPTER 15

THE SURFACE
OF THE MOON

GERARD P. KUIPER

The University of Arizona

The principal source of information on the physical constitution of the moon is the lunar surface. It is accessible to detailed investigation since no atmosphere (1) obscures it or has modified it by erosion or weathering. The number of discrete structures shown by the lunar surface is large—already well in excess of 10^5 within the severe limitations of earth-based telescopes. Nevertheless, these gross or macrostructures (dimensions $>10^4$ cm) reveal a pattern that appears subject to interpretation. Thus a history of development is read off from these structures that reveals much about the composition and thermal history of the moon as a separate astronomical body.

The microstructure of the lunar surface is also accessible to observation. The photometric (2), the colorimetric, and particularly the polarization (3) properties of the different lunar provinces broadly define the microstructure for dimensions 10^{-5} to 10^{-1} cm. Besides, spectral measures in the atmospheric transmission band 8 to 14 μ are informative on the presence or absence of silica (which has a low absorptivity and emissivity near 9 μ); thermal measures through various lunar phases and through total lunar eclipses determine the thermal conductivity of the outermost surface layers (4). Microwave measures of the moon's thermal emissivity, again with lunar phase and through eclipses, add information about the deeper layers, down to say 10 cm (5).

A gap in our knowledge, including structural features from about 1 to 10^4 cm, remains. Some statistical information within this gap is at hand from lunar radar echoes (6) which indicate that the visually observed macrostructure probably continues on down to sizes of about 10 cm; that is, the moon is rather smooth down to such dimensions, with slopes in excess of 10 to 15° covering only roughly 1 percent of the lunar surface. Only well below 10 cm does the moon get the extreme roughness evidenced by the photometric and polarimetric properties, derived at optical wavelengths.

The mean density of the moon (3.33) is known with precision from the mass ($\frac{1}{81.5}$ of the earth) and average diameter (3476 km, or 2160 miles). Since, however, the average moment of inertia is not known with any precision (only the *differences* between the three principal moments) (7), the density gradient within the moon is not well known, hence is neither the precise dimension (or mass) of a central iron core nor the average density of the lunar rock in the surface layers.

15-1 THE TELESCOPICALLY OBSERVED MACROSTRUCTURE

The telescope reveals three main types (8) of lunar terrain (9) and a number of lesser types:

1. Dark areas, which comprise the so-called maria and the "flooded" crater bottoms.

2. Bright adjacent areas covered with irregular masses of debris. There is often a clear geometrical relationship between a mare and its bright, debris-covered surroundings (circular ring walls, radial structures, degree of concentration of debris depending on distance from the mare). Such relationships indicate a common origin, presumably by large impacts, of the mare and its surrounding wall of deposits. Not all the maria have such walls associated with them. This fact is one of several indications that two kinds of maria exist (10), those caused by impact and those caused by flooding.

3. The (bright) highlands, or *terrae*. The terrae differ from the maria not merely in brightness and lack of gross or systematic structural features, they also contain vastly more lunar *craters*. The craters are not aligned, as are volcanic craters on the earth. Instead, they appear quite random in any given area, though the crater density may vary from area to area. The randomness of crater distribution and the structural features of the craters themselves have suggested that they were formed by *meteoritic impact*. Although this explana-

tion has not yet been universally adopted (9), it appears to have an increasing number of adherents and in the writer's view is well supported. It follows that the *surface density* of impact craters may be used as a measure of the *age* of the lunar terrain. On this basis the terrae are older than the maria.

4. Superposed on the three main types of terrain are several classes of lesser features. We have already mentioned the craters. They have a lesser density per unit area on the maria and their associated walls than on the terrae, which indicates a difference in age, but the craters are not structurally related to either type of terrain, consistent with the supposed view of crater origin by random impacts (10). Associated with many of the more recently formed (only slightly damaged) craters are systems of *crater rays*. These appear to be composed of fine white fragments shot out from the impact area.

Other classes of subsidiary features are structurally related to the terrain in which they occur.

5. *Rilles* occur commonly in the maria, large and small, and in the larger flooded craters, usually just within the shore lines, roughly parallel to them; they often appear in sets of two or three or even more, branching and merging again, as might be expected from the tension cracks which they probably are (11, 12). Some features occurring on the terrae are sometimes called rilles also, but it seems more likely that they are actually graben. The rilles have jagged edges, like a broken rusk, and sometimes branch like lightning strokes.

6. *Ridges* occur in the maria and appear to be the result of compressional forces, like folded mountains. Their geometry is clearly related to the geometry of the mare basin in which they occur (13, 14).

7. *Faults* may occur either in the maria (Straight Wall; Cauchy Fault), flooded craters (Boscovich, Burg), or terrae.

8. *Graben* occur in the walls of the maria (Apennines, Haemus Mts.) and in the terrae (Rheita Valley). Many graben are narrow and long (say, 2 x 50 miles: Ariadaeus (15), Hyginus, and the Mare Nubium Rilles).

9. *Volcanoes* are often about 4 to 6 km at the base, about 0.5 km high, and have a central caldera 0.5 to 1 km in diameter. They occur only in the maria, usually near the shores. Several dozen have been found (16). They differ from the impact craters in that they are clearly additions of new material to the landscape, not merely a result of displacing old crushed material sideways by impact.

10. *Crater chains* are usually bright clefts lined with a dozen or more small craters that show bright near full moon. They occur

near the borders of maria and may be tectonic features lined with fumaroles.

The macrostructure of the lunar surface is best studied by direct telescopic inspection, with the aid of photographic atlases that show coordinates and the linear dimensions of the various structures:

1. *The Photographic Lunar Atlas,* University of Chicago Press, 1960, contains 230 sheets, 16 x 20 in., on a scale of 100 in. to the lunar diameter, or 1:1,370,000, or 1 in. = 21.6 miles, or 1 mile = 1.2 mm.

2. *The Orthographic Atlas of the Moon,* University of Arizona Press, 1961, contains 62 sheets on the same scale, showing superposed orthographic and latitude-longitude grids.

Figure 15-1 Full moon, reprojected to place Mare Imbrium central on disk.

Figure 15-2 Earth-based photograph of limb region near Mare Crisium, reprojected for comparison with Figure 15-3.

3. *The Rectified Lunar Atlas*, University of Arizona Press, 1962, shows the visible 59 percent of the lunar surface at scale 1:3,500,000, with the foreshortening removed by projection. This atlas divides the visible hemisphere into 30 fields of 30 x 30 degrees each (except that the polar sectors are 60 degrees in longitude each). Each field is shown in three illuminations, morning, noon, and late afternoon. Eight supplementary fields are provided for limb areas. The co-

ordinate grids, in longitude and latitude, are given at 2-degree intervals on 30 separate sheets, also showing the internationally adopted nomenclature. There are thus 128 sheets in the altas.

These atlases have been produced at the Lunar and Planetary Laboratory in collaboration with the Air Force Aeronautical Chart and Information Center at St. Louis. Very good hand-drawn charts at scale 1:1,000,000, are also being issued by ACIC. To date, four

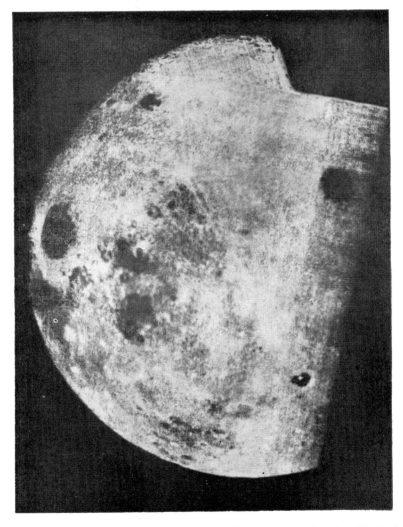

Figure 15-3 Synthesis of Russian photography from Lunik III with 20-in. camera.

fields have been published for the general region of Copernicus, Kepler, Riphaeus, and Letronne. Among the older atlases, the Paris photographic atlas deserves special mention for its several exquisite photographs.

A few illustrations are now described to amplify the remarks made above.

Figure 15-1 is a photograph of the full moon reprojected to place Mare Imbrium central on the disk, with the result that the surrounding mountain walls, such as the Apennines and the Alps, show their true circular forms. The dark-floored crater above the center is Plato; the ray crater well below the center, Copernicus. Other fea-

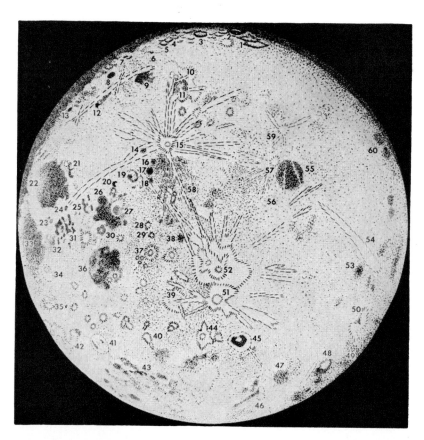

Figure 15-4 Schematic map of reverse side of moon by E. Whitaker, based on rediscussion of Lunik III photography. Numbers on map are explained in the key.

1. Two large contiguous walled plains, rendered visible by the shadows cast by the walls.
2. A prominent ring plain, filled with shadow, except possibly for a central peak; situated close to the north pole.
3. A large, anonymous walled plain, visible in the recentered photograph. It contains Franz's measured point Meton E, apparently a peak.
4. Petermann.
5. Cusanus. There are numerous shadows of crater walls visible in the region between here and No. 1.
6. Strabo E.
7. Strabo and Thales.
8. Endymion.
9. The dark portion of the floor of Mare Humboldtianum. It must be noted that the mountain boundary of this mare does not coincide with the limits of the dark area.
10. A bright area, crossed by several narrow, bright rays.
11. A gray area of distinctive shape, outlined and crossed by the rays just noted.
12. Struve, a dark patch without walls.
13. Franklin, shadow-filled.
14. Franz's "Mare trans Hahn," a small, dark patch situated between two bright rays.
15. Giordano Bruno, the center of a ray system rivaling that of Tycho. Some of the rays extend well on to the earthward hemisphere and may be seen in the recentered photograph.
16. Maxwell, an irregular patch of dark material.
17. Lomonosov, a circular patch of dark material.
18. Edison, an irregular patch of dark material.
19. Joliot-Curie, a dark marking with a distinctive shape. This is the Mare Novum of Franz and the IAU; a photograph taken at the Pic-du-Midi Observatory on December 21, 1961, shows that the dark markings are situated on the level floor of a magnificent walled plain, some 90 miles in diameter, with a grand central cluster of peaks.
20. A dark, horseshoe-shaped marking situated on the floor of the prominent ring plain Plutarch A.
21. Mare Anguis and the bright crater Eimmart.
22. Mare Crisium.
23. Firmicus and an adjacent dark patch.
24. Dark patch on the floor of Condorcet.
25. Dark areas of distinctive shape; Franz's Mare Marginis a, b, c, d, and e.
26. Mare Marginis.
27. A circular dark patch surrounded by an eccentric bright area. Actually a large, dark-floored ring plain, Franz's Mare Marginis k.
28. Popov, a vague bright nimbus.
29. Hertz, a distinct bright nimbus.
30. Neper, a large walled plain with irregular dark floor, bright walls, and a bright central peak.
31. Mare Undarum, a series of "flooded" valleys and craters.
32. Mare Spumans.
33. Mare Fecunditatis.

34. Langrenus, with bright walls and central peak.
35. Petavius B and its small ray system.
36. Mare Smythii. Bright craters and other markings on the surface are well known.
37. A bright area, with several small, well-resolved bright spots nearby. The smallest of these are slightly less than 10 miles across and probably represent individual bright craters.
38. Lobachevsky, a distinct dark patch.
39. Pasteur, an irregular bright area.
40. Sklodowska-Curie, a distinct bright patch; possibly two bright craters with surrounding nimbus.
41. Humboldt.
42. The bright ray systems centered on Stevinus A and Furnerius A.
43. Mare Australe, a large region of dark-floored ring plains and irregular dark patches.

     a. Franz's Abel, the dark floor of a large ring plain. The hook-shaped dark formation to the NW is Franz's measured point No. 1111.
     b. Marinus D, a distinct circular ring plain with a dark floor.
     c. Oken, similar to Marinus D but somewhat larger.
     d. Marinus K, which is Franz's Kelvin and Wilkins' Ibañez; a distinct, deep ring plain with bright walls.
     e. Brisbane G (Wilkins' Pratdesaba), a large, dark-floored formation with low walls.
     f. A circular formation with distinct bright walls and a dark floor.

44. Bright areas, presumably nimbi.
45. Tsiolkovsky, a prominent and unique formation. It has broad, bright walls, a dark floor, and a bright central peak or crater connected to the north wall by a bright isthmus.
46. Possibly a small ray system lying next to a distinctive linear dark marking. The region between these features and the south limb is bright, suggesting the existence of a ray center near the south pole. This supposition is confirmed by the fact that earth-based, full-moon photographs exhibit several bright rays in the south polar region which appear to radiate from a center just beyond the pole and thus on the averted hemisphere.
47. Jules Verne, a distinct dark circular patch situated near the antipodes of the center of Mare Imbrium.
48. A small bright area bounded on the south by a distinct dark patch. A light area stretches from here to No. 46, possibly rays.
49. Mare Ingenii, an extensive region of irregular dark patches.
50. A bright area with a distinctive shape.
51, 52, 58. The so-called Soviet Range, an area of bright rays and extensive nimbi.
51. A bright area surrounded by a large nimbus; it is the center of a major ray system.
52. A similar bright area surrounded by an even more extensive nimbus. Rays emanating from this center may be traced for considerable distances, mainly towards more northerly latitudes.
53. Mendeleev, a distinct dark patch.

54. A prominent and extensive bright ray.
55. Mare Muscoviense, a true lunar mare. It is somewhat smaller than Mare Humorum and approximately circular in outline. The existence of Astronauts' Bay, supposedly situated on the SE (astronomical direction) shore, is not confirmed. Two bright rays may cross the Mare as shown.
56. The location of Tsu Chung-Chi, a vague area that is slightly brighter than the surroundings.
57. Kurchatov, a distinct bright area, possibly a ray center.
58. Rays from Giordano Bruno and ray center No. 52 overlap in this general area.
59. An indistinct bright area, possibly a ray center.
60. Dark patches near the limb and terminator. Several gray areas are situated near the limb between this location and Mare Ingenii.

tures are readily identified with any standard lunar map. Mare Crisium is on the extreme right, close to the limb.

Figure 15-2 continues the view to the right. Mare Crisium is now on the left edge, Mare Marginus on the terminator (center), with Mare Smythii just below. Mare Australe is near the lower cusp, Mare Humboldtianum near the upper cusp. This illustration is obtained by reprojection of an earth-based photograph and serves incidentally to verify the details recorded from the Russian spacecraft Lunik III for the region of overlap. The Russian photography is shown in Figure 15-3, based on the original Russian records combined and synthesized by Mr. E. Whitaker of the Lunar and Planetary Laboratory. The correspondence between Figures 15-2 and 15-3 is seen to be remarkably good, a great tribute to the Russian work.

Figure 15-3 is limited to the photographs obtained with the 20-in. camera on Lunik III. The results obtained on both the 8- and 20-in. cameras are used in Figure 15-4, also due to Mr. Whitaker. The numbers refer to nomenclature published in Communications of the Lunar and Planetary Laboratory No. 13, in which Mr. Whitaker describes and analyzes the Russian work in some detail.

There is a gap of some 60 degrees in longitude between the Russian coverage of the back of the moon and the best earth-based photography of the other limb. Figure 15-5 shows this limb region on a reprojected photograph. The dark spots above the center are Grimaldi and Riccioli; the bright ray crater is Byrgius. At the center of the terminator a remarkable structure is seen (Mare Orientale) that is shown in Figure 15-6 and analyzed in some detail in Figure 15-7. This plate is taken from a joint study of this feature by Mr. W. Hartmann and the writer, published in Communications, Lunar and Planetary Laboratory, No. 12, 1962. The central mare basin is surrounded, on the visible side, by as many as seven concentric walls or scarps. A dozen or so other basins were found in this same paper to exhibit

Figure 15-5 Reprojected earth-based photography of east limb.

two or more concentric ring walls or fault scarps. There is evidence
that these walls or scarps only during a later phase in the moon's
history developed occasional local flooding, often in crescentlike basins
near the foot of the scarp. Several such new lava basins are shown
on Figure 15-7 by Hachures. The Altai Scarp of Mare Nectaris, often
regarded as an exceptional feature, is one of the more pronounced
structures in this class. Actually, Mare Nectaris is in part surrounded
by three walls, of which the Altai Scarp is the outer. This may be
seen in Figure 15-8 (lower-left quadrant). Another example of a
double scarp is shown in Figure 15-9 (Mare Humboldtianum).

We conclude the illustrations with Figures 15-10 and 15-11 which
show the ridge system in Mare Imbrium and the subsidiary system
in the Rainbow Bay (Sinus Iridum). These photographs demonstrate

how rough a typical mare floor is and how the mare is a single dynamical unit, with a multiple array of structural features (ridges, surrounding mountains, more ridges, shelves, etc.), rather than a featureless basin. The vast number of small white specks on Figure 15-10 represent minor impact craters, probably largely of meteoritic origin, though in the crater rays to the right some secondary craters apparently originating from the Copernicus impact are present also. A close study of lunar photographs and, particularly, of the moon through a good telescope is more rewarding and informative than any verbal description can be.

15-2 THE MICROSTRUCTURE OF THE LUNAR SURFACE

Sources of information on the microstructure are the following:

1. Photometry of the maria, terrae, crater rings, etc., as a function of phase angle. The striking differences between full-moon photographs and those taken at low sun suggest the potentialities of this method. The fact that the full moon shows no darkening toward the limb indicates a rough surface at the scale of the wavelengths used, $10^{-5} - 10^{-4}$ cm. Another fact that proves the same is the steep increase of brightness of the moon as a whole, or any of its parts, toward full moon. Models of the surface have been constructed (2) to represent the photometric data quantitatively.

2. Radar reflection data give corresponding information at the centimeter and decimeter wavelengths and relate to correspondingly larger surface elements (6). At these dimensions the moon is found to be about as smooth as it appears on photographs; steep slopes ($>15°$) account for not more than about 0.01 of the lunar surface.

3. Color differences on the moon, when measured in the visual range, are small but not entirely absent (2). R. W. Wood, half a century ago, found that the region near Aristarchus is somewhat yellowish and quite deficient in reflected ultraviolet light. We have found several islands in Mare Nubium that are similarly colored—apparently segments of an older crust not covered by the general lava flows that formed the mare. The coloring substance has not yet been identified.

4. Polarization measures, made for all accessible phases, coupled with matching laboratory data, have shown (3) the lunar surface to be covered with a fine powdery substance.

5. Thermal measures, made in the 10 μ atmospheric window, of selected regions on the moon at various phases of lunation and through total eclipses. They have shown (4) that the thermal conductivity

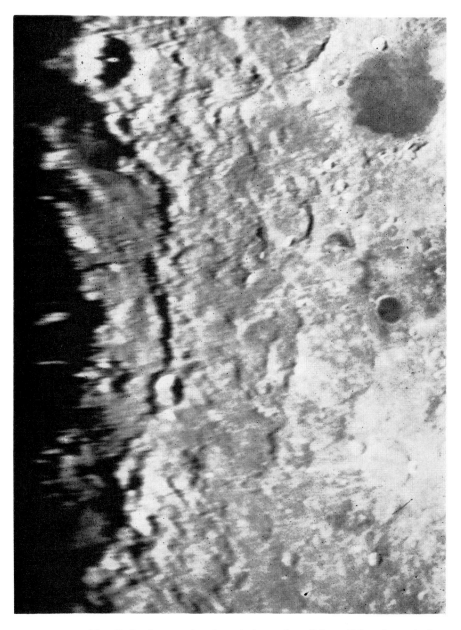

Figure 15-6 Rectified photograph of central portion (Mare Orientale region) of Figure 15-5.

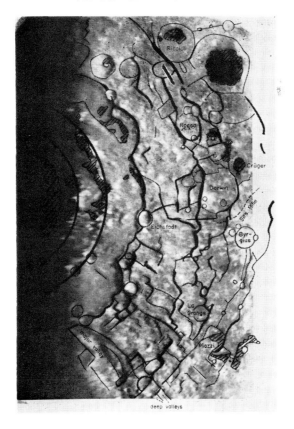

Figure 15-7 Analysis of Mare Orientale region.

of the surface layer is extremely low, about $\frac{1}{2000}$ of that of basalt.

6. Similar measures made at millimeter and microwave frequencies (wavelengths 1 mm to 1 meter) show that the deeper layers have larger conductivity. On the basis of 5. and 6. combined, it was found by Gibson (5) that the moon is covered with about 5 mm ($\frac{1}{5}$ in.) of fine dust, below which is a layer of a few inches of highly conducting material (presumably meteoritic in origin); below that rock is found.

7. Near the large ray craters (Copernicus, Tycho) the dust layer is much thinner, about 0.2 mm or 0.01 in., and causes the crater surroundings to be warmer than the moon as a whole during a total lunar eclipse (the difference is about 40°C). This was discovered by Shorthill, Borough, and Conley, 1960 (17), at the Dominion Astro-

Figure 15-8 Mare Nectaris and three concentric rings.

Figure 15-9 Double ring surrounding Mare Humboldtianum.

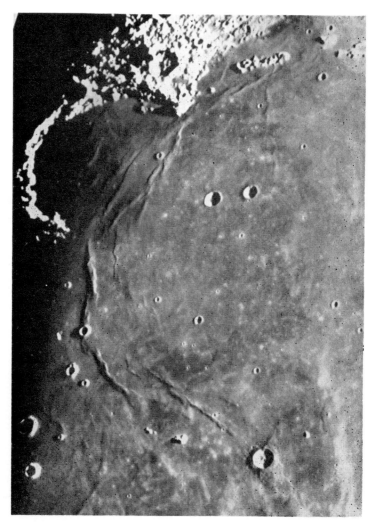

Figure 15-10 Western half of ridge system surrounding inner basin of Mare Imbrium.

Figure 15-11   Eastern half of ridge system surrounding inner basin of Mare
Imbrium.

physical Observatory, Victoria, B. C., and by Sinton at the Lowell Observatory (18).

Some data on the structure and composition of the lunar interior is found from the observed differences of the moments of inertia, and recent data on the radioactive contents of meteorites (or asteroids) lead to conclusions on the thermal history of the moon. This history is to some extent reflected in the surface structures observed and is therefore accessible to verification.

15-3 SUMMARY

The development of the moon and its observable surface, as it is interpreted by the writer, is approximately as follows. The earth and the moon seem to have formed, as a double planet, about 4.7 billion years ago, at a mutual separation that is not well known but is estimated to have been between 5 and 20 percent of the present distance. The original earth rotation was then rapid (5 to 6 hr) and the month short (a few days). Since the "month" was longer than the "day," tidal friction caused a retardation of the earth rotation, a transfer of angular momentum from the rotating earth to the moon's orbit, and an increase in the moon's distance. In its outward journey the moon appears to have swept through a ring of minor satellites initially surrounding the earth outside the moon's orbit. This is believed to have caused the initial stage of heavy bombardment on the lunar surface, evidenced by the exceptional crater density on the terrae, and also the formation of the impact maria. Most of the post-mare craters are small and supposed to be of meteoritic origin. The surface density of these craters is compatible with this hypothesis. The flooding of the maria, however, is not believed to have been the direct result of the impacts themselves, but rather of the availability of lavas just below the surface during a certain period only, since neither very ancient nor very recent impacts, even large ones, have led to any visible flooding. This period of flooding is identified (7) with the time during which a thorough change in the texture of the lunar surface materials appears to have occurred, probably caused by hydrothermal action. Observation shows the approximate simultaneity of these two developments from numerous relationships of the surface features. There is strong evidence that the moon went through a hot period, which, in turn, is tentatively identified (7) with that observed from the melting and solidification of the meteorites, believed to be asteroidal fragments. The date thus fixed is 4.5 to 4.6 billion years ago. The postmare history is therefore essentially equivalent in age to geologic history.

The maria give us the opportunity to study the surface erosion, by particle impacts and radiation, during this long interval of 4.5 billion years; the terrae give information on the ancient but rather brief premare history, roughly 0.1 billion years. The surface of the moon thus contains precious records, the equivalents of which are not available on earth. The exploration of these records during the coming decades will be one of the most fascinating episodes in the history of science.

REFERENCES

1. The upper limit, deduced from radio observations of the Crab nebula occulted by the moon, is about 10^{-13} terrestrial atmospheres. Cf. C. H. Costain, B. Elsmore, and G. R. Whitfield, *M.N.*, **116**, 380, 1956; B. Elsmore, *Phil. Mag.*, **2**, 1040, 1957. The actual atmosphere is likely to be much below this limit.

2. Cf. *Planets and Satellites,* The Solar System, Vol. III, University of Chicago Press, Chicago, 1961; Chapter 6, Photometry of the Moon, M. Minnaert, Sections 4 and 6; Chapter 8, Photometry and Polarimetry of Planets and Satellites, Daniel L. Harris, Section 8.

3. *Ibid.,* Chapter 9, Audouin Dollfus, Polarization Studies of Planets, Section **4**.

4. *Ibid.,* Chapter 10, Edison Pettit, Planetary Temperature Measurements; Chapter 11, William M. Sinton, Recent Radiometric Studies of the Planets and the Moon.

5. *Ibid.,* Chapter 12, Cornell H. Mayer, Radio Emission of the Moon and Planets; J. E. Gibson, Lunar Surface Characteristics Indicated by the March, 1960, Eclipse and Other Observations, *Ap. J.,* **133**, 1072 (1961).

6. Cf. *The Moon, Meteorites, and Comets,* The Solar System, Vol. IV, University of Chicago Press, Chicago, 1962; Chapter 5, J. V. Evans and G. H. Pettingill, The Scattering of the Lunar Surface at Radio Wavelengths.

7. E.g., G. P. Kuiper, *Proc. Natl. Acad. Sci.,* **40**, 1097 ff. (1954).

8. Kuiper, G. P., *J. Geophys. Res.,* **64**, 1715 (1959).

9. An excellent review of the lunar surface features is contained in *Structure of the Moon's Surface,* G. Fielder, Pergamon Press, 1961, which became available after this chapter had been written.

10. Baldwin, R. B., *The Face of the Moon,* University of Chicago Press, Chicago, 1949.

11. E.g., T. G. Elger, *The Moon,* London, 1895, pp. 20–26.

12. Fielder, G., *op. cit.,* Section 12.

13. Elger, T. G., *op. cit.,* pp. 7–9.

14. The relationship is well shown, e.g., in the writer's photographs reproduced in *Vistas in Astronautics,* Vol. 2, Pergamon Press, 1959, ed. M. Alperin and H. F. Gregory, pp. 280, 283, 287, 288, 289, 291, 292, and 293.

15. For an excellent sketch of the Ariadaeus Rille, cf. Fielder, *op. cit.,* p. 204.

16. For reproductions, see *Vistas in Astronautics,* Vol. 2, pp. 307, 308.

17. Shorthill, R. W., H. C. Borough, and J. M. Conley, *Publ. Astron. Soc. Pacific,* **72**, 481 (1960).

18. Sinton, W. M., *Lowell Obs. Bull.,* **5**, 1 (1960).

CHAPTER 16

BIOASTRONAUTICS

BRIGADIER GENERAL DON D. FLICKINGER

U.S.A.F.M.C. (Ret.)

The prospect of successful manned space flight and subsequent exploration of outer space and nearby lunar and planetary surfaces has excited the interest and imagination of people the world over. Few, if any, events in the history of mankind have created such a dramatic impact on current thinking and future hopes as has man's successful breaching of the space frontier.

Because man is a dynamic biological system, capable of thinking and reasoning, it is natural that the medical, biological, and behavioral scientists would become deeply involved in this particular facet of our space program. Valid knowledge was needed on human needs, tolerances, and capabilities to survive the forces of orbital flight and to perform useful tasks in the space environment. When precise scientific knowledge was lacking, the life scientists attempted either to research the data within the time required or to make reasonable extrapolations and estimates that would be usable and acceptable by the engineers.

With the successful ballistic flights of Astronauts Shepard and Grissom, that portion of the "corridor into outer space," using the Mercury Redstone vehicle, was proved in all technical, operational, and human aspects. The orbital flights of Cosmonauts Gagarin and Titov and Astronaut Glenn extended this flight spectrum into the regime of actual space travel wherein the manned vehicle became an earth satellite. The objectives of this chapter are basically twofold: first, to review the biomedical findings as we know them from these recent events and, second, to discuss those problem areas that appear most important to future progress and extensions in manned space-flight technology.

16-1 DISCUSSION OF TERMS

In the strict sense of the word, there is no such scientific entity as space biology or space medicine, despite their widespread use and acceptance. What we are dealing with is the application of medical knowledge and techniques to ensure the safety and performance of the astronaut during the entire space mission. In a similar manner, "space" biology should properly connote those biological research activities in outer space and on planetary surfaces that are designed to elucidate further our knowledge of terrestrial living processes and to discover evidences of extraterrestrial life or prelife forms and substances.

Astronautics, though not in itself a specialized field of science or engineering, has become a useful term to categorize an interdisciplinary area of work requiring contributions from many specialized fields of traditional scientific and engineering disciplines. In a similar manner bioastronautics has been used to delineate those specialized areas of the life, physical, and mathematical sciences that have been brought to bear on the technological requirements contained in successful exploration of space, manned or otherwise. Because of its primary connotation with engineering applications and, further, because it is least likely to offend the sensitivities of the purists, the term bioastronautics is perhaps the most useful one.

16-2 BIOMEDICAL FACTORS IN MANNED ORBITAL FLIGHTS

A brief review of the real and potential hazards to viability and performance to which man is exposed during a near-earth orbital mission will be useful in evaluating results later discussed. Simply stated, they are as follows:

1. Dynamic energy forces intrinsic to launch, re-entry, and landing, under both routine and emergency conditions. These forces include accelerations, decelerations, noise, vibrations, and temperature extremes.

2. Environmental phenomena peculiar to the orbiting phase of the mission. These phenomena cover the so-called mysteries or unknowns of space flight which have no valid extrapolations from human exposure to the stress factors incident to operating high-performance aircraft in the earth's atmosphere. Included are the factors of pro-

viding a life-support system in the hard vacuum of space, tolerance to weightlessness, isolation and confinement, and exposure to unattenuated electromagnetic radiations.

16-3 BIOMEDICAL TECHNIQUES AVAILABLE

Over the last 15 to 20 years, military life scientists and engineers have worked extensively on the many faceted problem of providing safety and performance capability to human operators of weapon systems. Submarines, tanks, aircraft carriers, and both operational and research aircraft imposed their own individual spectrum of psychological and physiological stresses on their military crews. Though many of these problems remain incompletely solved, it is not an overstatement to say categorically that at the close of World War II the United States had far surpassed all other nations in this field of crew protection and recovery under both routine and emergency conditions.

From this body of knowledge, sufficient accurate data on human tolerances and limitations were available to assure uncomplicated survivability of the astronaut through the orbital-flight phases. Of primary concern was the potentially disabling effect, either temporary or permanent, of certain configurations of launch accelerations (4 to 9 g's) with slow rates of onset but of fairly long duration (70 to 120 sec) and other patterns of decelerations (7 to 16 g's) including impact (11 to 21 g's), both of shorter duration but during which multidirectional force loads could be imposed on the body.

Additional animal and human biodynamic studies were expeditiously carried out, which indicated that with the Atlas booster and Mercury vehicle irreversible disabilities would not be expected under the majority of expected conditions. However, the conception and development of the Faget contoured couch (see Figure 16-1) by the Mercury Task Group under Mr. Robert Gilruth provided an unexpected but tremendously important safety factor for the astronaut against these borderline force patterns. The subsequent addition of the landing bag to the bottom of the capsule, to be deployed after reentry had been completed, provided the final margin of safety needed under any and all impact conditions, either on land or sea.

The requirement to provide a livable environment within the Mercury capsule presented rather straightforward engineering problems soluble by existing techniques and equipment. Somewhat restrictive limitations in orbital-payload weight imposed by the Atlas booster capability dictated that instead of providing a sea-level pressure and two-gas (nitrogen and oxygen) system greater reliability and re-

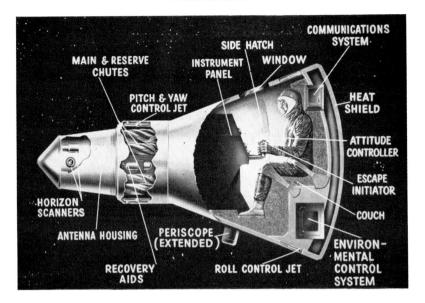

Figure 16-1 Mercury capsule.

dundancy could be obtained from using a single-gas, 100 percent oxygen system in a pressure of one third atmosphere. Two separate environmental control systems, one for the cabin and the other for the full-pressure suit, provided the necessary margin of safety against equipment failures, unexpected capsule rupture, or excessive heat-pulse transmitted to the interior of the capsule during re-entry.

The question of weightlessness, and its effect on sensory perception and psychomotor-response (performance) capability during the period of an orbital mission, was incompletely resolved for the simple reason that this unnatural condition could not be produced for the time duration required by any other means than that of actually putting the subject into orbital flight. From the early work of the Henry group in 1949, and the subsequent exposures of animal specimens to prolonged periods of hypogravity, the consensus was that, properly restrained, the astronaut should experience no difficulty in either maintaining adequate equilibrium and orientation or carrying out whatever observations and control maneuvers would be required.

Shielding against ionizing particles or electromagnetic radiations unattenuated by the earth's atmosphere was not considered a requirement for near-earth equatorial orbital flights of durations up to 18 to 24 orbits, assuming no major solar flare occurred during the period of the flight. The question of biomedical monitoring for both safety of flight and acquisition of medical data was considered and discussed extensively. Here, again, restrictions on payload, volume, and on-board power supply were significant factors; yet perhaps the determining factor was to be found in reviewing the basic objective and underlying philosophy of the Mercury project. The tenet underlying the entire undertaking was that it was technologically feasible and practical to put a manned vehicle into orbit, have the occupant perform useful mission tasks, and be recovered with no greater danger than that involved in the first flight of an experimental test aircraft. The project was not designed as a biomedical research experiment, and for obvious reasons the primary objectives were to provide greatest reliability of the booster, capsule systems, and ground command and control facilities. Therefore, biomedical sensing, recording, and transmitting facilities were kept to an acceptable minimum in consonance with the comfort requirement of the astronaut and logical medical diagnostic procedures. The voice link between the astronaut and his counterparts in the monitoring stations was considered perhaps the most important factor in reaching a critical medical decision regarding his state of health, well-being, and capability to continue the flight to preplanned mission objectives.

16-4 RESULTS OF MANNED SPACE FLIGHTS TO DATE

The successful Mercury-Redstone ballistic flights completed by Astronauts Shepard and Grissom were extremely useful and vital preludes to the subsequent orbital flight by Astronaut Glenn (see Figure 16-2). The detailed results have been excellently summarized and widely distributed by NASA (see General References). Two principal points concerning these results should be mentioned. First, these flights proved the basic soundness of both the space-vehicular and ground-support systems and procedures. Second, there were no abnormal physiological or psychological reactions either objectively observed and recorded or subjectively experienced by the astronauts. Of considerable interest was the wide range of observational and performance capabilities demonstrated by both astronauts. Instead of just "going along for the ride," he became perhaps the most important single component in the entire system, capable of taking over from any of the automatic modes and precisely controlling the vehicle's attitude whenever desired or required.

Analysis and evaluation of the results of Colonel Glenn's three-orbit (4 hr, 30 min) mission presents no problem, since NASA has published an excellent monograph summarizing all data, both medical and otherwise, which is available to the international scientific community (see General References). The following significant points can be quite succinctly extracted from these published results:

1. No physiologic or psychologic abnormalities were observed in, recorded from, or experienced by Colonel Glenn either before, during, or after his earth-orbital flight.

2. Throughout all phases of the mission, launch, preflight, re-entry, and recovery, Colonel Glenn retained full possession of his mental faculties and was able to make intelligent observations and timely

Figure 16-2 Specialist making adjustment to Astronaut John H. Glenn, Jr.'s spacesuit prior to MA-6 launch operations.

decisions and to perform all control functions with precision and accuracy.

3. During the entire period of zero gravity (approximately 4 hr) Colonel Glenn experienced no disorientation, vertigo, impaired body function (i.e., eating, drinking, and urination), or any other symptom or subjective sensation that could be classified as either disabling or annoying in any degree. In fact, Colonel Glenn found that the status of weightlessness was not only pleasant and comfortable but it was also useful to him.

4. Of perhaps greatest importance was the finding that the flight objective of completing three earth orbits would not have been achieved without Colonel Glenn in the capsule. Various malfunctions occurred during the mission that would have resulted in aborting the mission, or even possibly losing the capsule, had it not been for the presence of the human component to analyze the unexpected situation, make an on-the-spot logical decision, and finally to take over from the automatic equipment with the required corrective action.

Obviously, the successful completion of the Glenn orbital mission constituted the most significant and important milestone in manned space-flight technology that has yet been recorded. It has proved beyond doubt that man can and will explore and exploit space, just as he has the ground, sea, and air, with purpose, safety, and effectiveness. As on other exploratory exercises, the risks and hazards involved are dependent on the thoroughness of preparations, the suitability and reliability of the equipment used, and the adequacy of the ancillary support provided for both routine and emergency operations.

A review of the information released on the Soviet cosmonauts Gagarin and Titov indicated general agreement with the results and conclusions discussed above. However, the so-called "space-sickness" episode reported by Gherman Titov after he had completed six earth orbits deserves some brief mention.

After having been in the zero-gravity condition for approximately 9 hr, Titov reported that he was having some sensations of vertigo along with mild nausea and stomach discomfort. Advised to immobilize his head in the couch and refrain from rapid head movements, he complied and shortly thereafter reported improvement and was able to sleep, eat, and perform the prescribed operational tasks. However, the symptoms did not disappear completely until an earth gravity vector had been re-established with re-entry.

The significance of this reported finding is not clear at this point, and the question of a time-dependence factor being critical in man's tolerance to the weightless state must remain unresolved until more people undergo similar periods of exposure and more basic laboratory investigations are completed. With our current state of knowledge and limited practical experience, attempts to predict types and degrees of brain or body-system degradation after specific periods of zero-gravity exposure represent rather highly speculative exercises. It is the writer's opinion that with proper selection, training, and the use of in-flight control measures the astronaut will be able to adapt himself to weightlessness for periods of several weeks' duration. However, this opinion also represents fairly pure speculation and intuition, not fact.

16-5 FUTURE TRENDS IN BIOASTRONAUTICS

The parameters and premises on which the consideration and discussion of future requirements for bioastronautic research and advanced technology will be based are defined as follows:

1. Mission objectives—those estimated for realization in the next 10 to 12 years, namely manned lunar landing and return and manned orbital observatories or laboratories with crew station times of 10 to 14 days.
2. Advances in propulsion, vehicles, and components to be linear rather than exponential in this time period.
3. Reliability (risk) factor approximately the same as that for the Mercury system.
4. Maximum mobilization and utilization of national scientific and technological resources.
5. International cooperation in space exploration with no denial of space, lunar, and planetary surfaces to our own national objectives or exploratory activities.

With the foregoing criteria serving as rather rough but useful guide lines for further considerations, some general, yet pertinent, questions are in order:

1. Are we reasonably cognizant of the responsibilities and opportunities contained in the National Space Program?
2. As a corollary to 1., have we received and are we receiving scientific and technical guidance on the interests and needs of the life sciences in the National Space Program toward which our efforts might be channeled even without contractual support?

3. Are the current facilities and procedures established for the acquisition, treatment, and dissemination of scientific information within our national body of scientists and engineers adequate for the job?

4. When we consider the total bioastronautic research and development potential in the nation as it currently exists in governmental, industrial, and academic laboratories, is it properly mobilized to the various principal tasks and is *each segment doing what it can do best?*

5. Are we accurately estimating our future manpower needs and evaluating without bias, traditional complacency, or proprietary interests the current educational and training programs against these needs?

It is doubtful that any of these questions can be answered in the unequivocal affirmative. The point is that even before specific areas of bioastronautic requirements to support national space programs are considered, clearly defined national space objectives must be established.

Specific examples of work needed to further bioastronautic research and development are cited below, followed by what might be attempted if a cooperative international space program were established.

Bioastronautic research

1. Physiological and behavioral studies on human responses, adaptive processes, and performance capabilities under such combined stresses as temperature and pressure variations, noise, vibration, heat, g-loadings, and isolation.

2. Studies to establish firmly the relative biological effectiveness of high- and low-energy protons and the heavy primary component of cosmic rays.

3. Studies on biological rhythms in man and their application to natural and artificially induced work-rest cycles.

4. Studies on hibernation and related procedures available to reduce metabolic requirements in man without producing irreversible changes in vital function.

5. Studies of nervous system and brain pathways along with areas of activating and coordinating mechanisms as they relate specifically to predictable response and behavior patterns.

6. Studies embracing a wide range of scientific talents to identify with much greater specificity the neurologic, digestive (metabolic), and circulatory alterations induced by zero or simulated subgravity states.

7. Studies, again embracing a wide range of interdisciplinary talent, to identify those potentially measurable and transmissable vital human functions that most accurately indicate the true state of man's viability and functional level.

Bioastronautic technical developments

1. Space suits for extravehicular and planetary surface wear. Far too little is being done in this important area, and the problem of temperature control (i.e., providing a means of dissipating body-produced heat) is a major one (see Figure 16-3).

2. Simple reliable monitoring and transmitting equipment that will give us on a continuous, real-time basis the following information about our space man: Where is he? How is he doing? What is he doing? If he is not where he is supposed to be and/or not doing what is required of him, why not?

3. Environmental control (life-support) systems that are logistically practical (weight and power requirement) and that will provide reliable, livable, and workable environments for a period of 60 days. These systems will obviously entail electrochemical components that will reconstitute at least a major portion of exhaled and excreted liquids and gases into usable and acceptable material for reingestion and inhalation. The average man turns over a little more than 8 lb of material a day, and if a pure replenishment system without any reclamation process were used we would shortly run out of both volume and weight available for the purpose.

4. Human engineering of space capsules and crew duty stations. This is admittedly a broad and somewhat all-inclusive requirement, but it should be emphasized nonetheless, for there is so much to be gained and learned by applying well-established and proven techniques from past military aircraft experience to current spacecraft design specifications. A "systems" approach is urgently needed for the important problem of man-machine-environment integration. With such a premium now being paid for payload, volume, and power supply, it would seem not only useful but almost mandatory that we look at the total spectrum of sensory (information) inputs and motor (response) outputs required as they relate, on the one hand, to man's physiologic needs and tolerances and, on the other, to his demonstrated capability to perform the necessary tasks with the equipment. Approaching it from an integrated systems standpoint would result in considerable savings of equipment complexity and redundancy.

Figure 16-3 Mercury astronauts.

Possibilities for cooperative international bioastronautic programs

1. Establishment of an International Institute for Advanced Biomedical Studies. Recent strides made by life scientists working in interdisciplinary teams with physical, mathematical, and engineering scientists toward quantifying living processes, functions, and behavior are most encouraging and exciting. The exacting requirements of manned space flight point to the urgent need for a vastly broadened and augmented program in this general area. International participation would provide not only a great depth of talent but also would

ensure maximum utilization of results in many areas other than space exploration. As an adjunct of this Institute, a laboratory of performance physiology could very well be set up in which to select, train, and perform longitudinal studies on an international group of astronauts.

2. A series of international space "test-beds" to be developed and standardized on the basis of available military (and civilian) boosters, vehicles, and components, which could be allocated on a priority basis to the test of manned space-vehicle components. Advanced life-support equipment and various types of monitoring, control, and communications equipment could be expeditiously and reliably "space qualified" in this manner. When necessary, suitable biological specimens could be used as "exercisers" of the component rather than attempting costly fabrication of a "mechanical man." The point is plain enough; what we lack most right now, whether we are thinking of Dyna-Soar, Gemini, Apollo, or a manned lunar station, is advanced missile qualified components of proven capability to support human life and activity in space. Larger boosters will be of little avail unless we develop and proof-test more and better hardware to be "put on the shelf" against future vehicular and mission requirements.

3. An international manned-orbital biomedical laboratory designed and operated specifically to conduct critical human and animal experiments in the space environment. With the questions being raised regarding man's ability to function efficiently and dependably as an observer, controller, and fixer, and considering the extremely short period of time available to obtain definitive and conclusive answers, there seems to be no alternative to launching a 5-to-7-man orbiting biomedical laboratory with the least possible delay.

4. An earth-based planetary and lunar test station. There are several mountain ranges in the world (e.g., the Himalayas and possibly Mt. McKinley in Alaska) on which a test station could be established at a level of about 20,000 feet. The point of interest regarding this specific altitude is not so much its environmental effect on man but rather that the natural ecology (so-called aeolian or wind-borne) above this level differs considerably from the standard green-plant-animal ecology that exists at lower levels. Tools, vehicles, men, equipment, and remote-monitoring devices destined for use in future lunar and planetary expeditions could be quite thoroughly tested and "qualified" under such conditions at reasonable cost and minimum hazard. Temperature variations and reduced atmosphere oxygen pressures would provide additional and useful features to the test program. The logistical problems of resupply and rotation of

personnel through means of aerial delivery and pickup might well have some counterpart in future lunar and planetary operations. The returns from establishing and operating an international test station, not only in terms of useful knowledge and experience gained but also in creating yet another avenue leading toward mutual trust and cooperation amongst global communities, could far outweigh the monetary costs involved.

16-6 SUMMARY

Successful orbital flights of both United States and Soviet manned spacecraft completed during the last year have marked a significant milestone in the exploration of space.

Complete biomedical data obtained on the U. S. Mercury three-orbit flight of Astronaut John Glenn reveals no degradation in vital body functions or performance capability during launch, orbit, re-entry, or landing phases of the mission.

The combined experiences and data acquired from the orbital space missions of Astronaut Glenn and Cosmonauts Gagarin and Titov represent insufficient objective material to allow accurate estimates on human tolerance limits to zero gravity. Further laboratory and in-flight observations will be required to resolve this question.

Future requirements for bioastronautic research and technology in support of manned space flight covering a period of 7 to 10 years falls generally into two categories: (1) biosciences research to quantitate, whenever possible, human needs, tolerances, and capabilities to survive and perform effectively during space missions and (2) advanced biotechnology to provide more efficient and reliable life-support and monitoring systems and to optimize man-machine systems integration.

The Nation's community of life scientists has accepted in the past and will continue to accept in the future the many challenges and responsibilities presented by the national space program and to make its share of contributions. Complacency and disciplinary chauvinism, however, should not deter us from critically evaluating our organizational, procedural, and educational methods to ensure their full support and responsiveness to national space interests and needs.

GENERAL REFERENCES

Proceedings of a Conference on Results of the First United States Manned Suborbital Space Flight, National Aeronautics & Space Administration, June 6, 1961, Washington, D. C.

Results of the First United States Manned Orbital Space Flight, February 20, 1962, National Aeronautics & Space Administration, Washington, D. C.

Lectures in Aerospace Medicine, January 16–20, 1961, USAF Aerospace Medical Center, Brooks Air Force Base, Texas.

Technical Note NASA D-588, Proceedings of Conference on Radiation Problems in Manned Space Flight, National Aeronautics & Space Administration, Washington, D. C.

Technical Note NASA D-781, February 1961, First Planning Conference on Biomedical Experiments in Extraterrestrial Environments, National Aeronautics & Space Administration, Washington, D. C.

INDEX